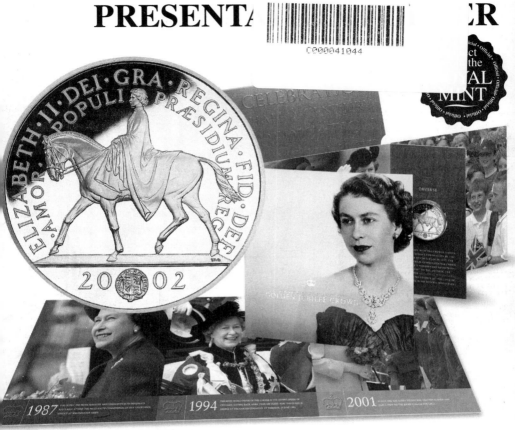

| Tel:
01543
473073
between
2pm and 8pm | **J. WELSH**
P.O. Box 150, Burton-on-Trent
Staffs DE13 7LB
Callers by appointment only as all coins banked | Est. 1968
Fax No.
(24 hrs)
01543
473234 |

COINS FOR SALE

GOLD PR. SETS IN ORIG R. MINT BOX
1980 Gold (£5, £2, Sov, ½ Sov) £895.00
1982 Gold (£5, £2, Sov, ½ Sov) £750.00
1885 Gold (£5, £2, Sov, ½ Sov) £725.00
2000 £2 down £375.00
2001 Gold £5, £2, Sov, ½ Sov) £975.00

£5 & £2 PIECES
1984 Proof £5 GEM UNC £375.00
1985 £5 Nice UNC £325.00
1988 £5 Nice UNC £325.00
1986 Proof £2 Nice UNc £185.00
1990 Proof £5 Nice UNC £350.00
1991 Proof £2 Nice UNC £195.00
1993 £5 Nice UNC £350.00
1994 £5 Nice UNC £350.00
1995 £5 Nice UNC £350.00
1996 £5 Nice UNC £350.00
2000 £5 UNC £300.00

5 GUINEAS, 2 GUINEAS, ETC
1713 Gn. Anne, BU Proof like. Rare in this
grade £1000
1714 Gn. Anne. EF Nice. Scarce date .. £950.00
1715 Geo. I Gn. Near GVF+ Very rare . £495.00
1725 Geo. I. Gn. NVF/VF rare £350.00
1726 Geo. I. Gn. BU extr. rare especially in
this grade £1850.00
1731 George II. Gn. Young Hd. EF Nice very
rare £750.00
1739 2 Gn. Nice BU Extr. rare in this grade£1250.00
1748 George II. Old Hd. Gn. EF very rare
.... £995.00
1751 George II. Old Hd. Gn. EF/AUNC very
rare £750.00
1785 George III. Gn GVF+ £195.00
1785 Gn. BU £495.00
1788 Gn. ABU £275.00
1791 Gn. GVF £175.00
1813 Military Abt VF Extr. rare £550.00
1813 Military BU £995.00

£5 & £2 PIECES
1887 £5 EF/ABU £550.00
1887 £5 BU £875.00
1893 £5 BU very rare £1250.00
1893 £2 BY Very rare £575.00
1937 Pr. £2 BU £350.00

GUINEAS ETC
1676 Charles II. UNC Attractive and
extremely rare in this grade £2950.00
1760 Superb BU Good strike and proof like.
Extremely rare in this grade £1400.00
1798 Gn. EF £225.00
1793 H Gn. VF £100.00

SOVEREIGNS
George III
1817 EF/ AUNC £300.00
1817 Nice BU £595.00
George IV
1821 Proof BU GEM Extr. rare, very few
known £2500.00
1829 ABU £395.00

HALF SOVEREIGNS
1821 Superb BU £1850.00
1835 BU GEM, Good strike £650.00
1893 Proof BU GEM £450.00
1912 BU £48.00

1937 PR BU £160.00
CROWNS
Charles I Briot EF Nice Extr. rare in this grade
.... £1250.00
1688 GVF+ £495.00
1821 GVF £65.00
1845 BU Strong hair detail Extr. rare .. £1250.00
1888 UNC Nice tone Rare £140.00
1896 LIX Abt VF Rare £25.00
1896 LIX EF Very rare £125.00
1902 Nice VF £38.00
1902 EF £65.00
1902 Nice UNC Very light tone £135.00
1928 EF £110.00
1928 Superb BU £185.00
1929 Superb BU Very rare in this grade £250.00
1936 Abt. BU Very rare £325.00
1937 BU £18.00
1953 BU £45.00
1960 Poldic UNC £12.00
1960 V.I.P. BU GEM Very few minted ... £395.00
1960 BU £45.00

HALFCROWNS
1551 Edward VI. Ex-Ling VF £495.00
Charles I GVF/VF S.2771 MM Crown .. £120.00
1658 Cromwell Nice NVF Very rare . £595.00
1663 EF Superb tone £650.00
1836 GVF £35.00
1836 F £14.00
1905 F Very rare £135.00
1913 BU Very rare £125.00
1930 BU Extr. rare £275.00
1958 BU £20.00

SHILLINGS
Eliz. I Milled VF Good portrait £350.00
Eliz. I EF Attractive £450.00
James I EF Good portrait £450.00
Ph. & Mary NVF Extr. rare £450.00
1658 Cromwell GVF Extr. rare £550.00
1668 Charles II BU Extr. rare in this grade
.... £850.00
1693 Wm & Mary GVF/NEF Very rare .. £395.00
1711 F £20.00
1723 SSc 2nd Bust NEF Rare £95.00
1743 Nice VF £40.00
1787 EF/UNC £32.00
1839 2nd Bust BU £120.00
1845 UNC Nice tone Very rare £140.00
1846 Nice UNC Nice tone Very rare £150.00

CARTWHEEL 2d
1797 Nice UNC Very rare in this grade £295.00
1797 Pr. Nice UNC Extr. rare £450.00

SOVEREIGNS
George IV (Bare Head)
1821 ABU £395.00
1822 LING/BU £485.00
1825 Bear Head BU Nice Very rare in this
grade £796.00
1826 BU nice £685.00
1827 GVF Scarce £185.00
1830 NEF £350.00

VICTORIA 1838–1887
Young Head Shield Rev.
1838 Proof Plain Edge Extgr. rare. Only a few
known GEM UNC £4950.00
1853 Nice BU really good strike £225.00
1855 EF/ABU Scarce £425.00

1855 Sidney NVF Extr. rare only £550.00
1858 Nice BU £195.00
1862 BU £150.00
1868 Syd. GVF+ rare £150.00
1870 NEF/EF Scarce £95.00
1872 M BU Rare £195.00
1873 S Abt. BU £100.00
1875 S EF scarce £110.00
1877 S BU £140.00
1878 S BU Scarce £150.00
1879 S ABU/BU £110.00
1880 S ABU Rare £125.00
1883 M Nice VF Very rare £195.00
1884 S ABU £80.00
1884 S BU Scarce £125.00

Veiled Head 1893–1901
1893 Pr. BU GEM Extr rare £595.00

Elizabeth II 1953–
1958 BU £55.00
1959 BU Rare £60.00
1962 BU £55.00
1963 BU £55.00
1964 BU £55.00
1965 BU £55.00
1966 BU £54.00
1967 BU £54.00
1968 BU £54.00
1974 BU £56.00
1976 BU £55.00
1978 BU £55.00
1979 BU £55.00
1980 BU £55.00
1981 BU £55.00
2000 BU £57.00
2001 BU £58.00

CROWNS
Eliz I. MM 2 Extr. rare GF/NVF £1400.00
1667 GF £90.00
1687 James II GVF Very rare £250-.00
1695 GF Scarce £75.00
1732 George II NEF/EF rare. Attractive ....
.... £650.00
1741 Nice EF £880.00
1741 George II YHd GVF £425.00
1804 BE Doll. Nice UNC £375.00
1804 BE Doll. EF A/UNC Light tone . £225.00
1804 BE Doll. GVF+ £140.00
1804 BE Doll. EF/ABU £185.00
1804 BE Doll. Nice ABU £250.00
1804 BE Doll. Nice BU £325.00
1815 LVIII UNC Nice tone £250.00
1819 LIX Nice UNC £325.00
1821 GF £32.00
1821 Nice GVF+ £85.00
1822 Tert. VF Scarce £25.00
1844 NEF £125.00
1844 EF Rare £250.00
1845 GVF £75.00
1887 UNC Nice tone £50.00
1893 LVI Nice BU £150.00
1893 LVI NEF/EF £45.00
1895 LX Nice BU £175.00
1900 LXIV GVF+ £28.00
1902 MP Nice UNC £110.00
1929 NVF £85.00
1930 Firm rare £65.00
1935 Raised Pr. Nice UNC Orig box £240.00
1935 BU £15.00

3

"THE I.A.P.N. dealer, your guide to the world of numismatics"

"More than one hundred of the world's most respected coin dealers are members of the I.A.P.N. (International Association of Professional Numismatists).

I.A.P.N. members offer the collector an exceptional selection of quality material, expert cataloguing, outstanding service, and realistic pricing. The I.A.P.N. also maintain the International Bureau for the Suppression of Counterfeit Coins (I.B.S.C.C.) which, for a fee can provide expert opinions on the authenticity of coin submitted to it. A booklet listing the name, address and specialities of all I.A.P.N. members is available without charge by writing to the I.A.P.N. Secretariate". Jean-Luc van der Schueren, 14, Rue de la Bourse, B-1000, Bruxelles.

Tel: +32–2–513 3400   Fax: +32–2–512 2528   E-mail: iapnsecret@compuserve.com   Web site: http://www.iapn.ch

ARGENTINA
DERMAN, Alberto José, Avenida Corrientes 368, BUENOS AIRES

AUSTRALIA
NOBLE NUMISMATICS Pty Ltd (Jim Noble), 169 Macquarie Street, SYDNEY NSW 2000

AUSTRIA
HERINEK, G., Josefstädterstrasse 27, A–1082 WIEN VIII
MOZELT, Erich, Postfach 19, A–1043 WIEN

BELGIUM
ELSEN SA, Jean, Avenue de Tervuren 65, B–1040 BRUXELLES
FRANCESCHI & Fils, B, 10, Rue Croix-de-Fer, B–1000 BRUXELLES
VAN DER SCHUEREN, Jean-Luc, 14, Rue de la Bourse, B–1000 BRUXELLES

CANADA
WEIR LTD., Randy, PO Box 64577, UNIONVILLE, Ontario, L3R 0M9

EGYPT
BAJOCCHI, Pietro 45 Abdel Khalek Sarwat Street, 11111 CAIRO

ENGLAND
BALDWIN & SONS LTD., A.H. ,11 Adelphi Terrace, LONDON WC2N 6BJ
DAVIES LTD, Paul, 70 Box 17, ILKLEY, West Yorkshire LS29 8TZ
CHRISTOPHER EIMER, PO Box 352, LONDON NW11 7RF
FORMAT OF BIRMINGHAM LTD 18 Bennetts Hill, BIRMINGHAM B2 5QJ
KNIGHTSBRIDGE COINS, 43 Duke Street. St. James's, LONDON SW1Y 6DD
LUBBOCK & SON LTD, 315 Regent Street, LONDON W1R 7YB
RUDD , Chris, PO Box 222. Aylsham, NORFOLK NR11 6TY
SPINK & SON LTD, 69, Southampton Row, Bloomsbury, LONDON WC1B 4ET

FRANCE
BOURGEY, Sabine, 7, Rue Drouot, F–75009 PARIS
BURGAN, Claude—Maison Florange, 8, Rue du 4 Septembre, F–75002, PARIS
MAISON PLATT SA, BP 2612, F–75026, Cedex 01, PARIS
NUMISMATIQUE et CHANGE DE PARIS, 3, Rue de la Bourse, F–75002 PARIS
O.G.N., 64, Rue de Richelieu, F–75002 PARIS
A POINSIGNON-NUMISMATIQUE, 4, Rue des Francs Bourgeois, F–67000 STRASBOURG
SILBERSTEIN, Claude, 39, Rue Vivienne, F–75002 PARIS
VINCHON-NUMISMATIQUE, Jean 77, Rue de Richelieu, F–75002 PARIS
WEIL, Alain, SPES NUMISMATIQUE, 54, Rue de Richelieu, F–75001 PARIS

GERMANY
DILLER, Johannes, Postfach 70 04 29, D–81304 MÜNCHEN
GARLICH, Kurt B, Albert Schweizer Strasse, 24A, D–63303, DREIEICH-GOTZENHAIN
GIESSENER MÜNZHANDLUNG DIETER GORNY GmbH, Maximiliansplatz 20, D–80333 MÜNCHEN
HIRSCH, NACHF., Gerhard, Promenadeplatz 10/11, D–80333 MÜNCHEN
JACQUIER,Paul-Francis, Honsellstrasse 8, D–77694 KEHL
KAISER, Rüdiger, Münzfachgeschaft, Mittelweg 54, D–60318 FRANKFURT

KRICHELDORF Nachf., H.H.Gunterstalstrasse 16, D–79102 FREIBURG i.Br.
KÜNKER, Fritz Rudolf, Münzenhandlung, Gutenbergstrasse 23, D–49076 OSNABRÜCK
KURPFALZISCHEMÜNZENHANDLUNG—KPM, Augusta-Anlage 52, D–68165 MANNHEIM,
Numismatik LANZ, Luitpoldblock-Maximiliansplatz 10, D–80333 MÜNCHEN
MENZEL, Niels, Dachsteinweg 12, D–12107, BERLIN-MARIENDORF

MÜNZENETAGE–ANTIKE NUMISMATIK (Herrn Dr. M. Brandt), Marktplatz 14, D–70173 ,STUTTGART
MÜNZEN-UND MEDAILLENHANDLUG STUTTGART, Charlottenstrasse 4, D–70182 STUTTGART
NEUMANN, Ernst, Watteplatz 6, Postfach 1423, D–89312, GUNZBURG
PEUS NACHF., Dr. Busso Bornwiesenweg 34, D–60322 FRANKFURT/M,
Münzhandiung RITTER GmbH Postfach 24 01 26, D–40090 DÜSSELDORF
TIETJEN + CO, Spitalerstrasse 30, D–20095 HAMBURG
W E S T F A L I S C H E AUKTIONSGESELLSCHAFT oHG, Nordring 22, D–59821, ARNSBERG

ISRAEL
EIDELSTEIN, Adolfo, 61 Herzl St., HAIFA, Postal address: POB 5135, 31051 Haifa
QEDAR, Shraga, 3, Granot Street, Entrance 6, JERUSALEM. Postal address: PO Box 520, 91004 Jerusalem

ITALY
BARANOWSKY s.a.s, Via del Corso 184, I–00187, ROMA
BERNARDI, Giulio, Via Roma 3 & 22c, PO Box 560, I–34 121 TRIESTE
CARLO CRIPPA s.n.c., Via degli Omenoni 2 (angolo Piazza Belgioioso). I–20121 MILANO
DE FALCO, Corso Umberto 24, I–80138 NAPOLI
FALLANI , Via del Babuino 58a, I–00187, ROMA
MARCHESI GINO &Figlio (Guiseppe Marchesi), V. le Pietramellara 35, I–40121, BOLOGNA
PAOLUCCI, Raffaele, Via San Francesco 154, I–35011 PADOVA
RINALDI & Figlio, O.,Via Cappello 23 (Casa di Giulietta), I–37121 VERONA
VARESI Numismatica s.a.s., Alberto Varesi, Via Robolini 1, I–2-7100, PAVIA

JAPAN
DARUMA INTERNATIONAL GALLERIES, 2–16-32-301, Takanawa, Minato-ku, JP-TOKYO 108-0074
WORLD COINS, 1-15-5, Hamamatsu-cho, Minato-Ku, TOKYO 105-0013.

LUXEMBOURG
LUX NUMIS, 20, rue J.P Kommes, L–6988 HOSTERT, LUXEMBOURG

MONACO
GADOURY Editions Victor, 57 rue Grimaldi, Le Panorama, MC–98000
LE LOUIS D'OR, 9, Ave. des Papalins, MC–98000 MONACO

THE NETHERLANDS
MEVIUS NUMISBOOKS Int. BV Oosteinde 97, NL 7671
VRIEZENVEEN SCHULMAN BV, Laurens, Brinklaan 84a, NL–1404 GM BUSSUM
WESTERHOF, Jille Binne, Trekpad 38–40, NL–8742 KP, Burgwerd

NORWAY
OSLO MYNTHANDEL AS, (Jan Aamlid) Postboks 355, Sentrum, N–0101, OSLO

PORTUGAL
NUMISPORTO LDA, Mr. Ferreira Leite, Av. Combantes Grande Guerra 610 LJ6, P–4200 PORTO

SINGAPORE
TAISEI STAMPS & COINS (S) PTE LTD, 116 Middle Road, #09–02, ICB Enterprise House, SINGA- 188972

SPAIN
CALICO, X. & F., Plaza del Angel 2, E-08002 BARCELONA
CAYON, Juan R., JANO S.L., Alcala 35, E–28014 MADRID
SEGARO, Fernando P, Plaza Mayor 26, E–28012, MADRID
VICO SA, Jesus, Jorge Juan, 83 Duplicado, E–28009 MADRID

SWEDEN
AHLSTRÖM MYNTHANDEL, AB, Norrmalmstorg 1, 1, PO Box 7662, S–103 94 STOCKHOLM
NORDLINDS MYNTHANDEL AB, ULF, Karlavagen 46, PO Box 5132, S–102 43 STOCKHOLM

SWITZERLAND
HESS, Adolph A. G (H. J. Schramm) Postfach 7070, CH-8023, ZÜRICH
HESS—DIVO AG, Postfach 7070, CH-8023, ZÜRICH
LEU NUMISMATIK AG, Postfach 4738, CH-8022 ZÜRICH
MÜNZEN UND MEDAILLEN AG, Malzgasse 25, BASEL. Postal address: Postfach 3647, CH-4002 BASEL
NUMISMATICA ARS CLASSICA AG, Niederdorfstrasse 43, Postfach 745, CH–8025 ZÜRICH
STERNBERG AG, Frank Schanzengasse 10 (Bhf. Stadelhofen), CH–8001 ZÜRICH

UNITED STATES OF AMERICA
BASOK, Alexander, 1954 First Street #186, HIGHLAND PARK, IL 60035
BERK, LTD., Harlan J, 31 North Clark Street, CHICAGO, IL. 60602
BULLOWA, C.E. COIN HUNTER, 1616 Walnut Street, PHILADELPHIA, PA 19103
COIN AND CURRENCY INSTITUTE INC, PO Box 1057, CLIFTON, NJ 07014
COIN GALLERIES, 123 West 57 Street, NEW YORK, NY 10019
CRAIG, Freeman, PO Box 4176, SAN RAFAEL, CA 94913
DAVISSON'S LTD, COLD SPRING, MN 56320
DUNIGAN, Mike, 5332 Birchman, Fort Worth, TX 76107
FORD, John J. Jr, PO Box 10317, PHOENIX, AZ 85064
FREEMAN & SEAR, PO Box 641352, LOS ANGELES, CA 90064–6352
FROSETH INC., K.M., PO Box 23116, MINNEAPOLIS, MN 55423
GILLIO Inc., Ronald J., 1103 State Street, SANTA BARBARA, CA 93101
HARVEY, Stephen, PO Box 3778, BEVERLEY HILLS, CA 90212
HINDERLING, Wade, PO Box 606 MANHASSET, NY 11030
KERN, Jonathan K. Co., 441, S. Ashland Avenue, Lexington, KY 40502
KOLBE, George Frederick, PO Drawer 3100, CRESTLINE, CA 92325–3100
KOVACS, Frank L., PO Box 25300 SAN MATEO, CA 94402
KREINDLER, Herbert, 15, White Birch Drive, Dix Hills, NY11746
MALTER & CO. Inc., Joel L., 17005 Ventura Blvd., ENCINO, CA 91316
MARGOLIS, Richard, PO Box 2054, TEANECK, NJ 07666
MARKOV, Dmitry, Coins & Medals, PO Box 950, NEW YORK, NY 10272
MILCAREK, Dr. Ron, PO Box 1028, Greenfield, MA 01302
PONTERIO & ASSOCIATES, Inc, 1818 Robinson Ave., SAN DIEGO, CA 92101-1683
RARE COIN COMPANY OF AMERICA, Inc, 6262 South Route 83, WILLOWBROOK, IL 60514
RARE COIN GALLERIES, Robert van Bebber, 228, South Brand Boulevard, GLENDALE, CA 91204
ROSENBLUM, William M., EVERGREEN, CO. 80437–0355
RYNEARSON, Dr Paul, PO Box 4009, MALIBU, CA 90264
SINGER, Dr Gordon Andreas, PO Box 235, GREENBELT, MD20768–0235
STACK'S, 123 West 57 Street., NEW YORK, NY 10019
STEPHENS Inc., Karl, PO Box 3038, Fallbrook, CA 92088
STREINER, Eric Inc, 119 West 57th Street, Suite 1218, NY 10019, NEW YORK
SUBAK Inc., 22 West Monroe Street, Room 1506, CHICAGO, IL 60603
TELLER NUMISMATIC ENTERPRISES 16027 Ventura Blvd., Suite 606, ENCINO, CA 91436
WADDELL, Ltd., Edward J., Suite 316, 444 N. Frederick Ave., GAITHERSBURG, MD 20877
WORLD-WIDE COINS OF CALIFORNIA, PO Box 3684, SANTA ROSA, CA 95402

VENEZUELA
NUMISMATICA GLOBUS, Apartado de Correos 50418 CARACAS 1050–A

THE
COIN
YEARBOOK
2002

Edited by
James Mackay, MA, DLitt
John W. Mussell
and the Editorial Team of COIN NEWS

ISBN 1 870 192 37 0

Published by
TOKEN PUBLISHING LIMITED
Orchard House, Duchy Road, Heathpark, Honiton, EX14 1YD
Telephone: 01404 46972   Fax: 01404 44788
e-mail: info@tokenpublishing.com. Website: http://www.tokenpublishing.com

Printed in Great Britain by Polestar Wheatons Ltd., Exeter EX2 8RP

Let Coincraft help you in three ways...

In person

Publishers of the Standard Catalogues

Coincraft are the publishers of the Standard Catalogues of English, Scottish and Irish coins and other numismatic books.

Call in person at either of our two shops at 44 & 45 Great Russell Stree just across from the British Museum. Open Monday to Friday 9.30 to 5.00 and Saturday from 10.00 till 2.30.

Friendly, personal service and an interesting display of coins, banknotes medallions, ancient coins and antiquities, to tempt and delight you.

We always need to buy

Coincraft needs to buy: single items to entire collections, dealers inventories, hoards, accumulations, you name it and we will make you an offer. Over 90% of our offers are accepted. Sell where the dealers sell.

By post

Coincraft publishes Britain's only coin newspaper, The Phoenix, published every three weeks. It contains 24 tabloid sized pages of special offers and rare items, many not available anywhere else.

You can't buy a subscription, but you can get a complimentary copy free, just for the asking.

If you like numbers:

Coincraft has 2 buildings, 25 staff, in the past 5 years we have spent over £900,000 on advertising and added over 52,000 collectors to our mailing list. We are listed in the Guinness Book of Records for buying the largest, heaviest, and most expensive lot of banknotes ever sold.

On the internet

Our website, www.coincraft.com is available 24 hours a day. There are many interesting features including a comprehensive numismatic glossary.

Keep looking, more is being added every day.

Coincraft
FRIENDLY PROFESSIONAL SERVICE SINCE 1955

44 & 45 Great Russell Street, London WC1B 3LU
(opposite the British Museum)

Tel 020 7636 1188 and 020 7637 8785
Fax 020 7323 2860 and 020 7637 7635
Web www.coincraft.com Email info@coincraft.com

Find out why collectors say;
Coincraft, nice people to do business with.

Contents

Index to advertisers

Foreword

WELCOME to the ninth edition of the COIN YEARBOOK. In each edition we continue to mirror the market trends in the coin hobby, reflecting the upward, as well as the occcasional downward, movements in the prices of coins as well as English medals and banknotes.

As we went to press sterling has remained strong against the US dollar, in fact, during the past year, the pound dropped from an average of $1.60 to $1.40, but has remained fairly steady around that level ever since and, indeed, had shown a slight increase by the autumn of 2001, to stand at $1.45. Meanwhile, the euro had a rather mixed year, although it was also showing signs of recovery against the dollar while maintaining its position in regard to the pound. Hitherto, the strong pound had had a deterrent effect on overseas buyers at the major London salerooms, but now that sterling has dropped to a more sensible level both European and American bidders have returned, and this in turn has had the effect of sending the prices of top-quality material sharply upwards.

Inflation has remained at a very low level throughout the past year, while mortgage rates are now the lowest in forty years. Interest in coins and medals as "alternative investments" received a boost from the continuing poor performance of the stock market, dragged down to a 17-year low largely by the fall in the shares of computer industries. At the same time, however, uncertainty about the global economy in general, and the US economy in particular, has tended to have a depressing effect on the lower reaches of the coin market. While there appears to be no shortage of money for the finest and rarest pieces, it has been noticed that when it comes to the cheaper coins and the middle ranges of the market, people are either spending less or are becoming much more selective in what they purchase. This situation has largely been psychologically induced. There has been much loose talk about an impending recession, and recent job losses in the volatile world of IT have tended to reinforce this; but there is always the danger that the world can actually talk itself into a recession.

At the same time, it is heartening to note that numismatics has now enthusiastically embraced the world of e-commerce. Our website (www.tokenpublishing.com) is visited by several hundred browsers every day! Those dealers who took a gamble and set up websites now report the astonishing interest and corresponding volume of business which have arisen as a result. Coin collecting transcends all national, social, political and economic boundaries. Ironically all this is made possible by those pieces of plastic which we so often regard as the rival and enemy of traditional coinage. But so long as credit cards attract a service charge and there remains a monetary lower limit on transactions, coins as we have known them for almost three millennia, are assured of a future.

Numismatically speaking, the biggest event of the past 3,000 years is just around the corner, for never before in the entire history of the world have 11 countries, representing over 200 million people of disparate cultures, languages, history and ethnic origin, banded together to use the same currency, and by the time all 15 countries of the European Union sign up for the euro it will represent the most powerful trading bloc in the world. Whether it actually matches, far less surpasses, the almighty dollar remains to be seen. Its notional value has drifted considerably since it was launched two years ago, but now that the euro is an accomplished fact, and there are coins to prove it, it will hopefully go from strength to strength.

The official launch of the euro, at the beginning of September, was well publicised in the world's media and doubtless this helped to dispel many of the myths and fears which have surrounded it. One of the less informed comments in the UK concerned the fact that we would lose the Queen's head from our coins if we were to join the euro system, and that this symbol of British sovereignty must never be surrendered. This ignored the fact that although one side of the euro coins will bear the standard motifs designed by Luc Luycx of Belgium, the other side would be distinctive to each of the issuing countries. We would go so far as to say that the advent of the euro coinage will be a tremendous shot in the arm to the hobby and many people will be encouraged to start a collection of euro coinage on the ground floor.

After the hullabaloo of the Millennium and the euphoria surrounding the Queen Mother's hundredth birthday last year, 2001 has been a relatively quiet year apart from celebrations marking the Queen's 75th birthday; but now we can look forward to a great deal of numismatic activity surrounding the forthcoming Golden Jubilee, with new commemorative coins from many Commonwealth countries as well as the UK and the offshore islands. And then, hard on the heels of the Sydney Olympics are the next Winter Olympics as well as the World Cup football championships to satisfy the cravings of those who collect coins with a sporting theme. And so it goes on. The market for new issues appears to be insatiable although we suspect that there is a relatively high turnover in the purchasers of this material. Of course, many of the people initially attracted to the hobby by these issues subsequently turn to older coins. However, it is a disappointing fact that in the United Kingdom the trade tend not to get excited about new issues—few dealers now stock the latest issues from countries other than the United Kingdom and thus the coins themselves are becoming more difficult to source. However, many of the mints are happy to supply to collectors direct, although not all are geared up for this so collectors are turning to the many overseas dealers who provide a complete new issue service. The contact details of the mints of the world can be found in the directory pages of this YEARBOOK and advertisements from overseas dealers and new issue dealers regularly appear in COIN NEWS and of course many can be found on the internet.

Like other hobbies and pastimes, there is a constant worry about attracting the young who will be the collectors of the next generation. Personally we feel that these fears are groundless. Rather than attempt to woo youngsters away from their computer games we should perhaps be looking at ways of introducing the hobby to people taking retirement earlier and earlier each year. These are the people who are still active, generally have a reasonable surplus disposable income, and the time to devote to an interesting and rewarding hobby. It is significant that much of the feedback we get for COIN YEARBOOK comes from people in that category. We welcome constructive comments and criticism that will help keep the COIN YEARBOOK at the forefront of the hobby and look forward to hearing from readers throughout the year. In addition, our parent magazine COIN NEWS (which has a healthy letters page and a free coin identification service) continues to lead the hobby—readers who are not acquainted with this colourful monthly magazine are invited to write in for a free sample copy. The magazine is published each month on the last Friday of the month preceding the cover date, e.g. the January edition is available from the last Friday of December.

When putting together a publication such as COIN YEARBOOK we inevitably have to call on a number of experts for advice and assistance. We are indebted to the many people who have helped in the compilation of this edition, particularly to Royston Norbury of West Essex Coins, Steven Mitchell of Studio Coins, Chris Rudd and many other dealers who have generously given advice on the pricing of coins, and Nick Swabey for revising the section on the Maundy series. Thanks also to the various auction houses and dealers who have allowed us to reproduce illustrations from their publications.

13

The First
Ireland Euro Coin Set

The national design

On 1 January 2002, the first euro denominated notes and coins were issued into circulation. They will circulate freely throughout the twelve monetary union member states. Each coin features a common European design on one side and a design unique to each individual country on the other. The first Irish euro coins continue a long tradition of coins bearing the harp.

The harp has appeared on all Irish coins since the issue of national coinage in 1928. To commemorate this momentous and historic occasion the first ever Irish Euro coins are available in a colourfully illustrated presentation folder. This coin set is designed to preserve the past and celebrate the future. Guarantee your memento of Irish and European history. Place your order today.

Please return your completed order form to: Central Bank of Ireland, PO Box 61, Sandyford, Dublin 16, Ireland.

For faster service you may place your order by telephone 00 353 1 2955666 or fax 00 353 1 2956536. Please remember to quote your credit card number, security number and expiry date.
We will despatch your order within 28 days.
The Central Bank of Ireland retains the right to limit the number of Currency Sets on any order, if necessary.
Please include postage charges on your order.
Please complete in black ink.

Description	Price €	Qty	Value
The First Ireland Euro Coin Set 2002	€18.00		
Postage: €5.00 within Europe			
€12.00 rest of the World			
Total Value of Order £			

Name:

Address:

Postcode: Country:

Daytime Tel. No.:

Date:

Signed

It is essential that all credit card orders are signed.

Please indicate your preferred method of payment.

☐ Cheque   ☐ Bank Draft/Money Order

☐ MasterCard   ☐ Visa

Cheques should be made payable to the Central Bank of Ireland. Please put your name and address on the back of all Cheques/Bank Drafts/Money Orders.

Credit Card No.

☐☐☐☐ ☐☐☐☐ ☐☐☐☐ ☐☐☐☐

Security No.   Expiry Date

☐☐☐   ☐☐☐☐

That was *the year* that was!

An at-a-glance résumé of the main events and occurrences that affected the coin hobby during the past months, as reported in COIN NEWS . . .

May 2000

At a special ceremony on board HMAS *Sydney IV*, the Royal Australian Mint unveils the latest $1 coin depicting the ship's famous namesake which was lost with all hands in 1941. Those attending the poignant ceremony received an example of the coin with a special mintmark commemorating the occasion.

The Royal Australian Mint's HMAS Sydney II $1 fine silver proof coin.

June 2000

The sale held by Jean Elsen of Belgium on June 24 in Brussels tops the 1 million euro mark (over 40 million Belgian francs). Two extremely rare medieval gold coins realised 23,000 and 21,000 euros respectively.

HRH Prince Andrew, Duke of Kent, presents medals to drivers who take part in a rally to promote British Bosnian friendship.

July 2000

Dr Michael Matzke becomes an Assistant Keeper in the Department of Coins and Medals at the Fitzwilliam Museum, Cambridge, with special reference to the Greek and Roman coins.

On July 13 a cheque for £15,088 is presented to the medical charity Medicins sans Frontieres at Spink's London Galleries, the proceeds of the sale of 37 coins from the kingdom of Aksum, part of the Dr Anton Dreesmann Collection of Ancient Coins.

August 2000

The Royal Mint releases a piedfort version of the silver £5 crown to celebrate the actual hundredth birthday of Her Majesty Queen Elizabeth the Queen Mother.

Hailed as the greatest marine archaeological discovery of all time, the long-lost city of Heraklion is found at the bottom of the sea, four miles off the coast of Egypt under five feet of sand and silt. The ancient Greek city, founded in the 5th century BC, is believed to have vanished without trace as the result of an earthquake. Among the valuable artefacts recovered from the site is a large hoard of bronze coins which positively identify the legendary city.

The Royal Mint's annual report for 1999–2000 reveals that it has invested heavily in new plant and machinery. At the same time, new working practices have been introduced. These changes have inevitably affected profitability for the financial year, the operating profit dropping to £300,000 in place of £5.8 million in the previous year. During the period under review the Mint struck coins for more than 60 countries. Sales of collector coins rose by 23 per cent, while production of UK circulating coins rose sharply to 1,986 million, an increase of 47 per cent.

Australia introduces a consumer tax (equivalent of VAT) but Jim Noble, the leading Australian auctioneer, is confident that this will make no appreciable difference to bidding levels. In his latest sale the top price is $98,500 for the 1937 Royal Mint pattern penny.

Following the entry of Greece into the euro zone in June, the designs of the forthcoming Greek euro coins are revealed. Unlike the other euro coins, which are inscribed in the Roman alphabet and denominated in cents, the Greek coins have retained their own alphabet and are denominated in lepta. Different motifs are used for the "national" side and range from classical mythology to modern shipping, with a portrait of the great patriot Eleftherios Venizelos on the 50 lepta. Appropriately, the motifs of the bimetallic denominations are an Athenian "owl" tetradrachm—a forerunner of the euro as a coin which enjoyed international acceptance in the classical period (1 euro), and Europa and the Bull (2 euro).

Kevin Elliot and his cousin, Martin.

Kevin Elliott and his cousin Martin, who unearthed a hoard of 9,213 Roman denarii in a Somerset field in 1998, receive £265,000 from their local museum as their reward. The hoard is believed to be the largest cache of denarii ever discovered in Britain.

Celtic specialist Chris Rudd of Aylsham, Norfolk introduces a mail bid system.

Bonham's close down their coin and medal department. Daniel Fearon, who had headed the department since its inception in 1993, sets up as an auction consultant and dealer in coins and medals.

September 2000

The New Millennium Experience Company launches a series of medals. Designed by Jacqueline

The "Public Libraries" 50p coin from the Royal Mint.

Stieger, the gold, silver and nickel medals have a convex-concave shape simulating the Millennium Dome featuring the exterior and interior of the controversial building.

The Royal Mint releases a special 50p coin to mark the 150th anniversary of the public library system in the UK. The reverse, designed by Mary Milner Dickens, shows the flicking pages of a book over the classical façade of a public library.

The Shetland Museum launches a replica of the medieval Rhenish gulden to raise funds to purchase a genuine original of the coin which was at one time one of the most popular trade coins of Europe.

The Sydney Olympic programme is completed magnificently by a one-kilo silver $50 coin with the Games' logo in full colour, surrounded by motifs of all the different athletic disciplines represented at the Games.

The Royal Mint launches an uncirculated version of the gold sovereign in an edition of 2000. Alongside the date appears the letter U in a circle to distinguish the uncirculated coin from the proof version, released simultaneously.

Whyte's of Dublin hold an extremely successful sale on September 23, most of the lots selling for 50 per cent over the pre-sale estimate. Among the more interesting lots is a group of George III coins dated 1805, retrieved from the foundation stone of Nelson's column in O'Connell Street which was demolished by the IRA in 1966. Estimated at £400-500, the trio fetch £1,500.

October 2000

The BNTA annual show, Coinex, takes place over the weekend of October 7–8, preceded by a Spink sale (October 4–5), and followed by sales at Baldwin's (October 9–10) and Glendining's (October 11).

The first three-part sale of the newly formed auction house of Gorny & Mosch takes place at Munich, October 9–11.

The Royal Mint releases its seasonal giftware range, including coin-related jewellery and a desk clock mounted with a Queen Mother crown alongside.

Exhibits of the "Collecting 2000" exhibition at the Museum of London.

The Museum of London hosts an exhibition entitled "Collecting 2000" the result of a project to discover what Londoners do in their spare time. Needless to say, coins and medals feature prominently among the diverse range of collectables. The show remains open until April 29, 2001.

Timothy Millett leaves Baldwin's after 17 years and sets up as an independent dealer, specialising in historical medals.

The skeleton of a man covered in medieval coins, discovered below Florence Cathedral about 30 years ago, is finally identified as that of Giotto di Bondone, one of the most important precursors of Renaissance painting.

The Royal Mint unveils the design of the £2 coin honouring Guglielmo Marconi and marking the centenary of his first trans-Atlantic radio transmission. The winning reverse motif was designed by Robert Evans.

Patrick Finn, the specialist in Irish and hammered coinage, dies on October 21 after a long illness.

Dr John Kent, formerly Keeper of Coins and Medals at the British Museum (1983–90) and one of the world's leading authorities on Roman coinage, dies at the age of 72.

November 2000

Glendining's sale on November 3 features arguably the best collection of 17th and 18th century tokens from Bedfordshire and Hertfordshire to come on the market for many years.

The very first Millennium £5 coin struck by the Royal Mint at the Millennium Dome fetches £3,500 on Terry Wogan's BBC Radio 2 "Children in Need Appeal" on November 15.

Taisei, organisers of the Singapore International Coin Convention, sell the show to a consortium including the Singapore Mint, MP Asia and VDN Euro Coin AG. The show is being re-organised under the new name of the Asia Money Fair.

Sotheby's hold an important sale of world coins on November 16–17.

Spink hold a couple of open days on November 24–25, offering free advice and valuations at their impressive new premises in Southampton Row, Bloomsbury.

The Pobjoy Mint takes one of the Coin of the Year Awards for the third consecutive year, being awarded the prize for the most inspirational coin, the silver 14 euro of Bosnia and Herzegovina, featuring a peace dove. The overall winner of Coin of the Year, however, is Italy's 5000 lire Millennium coin.

A magnificent exhibition of the treasures of Catherine the Great opens at the new Hermitage Rooms in Somerset House, London on November 25 and runs until September 25, 2001. It includes 40 of the superb commemorative medals struck during her reign.

December 2000

Classical Numismatic Group hold an impressive Triton sale on December 5–6, including a notable collection of Polish coins

A gallery of the "Treasures of the Hermitage" exhibition at Somerset House, London.

The 2001 Shakespeare Calendar Medal.

The Royal Mint releases its first ever calendar medal, with a bust of Shakespeare and the Globe Theatre on the obverse.

The second auction held by Renaissance, the recently formed consortium of leading international dealers, takes place on December 6 in New Jersey.

The Great Court at the British Museum, a £100m development to convert the former Reading Room, is inaugurated on December 7, providing new museum accommodation on the two-acre site.

Spink America, in association with Christie's of New York, hold a sale on December 14, featuring gold coins from the wreck of the SS *Central America* which foundered in 1857 en route from Panama to New York with a valuable cargo of gold from California.

The National Art Collections Fund assists the Museum of Reading to acquire the Wokingham Roman coin hoard which had been discovered in 1970.

A website Antiquestall.com is launched as a medium for the sale of coins, medals and other collectables.

January 2001

Mark Rasmussen, formerly of Spink's and an acknowledged authority on English milled coinage as well as patterns and proofs, sets up his own numismatic consultancy on January 1.

The Royal Norwegian Mint becomes a private limited company wholly owned by the Central Bank of Norway, with effect from January 1.

The Pobjoy Mint establishes a website on which over 700 coins produced by the Mint in recent years can be viewed.

The British Numismatic Society's website goes on line with the aid of the Fitzwilliam Museum and Dr Sean Miller.

Chris Rudd celebrates his tenth anniversary in business by producing his largest catalogue to date, listing more than 200 Celtic and Gaulish coins. He establishes a new record price for a British Celtic coin when he purchases the famous Norfolk stater, discovered in 1991, for £7,000 at a sale in Zurich.

A Wreck Amnesty is proclaimed by the Receiver of Wrecks, running from January 23 till April 24, to give divers and others the opportunity to declare their finds and legalise them.

The Morley Coin Fair organised by Eddie and Cindy Smith, moves to a larger venue at the Cedar Court Hotel, Wakefield on January 28.

A civil action for the forfeiture of a 1933 gold eagle was due to start in a US federal court on January 29, but as the result of an out-of-court settlement, permission to dispose of the coin was granted to Stephen C. Fenton of Knightsbridge Coins. The coin, which had been acquired by Fenton from the collection of the late King Farouk, was allegedly one of several 1933 gold eagles stolen from the US Mint in Philadelphia some time in the 1930s. Several other coins had been tracked down in the interim and destroyed but this coin, seized by Secret Service agents in 1996, is the only one to have been granted a reprieve. It was expected that the world's rarest coin would establish a new record price when it ultimately went under the hammer.

February 2001

The 30th World Money Fair takes place at the Convention Centre, Basel over the weekend of February 2–4.

Mark Rasmussen.

At the annual Mint Masters' Conference, held in Canberra, the Polish State Mint is awarded a special prize for technical achievement, in producing their three-metal 200 zloty Millennium coin with latent imaging on both sides.

Dix Noonan Webb expand, with the recruitment of Peter Preston-Morley and Andy Webb, together with the appointment of three regional representatives.

William Gardner, the celebrated designer and engraver of coins, dies at the age of 86. Among the British coins for which he was responsible were the threepence and both shillings of 1953 as well as the 20p coin.

March 2001

The first Asia Money Fair takes place at the Raffles City Convention Centre in Singapore on March 9-11, coinciding with a Baldwin's sale on March 8.

Sheffield Coin Auctions hold their 100th sale.

Baldwin's hold their second "argentum" sale on March 22.

Dr Mark Jones is appointed Director of the Victoria and Albert Museum. An Assistant Keeper at the Department of Coins and Medals in the British Museum (1974–92), he was subsequently Director of the National Museums of Scotland and responsible for the opening in 1999 of the new Royal Museum of Scotland. A leading authority on commemorative and art medals, he has published a number of books on the subject.

HRH Prince Philip stands down as the President of the Royal Mint Advisory Committee. A position he had held for 47 years. He is succeeded by Professor Sir Christopher Frayling, Rector of the Royal College of Art and Chairman of the Design Council who is appointed to the new post of Chairman of the Committee.

Mavin International Pte Ltd is formed in Singapore by a retired High Court judge and four lawyers to provide numismatists worldwide with legal advice as well as grade and sell a wide range of high-class coins and medals.

Spring Coinex, sponsored by the BNTA, takes place at Harrogate on March 31.

April 2001

The Annual Congress of the British Association of Numismatic Societies takes place at Woolton Hall, University of Manchester, over the weekend of April 6–8.

Numismatists from all over the world gather in Esztergom, home of the first Hungarian Mint, to celebrate the 1000th anniversary of Hungary. Andrew Burnett, Keeper of Coins and Medals at the British Museum and President of the International Numismatic Commission, delivers a paper on monetary union in the Roman Empire.

May 2001

Sotheby's (pictured above) close down their coin and medal department after their sale on May 2. Leading experts James Morton and Tom Eden set up the firm of Morton & Eden to carry on auctions in association with Sotheby's.

The Fitzwilliam Museum acquires the outstanding Conte Collection of 750 Norman and Angevin coins dating between 1066 and 1279, for £550,000 with the help of a £95,000 grant from the National Art Collections Fund.

Every schoolchild in Australia is presented with a medal commemorating the centenary of the federation of the six colonies to form the Commonwealth of Australia. The medals, each contained in a special presentation pack, are distributed on May 9.

The £2 coin used by the referee to decide the kick-off at the FA Cup Final is sold for £750 at a charity auction organised by Sky Television on May 18.

The rare Oak Tree twopence, sold at DNW on June 20.

June 2001

A rare example of an Oak Tree twopence, one of the earliest coins of the American colonies, comes under the hammer at the Dix Noonan Webb sale on June 20. The coin, struck in Massachusetts in 1662, was discovered in a garden in Devon near an ancient Quaker burial ground which may explain how the coin came to be there. Estimated at £1,500, it actually realised £4,400.

Graham Dyer, Librarian and Curator at the Royal Mint, is awarded the OBE in the Queen's Birthday Honours List.

Graham Dyer, OBE.

The last London Coin Fair at the Cumberland Hotel takes place on June 23. Due to a change of ownership of the hotel, the long-running fair organised by Howard and Frances Simmons is compelled to seek a new venue at the Posthouse, Bloomsbury.

July 2001

The British Art Medal Society's annual conference takes place on July 6–8 at the Cork Vision Centre, Cork, Ireland.

Spink dispose of the Patina Collection of official and private pattern coins covering the period from 1801 to the present day, on July 11, including a complete mintage of 174 unique gold pieces created by the British sculptor Donald R. Golder.

London Coin Auctions hold their biggest ever sale on July 15, offering 1,456 lots which realise a grand total of £53,126. The highest price is £1,153 for a parcel of 447 Roman bronze coins.

A retrospective exhibition of the work of sculptor and medallist Arnold Machin takes place at the Royal Academy Schools, Burlington House, London from July 17 to August 3. Tools and dies are on loan from the Royal Mint, for whom Machin produced the bust portrait of the Queen widely used on British and Commonwealth coins. His name, of course, is a synonym for the world's most prolific stamp series, used in Britain since 1967, for which he sculpted the Queen's portrait.

The British Museum mounts a lavish display of Mughal gold coins as part of the exhibition entitled Treasury of the World Jewelled Arts of India in the Age of the Mughals.

The Royal Mint's annual report, covering the twelve-month period to the end of June, reveals increased productivity and an all-time production record. Sales rose to $96.2m and production of circulating coins rose by 31 per cent to 4,907 million. Exports accounted for 48 per cent of total sales. UK circulating coinage rose a further 4 per cent on last year's record to a new level of 2,068 million. Nevertheless the Mint had an operating loss of £500,000, largely as a result of the restructuring and capital investment programme initiated last year.

August

Peter "Maundy" Allen dies on Saturday, August 4. He was a prominent dealer for many years, specialising in Maundy money which accounts for his popular nickname.

September 2001

"From Lire to Euro" is the title of an exhibition at the 51t National Numismatic Show in Riccione, Italy over the weekend of September 8–9.

The Royal Mint unveils the design by Ian Rank-Broadley for the coin to mark the Golden Jubilee of the Queen in 2002.

The
best
and *worst*
of recent coin designs

Royalty, always a very popular and therefore highly marketable commodity, dominated the new issues of the past year. Three occasions in particular seem to have caught the imagination of the world's mints and all were associated with queens, namely the centenary of the birth of the Queen Mother, the centenary of the death of Queen Victoria and the 75th birthday of Queen Elizabeth. Remarkably the success of the Queen Mother hundredth birthday coins in August 2000 had a considerable knock-on effect, and coins celebrating the event continued to appear well into 2001, the latest being a stunning £10 coin from Alderney, the reverse designed by David Cornell, featuring the Queen Mum surrounded by members of the Royal Family. By contrast the coming of age of HRH Prince William of Wales excited little numismatic interest, although Gibraltar loyally produced a trio of crowns in gold, silver or cupro-nickel to mark his 18th birthday.

Mary Milner Dickens, who is rapidly establishing herself as one of the outstanding contemporary coin designers, was responsible for the £5 coin released by the Royal Mint in honour of Queen Victoria. The theme of this was not so much the death, but the achievements of her long reign. Against a background of the framework of the Crystal Palace (and this neatly marking the 150th anniversary of the world's first great international exhibition) a V enclosed the profile of the young Victoria as shown on the world's first adhesive postage stamp, the Penny Black, subtly identified by a fragment of the value inscription which appeared at the foot of the stamp. It is interesting to see the stamp effigy, which was ultimately derived from William Wyon's Guildhall Medal of

1838, turned back to its origins, and one wonders whether on this occasion the Mint used the Wyon medallic original rather than the two-dimensional engraving by Charles and Frederick Heath who had the job of adapting the effigy for postal purposes.

Alderney's £10 coin struck to mark the Queen Mother's 100th birthday. Actual size 65mm.

The Royal Mint's new £5 to commemorate the Victorian Age. Actual size 38mm.

23

Due to the modest policy of the Royal Mint, designers are tasked with the problem of conveying as much as possible within the confines of a single coin. This problem does not apply to some other countries which habitually produce long sets for the same purpose. A good example of this was the prolix series of 16 crowns from Gibraltar, providing a veritable portrait gallery of the great and good of Victoria's reign. No doubt it will please thematic collectors to find Florence Nightingale, Disraeli or Gladstone represented.

The Queen's 75th birthday provoked a rash of crown-sized coins from the Channel Islands and some of the smaller remaining colonial territories. The problem with any coin celebrating Her Majesty is that she already graces the obverse. Is it necessary to portray her on both sides, or should a symbolic or purely pictorial motif be used on the reverse? This dilemma was evident in some of the coins produced by Valcambi. Whereas Ascension had the Queen's cypher over a spray of roses, the reverse designs of the Falkland Islands and Tristan da Cunha had a second go at portraiture, a profile and a facing bust respectively. The profile was marred by the inclusion of a rather fussy floral border with a cramped circular inscription for good measure, but the Tristan design was much more pleasing and for once the facing portrait worked extremely well. This is always a tricky thing for sculptors and seldom produces entirely satisfactory results.

There were reverberations of the long-running Millennium saga, with latecomers celebrating 2000 years of Christianity and therefore stressing the religious aspects of the event, together with a more secular approach in coins marking the "true" Millennium or the dawn of the 21st century in 2001. It may be remembered that the United States launched its tribute to the Millennium or new Century in the form of a series of quarters, one for each state—a programme which is destined to run and run. Canada came up with the brilliant notion of "Create a Centsation", a series of quarters with different symbolic or allegorical motifs on the reverse. Now Australia has followed suit, with a series of coins for each state in a similar vein.

Inevitably the Olympic Games loomed large over this period with a prolific series from the host country, and a number of issues from other

Coins with inlaid jewels. Top: Pobjoy's Queen Mother 1/5 crown with pearl inlaid. Right: Poland's 20 zloty with amber inlaid.

The Rhode Island quarter. Part of the US Mint's hugely popular "State's Quarters" series.

From the Canadian "Create a Centsation" series. From top: coins to represent Community and Creativity.

countries. The best coin in this category was the 25 florins from Aruba showing a Tornado sailboat performing at the Games. The only other event in the period under review which was at all noteworthy was the 60th anniversary of the Battle of Britain, ignored in Britain itself but the subject of crowns from Gibraltar and the Isle of Man.

This was also a year in which gimmickry was well to the fore. The novelty of colour has not worn off by any means, as witness the rash of coins with a multicoloured reverse released in recent months; but there is a danger that pretty pictures may become a substitute for good design and competent sculpting, and it has to be admitted that some of the colourful coins lack the overall quality of coins struck in more conventional styles. Is the Cook Islands dollar celebrating the Queen Mother better than the coins from the British Virgin Islands? The first, struck by the Perth Mint, has the portrait in

"Big is beautiful"! The Perth Mint's 1 kilo silver coin.

full colour, whereas the latter, from the Pobjoy Mint, is sculpted in the traditional manner. Actually Pobjoy also utilised this portrait in a gold coin from the Isle of Man, embellishing it with a pearl inset into the Queen's brooch. Inlay seems to be the name of the game just now. Poland's 20 zloty coin celebrating the medieval amber trade actually has a piece of amber inset on the reverse.

There is an analogy with postage stamps, in which multicoloured photogravure or offset lithography now dominate the scene, but still the finest and most prestigious stamps are those which are recess-printed in monochrome, just like the Penny Black, in fact.

"Big is beautiful" seems to be a slogan of the new century, with a number of excessively large coins; but big for the sake of bigness alone is a

Zambia's revolutionary upright oval coins. This series, commemorating 100 years of exploration also includes colour designs on the reverse.

sterile concept which generally leads us nowhere. To be sure, there are some exceptions, and one of these was the one-kilo silver coin issued by Australia in connection with the Sydney Olympic Games. Aside from the Games' logo in colour in the centre, this coin was notable for the circular frieze representing all the sporting disciplines, the grandiose motif being somewhat reminiscent of Pistrucci's Waterloo Medal.

It may be remembered that the Pobjoy Mint achieved a notable success in 1990 with coins of Gibraltar and the Isle of Man which not only reproduced the Penny Black but contrived to create the illusion of black in the coins. In an attempt to surpass this, two coins were released by Gibraltar last year reproducing the "Post Office" Mauritius 2d of 1847. Ostensibly the pretext for this was the 160th anniversary of uniform penny postage (or,

Bermuda's triangular coins.

as the coin incorrectly put it THE UNIFORM PENNY POST), though why an event in Britain in 1840 should be marked by a colonial stamp of 1847, and by a third country at that, seems rather specious. The £5 coin was struck in titanium with the centre of the design entirely in blue, but unfortunately the treatment did not quite work.

Apart from the excessive and not always judicious use of colour, there has also been an upsurge in unusual formats. Zambia appears to have carved a niche in upright ovals, often combined with colour. The latest in this genre was a series portraying famous explorers through the ages, alongside their distinctive ships. None of this, of course, had any relevance to Zambia itself, but who cares nowadays?

Triangular coins have been issued in the past by the Cook Islands and Bermuda, with rounded corners or curved sides respectively, and it is the latter shape which was adopted by Slovakia for the 5000 crowns coin celebrating the true Millennium (i.e. beginning in 2001 rather than 2000). This would have been quite a remarkable coin for its reverse

Gibraltar's crown celebrating the 21st century by Pobjoy Mint. The trimetallic coin has a silver inner ring, a gold middle ring and a platinum outer ring.

alone, showing three human hands inspired by the frescoes of Michelangelo in the Sistine Chapel, but the obverse is one of the most dramatic of recent times, with its motif of the planets and astrological symbols.

From the purely technical viewpoint, this coin also broke new ground. Bimetallic coins, which were few and far between not so many years ago, are now commonplace, so the world's mints have to go a step farther, hence trimetallic coins. The Slovak Millennium coin was struck in silver, with a central gold disc on the obverse and, within that, a central core of platinum. The same combination of precious metals can be found on Gibraltar's crown celebrating the 21st century only in this instance the order is reversed: a Celtic ring in silver at the cenre, a gold ring featuring inventions of the Second Millennium and an outer ring of platinum with futuristic ornament.

Poland also produced a trimetallic coin for the Millennium, using a combination of gold, copper and silver, the coin was arguably the best of the trimetallic confections with its obverse of the state emblem within a vortex and a reverse of a man and woman entering the tunnel of the unknown future. Andorra had much the same idea for its Millenium coin but the idea has yet to become wholly practical in the difficult medium of coinage. Canada included tiny gold-plated holographic

symbols in the reverses of the silver $20 coins showing historic modes of transport. The Bluenose, of course, already graces the humble dime, but the Toronto locomotive of 1853 and the Taylor steam buggy of 1867 were pleasing newcomers to the theme of transport.

At the other end of the spectrum, however, it was pleasing to note that traditional numismatic values were still flourishing. Austria produced a silver 100 schilling coin bearing the bust of Marcus Aurelius, a faithful reproduction of a Roman coinage effigy, while the Czech Republic struck a 200kc coin to celebrate the 700th anniversary of the famous Prager groschen of Wenceslas. The best series in this genre came from France which celebrated 2000 years of French coins by reproducing three of them, a stater of the Parisii, a denier of Charlemagne and an ecu of St Louis, with a common reverse showing the first franc of the French Revolution.

One of the most striking reverses came from Ireland whose Millennium pound featured the Broighter boat. This struck just the right balance, with a fine motif uncluttered by unnecessary ornament or inscriptions. When it comes to minimalism in coin design, the prize must go to Switzerland whose gold 50 francs honouring the children's stories of Johanna Speyri showed a barefoot Heidi running alongside a goat, with the absolute minimum of minuscule text. The same country's Millennium coin was the ultimate in obscurity. The twisted mass in the centre is officially described as "a rune-like image of a new-born baby" but it could equally well have been one of those ink blobs devised by the Swiss neurologist Hermann Rorschach and which you can interpret how you will.

The Swiss Mint's minimalist design on the 50 franc "Heidi" coin.

Canada's 20 dollars as part of the 2001 Land, Sea and Rail series. The coin includes a small holographic symbol at top left. The coin featured here depicts the Marco Polo.

Harry Potter ™

27

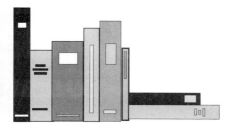

Books
of the year

Every coin collector knows that knowledge is the key to forming a good collection and each year new books or new editions of older works, as well as standard reference works, are up-dated by dedicated specialists. Here we list the most important numismatic titles that have appeared during the past year. Most have been reviewed in COIN NEWS.

ANCIENT GREEK NUMISMATICS: A GUIDE TO READING AND RESEARCH, by Bill Daehn. 400 pages. Casebound. Davisson's Ltd, Gold Spring MN 56320, USA. Price £60.

Seven years of research have gone into the production of this volume which should be a major boon to all collectors of Greek coins. The book provides an exhaustive bibliography of all books, catalogues, articles and monographs on every aspect of Greek numismatics published in the English language. As well as mainstream classical Greek coins, it encompasses such by-ways as Celtic, Parthian, Indo-Greek and early Judaean coinage.

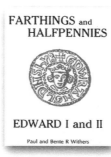

FARTHINGS and HALFPENNIES

EDWARD I and II

Paul and Bente R Withers

FARTHINGS AND HALFPENNIES OF EDWARD I AND II, by Paul and Bente R. Withers. 60 pages. Paperback. Galata Print. The Old White Lion, Market Street, Llanfyllin, Powys, SY22 5BX. Price £10.

An extremely useful classification guide to the complex and varied series of halfpennies and farthings from the reigns of the first two Edwards. The fully illustrated guide is based on a lecture given by Paul Withers at the BANS Congress, using many of the coins from the collection of the late David Rogers.

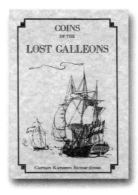

COINS OF THE LOST GALLEONS

CAPTAIN KATHRYN BUDDE-JONES

COINS OF THE LOST GALLEONS by Captain Kathryn Budde-Jones. 30 pages. World Treasure Books, PO Box 5, Newport, Isle of Wight.

This little book provides an admirable introduction to the world of shipwrecked Spanish galleons and the treasure they conveyed from the New World. In particular it lists and describes the cobs, bars and primitive pieces of eight which have been brought to the surface in more recent years.

MEDIEVAL ENGLISH GROATS, by Ivan Buck. Greenlight Publishing, 119 Newland Street, Witham, Essex CM8 1WF. Price £15.

MEDIEVAL ENGLISH GROATS

Ivan Buck

This colourful book surveys the origins and development of the groat, from its introduction in the reign of Edward I to its decline and demise under the Tudor monarchs. A very readable and entertaining text is admirably illustrated in full colour.

RENNICK'S AUSTRALIAN COIN & BANKNOTE VALUES, edited by Ian Pitt. 192 pages. Price £10 (soft covers) or £15 (casebound), plus £2 p&p.

SPANISH COLONIAL SILVER COINS IN THE FLORIDA COLLECTION, by Alan K. Craig. Florida University Press. Price $49.95.

This is the favourite currency catalogue of all knowledgeable collectors in the Antipodes and although the prices are given in Australian dollars it provides a valuable and authoritative guide to all Australian coins and banknotes. Every item is well illustrated and includes rare patterns and 19th century trade tokens. The modern issues of the Royal Australian Mint and the Perth Mint are covered in considerable detail.

The State of Florida owns a vast collection of nearly 23,000 pieces of Spanish treasure coins salvaged from ships wrecked off the coast. It is the largest collection in the world of its kind and makes a fascinating area for study. A companion volume dealing with the gold coins is currently in production.

ROMAN COIN PRICE YEARBOOK 1996/97, compiled by Morten Eske Mortensen. Auction Corporation-DK, Grelberg Forlagsekspedition, Drejogade 26 F 501, DH-2100, Copenhagen Ø, Demark.

STANDARD CATALOG OF WORLD COINS 2002. 2048 pages. Card covers. Krause Publications, 700 East State Street, Iola, Wisconsin. Price £40 plus £8 p&p, from Token Publishing.

This book covers Roman Republican coins at auction world-wide in the period 1996–97 and is a companion volume to a previous yearbook dealing with Roman Imperial coins. The information has been collated and tabulated to show both estimates and prices realised. As well as auction prices it contains a number of features and other information by leading experts in this field.

SCANDINAVIAN COIN PRICE YEARBOOK. 650 pages. Auction Corporation-DK, Grelberg Forlagsekspedition, Drejogade 26 F 501, DK-2100 Copenhagen Ø, Denmark. Price £68.

A new edition of a well-established price guide to the coins of Denmark, Norway, Sweden, Schleswig-Holstein and the various overseas territories, containing auction realisations over the period 1998–99. Over 17,000 prices are recorded from sales all over the world.

This massive book details all the coins of the world which have been issued from 1901 to the present time, with over a million prices and tens of thousands of price updates and revisions since the previous edition.

SYLLOGE OF COINS OF THE BRITISH ISLES: THE NORWEB COLLECTION, TOKENS OF THE BRITISH ISLES 1573–1750, Part VI, by R.H. Thompson and M. J. Dickinson. 264 pages. Casebound, Spink. £25.

This part deals with the tokens of the English counties from Wiltshire to Yorkshire, together with those of Scotland, Ireland, Wales and the offshore islands. The project began in 1973 when Mrs Mary Norweb and her husband Henry invited Robert Thompson to examine their collection of 17th century British tokens. Mrs Norweb had first become interested in coins as long ago as 1905 and over the ensuing half century she built up one of the most remarkable collections ever formed. From 1953 onwards, however, she and her husband concentrated on British 17th century tokens. Following her death, her collection of coins was sold at auction, but the tokens remained intact. Originally Thompson planned to produce a mere check list but it was the late Christopher Blunt who proposed that a full catalogue of the collection should be incorporated in the British Academy's Sylloge series, and as a result the first part covering the tokens was published in 1984. The Norweb collection comprises some 13,000 specimens and this handsome volume now brings this monumental project to a highly satisfactory conclusion.

TOKENS OF THE INDUSTRIAL REVOLUTION, FOREIGN SILVER COINS COUNTERMARKED FOR USE IN GREAT BRITAIN, by Harrington E. Manville. 328 pages. Casebound. Spink. Price £40.

This impressive volume is the first ever produced on the subject of foreign silver coins countermarked for circulation in Great Britain during the late 18th and early 19th centuries at a time of shortage of indigenous coins during the Napoleonic Wars. Whereas the Bank of England was responsible for the countermarked silver which circulated in England, many coins were privately countermarked in Scotland by various commercial enterprises. A few privately countermarked coins were produced in the Midlands and north of England but the only examples in Ireland hailed from Belfast and County Kilkenny. Despite prohibition by several Acts of Parliament, countermarking continued unabated until such times as the government replenished the supply of British silver coins in everyday circulation.

This magnificent book is a distillation of more than 35 years of research in both private collections and the collections of the great national and provincial museums.

THE WORLD'S SHOW, by Leslie Allen. 280 pages. Casebound. Coincraft. Price £29.50 plus £2.50 p&p.

A splendid treatise on the tokens, medals and advertising pieces produced in connection with exhibitions and other events at the Crystal Palace, from its inception during the Great Exhibition of 1851 up to the time it was destroyed by fire in November 1936. The authoritative text is matched by lavish illustrations.

And don't forget the companion titles to the COIN YEARBOOK, from Token Publishing:

BANKNOTE YEARBOOK. Softbound. 232 pages. Price £14.95.

MEDAL YEARBOOK. Softbound. 472 pages. Price £16.95.

For further information on these popular annual titles, telephone 01404 44166.

VIGO
Tercentenary

COLLECTORS of early British milled coinage will be familiar with the coins of Queen Anne with the name VIGO inscribed below the Queen's bust, and that this denotes bullion which was captured from the Spaniards there—but little else. One standard numismatic reference work even states that Vigo is a town in Portugal, while such works as Lloyd Laing's monumental *Coins in History*, C. H. V. Sutherland's *English Coinage 600–1900* and Howard Linecar's *British Coin Designs and Designers* dismiss the Vigo coins in a single sentence, merely stating that they exist. To the uninitiated, the appearance of a Spanish name on British coins is intriguing to put it mildly. As the tercentenary of the battle which gave rise to the coins occurs this year it seems timely to look at the background of the coins and the events which gave rise to them.

The coins were the outcome of certain economic and political developments. The chief economic factor was the chronic shortage of silver which developed in the 17th century and continued throughout the 18th. This seems paradoxical, in view of the vast quantities of silver mined in South and Central America, but the simple truth was that it was insufficient to keep pace with the demand in Europe where industrial progress and material prosperity were matched by a tremendous population explosion. The general scarcity of silver from the Restoration onwards was reflected in the somewhat sporadic output of the Mint and, interestingly, in the marking of coins with symbols to denote the sources of supply: the plumes (Wales), roses (West of England), the elephant and castle

Other provenance marks. From left: roses and plumes on a 1707 crown; SSC on a 1723 crown.

(the African Company) or the letters SSC (the South Seas Company). The word VIGO which appeared on gold and silver coins in 1702–3 was put there primarily to identify the source of the bullion, but it may also have been intended to celebrate a brilliant coup—although this is nowhere stated in the warrant authorising the coins. Certainly posterity tends to regard the coins as quasi-commemorative.

The chief political factor was the overweening ambition of Louis XIV to become a second Charlemagne, creating an empire covering the whole of western Europe. Matters came to a head when Charles II, King of Spain, was persuaded, on his death-bed, to name Philip of Bourbon, grandson of Louis, as his successor. With Philip on the Spanish throne, Louis could claim with some justification that the Pyrenees had ceased to exist. He could have said much the same of the Alps, for he now gained control of the extensive Spanish territories in Italy. This extension of Bourbon power not only threatened to turn the western Mediterranean into a French lake, but threatened British interests farther north, for it meant that the French now gained control of the Spanish Netherlands (modern Belgium). In March 1701 all of the fortresses in that area were taken over by French troops. William of Orange, as Stadholder of the United Netherlands (i.e. Holland) as well as being William III of Britain, was very quick to perceive the threat. Indeed, he had feared that something of this sort might eventually happen and during the last years of his life he had been laying the foundations of an anti-French coalition involving not only Britain and Holland but also Austria (whose Archduke Charles was put forward as a rival candidate to the Spanish throne), some of the German states, Denmark and Portugal. France, on the other hand, had the backing of Spain, Bavaria and Cologne.

Immediately after the French take-over of the Belgian fortresses, Britain and Holland began preparing for war, but at that time neither possessed land forces which could have taken on the might of the French army, arguably the largest, best-equipped and trained in Europe. In the war, which dragged on for 12 years, the chief opposition to the French from the outset came from Austria whose armies under their brilliant commander, Prince Eugene, drove the French out of Italy. From 1702 onwards, however, Eugene shared the honours with John Churchill, later first Duke of Marlborough, whose victories at Blenheim, Ramillies, Oudenarde and Malplaquet helped to determine the outcome of the war.

At the outset, however, Britain and Holland put their faith in their navies. A generation earlier they had fought each other but now they were allies in the common cause against France and Spain. In fact, the War of the Spanish Succession was essentially a series of land campaigns, "a monotonous round of marches and sieges" as one historian has dismissed it, and there was very little activity at sea. But it did yield one spectacular sideshow which, in monetary terms, was one of the most profitable ventures since Elizabethan times, an exploit of which Sir Francis Drake himself would have been proud.

Sir Francis, in fact, had twice attacked the Spanish port of Vigo, situated on the north-western coast in the province of Pontevedra. In 1585 and again four years later, Drake had sailed into Vigo Bay and destroyed galleons under the very muzzles of the gun batteries that bristled round the shore. Vigo was one of the chief ports of entry for the treasure fleets sailing from the Caribbean and when British naval intelligence got wind of a rumour that a "plate fleet" was on its way from the Spanish Main, a fleet of 50 warships was hastily assembled and despatched south.

The French, anticipating an attack from the British and Dutch, had provided a screen of frigates across the Bay of Biscay to protect the treasure ships, but Admiral Sir George Rooke skilfully evaded the enemy and boldly sailed into Vigo Bay. The ensuing battle was a splendid example of what later came to be called combined operations. Transport ships landed an army under the command of James Butler, the second Duke of Ormonde, and his crack troops swiftly overran the ring of fortresses and silenced their guns.

The power of the British Navy. A man-of-war attacks a Spanish Galleon off Cartagena, May 28, 1708.

The naval engagement was virtually a turkey shoot, as the British and Dutch battleships and frigates bombarded the treasure fleet. No fewer than 37 French and Spanish ships were captured or destroyed and many more were severely disabled. It was a major blow from which the French and Spanish navies never recovered. Two years later Sir George Rooke and his Dutch allies pulled off another major victory when they seized the Rock of Gibraltar, the key to the Mediterranean and of immense strategic value.

But the exploit at Vigo on October 22, 1702 did more than merely enhance the naval prestige of Britain. The treasure and other property seized was valued in excess of a million pounds, but by the time the prize money had been paid out to those who had taken part in the expedition, the Treasury received only £95,000 in silver and gold bullion. Nevertheless, for a government which was chronically short of cash, this was a significant windfall.

In his capacity as Chief Engraver of the Mint, John Croker (previously Johann Crocker) was extremely busy that year. The sudden death of William III in a riding accident at the early age of 54 brought to the throne his sister-in-law Anne, the younger daughter of James II, and now her buxom left-facing bust replaced the bewigged profile of William on the coinage.

The rarest of all the Vigo coins is the gold five guinea piece. None was struck in 1702 but a small quantity was produced the following year. Remarkably, no fewer than four different types

Rare 1703, pre-Union five guineas with "VIGO" below bust. For more on the coins of the reign of Anne see COIN NEWS August 2001.

have been identified. In the first group, with stops on the obverse, minute variations in the positioning of the VIGO mark reveal that three dies were produced. To this may be added a fourth variety in which no stops are present. All of the Vigo five-guineas are of the greatest rarity, fewer than 20 in total being said to exist. An unspecified but small quantity of guineas was also struck in 1703 with VIGO on the obverse, but only one type has been recorded. Similarly a handful of half-guineas was minted. In total, some 34 pounds of gold from the Vigo treasure was coined—less than one per cent of the gold coined the previous year.

The first crowns of Anne's reign likewise appeared in 1703 and were entirely produced from Spanish booty, but only one type with the VIGO mark is known. Half-crowns were struck in considerable quantities and a high proportion of them have apparently survived in VF or EF condition, suggesting that they appealed to the public on account of their source and were hoarded accordingly rather than spent. Conversely half-crowns of 1703 without the VIGO mark are very much scarcer, and collectors have to be on their guard for coins which have had the mark erased.

The only coin which actually appeared in the year of the battle was the shilling. To have produced coins dated 1702 so soon after the victorious fleet returned to England must have been quite a feat. The Vigo shillings of 1702 are the commonest of the three types of shilling struck that year, having been preceded by coins without any provenance mark and then coins with Welsh plumes. In 1703, however, production of shillings was confined to those from the Spanish silver and these are by far the commonest of all the Vigo coins, offering even the collector of modest means the opportunity to possess at least one of the pieces which stand as a lasting testament to one of Britain's greatest naval exploits.

The Jubilee coinage
of 1887

THE last time that a British monarch celebrated her Golden Jubilee was in 1887, and it could be argued that the country which Victoria ruled bore just as little resemblance to the kingdom at her accession as the UK of 2002 does to the UK of 1952. Both half centuries witnessed the most momentous changes at every level of society and in every walk of life. A Golden Jubilee is a rare event and one which, like the Millennium, is a time for looking back as well as forward.

So far as Victorian Britain was concerned, there had been immense political changes between 1837 and 1887. The Whigs and Tories had given way to the efficient party machines of the Liberals and Conservatives. The franchise was considerably extended by the Reform Act of 1885 but the working classes were now becoming disenchanted with the Liberals and realising that they needed a party of their own. This was actually advocated by Keir Hardie in 1887 but did not come to fruition until his election to parliament in 1892. The great Dock Strike of 1889 over the docker's tanner—an extra sixpence a day—led to a tremendous extension of trade unionism and thereafter socialism became less of an intellectual exercise and more concerned with organising the class struggle along political and industrial lines. In the general election of 1895, however, all of the ILP candidates were defeated. Rising prosperity and full employment, after the depression of the 1880s, booming industry and rapidly expanding overseas markets all combined to raise standards of living.

It was in this atmosphere, beginning with the promise of happier times around the corner and continuing with the mounting euphoria of the 1890s, that the two Jubilees of Queen Victoria should be seen. In retrospect the "Jubilee Period" came to be seen as an era of unprecedented material prosperity and progress, a golden age at the close of a very long reign. The crown had come to Victoria as a symbol of political ineptitude and moral degradation; by the time of the Golden Jubilee she had come to make it a unique symbol of national honour.

Her rigid devotion to duty and unflagging industry were qualities which the Victorians prized and respected. To be sure, in the period immediately before her Jubilee, the Queen was still somewhat remote from her people, the Widow of Windsor, grieving for her beloved Albert who had died in 1861. On her rare appearances in public she was seen as a small, rather dumpy figure of forbidding mien, severely clad in black. For formal occasions she favoured a tiny crown which may have been more comfortable than the traditional crowns but tended to create a ludicrous effect, especially when viewed in profile.

This was taken as the model for a new coinage effigy, sculpted by Sir Joseph Edgar Boehm. Leonard Charles Wyon had the unenviable task of translating this into the dies engraved for an entirely new series of gold and silver coins. It is difficult to apportion blame for the results as, to a large extent, the engraving of dies had become mechanical, thanks to the use of the pantographic reducing machine. Moreover, it should be remembered that the great outcry that greeted the issue of the coins was provoked largely by the shock of seeing the queen as she really was, and not the somewhat idealised teenager as she was portrayed on stamps and the smaller silver coins.

What was remarkable about the Jubilee series was the inclusion of five-and two-pound coins. No two-pound coin had circulated since 1823 and

The Jubilee two-pounds, 1887.

37

The Jubilee five-pounds, 1887.

no circulating coin of comparable value to the five-pounds since the five-guineas of George II in 1753. Now both of these high values were struck in circulating and proof versions. Another feature of the Jubilee series was the extension of the George and Dragon motif to the two largest gold coins as well as the sovereign. The issue of these high-value coins was confined to Jubilee Year itself, but sovereigns with the Boehm profile and George and Dragon reverse were issued until 1892 (Royal Mint) and 1893 (Sydney and Melbourne). The half-sovereign retained a heraldic reverse, though the shield was redesigned and the Victorian small crown substituted for the imperial crown previously used. The date was also transferred from the obverse to the reverse and placed below the point of the shield. Half-sovereigns were not minted again until 1890–93 (Royal Mint), but were also struck at Sydney (1889 and 1891) and Melbourne (1893).

The same spirit of nostalgia that inspired the high-value gold coins probably tipped the balance in favour of the inclusion of a crown in the Jubilee silver series. This cumbersome coin had not been issued for general circulation since 1847, though a proof crown had been included in the 1853 set. For the Jubilee crown, the Mint went back to Pistrucci's St George and Dragon, last used for a crown in 1822. They were struck in circulating as well as proof versions, the former continuing annually until 1892.

As yet another round in the battle for decimalisation, a coin tariffed at four shillings was introduced at this time. The double florin was soon dubbed the Barmaid's Grief, on the grounds that barmaids were frequently confused into regarding this coin as a crown and giving drinks or change equivalent to five shillings. It is hard to imagine Victorian barmaids being any less astute than their modern counterparts, and this tale ignores the fact that no confusion ever seems to have been associated with the half-crown and its slightly smaller partner, the florin. Moreover, the double florin had a totally different reverse from the crown, with a cruciform arrangement of

heraldic shields. The truth of the matter is that the public, while ready to accept crowns which had existed in the past, were ever hostile to an entirely new denomination. Two versions of this coin exist, with Arabic or Roman numeral (1 or I) in the date. The Arabic version was used for proofs and retained for the double florins of 1888–90. Significantly, far fewer double florins were minted in these three years and the experiment was then abandoned.

The Jubilee half-crown followed the pattern of its predecessor and had a crowned shield on the reverse though this, too, harked back to the reign of George IV and closely resembled the design used in 1823–4, the shield being surrounded by the insignia of the Garter, though the crown was modernised. Jubilee half-crowns were minted each year until 1892.

The florin was a scaled down version of the double florin, with the same cruciform shields on the reverse, with sceptres crossing the angles. Two of these sceptres had the usual royal top, while the others were topped by a harp and thistle respectively, and the star of the Garter appeared in the centre. The florin was struck annually until 1892.

The shilling and sixpence abandoned the wreathed value concept of earlier years and returned to the shield in Garter motif used in the 1820s, with suitable modifications to update the details. The inclusion of the queen's titles in full cramped the effigy on the shillings of 1887–89 but a new obverse, with a larger portrait and smaller lettering, was adopted in 1889 and continued till 1892. No sooner had the Garter shield version of the sixpence been released than dishonest people began gilding them and passing them off as half-sovereigns. The authorities promptly reverted to the wreathed value reverse employed since 1838, but this was updated with the new Victorian crown at the top. Sixpences of this type were struck till 1893, though the mintage decreased each year from 1891.

Since the Maundy ceremony of 1887 took place before the Jubilee festivities commenced, the Maundy money that year had been in the style of the young head coinage. The Jubilee profile was not adopted for the Maundy series until 1888, and thereafter the four smallest silver coins with Victorian crowns surmounting the values were struck until 1892. There was, however, a threepence, intended for general circulation, and this appeared as part of the Jubilee set in 1887, in both proof and circulating versions. The circulating version in subsequent years can be distinguished from the Maundy coin by its relatively dull surface. Groats, last minted in 1836, were fleetingly revived in 1888 for use in British Guiana. These had the Jubilee obverse and Britannia reverse.

Talking
Tokens

Strictly speaking, a token is any piece of money whose intrinsic value is less than its face value. In that sense, therefore, all modern coins are mere tokens, because their metallic worth is invariably less than their nominal, legal tender value. Until the 19th century, however, most countries issued coins which contained metal up to the value at which they circulated. This applied mainly to gold and silver coins, but it should be noted that Britain's first copper penny and twopence (1797) were so cumbersome because they contained one and two ounces of metal respectively, copper being then valued at a penny an ounce.

The desire for parity between intrinsic and nominal value led to copper coins containing a small plug of silver to bring them up to their full value. The UK abandoned full value in 1816; as a result of the recoinage of that year the gold sovereign became the absolute standard and all silver and copper coins became mere tokens. The difference between real and nominal value widened in subsequent years with the debasement of silver coins and finally the replacement of silver altogether by cupro-nickel and other base alloys. Oddly enough, there have been many instances of small copper or bronze coins in recent years which had a greater intrinsic value than their face value and actually cost twice as much to produce as they were worth in circulation.

A token is an outward sign or pledge, something given or shown as a guarantee of authority or good faith. The word comes from German *zeichen* and Old English *tacen*, meaning a sign or mark. From this developed the notion of a promise, symbol or keepsake. In the numismatic sense, however, the term is restricted to any coinlike object, either issued by a body other than a government, or something which is used in place of money and can be exchanged for specified goods and services. Broadly speaking, tokens include any unofficial coins supplied by local bodies or occasionally even private individuals and tolerated in general circulation at times of shortage of government issues of small change.

Tokens go back a surprisingly long way. The earliest issues in base metal with limited local validity were produced by Sicily in the middle of the fifth century BC, the bronze litra being easier to handle than its tiny silver counterpart. Himera was one of the first towns to issue such tokens, but by the end of the century many Sicilian towns had adopted small bronze pieces as token currency, the intrinsic value of which was considerably below the circulating value placed on them by the issuing authorities.

This concept gradually spread to all other parts of the Greek world. Under the Roman Empire, base-metal tokens were issued from the time of Augustus to the late third century AD. Sometimes referred to as quasi-autonomous coinage, these pieces were struck mostly in bronze with the nominal value of drachmae or sestertii, and have portraits of local deities instead of the Roman emperor and members of his family. These tokens were struck by every town and city and their range and variety is enormous.

This concept survived the fall of the Roman Empire and many towns in medieval Europe continued to strike small base-metal pieces for use as local currency. They were usually accorded a measure of legality because they were authorised by the royal or imperial government, even if their actual design and metal content were decided by the municipal authorities. In addition to the tokens which served as small change there are other categories of coinlike material which deserve comment.

Jetons (from French *jeter*, to throw) originated in medieval France as counters used on the chequerboard by merchants and bankers as well as royal treasurers to do their monetary calculations. These pieces spread rapidly all over Europe, but found their greatest expression at Nuremberg where, in the hands of Hans Krauwinckel (flourished 1580–1620), they attained the status of an art form and were often produced in thematic sets.

While many jetons were struck in gold or silver and were eventually used (especially in France) as a form of New Year bonus to servants, the vast majority of them were struck in debased silver alloys (billon) or in copper, bronze, brass or pewter. Base-metal Nuremberg jetons, in fact, often circulated as small change in countries where there was a shortage of total lack of government issues of small change. This situation arose in England early in the 14th century, Nuremberg jetons circulating freely until 1335 when they were banned by statute.

English tokens

The first indigenous tokens in England were cast or struck in lead and have been recorded as circulating in 1404. For many years these local farthings and half-farthings were tolerated but had no official sanction. They were certainly well-established in Tudor times and it was not until 1598 that any attempt was made to regulate them.

The prolific issues of 18th century tokens were banned on the introduction of the "Cartwheel" coinage in 1797.

Queen Elizabeth then licensed Bristol to issue lead tokens, to be valid within a ten-mile radius of the city. At the same time, private tokens were expressly forbidden, so that the municipal tokens were given a monopoly. By the end of the Civil War (1649) there was an acute shortage of small change, and illicit tokens, mainly in lead and including pewter, brass, copper or even leather pieces, were revived in England and Wales.

Almost 4,000 types of token were issued in London alone, by tradesmen and shopkeepers of all kinds, and often circulating no farther than the end of the street. As the vast majority were produced before the Great Fire of 1666 they form an invaluable record of London streets and their occupants from this period. Following the introduction of regal copper farthings and halfpence in 1672 these tradesmen's tokens were banned, but they continued in some parts of England until 1674, and survived in Ireland until 1679. By contrast there was virtually no need for tokens in 17th century Scotland because of an abundant supply of copper coinage, and only two Scottish tokens (c. 1668) have so far been recorded.

In many ways tokens benefited the poor, who were no longer compelled to purchase more than they actually required because the smallest coin available was a penny. Tokens were also used as alms, as people would gladly give a farthing but would think twice about giving a halfpenny or penny. For this reason many tokens of the 17th century were inscribed "Remember the Poore",

17th century tokens come in a variety of shapes and sizes.

"For the Poore's Advantage" or "For Change & Charitie" or some other pious slogan.

There were even tokens inscribed in verse: "To supply the poore's need is charitie indeed". Other poetic inscriptions include "When you please, I'll change thee", "Although but brass, yet let me pass", "Welcome you be to trade with me" or "Take these that will, I'll change them still".

Eighteenth century tokens

Tokens were revived in the British Isles in 1787 to fill a gap in the regal coinage. Silver pennies for general circulation were only sporadically produced in the reign of George III and none at all was minted after 1786. The dearth of copper halfpence and farthings was even greater as none was minted after 1775. On this occasion the way was led by the Angelsey Copper Mining Company which began striking pennies with the effigy of a Druid on the obverse. This triggered off an immense deluge of token pennies, halfpennies and farthings. The range was not as great as it had been in the 17th century as fewer individual shopkeepers now issued them.

There was a greater concentration of tokens issued by municipal authorities and the more important merchant companies. On the other hand, the quality of design and execution improved beyond all recognition and latterly they were aimed at the contemporary collector market, with emphasis on heraldry, landmarks, scenery, historic events and portraits of local and national celebrities. These tokens enjoyed a decade of use before they were banned following the introduction of the "Cartwheel" coinage in 1797.

Nineteenth century tokens

Silver tokens were issued between 1804 and 1816 as a result of a continuing shortage of silver coins. At first countermarked Spanish dollars and half-dollars were issued but in 1811–12 the Bank of England released silver pieces inscribed BANK TOKEN on the reverse, with the value and date below. The obverse portrayed George III and had his name and titles round the circumference like the proper silver coins. Denominations of 1s6d and 3s were issued; though 9d pieces exist they were only patterns. The Bank of Ireland had silver tokens in the same period, but denominated in a decimal system of 5, 10 and 30 pence, as well as 6 shillings. Many private silver tokens were issued in 1811–12 in denominations from 3d to 5s, mainly by private banks, local authorities and large companies.

Copper or bronze tokens were again issued in the British Isles from 1811 to the 1830s. As no copper subsidiary coins were issued between 1807 and 1821 (no halfpence or pennies until 1825–26) the range of tokens in this period was far greater than ever. Significantly a high proportion of these tokens were now issued by banks rather than by private individuals.

Other types of tokens

Tokens have been produced in most countries at some time or another. Very extensive series, for example, were produced in Canada and Australia before these countries introduced subsidiary coinage. They were also produced on a number of occasions in the USA, from the revolutionary period onwards, and notably during the Hard Times (1834–44) during a shortage of copper cents and half-cents. There was a further spate of local tokens during the Civil War (1861–65), often with patriotic motifs and having a propaganda purpose as well as filling the gap in the coinage. Many countries issued tokens during and after the First World War, every type of material from pasteboard and wood to leather and even rubber being pressed into service. A special category consists of trade dollars issued all over Canada. These are often commemorative or intended as tourist mementoes, but they have a nominal value, redeemable for cash within a certain area

Banks and local authorities produced hundreds of different tokens in the early 19th century.

Hop tokens, although simple and sometimes crudely made, can make an interesting collection.

Another vast area consists of the checks and tokens issued by co-operative societies, often in proportion to the money spent by the member in the societies' stores, as a form of dividend. When a certain quantity of checks had been accumulated they could be exchanged for goods or services. The same concept underlay the discount schemes, premium giveaways and trading stamps of more recent items.

Tokens of metal, pasteboard or even plastic have been used as a method of controlling the use of public transport by employees of companies, the Post Office or local authorities, being given out whenever it was necessary for an employee to travel on official business. Such tokens were produced by local authorities or the private companies operating buses, ferries, trams and other services. At the other end of the spectrum are the tokens and passes, often in silver or even gold, or ivory, which were issued to directors of the railway companies to enable them to travel free of charge. Tokens in the same materials, and for the same purpose, were produced for the use of the directors and shareholders of theatres and other places of entertainment, and were often highly ornate in design.

and over a fixed period, usually twelve months. They are immensely popular and now have a wide following in North America.

In Britain from the 18th century onwards tokens were often issued by textile mills, collieries, iron foundries and other industrial undertakings in exchange for a day's work. These tokens could only be used to obtain goods from the company stores, and were eventually outlawed by the Truck Act in 1844. Nevertheless they survived in various parts of Britain, often in specific forms of labour. A very prolific series, for example, consists of hop-pickers' tokens, associated mainly with the hopfields of Kent and Sussex. In Scotland, however, fruit-pickers' tokens were also issued by many of the farms in the Clyde Valley and the fruit-growing areas of Perthshire and Angus.

Gaming tokens

This is another vast field, ranging from the brass halfpenny and penny tokens issued by many pubs and taverns in the 19th century for use in games of chance, to the modern tokens, often in cupro-nickel, bronze or aluminium-bronze, used in one-armed bandits and fruit machines. These tokens range from the fairly utilitarian designs showing perhaps a company name and a unit of value only, to the very elaborate tokens used by casinos and gaming clubs, often with special security features built into their design and composition. Many of the gaming tokens of more recent years have a quasi-commemorative or publicity character.

A new world record price for a British token was set at Noble Numismatic's sale on July 7/8, 1998, when Richard Orchard's Sawbridgeworth token realised £24,400.

Dates
on coins

The vast majority of modern coins bear the date prominently on one side. In most cases dates are expressed in modified Arabic numerals according to the Christian calendar and present no problem in identification. There have been a few notable exceptions to this general rule, however. Morocco, for example, has used European numerals to express dates according to the Moslem calendar, so that a coin dated 1321 actually signifies 1903. Dates are almost invariably written from left to right—even in Arabic script which writes words from right to left. An exception, however, occurred in the Philippines quarto of 1822 where the date appeared as 2281, and the "2s" back to front for good measure.

	ARABIC-TURKISH	CHINESE, JAPANESE KOREAN, ANNAMESE (ORDINARY)	CHINESE, JAPANESE KOREAN, ANNAMESE (OFFICIAL)	INDIAN	SIAMESE	BURMESE
1	١	一	壹	٩	๑	၁
2	٢	二	貳	۲	๒	၂
3	٣	三	叁	۳	๓	၃
4	٤	四	肆	٨	๔	၄
5	٥	五	伍	٤	๕	၅
6	٦	六	陸	٤	๖	၆
7	٧	七	柒	٥	๗	၇
8	٨	八	捌	८	๘	၈
9	٩	九	玖	९	๙	၉
0	٠			٥	๐	၀
10	١٠	十	拾		๑๐	
100	١٠٠	百			๑๐๐	
1000	١٠٠٠	千				

Dates in Roman numerals have been used since 1234 when this practice was adopted by the Danish town of Roskilde. Such Roman numerals were used sporadically throughout the Middle Ages and in later centuries and survive fitfully to this day. This was the system used in England for the first dated coins, the gold half-sovereigns of Edward VI struck at Durham House in 1548 (MDXLVIII). This continued till 1550 (MDL) but thereafter Arabic numerals were used, beginning with the half-crown of 1551. Notable exceptions of more recent times include the Gothic coinage of Queen Victoria (1847–87).

The first coin with the date in European numerals was a plappart of St Gallen, Switzerland dated 1424, but this was an isolated case. In 1477 Maria of Burgundy issued a guldiner which bore a date on the reverse, in the form of two pairs of digits flanking the crown at the top. The numerals in this instance were true Gothic, an interesting transition between true Arabic numerals and the modified Arabic figures now used in Europe. The Tyrolese guldengroschen of 1484–6 were the first coins to be regularly dated in European numerals and thereafter this custom spread rapidly.

For the numismatist, the problem arises when coins bear a date in the numerals of a different alphabet or computed according to a different era. Opposite is a table showing the basic numerals used in different scripts. The various eras which may be found in coin dates are as listed and explained overleaf.

Hijra

The era used on Moslem coins dates from the flight of Mohammed from Mecca to Medina on July 15, 622 and is often expressed as digits followed by AH (*Anno Hegirae*). Moslems employ a lunar calendar of twelve months comprising 354 11/30 days. Tipu Sultan of Mysore in 1201 AH (the fifth year of his reign)introduced a new era dating from the birth of Mohammed in AD 570 and using a luni-solar system. Tipu also adopted the Hindu cycle of sixty years (the Tamil Brihaspate Cycle), but changed this two or three years later, from Hijra to Muludi.

Afghan coins used the lunar calendar until 1920 and during 1929–31, but at other times have used the solar calendar. Thus the Democratic Republic began issuing its coins in SH 1358 (1979).

To convert an AH date to the Christian calendar you must translate the Arabic into European numerals. Taking an Arabic coin dated 1320, for example, first deduct 3% (to convert from the Moslem lunar year to our solar year). This gives 39.6 which, rounded up to the nearest whole number, is 40. Deduct 40 from 1320 (1280), then add 622. The answer is 1902.

There have been a few notable exceptions. Thus the Khanian era of Ilkhan Ghazan Mahmud began on 1st Rajab 701 AH (1301). This era used a solar calendar, but was shortlived, being confined to coins of Mahmud and his nephew Abu Said down to year 34 (1333).

The era of Tarikh Ilahi was adopted by the Mughal emperor Akbar in the thirteenth year of his reign (922 AH). This era dated from his accession on 5th Rabi al-Sani 963 AH (February 19, 1556). The calendar had solar months and days but no weeks, so each day of the month had a different name. This system was used by Akbar, Jahangir and Shah Jahan, often with a Hijra date as well.

Saphar

The era of the Caesars began on January 1, 38 BC and dated from the conquest of Spain by Augustus. Its use on coinage, however, seems to have been confined to the marabotins of Alfonso VIII of Castile and was expressed in both Latin and Arabic.

Samvat

The era of Vikramaditya began in 57 BC and was a luni-solar system used in some Indian states. Coins may be found with both Samvat and Hijra dates. Conversion to the Christian date is simple; merely subtract 57 from the Samvat to arrive at the AD date.

Saka

This originated in the southwestern district of Northern India and began in AD 78. As it used the luni-solar system it converts easily by adding 78 to the Saka date.

Nepal

Nepalese coins have used four different date systems. All coins of the Malla kings were dated in Nepal Samvat (NS) era, year 1 beginning in 881. This system was also used briefly by the state of Cooch Behar. Until 1888 all coins of the Gurkha dynasty were dated in the Saka era (SE) which began in AD 78. After 1888 most copper coins were dated in the Vikram Samvat (VS) era from 57 BC. With the exception of some gold coins struck in 1890 and 1892, silver and gold coins only changed to the VS era in 1911, but now this system is used for all coins struck in Nepal. Finally, dates in the Christian era have appeared on some commemorative coins of recent years.

Ethiopian

This era dates from August AD 7, so that EE 1885 is AD 1892. Ethiopian dates are expressed in five digits using Amharic numerals. The first two are the digits of the centuries, the third is the character for 100, while the fourth and fifth are the digits representing the decade and year. On modern coins dates are rendered in Amharic numerals using the Christian era.

Thailand

Thai coins mainly use the Buddhist era (BE) which dates from 543 BC, but some coins have used dates from the Chula-Sakarat calendar (CS) which began in AD 638, while others use a Ratanakosind Sok (RS) date from the foundation of the Chakri dynasty in AD 1781.

Hebrew

The coins of Israel use the Jewish calendar dating from the beginning of the world (Adam and Eve in the Garden of Eden) in 3760 BC. Thus the year 1993 is rendered as 5753. The five millennia are assumed in dates, so that only the last three digits are expressed. 735 therefore equates with AD 1975. Dates are written in Hebrew letters, reading from right to left. The first two characters signify 400 and 300 respectively, totalling 700. The third letter denotes the decades (*lamedh* = 30) and the fourth letter, following the separation mark (") represents the final digit (*heh* = 5). The Jewish year runs from September or October in the Christian calendar.

Dates from the creation of the world

This system was also used in Russia under Ivan IV. The dating system *Anno Mundi* (AM) was established by the Council of Constantinople in AD 680 which determined that the birth of Christ had occurred in 5508 AM. Ivan's coins expressed the date as 7055 (1447).

Dynastic dates

The system of dating coinage according to regnal years is a feature of Chinese and Japanese coins. Chinese coins normally have an inscription stating that they are coins of such and such a reign period (not the emperor's name), and during the Southern Sung dynasty this was joined by the numeral of the year of the reign. This system was continued under the republic and survives in Taiwan to this day, although the coins of the Chinese Peoples Republic are dated in western numerals using the Christian calendar.

Early Japanese coins bore a reference to the era (the title assumed by each emperor on his accession) but, like Chinese coins, could not be dated accurately. From the beginning of the Meiji era (1867), however, coins have included a regnal number. The Showa era, beginning in 1926 with the accession of Hirohito, eventually ran to sixty-three (expressed in western numerals on some denominations, in Japanese ideograms on others) to denote 1988, although the rest of the inscription was in Japanese characters.

Dynastic dates were used on Korean milled coins introduced in 1888. These bore two characters at the top *Kae Kuk* (founding of the dynasty) followed by quantitative numerals. The system dated from the founding of the Yi dynasty in 1392.

Curiously enough, some Korean banknotes have borne dates from the foundation of the first dynasty in 2333 BC.

Iran adopted a similar system in 1975, celebrating the 15th anniversary of the Pahlavi regime by harking back to the glories of Darius. The new calendar dated from the foundation of the Persian Empire 2535 years earlier, but was abolished only three years later when the Shah was overthrown.

Political eras

France adopted a republican calendar in 1793 when the monarchy was abolished. Coins were then inscribed L'AN (the year) followed by Roman numerals, but later Arabic numerals were substituted. This continued to the year 14 (1806) but in that year the Emperor Napoleon restored the Christian calendar.

The French system was emulated by Haiti whose coins dated from the revolution of 1803. The date appeared as AN followed by a number until AN 31 (1834) on some coins; others had both the evolutionary year and the Christian date from 1828 until 1850 (AN 47). Coins with a date in the Christian calendar appeared only in 1807–9 and then from 1850 onwards.

Mussolini introduced the Fascist calendar to Italy, dating from the seizure of power in October 1922. This system was widely employed on documents and memorials, but was first used on silver 20 lire coins of 1927 and then only in addition to the Christian date and appearing discreetly as Roman numerals. Subsequently it was extended to gold 50 lire and 100 lire coins in 1931 and the subsidiary coinage in 1936, being last used in the year XXI (1943).

Around the *World*

Listed here are the names of all the coins of the world, many of which have been around for hundreds of years, others are no longer in use. Some of the denominations have been introduced only recently, whilst others are familiar household words. A number of the names are shared by different countries and a few have even been used by different civilisations.

Abazi Caucusus
Abbasi, Abbassi Afghanistan, Georgia, Persia
Ackey Gold Coast
Adli Altin Ottoman Empire
Afghani Afghanistan
Agnel France
Agora (ot) Israel
Ahmadi Mysore, Yemen
Akce Turkey
Akcheh Turkestan
Albertusdaler Denmark
Albus German States, Swiss Cantons
Altin, Altun Egypt, Turkey
Altinlik Turkey
Altyn, Altynnik Russia
Amani Afghanistan
Amman Cash Mewar Udaipur, Pudukota, India
Angel England, Scotland, Isle of Man

Angel

Angelet France
Angelot France
Angster Lucerne
Anna Burma, India, Pakistan, Kenya, Muscat & Oman
Antoninianus Rome
Ardite Navarre
Argentino Argentina
Ariary Malagasy Republic
As Rome
Asarfi Nepal

Ashrafi Afghanistan, Awadh, Bahawalpur, Egypt, Hyderabad
Asper Algeria, Egypt, Libya, Trebizond, Tunisia, Turkey
Asses Luxembourg
At Laos
Atia Portuguese India
Atribuo Frankfurt
Att Cambodia, Laos, Siam (Thailand)
August d'Or Saxony
Augustale Sicily
Aurar (plural **Eyrir**) Iceland
Austral Argentina
Avo Macau, Timor
Bagarone Bologna
Bagattino Venice
Baggliangster Lucerne
Baht Thailand
Baiocco (plural **Baiocchi**) Papal States
Baisa Oman
Baiza Kuwait
Baizah Muscat & Oman
Balboa Panama
Ban (plural **Bani** or **Banu**) Roumania
Banica Croatia
Barbarina Mantua
Barbonaccio Lucca
Barbone Lucca
Barbuda Portugal
Barilla Philippines
Batzen German States, Swiss Cantons
Bawbee Scotland
Bazaruco Portuguese India
Bazaruk Dutch Settlements in India
Belga Belgium
Benduqi Morocco
Besa (plural **Bese)** Ethiopia, Somalia
Beshlik Soviet Central Asia
Bezant Byzantine Empire, Cyprus, Jerusalem
Bezzo Italian States

Bianco (plural **Bianchi**)   Bologna, Papal States
Biche   French Indian Settlements
Binio   Roman Empire
Bipkwele   Equatorial Guinea
Bir (r)   Ethiopia
Bisti   Caucasia
Bit   Guyana, West Indies
Bitt   Danish Virgin Islands
Black Dog   Nevis
Blaffert   Switzerland
Blanc   France
Blodsklipping   Sweden
Bluzger   Swiss Cantons
Bodle   Scotland
Bogach   Yemen
Bolivar   Venezuela
Boliviano   Bolivia
Bolognino   Papal States
Bonk   Ceylon, Dutch East Indies
Bonnet   Scotland
Boo   Japan
Braspenning   Flanders
Broad   England
Bu   Japan
Budju   Algeria
Buqsha   Yemen Arab Republic
Burbe(ns)   Tunisia
Butut   Gambia
Cache   French Indian Settlements
Cagliareso   Italian States
Calderilla   Spain
Candareen   China
Carbovanetz   Ukraine
Carlin   Sicily
Carlino   Papal States
Carolin   Austria,German States, Sweden
Cash   China, Hong Kong, India, Mysore,
   Travancore, Turkestan, Vietnam
Cassathaler   German States
Cauri   Guinea
Ceitil   Portugal
Cent   Australia, Bahamas, Barbados, Belize,
   Bermuda, Botswana, British East Caribbean
   Territories, British Honduras, British North
   Borneo, British Virgin Islands, Brunei,
   Canada, Cayman Island, Ceylon, China,
   Cochin China, Cocos (Keeling) Islands, Cook
   Islands, Curacao, Cyprus, Danish West Indies,
   East Africa, Ethiopia, Fiji, French Indochina,
   Gilbert and Ellice Islands, Guyana, Hawaii,
   Hong Kong, Indonesia, Jamaica, Kenya, Kiao
   Chau (Kiatschau), Kiribati, Laos, Liberia,
   Malaya, Malaysia, Malta, Mauritius,
   Netherlands, Netherlands Antilles,
   Netherlands Indies, New Zealand, Nova
   Scotia, Panama, Prince Edward Island,
   Sarawak, Seychelles, Sierra Leone, Singapore,

   Solomon Islands, South Africa, Sri Lanka,
   Straits Settlements, Suriname, Swaziland,
   Tanzania, Trinidad and Tobago, Tuvalu,
   Uganda, United States of America, Virgin
   Islands, Zanzibar, Zimbabwe
Centas (plural **Centa, Centu**)   Lithuania
Centavo   Angola, Argentina, Bolivia, Brazil,
   Cape Verde Islands, Chile, Colombia, Costa
   Rica, Cuba, Dominican Republic, Ecuador, El
   Salvador, Guatemala, Guinea-Bissau,
   Honduras, Mexico, Mozambique, Nicaragua,
   Paraguay, Peru, Philippines, Portugal,
   Portuguese Guinea, Portuguese India, Puerto
   Rico, St Thomas and Prince Islands, Timor,
   Venezuela
Centecimo   Bolivia
Cententionalis   Roman Empire
Centesimo   Bolivia, Chile, Dominican Republic,
   Ethiopia, Italian East Africa, Italy, Panama,
   Paraguay, San Marino, Somalia, Uruguay,
   Vatican
Centime   Algeria, Antwerp, Belgian Congo,
   Belgium, Cambodia, Cameroon, Cochin
   China, Comoro Islands, Djibouti, France,
   French Equatorial Africa, French Guiana,
   French Indochina, French Oceania, French
   Polynesia, French Somali Coast, French West
   Africa, Guadeloupe, Guinea, Haiti, Laos,
   Monaco, Morocco, New Caledonia, Reunion,
   Senegal, Switzerland, Togo, Tunisia, Vietnam,
   Westphalia, Yugoslavia, Zaire
Centimo   Costa Rica, Mozambique, Paraguay,
   Peru, Philippines, Puerto Rico, St Thomas and
   Prince Islands, Spain, Venezuela
Centu   Lithuania
Chaise   Antwerp, Bavaria, France
Chervonetz (plural **Chervontzy**)   Russia
Chetrum   Bhutan
Cheun   South Korea
Chiao   China, Formosa, Manchukuo
Chi'en   China
Chio   China
Cho-gin   Japan

Chomseh   Yemen
Chon   Korea
Christian d'Or   Denmark
Chuckram   Travancore
Colon   Costa Rica, El Salvador
Condor   Chile, Colombia, Ecuador
Cordoba   Nicaragua
Cornado   Spain
Cornuto   Savoy
Coroa de Prata   Portugal
Coroin   Eire
Corona   Austrian provinces of Italy, Naples
Coronato   Castile, Naples
Couronne d'Or   France
Crocione   Italian States
Crossazzo   Genoa
Crown   Ascension, Australia, Bermuda,
England, Ghana, Gibraltar, Ireland, Isle of
Man, Jamaica, Jersey, Malawi, New Zealand,
Nigeria, Rhodesia, Rhodesia and Nyasaland,
St Helena, Scotland, Southern Rhodesia,
Tristan da Cunha, Turks and Caicos Islands

Cruzadinho   Brazil, Portugal
Cruzado   Brazil, Portugal
Cruzeiro   Brazil
Cuartillo, Cuartino   Mexico
Cuarto   Bolivia, Spain
Daalder   Netherlands
DakBler   Danish West Indies, Denmark,
Sweden
Dam   Afghanistan, India, Nepal
Daric   Persia
Dauphin   France
Decime   France
Decimo   Argentina, Chile, Colombia, Ecuador,
Galapagos
Decussis   Roman Republic
Dekadrachm   Syracuse, Hellenistic kingdoms
Dekanummion   Byzantine Empire
Dekobolon   Greece
Demareteion   Syracuse
Demer   France

Demy   Scotland
Denar   Hungary
Denarius   Rome
Denaro   Italian States
Denga   Russia
Dengi   Roumania
Denier   France and colonies, Haiti, Swiss
Cantons
Denning   Denmark
Deut   Rhineland, Westphalia
Deutschemark   Germany
Dhofari Riyal   Yemen
Diamante   Ferrara
Diamantino   Ferrara
Dicken   Swiss Cantons
Didrachm   Greece
Dime   Canada, Hawaii, USA
Dinar   Afghanistan, Algeria, Bahrain, Hejaz,
Iraq, Kuwait, Morocco, Persia, Saudi Arabia,
Serbia, Tunisia, Turkey, Yugoslavia
Diner   Andorra
Dinero   Peru, Spain
Diobol   Greece
Dirham   Jordan, Libya, Morocco, United Arab
Emirates
Dirhem   Dubai, Iraq, Morocco, Qatar
Dio, Diu   Portuguese India
Disme   USA
Dobla   Genoa, Naples and Sicily
Doblado   Spanish colonies
Doblenca, Doblenga   Aragon, Barcelona
Dobler   Mallorca
Doblon   Chile, Spain, Urugay
Dobra   St Thomas and Prince
Dodekadrachm   Carthage
Doit   Netherlands, Netherlands Indies,
Indonesia
Dokdo   Junagadh, Kutch, Nawanagar (Indian
States)
Dollar   Anguilla, Antigua and Barbuda,
Australia, Bahamas, Belize, Bermuda, Canada,
Cayman Islands, China, Cocos (Keeling)
Islands, Cook Islands, East Caribbean
Territories, Fiji, Great Britain, Grenada,
Guyana, Hawaii, Hong Kong, Indonesia,
Jamaica, Japan, Kiribati, Liberia, Malaysia,
Mauritius, Montserrat, Newfoundland, New
Zealand, Panama, St Kitts-Nevis, St Lucia, St
Vincent, Scotland, Sierra Leone, Singapore,
Solomin Islands, Straits Settlements, Trinidad
and Tobago, Tuvalu, USA, Virgin Islands,
Western Samoa, Zimbabwe
Dolya   Russia
Dong   Annam, Vietnam
Doppia   Italian States
Doppietta   Sardinia
Double   Guernsey

Dou Dou   French Indochina
Douzain   France
Drachma   Crete, Greece
Dram   Armenia
Dreibatzner   Austria, German States
Dreigroscher   Lithuania, Prussia
Dreiling   German States
Dub   Hyderabad, India
Dubbeltje   Holland
Ducat   Austria, Austrian States, Courland,
   Czechoslovakia, Denmark, German States,
   Hungary, Italian States, Liechtenstein, Liege,
   Netherlands,Poland, Roumania, Sweden,
   Swiss Cantons, Russia, Yugoslavia
Ducaton   Belgium, Netherlands
Ducatone   Italian States
Dudu   India
Duetto   Italian States
Duit   Ceylon, German States, Netherlands,
   Netherlands Indies
Dukat   Czechoslovakia, German States,
   Hungary, Poland, Sweden, Yugoslavia
Duplone   Swiss Cantons
Duro   Spain
Dyak   Nepal
Ecu   Belgium, Bosnia, France, Gibraltar
Ekuele   Equatorial Guinea
Elisabeth d'Or   Russia
Emalangeni   Swaziland
Escalin   Belgium, Guadeloupe, Haiti, Liege,
   Martinique
Escudillo   Spain
Escudo   Angola, Argentina, Azores, Bolivia,
   Cape Verde Islands, Central American
   Republic, Chile, Colombia, Costa Rica,
   Ecuador, Guadeloupe, Guatemala, Guinea-
   Bissau, Madeira, Mexico, Mozambique, Peru,
   Portugal, Portuguese Guinea/India, St
   Thomas and Prince Islands, Spain, Timor
Espadin   Portugal
Esphera   Goa
Excelente   Spain
Eyrir (singular **Aurar**) Iceland
Fals   Iraq
Faluce   Ceylon
Falus   Afghanistan, China, India, Iran, Morocco,
   Turkestan
Fanam   Ceylon, Dutch East Indies, Travancore
Fano   Tranquebar (Danish Indian Settlements)
Fanon   French Indian Settlements
Farthing   Antigua, Ceylon, Great Britain, Isle of
   Man, Jamaica, Malta, Scotland, South Africa
Fels   Algeria
Fen   People's Republic of China, Manchukuo
Fenig (ow)   Poland
Feoirling   Eire
Ferding   Courland, Livonia

Filiberto   Savoy
Filippo   Italian States
Filler   Hungary
Fils   Bahrain, Iraq, Jordan, Kuwait, South
   Arabia, United Arab Emirates, Yemen
Fiorino   Italian States
Flitter   South German States
Floirin   Eire
Florin   Australia, Austria, East Africa, Fiji,
   Great Britain, Hungary, Ireland, Malawi, New
   Zealand, Rhodesia and Nyasaland, South
   Africa, Swiss Cantons
Follis   Rome, Byzantine Empire
Forint   Hungary

Franc   Algeria, Belgian Congo, Belgium,
   Burundi, Cambodia, Cameroon, Central
   African Republic, Chad, Comoro Islands,
   Congo, Danish West Indies, Djibouti,
   Dominican Republic, Ecuador,
   France, French colonies, Gabon, Guadeloupe,
   Guinea, Ivory Coast, Katanga, Luxembourg,
   Madagascar, Malagasy Republic, Mali,
   Martinique, Mauretania, Monaco, Morocco,
   New Caledonia, New Hebrides, Reunion,
   Ruanda-Urundi, Rwanda, St Pierre and
   Miquelon, Senegal, Switzerland, Togo,
   Tunisia, West African States
Francescone   Italian States
Franchi   Switzerland
Franco   Dominican Republic, Ecuador, Italian
   States, Swiss Cantons
Frang   Luxembourg
Frank(en)   Belgium, Liechtenstein, Saar,
   Switzerland, Westphalia
Franka Ara   Albania
Frederik d'Or   Denmark
Friedrich d'Or   German States
Fyrk   Sweden
Gabellone   Papal States
Gayah   Sumatra
Gazetta   Venice
Genovino   Genoa, Florence, Venice
Genevoise   Geneva

George Noble England
Georgstaler German States
Gersh Ethiopia
Gigliato Hungary, Naples, Rhodes
Gigot Brabant, Flanders
Gin Japan
Giorgino Ferrara, Modena
Giovannino Genoa
Girsh Hejaz, Nejd, Saudi Arabia, Sudan
Giulio Italian States
Golde Sierra Leone
Goldgulden German States, Swiss Cantons
Goldpfennig German States
Goryoban Japan
Gourde Haiti
Gourmier Morocco
Gram Afghanistan
Gramme Burma
Gramo Bolivia, Tierra del Fuego
Grana Italian States
Grano Italian States, Mexico,
Sovereign Order of Malta
Grenadino Colombia, New Granada
Greschl Roumania, Transylvania
Grivenka Russia
Grivennik Russia
Grivna (plural **Grivny**) Ukraine
Groat Great Britain
Groeschl Bohemia
Groot Netherlands
Gros France
Groschel German States
Groschen Austria, German States, Poland,
Swiss Cantons
Groshen Austria, German States
Grossetto Dalmatia, Illyria, Venice
Grosso Italian States
Grossone Italian States
Grosspfennig Pomerania, Rhineland
Grossus Courland, Poland
Grosz (plural **Grosze** or **Groszy**) Poland
Grote German States
Grush Albania
Guarani Paraguay
Guerche Egypt, Saudi Arabia
Guinea Great Britain, Saudi Arabia
Gulden Austria, Curacao, German States,
Netherlands, Netherlands Indies, Swiss
Cantons
Guldiner Austria, South German States, Swiss
Cantons
Gutegroschen North and Central German
States
Guterpfennig German States
Habibi Afghanistan
Halala Saudi Arabia, Yemen
Halbag Frankfurt

Haler (plural **Halere, Haleru**) Czechoslovakia,
Czech Republic
Halierov Slovakia
Haller Swiss Cantons
Hao China, Vietnam
Hapalua Hawaii
Hardhead Scotland
Hardi France, Turin
Hau Tonga
Hayrir Altin Iraq, Turkey
Hekte Lesbos, Mytilene
Heller Austria, German States, German East
Africa
Helm England
Henri d'Or France
Hryvnia Ukraine
Hsien China
Hvid Denmark
Hwan Korea
Hyperpyron Byzantine Empire
Ichibu-gin Japan
Ikilik Russia
Imadi Yemen
Imami Mysore
Imperial Russia
Isabella Spain
Ischal Russia
Ishu Gin Japan
Jacondale France
Jawa Nepal
Jeon Korea
Jerome d'Or Westphalia
Jiao People's Republic of China
Jedid Egypt
Jefimok (plural **Jefimki**) Russia
Joachimico Italy
Joachimik Poland
Joachimstaler Bohemia
Joao Portugal
Johanna Portugal
Johannes Portugal
Jokoh Kelantan, Malaysia
Judenpfennig Frankfurt
Justo Portugal
Kapang Sarawak
Kapeikas Latvia, Belarus
Karolin German States
Kas Danish Indian Settlements
Kasu Mysore
Kazbeg Caucasia, Safavid Persia
Khayriya Egypt
Khoum Mauretania
Kin Japan
Kina Papua New Guinea
Kip Laos
Koban Japan
Kobo Nigeria

Kopec Poland
Kopejek Outer Mongolia (Tannu Tuva)
Kopek Russia
Kori Kutch**Korona** Bohemia and Moravia, Hungary, Slovakia
Kortling German States
Korun(a) (plural **Koruny** or **Koruncic**) Czechoslo-vakia
Koula Tonga
Krajczar Hungary
Kran Iran, Persia
Kreu(t)zer Austria, Austrian States, Czechoslovakia, German States, Hungary, Liechtenstein, Poland, Roumania, Swiss Cantons
Krona (plural **Kronor** or **Kronur**) Iceland, Sweden
Krona (plural **Kroner** or **Kronen**) Austria, Denmark, German States, Greenland, Liechtenstein, Norway
Kroon(i) Estonia
Krugerrand South Africa
Kuna (plural **Kune**) Croatia
Kupang Malaysia, Thailand
Kurus Turkey
Kuta Congo-Kinshasa, Zaire
Kwacha Malawi, Zambia
Kwanza Angola
Kwartnik Poland
Kyat Burma, Myanmar
Kyrmis Russia
Lang Annam
Laree, Lari, Lariat or Larin Maldive Islands
Lati, Lats Latvia
Laurel England
Lei Roumania
Lek (plural **Leke** or **Leku**) Albania
Lempira Honduras
Leone Sierra Leone
Leopard England
Lepton (plural **Lepta**) Crete, Greece, Ionian Islands
Leu (plural **Lei**) Roumania
Lev(a) Bulgaria
Li Manchukuo
Liang China, Laos
Liard Belgium, France, Luxembourg
Libra Peru
Licente Lesotho
Likuta Zaire
Lilangeni Swaziland
Lion Scotland
Lion d'Or Austrian Netherlands
Lira (plural **Lire**) Eritrea, Italian East Africa, Italy, San Marino, Syria, Turkey, Vatican
Lira (plural **Lirot**) Israel
Lisente Lesotho

Litas (plural **Litai** or **Litu**) Lithuania

Litra Sicily, Syracuse
Livre France, Guadeloupe, Lebanon, Martinique, Mauritius, Reunion
Louis d'Argent France
Louis d'Or France
Luhlanga Swaziland
Lumma Armenia
Lweis Angola
Mace China
Macuta Angola
Magdalon d'Or Aix-en-Provence, Tarascon
Mahalek Ethiopia
Mahallak Harar
Mahbub Egypt, Ottoman Empire
Mahmudi Saudi Arabia
Makuta Zaire
Maloti Lesotho
Manat Azerbaijan
Manghir Crimea
Marabotin Moorish kingdoms, Southern Spain
Maravedi Spain
Marchetto Italian States
Marck German States
Marengo France
Mariengroschen German States
Mark Germany, German States, German New Guinea, Norway, Poland, Sweden
Marka Estonia
Markka(a) Finland
Mas Malaysia
Masriya Egypt
Masson Lorraine and Bar
Mat Burma
Matapan Venice
Mathbu Morocco
Maticaes Mozambique
Matona Ethiopia
Mattier German States
Maximilian d'Or German States
Mazuna Morocco
Medin Egypt
Mehmudiye Altin Ottoman Empire
Meinhard Austria, German States

Melgarejo Bosnia
Merk Scotland
Metica Mozambique
Meung Japan
Mil Cyprus, Hong Kong, Israel, Malta, Palestine
Milan d'Or Serbia
Miliarense Byzantine Empire
Milesima Spain
Millieme Egypt, Libya
Millime Tunisia
Milreis Brazil
Miscals China
Mohar Nepal
Mohur Afghanistan, Bikanir, Cooch Behar,
   Gwalior, Hyderabad, India (Mughal Empire),
   Maldive Islands, Netherlands Indies, Rajkot
Moidore (Moeda de ouro) Portugal
Momme Japan
Mon Japan, Ryukyu Islands
Mongo Mongolia
Mouton d'Or France
Mu Burma
Mun Korea
Mung Mongolia
Munzgulden Swiss Cantons
Muzuna Algeria
Naira Nigeria
Nami-sen Japan
Napoleon France
Naya Paisa Bhutan, India
Negotiepenning Netherlands
Neugroschen German States
New Pence Gibraltar, Great Britain, Guernsey,
   Isle of Man, Jersey
Ngultrum Bhutan
Ngwee Zambia
Nisar Afghanistan, India
Nisfiya Egypt
Noble Austria,England, Scotland, Isle of Man
Nomisma Byzantine Empire
Nonsunt Scotland
Nummion (plural **Nummia**) Byzantine Empire
Oban Japan
Obol Greece, Ionian Islands
Ochavo Spain
Octavo Mexico, Philippines
Omani Oman
Onca Mozambique
Oncia Italian States
Onlik Crimea
Onluk Turkey
Onza Bolivia, Chile, Costa Rica, Mexico
Or Sweden
Ore Denmark, Faroe Islands, Greenland,
   Norway, Sweden
Ort(e) Poland, Prussia
Ortug (plural **Ortugar**) Sweden

Ouguiya Mauretania
Pa'anga Tonga
Pagoda India (Madras)
Pahlavi Iran
Pai India, Siam (Thailand)
Paisa Afghanistan, Bhutan, India, Nepal,
   Pakistan
Panchia India
Pano Portuguese Africa
Paoli Italian States
Papetto Papal States
Para (plural **Paras** or **Parades**) Crimea, Egypt,
   Greece, Iraq, Libya, Nejd, Roumania, Saudi
   Arabia, Serbia, Sudan, Syria, Turkey,
   Walachia, Yugoslavia
Pardao Portuguese India
Parisis d'Or France
Pataca Macau
Pataco Portugal
Patagon Belgium
Patrick Ireland
Pavillon d'Or France
Pe Burma, Cambodia
Peca Portugal
Pengo Hungary
Penni(a) Finland
Penning(ar) Denmark, Sweden
Penny (plural **Pence**) Australia, Bahamas,
   Barbados, Bermuda, Biafra, British Guiana,
   British East Africa British West Africa, Canada,
   Ceylon, Falkland Islands, Fiji, Gambia, Ghana,
   Gibraltar, Gold Coast, Great Britain, Guernsey,
   Ireland, Isle of Man, Jamaica, Jersey, Malawi,
   Montserrat, New Guinea, New Zealand,
   Nigeria, Rhodesia and Nyasaland, St Helena,
   St Kitts-Nevis, South Africa, Southern
   Rhodesia, Trinidad & Tobago, Tristan da
   Cunha, Zambia
Pentekontalitron Sicily
Pentekontedrachm Hellenistic kingdoms
Pentenummion Byzantine Empire
Perper(a) Montenegro
Pesa German East Africa
Peseta Andorra, Equatorial Guinea, Peru, Spain
Pesewa Ghana
Peso Argentina, Bolivia, Cambodia, Chile,
   Colombia, Costa Rica, Cuba, Dominican
   Republic, El Salvador, Guatemala, Guinea-
   Bissau, Honduras, Mexico, Netherlands
   Antilles, Nicaragua, Paraguay, Peru,
   Philippines, Puerto Rico, Uruguay, Venezuela
Pessa Yemen (Lahej), Zanzibar
Petermannchen Trier
Pfennig(e) Austria, Bohemia, Germany,
   German States, Poland, Swiss Cantons
Pfenning Austrian States, German States
Philippeioi Macedon

Phoenix   Greece
Piastra   Italian States
Piastre   Annam, Cambodia, Cochin China,
   Cyprus, Denmark, Egypt, French Indochina,
   Hejaz, Iraq, Khmer, Lebanon, Libya, Nejd,
   Saudi Arabia, Syria, Sudan, Tonkin, Tunisia,
   Turkey, Vietnam, Yemen
Piataltynny   Russia
Picciolo   Sovereign Order of Malta
Piccolo   Italian States
Pice   Bhutan, Ceylon, East Africa, India, Kenya,
   Malaysia
Pinto   Portugal
Piso   Philippines
Pistole   France, German States, Ireland,
   Scotland, Swiss Cantons
Pitis   Brunei, Java, Sumatra, Siam
Plack   Scotland
Plappart   Switzerland
Poisha   Bangladesh
Poltina   Russia
Poltura   Hungary, Roumania
Poludenga   Russia
Polupoltinnik   Russia
Polushka   Russia
Pond   Transvaal
Pound   Ascension, Australia, Biafra, Cyprus,
   Egypt, Falkland Islands, Ghana, Gibraltar, Great
   Britain, Guernsey, Iran, Isle of Man, Israel,
   Jersey, Malta, Nigeria, Rhodesia, St Helena,
   South Arabia, South Africa, Sudan, Syria
Protea   South Africa
Pruta(ot)   Israel
Puffin   Lundy
Pul   Afghanistan, China, Turkestan
Pula   Botswana
Puli   Caucasia
Pultorak   Poland
Pya(t)   Burma
Pysa   Zanzibar
Qindar(ka)   Albania
Qiran   Afghanistan
Qirsh   Egypt
Quadrans   Roman Republic
Quan   Annam
Quart   Gibraltar, Swiss Cantons
Quart d'Ecu   France
Quartenses   Silesia
Quartillo   Spain
Quartinho   Portugal
Quarto   Ecuador, Mexico, Philippines, Spain
Quartuncia   Rome
Quaternio   Rome
Quattrino   Italian States
Qepiq   Azerbaijan
Quetzal   Guatemala
Quinarius   Rome

Quint   USA
Quinto di Scudo   Papal States
Rand   South Africa
Rappen   Switzerland
Rasi   Netherlands Indies
Reaal   Curacao
Real(es)   Argentina, Bolivia, Central American
   Republic, Chile, Colombia, Costa Rica,
   Dominican Republic, Ecuador, El Salvador,
   Venezuela
Real Batu   Indonesia
Reichsmark   Germany
Reichspfennig   Germany
Reichsthaler   Germany
Reis   Angola, Azores, Brazil, Madeira,
   Mozambique, Portugal, Portuguese India
Reisedaler   Denmark
Rentenmark   Germany
Rentenpfennig   Germany
Reul   Eire
Rial   Iran, Morocco, Muscat and Oman, Oman,
   Persia, Yemen Arab Republic
Rider   Scotland
Riel   Kampuchea
Rigsbankdaler   Denmark
Rigsbankskilling   Denmark
Rigsdaler,   Denmark, Norway
Rigsmontskilling   Denmark
Rijder   Friesland, Guelderland, United Provinces
Rijksdaalder   Netherlands
Riksdaler   Sweden
Riksdaler Riksmynt   Sweden
Riksdaler Specie   Sweden
Rin   Japan
Ringgit   Malaysia
Rio   Japan
Rixdollar   Ceylon
Riyal   Iran, Iraq, Saudi Arabia, United Arab
   Emirates, Yemen Arab Republic
Rose Noble   England
Rouble   Russia, USSR
Royal d'Or   France
Royalin(er)   Tranquebar, Danish Indian
   Settlements
Rub   Ethiopia
Rubel   German occupation of Russia
Rubiya   Egypt
Ruble   Poland, Transnistria
Rublis   Latvia
Rufiyaa   Maldive Islands
Rumi Altin   Ottoman Empire
Rupee   Afghanistan, Andaman Islands, Bhutan,
   Burma, China, Cocos Keeling Islands, India,
   Iran, Kenya, Mauritius, Nepal, Pakistan, Saudi
   Arabia, Seychelles, Sri Lanka, Tanzania, Tibet,
   United Arab Emirates, Yemen
Rupia   Portuguese India, Somalia

Rupiah   Indonesia
Rupie   German East Africa
Ruspone   Italian States
Ryal   England, Hejaz, Iran, Muscat and Oman,
   Nejd, Oman, Persia, Quaiti State, Saudi
   Arabia, Yemen, Zanzibar
Ryo   Japan
Rytterpenning   Denmark, Hanseatic League
Saidi   Oman
Saiga   Merovingian Empire
Salung   Siam (Thailand)
Salut d'Or   France
Sampietrino   Papal States
Sanar   Afghanistan
Sanese   Siena
Santa Croce   Italian States
Santim(at)   Morocco
Santims (plural **Santimi** or **Santimu**)   Latvia
Sapeque   Annam, Cochin China, French
   Indochina
Sar   Sinkiang
Sarrazzino   Crusader kingdoms
Satang   Siam (Thailand)
Sceat   Anglo-Saxon England
Scellino   Somalia
Schilling   Austria, German States, Poland,
   Swiss Cantons
Schoter   Breslau, Silesia
Schwaren   German States
Scilling   Eire
Scudo   Bolivia, Italian States, Mexico, Malta,
   Papal States, Peru, San Marino
Sechsling   German States
Semis   Rome
Semuncia   Rome
Sen   Brunei, Cambodia, Indonesia, Irian Barat,
   Japan, Kampuchea, Malaysia, Riau Lingga,
   West New Guinea
Sene   Samoa
Sengi   Zaire
Seniti   Tonga
Sent   Estonia
Sente   Lesotho
Senti   Estonia, Somalia, Tanzania
Sentimo   Philippines
Serebrnik   Bulgaria
Sertum   Bhutan
Sesena   Spain
Sesino   Italian States
Sestertius   Rome
Sestino   Italian States
Shahi   Afghanistan, Iran, Turkestan
Sheqal(im)   Israel
Shilingi   Tanzania
Shilling   Australia, Biafra, British West Africa,
   Canada, Cyprus, East Africa, Fiji, Gambia,
   Ghana, Great Britain, Grenada, Guernsey,
   Ireland, Isle of Man, Jamaica, Jersey, Kenya,

   Malawi, Malta, New Guinea, New Zealand,
   Nigeria, Scotland, Somalia, South Africa,
   Trinidad and Tobago, Uganda, Zambia
Sho   Nepal, Tibet
Shokang   Tibet
Shu   Japan
Siglos   Achaemenid Empire
Sik   Siam (Thailand)
Silbergroschen   German States,Luxembourg
Silbergulden   South Germany
Sizain   France
Skar   Tibet
Skilling   Danish West Indies, Denmark,
   Norway, Sweden
Skillingrigsmont   Denmark
Skot   Prussia, Silesia
Sol(es)   Argentina, Belgium, Bolivia, France,
   Haiti, Luxembourg, Mauritius, Peru, Reunion,
   Switzerland, Windward Islands
Soldo (plural **Soldi**)   Italian States, Swiss
   Cantons, Papal States, Yugoslavia
Solidus   Argentina, Bolivia, Peru, Rome
Solot   Siam
Som   Kyrgyzstan
Somalo   Somalia
Sosling   Denmark
Sou   Canada, French colonies, Guadeloupe,
   Mauritius, Reunion, Spain
Souverain d'Or   Austrian Netherlands
Sovereign   Australia, Canada, England,
   Falkland Islands, India, Isle of Man, Saudi
   Arabia, South Africa, United Kingdom

Sovrano   Italian States
Speciedaler   Denmark, Norway
Species Ducat   Denmark
Srang   Tibet
Stater   Greece
Stella   USA
Stiver   British Guiana, Ceylon, Demerara and
   Essequibo, Dutch East Indies, Netherlands
Stotinka   Bulgaria
Stuber   German States
Stuiver   Curacao, Dutch East Indies,
   Netherlands, Netherlands Antilles
Styca   Northumbria
Styver   Sweden
Su   South Vietnam
Sucre   Ecuador, Galapagos
Sueldo   Bolivia, Spain

Sukus   Indonesia
Sultani   Algeria, Libya, Tunisia
Surre Altin   Ottoman Empire
Syli   Guinea
Tackoe   Gold Coast
Tael   China, Laos
Taka   Bangladesh
Tala   Samoa, Tokelau
Talar(a)   Poland
Talaro   Ethiopia
Taler   German States, Poland, Swiss Cantons
Talirion   Greece
Tallero   Ethiopia, Italian States, Ragusa
Tambac-tron   Annam
Tambala   Malawi
Tamlung   Siam
Tanga   Portuguese India
Tangka   Tibet
Tanka   Nepal
Tankah   Burma
Tarin   Naples, Sicily
Taro (plural **Tari**)   Italian States, Malta
Tek Altin   Ottoman Empire
Tenga   China, Bokhara, Turkestan
Ternar   Poland
Tester   England
Testern   British East Indies
Testone   Italian States
Testoon   England
Tetartemorion   Greece
Tetarteron   Byzantine Empire
Tetradrachm   Greece
Tetrobol   Greece
Thaler   Austria, Austrian States, Courland,
  Czechoslovakia, German States, Hungary,
  Liechtenstein, Poland, Roumania, Switzerland
Thebe   Botswana
Theler   Frankfurt
Thistle Crown   England
Thistle Merk   Scotland
Thistle Noble   Scotland
Thrymsa   Anglo-Saxon England
Tical   Cambodia, Thailand
Tien   Annam, Vietnam
Tilla   Afghanistan, Sinkiang, Turkestan
Timasha   Afghanistan
Tostao   Portugal
Toea   Papua New Guinea
Tola   India, Nepal
Tolar   Slovenia
Toman   Iran, Persia, Azerbaijan
Tornese   Italian States
Tournois   France
Trade Dollar   Great Britain, Japan, USA
Trah   Malaysia
Tremissis   Rome, Byzantine Empire, Franks,
  Lombards, Visigoths

Tressis   Rome
Triens   Rome
Trihemiobol   Greece
Triobol   Greece
Tritartemorion   Greece
Tughrik   Mongolia
Turner   Scotland
Tympf   Poland
Tyyn   Kyrgyzstan
Unghero   Italian States
Unicorn   Scotland
Unit   Scotland, French West Africa
Unite   England
Van   Vietnam
Vatu   Vanuatu
Veld Pond   South African Republic
Venezolano   Venezuela
Vereinstaler   Austria-Hungary, German States
Victoriate   Rome
Vierer   Swiss Cantons
Vintem   Portugal
Wan   Korea
Wark   Ethiopia
Warn   Korean
Wen   China
Whan   Korea
Won   South Korea
Xerafim   Portuguese India
Xu   Vietnam
Yang   Korea
Yarim   Turkey
Yen   Japan
Yirmilik   Ottoman Empire
Yuan   China
Yuzluk   Ottoman Empire
Zaire   Zaire
Zalat   Yemen Arab Republic
Zecchino   Italian States, Malta
Zelagh   Morocco
Zeri Mahbub   Egypt, Libya, Turkey
Zloty (plural **Zlote** or **Zlotych**)   Poland

Zolota   Turkey
Zolotnik   Russia
Zolotoj   Russia
Zweidritteltaler   German States
Zyfert   East Friesland

Glossary of coin terms

In this section we list all the terms commonly encountered in numismatics or in the production of coins.

Abbey Coins Medieval coins struck in the abbeys, convents and other great religious houses which were granted coinage rights. These coins were often used also by pilgrims journeying from one monastery to another.

Abschlag (German for "discount") A *restrike* from an original die.

Accolated Synonym for *conjoined* or *jugate* and signifying two or more profiles overlapping.

Acmonital Acronym from *Aciaio Monetario Italiano*, a stainless steel alloy used for Italian coins since 1939.

Adjustment Reduction of metal in a *flan* or *blank* to the specified weight prior to striking, accomplished by filing down the face. Such file marks often survived the coining process and are occasionally met with in coins, especially of the 18th century.

Ae Abbreviation for the Latin *Aes* (bronze), used for coins made of brass, bronze or other copper alloys.

Aes Grave (Latin for heavy bronze) Heavy circular coins first minted at Rome in 269 BC.

Aes Rude (Latin for rough bronze) Irregular lumps of bronze which gradually developed into ingots of uniform shape and were the precursors of coins in Rome.

Aes Signatum (Latin for signed bronze) Bronze ingots of regular size and weight, bearing marks of authority to guarantee their weight (289–269 BC).

Agonistic (Greek) Term for coins issued to commemorate, or pertaining to, sporting events.

Alliance Coinage struck by two or more states acting together and having common features of design or inscription.

Alloy Coinage metal composed of two or more metallic elements.

Altered Deliberately changed, usually unofficially, with the aim of increasing the numismatic value of a coin, medal or note. This applies particularly to dates, where a common date may be altered to a rare date by filing or re-engraving one of the digits.

Aluminium (American *Aluminum*) Silvery lightweight metal, developed commercially in the late 19th century for commemorative medals, but used for tokens and emergency money during the First World War and since 1940 widely used in subsidiary coinage.

Aluminium-bronze Alloy of aluminium and copper. Hard-wearing and gold-coloured, it is now widely used in tokens and subsidiary coinage.

Amulet Coin or medal believed to have talismanic qualities, such as warding off disease and bad luck. Many Chinese and Korean pieces come into this category. See also *Touchpiece.*

Androcephalous Heraldic term for creatures with a human head.

Anepigraphic Coins or medals without a legend.

Annealing Process of heating and cooling applied to metal to relieve stresses and prepare it for striking into coins.

Annulet Small circle often used as an ornament or spacing device in coin inscriptions.

Antimony Brittle white metal, chemical symbol *Sb*, virtually impractical as a coinage metal but used for the Chinese 10 cents of Kweichow, 1931. Alloyed with tin, copper or lead, it produces the white metal popular as a medallic medium.

Antoniniani Silver coins minted in Imperial Rome. The name derives from the Emperor Caracalla (Marcus Aurelius Antoninus) in whose reign they were first struck. The silver content was progressively reduced and by the last issue (AD 295) they were reduced to *billon.*

Ar Abbreviation for Latin *Argentum* (silver), used for coins struck in this metal.

Assay Mark Mark applied to a medal struck in precious metal by an assayer or assay office as a guarantee of the fineness of the metal.

Assignat Type of paper money used in France

59

1789–96, representing the land assigned to the holders.

Attribution Identification of a coin by characteristics such as issuing authority, date or reign, mint, denomination, metal, and by a standard reference.

Au Abbreviation for *aurum* (Latin for gold), denoting coins of this metal.

AU Abbreviation for "About Uncirculated", often found in catalogues and dealers' lists to describe the condition of a numismatic piece.

Autodollar Name given to the silver yuan issued by Kweichow, 1928, and having a contemporary motor car as the obverse motif.

Auxiliary Payment Certificate Form of paper money intended for use by American military personnel stationed in overseas countries. See also *Baf* and *Scrip*.

Babel Note Nickname given to the paper money of the Russian Socialist Federated Soviet Republic (1919) because it bore the slogan "workers of the world unite" in seven languages, a reference to the biblical tower of Babel.

Baf Acronym from British Armed Forces, the popular name for the vouchers which could only be exchanged for goods in service canteens from 1945 onwards.

Bag Mark Minor scratch or abrasion on an otherwise uncirculated coin, caused by coins in mint bags knocking together.

Banknote Form of paper money issued by banks and usually promising to pay the bearer on demand in coin of the realm.

Barbarous Imitation of Greek or Roman coins by the Celtic and Germanic tribes who lived beyond the frontiers of the civilised world.

Base Non-precious metals or alloys.

Bath Metal Inferior bronze alloy, named after the English city where it was used for casting cannon. Used by William Wood of Bristol for Irish and American tokens and by Amos Topping for Manx coins of 1733/4.

Beading Ornamental border found on the raised rim of a coin.

Behalfszahlungsmittel German term for auxiliary payment certificates used in occupied Europe from 1939 to 1945.

Bell Metal Alloy of copper and tin normally used for casting bells, but employed for the subsidiary coinage of the French Revolutionary period.

Billon Silver alloy containing less than 50 per cent fine silver, usually mixed with copper. In Spain this alloy was known as *vellon*.

Bi-metallic Coins struck in two separate metals or alloys. Patterns for such coins exist from the 19th century but actual coins with a centre of one metal surrounded by a ring of another did not appear till 1982 (Italy, San Marino and Vatican). Canada introduced coins with a tiny plaque inset in a second metal (1990). See also *Clad, Plugged* and *Sandwich*.

Bi-metallism Monetary system in which two metals are in simultaneous use and equally available as legal tender, implying a definite ratio between the two. A double standard of gold and silver, with a ratio of 16:1, existed till the mid-19th century.

Bingle American term for a trade token, more specifically the US government issue of tokens for the Matacuska, Alaska colonization project, 1935.

Birthday Coins Coins celebrating the birthday of a ruler originated in Roman Imperial times, notably the reigns of Maximianus (286–305) and Constantinus I (307–37). Birthday talers were issued by many German states, and among recent examples may be cited coins marking the 70th, 80th and 90th birthdays of Gustaf Adolf VI of Sweden, 80th and 90th birthday coins from the British Commonwealth for the Queen Mother, and coins honouring Queen Elizabeth, the Duke of Edinburgh and the Prince of Wales.

Bit Term denoting fragments of large silver coins, cut up and circulating as fractional values. Spanish dollars were frequently broken up for circulation in the American colonies and the West indies. Long bits and short bits circulated at 15 and 10 cents respectively, but the term came to be equated with the Spanish real or eighth peso, hence the American colloquialism "two-bit" signifying a quarter dollar.

Black Money English term for the debased silver deniers minted in France which circulated freely in England until they were banned by government decree in 1351.

Blank Piece of metal, cut or punched out of a roller bar or strip, and prepared for striking to produce coins. Alternate terms are *flan* and *planchet*.

Blundered Inscription Legend in which the lettering is jumbled or meaningless, indicating the illiteracy of the tribes who copied Greek and Roman coins.

Bonnet Piece Scottish gold coin, minted in 1539–40. The name is derived from the obverse portraying King James V in a large, flat bonnet.

Bon Pour French for "good for", inscribed on Chamber of Commerce brass tokens issued in 1920–7 during a shortage of legal tender coinage.

Bouquet Sou Canadian copper token halfpenny of 1837 deriving its name from the nosegay of heraldic flowers on the obverse.

Box Coin Small container formed by *obverse* and *reverse* of two coins, hollowed out and screwed together.

Bracteate (Latin *bractea*, a thin piece of metal) Coins struck on blanks so thin that the image applied to one side appears in reverse on the other. First minted in Erfurt and Thuringia in the 12th century, and later produced elsewhere in Germany, Switzerland and Poland till the 14th century.

Brass Alloy of copper and zinc, widely used for subsidiary coinage. The term was also formerly used for bronze Roman coins, known numismatically as first, second or third brass.

Breeches Money Derisive term given by the Royalists to the coinage of the Commonwealth, 1651, the conjoined elongated oval shields on the reverse resembling a pair of breeches.

Brockage Mis-struck coin with only one design, normal on one side and *incuse* on the other. This occurs when a coin previously struck adheres to the die and strikes the next blank to pass through the press.

Broken Bank-note Note issued by a bank which has failed, but often applied more generally to banknotes which have been demonetised.

Bronze Alloy of copper and tin, first used as a coinage metal by the Chinese c. 1000 BC. Often used synonymously with copper, though it should be noted that bronze only superseded copper as the constituent of the base metal British coins in 1860.

Bull Neck Popular term for the coins of King George III, 1816–17.

Bullet Money Pieces of silver, *globular* in shape, bearing various *countermarks* and used as coins in Siam (Thailand) in the 18th and 19th centuries.

Bullion Precious metal in bars, ingots, strip or scrap (i.e. broken jewellery mounts, watch-cases and plate), its weight reckoned solely by weight and fineness, before being converted into coin.

Bullion Coin A coin struck in platinum, gold or silver, whose value is determined solely by the prevailing market price for the metal as a commodity. Such coins do not generally have a nominal face value, but include in their inscriptions their weight and fineness. Good examples of recent times include the Krugerrand (South Africa), the Britannia (UK), the Maple Leaf (Canada), Libertad (Mexico), the Nugget (Australia) and the Eagle (USA).

Bun Coinage British coins of 1860–94 showing Queen Victoria with her hair in a bun.

Bungtown Coppers Derisive term (from Anglo-American slang *bung*, to swindle or bribe) for halfpence of English or Irish origin, often

counterfeit, which circulated in North America towards the end of the colonial period.

Carat (American *Karat*) Originally a unit of weight for precious stones, based on carob seeds (ceratia), it also denotes the fineness or purity of gold, being 1/24th part of the whole. Thus 9 carat gold is .375 fine and 22 carat, the English sovereign standard, is .916 fine. Abbreviated as ct or kt.

A "Cartwheel" penny so called because of its cumbersome size.

Cartwheel Popular term for the large and cumbersome penny and twopenny pieces of 1797 weighing one and two ounces, struck by Matthew Boulton at the Soho Mint, Birmingham.

Cased Set Set of coins in mint condition, housed in the official case issued by the mint. Formerly leather cases with blue plush or velvet lining were used, but nowadays many sets are encapsulated in plastic to facilitate handling.

Cash (from Portuguese *caixa*, Hindi *kasu*). Round piece of bronze or brass with a square hole in the centre, used as subsidiary coinage in China for almost 2000 years, till the early 12th century. In Chinese these pieces were known as *Ch'ien* or *Li* and strung together in groups of 1000 were equivalent to a silver tael.

Cast Coins Coins cast from molten metals in moulds. This technique, widespread in the case of early commemorative medals, has been used infrequently in coins, the vast majority of which are struck from *dies*. Examples of cast coins include the Chinese cash and the Manx coins of 1709.

Check A form of *token* given as a means of identification, or issued for small amounts of money or for services of a specific nature.

Cheque (American *Check*) A written order directing a bank to pay money.

Chop (Hindi, to seal). Countermark, usually consisting of a single character, applied by Chinese merchants to precious metal coins and ingots as a guarantee of their weight and fineness. Coins may be found with a wide variety of chop´marks and the presence of several different marks on the same coin considerably enhances its interest and value. See also *Shroff mark*.

Christmas Coins issued as Christmas gifts date from the Middle Ages when the Venetian Doges struck *Osselle* as presents for their courtiers. In modern times, however, the custom has developed only since the late 1970s, several countries having issued attractive coins at Christmas since then.

Cistophori (Greek for chest bearing) a generic term for the coins of Pergamum with an obverse motif of a chest showing a serpent crawling out of the half-opened lid. Cistophori became very popular all over Asia Minor in the 3rd and 2nd centuries BC and were struck also at mints in Ionia, Phrygia, Lydia and Mysia.

Clad Coins Coins with a core of one alloy, covered with a layer or coating of another. US half dollars from 1965 to 1970, for example, had a core of 21 per cent silver and 79 per cent copper, bonded to outer layers of 80 per cent silver and 20 per cent copper. More recently, however, coins usually have a body in a cheap alloy, with only a thin cladding of a more expensive material, such as the British 1p and 2p coins of stainless steel with a copper cladding, introduced late in 1992.

Clash Marks Mirror image traces found on a coin which has been struck from a pair of dies, themselves damaged by having been struck together without a blank between.

Clipped Coins Precious metal coins from which small amounts have been removed by clipping the edges. It was to prevent this that *graining* and *edge inscriptions* were adopted.

Cob Crude, irregularly shaped silver piece, often with little more than a vestige of die impressions, produced in the Spanish American mints in the 16th–18th centuries.

Coin Piece of metal, marked with a device, issued by government authority and intended for use as money.

Collar Retaining ring within which the *dies* for the *obverse* and *reverse* operate. When the *blank* is struck under high pressure between the dies the metal flows sideways and is formed by the collar, taking up the impression of *reeding* or *edge inscription* from it.

Commemorative Coin, medal, token or paper note issued to celebrate a current event or the anniversary of a historic event or personality.

Communion Token Token, cast in lead, but later struck in pewter, brass, bronze or white metal, issued to members of a congregation to permit them to partake of the annual communion service in the Calvinist and Presbyterian churches. John Calvin himself is said to have invented the communion token in 1561 but they were actually referred to in the minutes of the Scottish General Assembly in 1560. Later they were adopted by the Reformed churches in many parts of Europe. They survived in Scotland till the early years of this century. Each parish had its own tokens, often bearing the names or initials of individual ministers, with dates, symbols and biblical texts.

Conjoined Term denoting overlapped profiles of two or more rulers (e.g. William and Mary).

Contorniate (from Italian *contorno*, edge). Late 4th and 5th century Roman bronze piece whose name alludes to the characteristic grooving on the edges.

Contribution Coins Coins struck by Bamberg, Eichstatt, Fulda and other German cities in the 1790s during the First Coalition War against the French Republic. The name alludes to the fact that the bullion used to produce the coins necessary to pay troops was raised by contribution from the Church and the public.

Convention Money Any system of coinage agreed by neighbouring countries for mutual acceptance and interchange. Examples include the Amphictyonic coins of ancient Greece, and the Austrian and Bavarian talers and gulden of 1753–1857 which were copied by other south German states and paved the way for the German Monetary union.

Copper Metallic element, chemical symbol *Cu*, widely used as a coinage medium for 2,500 years. Pure or almost pure copper was used for subsidiary coinage in many countries till the mid-19th century, but has since been superseded by copper alloys which are cheaper and more durable: *bronze* (copper and tin), *brass* (copper and zinc), *Bath metal* or *bell metal* (low-grade copper and tin), *aluminium-bronze* (copper and aluminium), *potin* (copper, tin, lead and silver) or *cupro-nickel* (copper and nickel). Copper is also alloyed with gold to give it its reddish hue, and is normally alloyed with silver in coinage metals. When the copper exceeds the silver content the alloy is known as *billon*.

Copperhead Popular term for a copper *token* about the size and weight of an American cent which circulated in the USA during the Civil War (1861–65) during a shortage of subsidiary coinage. Many different types were produced, often of a political or patriotic nature.

Coppernose Popular name for the debased silver shillings of Henry VIII. Many of them were struck in copper with little more than a silver wash which tended to wear off at the highest point of the obverse, the nose on the full-face portrait of the king.

Counter A piece resembling a coin but intended for use on a medieval accountancy board or in gambling. See also *jeton*.

Counterfeit Imitation of a coin, token or banknote intended for circulation to deceive the public and defraud the state.

Countermark Punch mark applied to a coin some time after its original issue, either to alter its nominal value, or to authorise its circulation in some other country.

Cowrie Small shell (*Cypraea moneta*) circulating as a form of primitive currency from 1000 BC (China) to the present century (East and West Africa) and also used in the islands of the Indian and Pacific Oceans.

Crockard Debased silver imitation of English pennies produced in the Netherlands and imported into England in the late 13th century. Edward I tried to prevent their import then, in 1299, allowed them to pass current as halfpennies. As they contained more than a halfpennyworth of silver this encouraged their trading in to be melted down and they disappeared from circulation within a year. Sometimes known as *pollards*. See also *Lushbourne*.

Crown Gold Gold of 22 carat (.916) fineness, so called on account of its adoption in 1526 for the English gold crown. It has remained the British standard gold fineness ever since.

Cumberland Jack Popular name for a counter or medalet of sovereign size, struck unofficially in 1837 in brass. The figure of St George was replaced by the Duke of Cumberland on horseback with the inscription "To Hanover" a reference to the unpopular Duke of Cumberland, uncle of Queen Victoria, who succeeded to the Hanoverian throne since Victoria, as a female, was debarred by Salic law from inheritance.

Cupellation (Latin *cupella*, a little cup). Process by which gold and silver were separated from lead and other impurities in their ores. A cupel is a shallow cup of bone-ash or other absorbent material which, when hot, absorbs any molten material that wets its surface. Lead melts and oxidises with impurities into the cupel, whereas gold and silver remain on the cupel. Cupellation is also used in assaying the fineness of these precious metals.

Cupro-nickel Coinage alloy of 75 per cent copper and 25 per cent nickel, now widely used as a base metal substitute for silver. A small amount of zinc is added to the alloy in modern Russian coins.

Currency Coins, tokens, paper notes and other articles intended to pass current in general circulation as money.

Current Coins and paper money still in circulation.

Cut Money Coins cut into smaller pieces to provide correspondingly smaller denominations. The cross on many medieval coins assisted the division of silver pennies into halfpence and farthings. Spanish dollars were frequently divided into *bits* which themselves became units of currency in America and the West Indies.

Darlehnskassen (German for "state loan notes"). Paper money issued during the First World War in an abortive bid to fill the shortage of coinage in circulation. These low-denomination notes failed to meet demand and were superseded by local issues of small *Notgeld* in 1916.

Debasement The reduction in the precious metal content of the coinage, widely practised since time immemorial by governments for economic reasons. British coins, for example, were debased from sterling (.925 fine) silver to .500 in 1920 and from silver to cupro-nickel in 1947.

Decimalisation A currency system in which the principal unit is subdivided into ten, a hundred, or a thousand fractions. Russia was the first country to decimalise, in 1534 when the rouble of 100 kopeks was introduced, but it was not till 1792 that France adopted the franc of 100 centimes and 1793 when the USA introduced the dollar of 100 cents. Most European countries decimalised their currency in the 19th century. Britain toyed with the idea, introducing the florin or tenth of a pound in 1849 as the first step, but did not complete the process till 1971. The last countries to decimalise were Malta and Nigeria, in 1972 and 1973 respectively.

Demidiated Heraldic term to describe the junction of two armorial devices, in which only half of each is shown.

Demonetisation The withdrawal of coins or paper money from circulation and declaring them to be worthless.

Device Heraldic term for the pattern or emblem on coins or paper notes.

Die Hardened piece of metal bearing a mirror image of the device to be struck on one side of a coin or medal.

Die Proof An impression, usually pulled on soft carton or India paper, of an *intaglio* engraving of a banknote, usually taken during the progress of the engraving to check the detail. Banknote proofs of this nature usually consist of the portrait or some detail of the design, such as the border, rather than the complete motif.

Dodecagonal   Twelve-sided, a term applied to the nickel-brass threepence of Great Britain, 1937–67.

Dump   Any primitive coin struck on a very thick *flan*, but more specifically applied to the circular pieces cut from the centre of Spanish dollars, countermarked with the name of the colony, a crown and the value, and circulated in New South Wales at 15 pence in 1813. See *Holey Dollar*.

Duodecimal   Currency system based on units of twelve, i.e. medieval money of account (12 denarii = 1 soldo) which survived in Britain as 12 pence to the shilling as late as 1971.

Ecclesiastical Coins   Coins struck by a religious authority, such as an archbishop, bishop, abbot, prior or the canons of a religious order. Such coins were common in medieval times but survived as late as the early 19th century, the bishops of Breslau (1817) and Gurk (1823) being the last prelates to exercise coinage rights. Coins were struck by authority of the Pope at Rome till 1870 but since 1929 coinage has been struck at the Italian state mint on behalf of the Vatican City State.

Edge Inscription   Lettering on the edge of a coin or medal to prevent clipping. Alluding to this, the Latin motto *Decus et Tutamen* (an ornament and a safeguard) was applied to the edge of English milled coins in the reign of Charles II.

Edge Ornament   An elaboration of the *graining* found on many milled coins to prevent clipping, taking the form of tiny leaves, florets, interlocking rings, pellets and zigzag patterns. In some cases the ornament appears between layers of more conventional reeding.

EF   Abbreviation for Extremely Fine.

Effigy   An image or representation of a person, normally the head of state, a historical personage, or an allegorical figure, usually on the *obverse* or "heads" side of a coin or medal.

Electrotype   A reproduction of a coin or medal made by an electrolytic process.

Electrum   Alloy of gold and silver, sometimes called white gold, used for minting the staters of Lydia, 7th century BC, and other early European coins.

Elongated Coin   An oval *medalet* created by passing a coin, such as an American cent, between rollers under pressure with the effect of squeezing it out and impressing on it a souvenir or commemorative motif.

Emergency Money   Any form of money used in times of economic and political upheaval, when traditional kinds of currency are not available. Examples include the comparatively crude silver coins issued by the Royalists during the *Civil War* (1642–49), *obsidional* money, issued in time of siege, from Tyre (1122) to Mafeking (1900), the *Notgeld* issued by many German towns (1916–23), *encased money, fractional currency, guerrilla notes, invasion, liberation* and *occupation money* from the two World Wars and minor campaigns.   Among the more recent examples may be cited the use of sweets and cheques in Italy (1976–77) and the issue of coupons and vouchers in many of the countries of the former Soviet Union pending the introduction of their own distinctive coins and notes.

Enamelled Coins   Coins decorated by enamelling the obverse and reverse motifs in contrasting colours was an art practised by many jewellers in Birmingham and Paris in the 19th century, and revived in Europe and America in the 1970s.

Encased Money   Postage and revenue stamps enclosed in small metal and mica-faced discs, circulated as small change in times of emergency. The practice was invented by John Gault, a Boston sewing-machine salesman, during the American Civil War (1862).   The face of the stamp was visible through the transparent window, while the back of the disc was embossed with firms' advertisements. This practice was revived during and after the First World War when there was again a shortage of small coins. Encased stamps have also been recorded from France, Austria, Norway, Germany and Monaco. See also *Stamp Money*.

Engrailing   Technical term for the close serrations or vertical bars round the edge of a coin, applied as a security device.

Engraving   The art of cutting lines or grooves in plates, blocks or dies. Numismatically this takes the form of engraving images into the face of the dies used in striking coins, a process which has now been almost completely superseded by *hubbing* and the use of *reducing machinery*. In the production of paper money, *intaglio* engraving is still commonly practised. In this process the engraver cuts the design into a steel die and the printing ink lies in the grooves.   The paper is forced under great pressure into the grooves and picks up the ink, and this gives banknotes their characteristic ridged feeling to the touch. Nowadays many banknotes combine traditional intaglio engraving with multicolour lithography or photogravure to defeat the would-be counterfeiter.

Epigraphy   The study of inscriptions, involving the classification and interpretation of coin legends, an invaluable adjunct to the study of a coin series, particularly the classical and medieval coins which, in the absence of dates and mintmarks, would otherwise be difficult to arrange in chronological sequence.

Erasion   The removal of the title or effigy of a ruler from the coinage issued after his or her death. This process was practised in imperial Rome, and applied to the coins of Caligula, Nero and Geta, as part of the more general practice of *damnatio memoriae* (damnation of the memory) ordered by the Senate.

Error   Mistakes on coins and paper money may be either caused at the design or engraving stage, or as a result of a fault in the production processes. In the first category come misspellings in legends causing, in extreme cases, *blundered inscriptions*, or anachronisms or inaccuracies in details of the design. In the second, the most glaring error is the *mule* caused by marrying the wrong dies. Faulty alignment of dies can cause obverse and reverse to be out of true. Although many coins are issued with obverse and reverse upside down in relation to each other, this can also occur as an error in coins where both sides should normally be facing the same way up. Other errors caused at the production stage include striking coins in the wrong metal or with the wrong *collar* thus creating a different edge from the normal (e.g. British 10p with scalloped Hong Kong edge).

Essay   (From the French *essai*, a trial piece). The term is applied to any piece struck for the purposes of examination, by parliamentary or financial bodies, prior to the authorisation of an issue of coins or paper money. The official nature of these items distinguishes them from *patterns*, which denote trial pieces often produced by mints or even private individuals bidding for coinage contracts.

Evasion   Close copy or imitation of a coin, with sufficient deliberate differences in the design or inscription to avoid infringing counterfeit legislation. A good example is the imitation of Sumatran coins by European merchants, inscribed SULTANA instead of SUMATRA.

Exergue   Lower segment of a coin or medal, usually divided from the rest of the *field* by a horizontal line, and often containing the date, value, ornament or identification symbols.

Exonumia   Generic term for numismatic items not authorised by a government, e.g. *patterns*, *tokens*, *medalets* or *model coins*.

Face   The surface of a coin, medal or token, referred to as the *obverse* or the *reverse*. The corresponding faces of a paper note are more correctly termed *verso* and *recto*, but the coin terms are often used instead.

An example of a "Facing" portrait on the obverse of a medallion of Henry Simms, 1901. Actual size 360mm.

Facing   Term for the portrait, usually on the obverse, which faces to the front instead of to the side (profile).

Fantasy   Piece of metal purporting to be the coinage of a country which does not exist. Recent examples include the money of Atlantis and the Hutt River Province which declared its independence of Western Australia.

FDC   Abbreviation for *Fleur de Coin*, a term denoting the finest possible condition of a coin.

Fiat Money   Paper notes issued by a government but not redeemable in coin or bullion.

Field   Flat part of the surface of a coin or medal, between the *legend*, the *effigy* and other raised parts of the design.

Fillet   Heraldic term for the ribbon or headband on the effigy of a ruler or allegorical figure.

Find   Term applied to an archaeological discovery of one or more coins. A large quantity of such material is described as a *hoard*.

Flan   Alternative name for *blank* or *planchet*, the piece of metal struck between dies to produce a coin or medal.

Forgery   An unauthorised copy or imitation, made with the intention of deceiving collectors. Forgeries intended to pass current for real coins or notes are more properly called *counterfeits*.

Fractional Currency   Emergency issue of small-denomonation notes by the USA in 1863–5, following a shortage of coins caused by the Civil War. This issue superseded the *Postage Currency* notes, but bore the inscription "Receivable for all US stamps", alluding to the most popular medium of small change at that time. Denominations ranged from 3c to 50c.

Franklinium   Cupro-nickel alloy developed by the Franklin Mint of Philadelphia and used for coins, medals and gaming tokens since 1967.

Freak An *error* or *variety* of a non-recurring type, usually caused accidentally during production.

Frosting Matt surface used for the high relief areas of many proof coins and medals, for greater contrast with the mirrored surface of the field.

Funeral Money Imitations of banknotes, used in China and Latin America in funeral ceremonies.

Geat (Git) Channel through which molten metal is ducted to the mould. Cast coins and medals often show tiny protrusions known as geat marks.

Ghost Faint image of the design on one side of a coin visible on the other. Good examples were the British penny and halfpenny of George V, 1911–27, the ghosting being eliminated by the introduction of a smaller effigy in 1928.

Globular Coins struck on very thick *dumps* with convex faces. The term is applied to some Byzantine coins, and also the *bullet money* of Siam (Thailand).

Godless (or *Graceless*) Epithet applied to any coin which omits the traditional reference to the deity, e.g. the British florin of 1849 which omitted D.G. (*Dei Gratia*, "by the Grace of God").

Gold Precious metal, atomic symbol and numismatic abbreviation *Au*, from the *Latin Aurum*, used as a coinage medium from the 7th century BC till the present day. The purity of gold is reckoned in *carats* or a decimal system. Thus British gold sovereigns are 22 carat or .916 fine. Medieval coins were 23.5 carat or .995 fine, and some modern bullion coins are virtually pure gold, denoted by the inscription .999. Canadian maple leaves are now struck in "four nines" gold and bear the inscription .9999.

Goodfor Popular name for token coins and *emergency money* made of paper or card, from the inscription "Good for" or its equivalent in other languages (e.g. French *Bon pour* or Dutch *Goed voor*) followed by a monetary value. They have been recorded from Europe, Africa and America during times of economic crises or shortage of more traditional coinage.

Gothic Crown Popular name for the silver crown issued by the United Kingdom (1847–53), so-called on account of its script (more properly Old English, rather than Gothic).

Grain The weight of a single grain of wheat was taken as the smallest unit of weight in England. The troy grain was 1/5760 of a pound, while the avoirdupois grain was 1/7000 pound, the former being used in the weighing of precious metals and thus employed by numismatists in weighing coins. A grain is 1/480 troy ounce or 0.066 gram in the metric system.

Graining Term sometimes used as a synonym for the *reeding* on the edge of milled coins.

Gripped Edge Pattern of indentations found on the majority of American cents of 1797, caused by the milling process. Coins of the same date with a plain edge are rather scarcer.

Guerrilla Money Money issued in areas under the control of guerrillas and partisans during wartime range from the *veld ponds* of the Boers (1900–2) to the notes issued by the Garibaldi Brigade in Italy and the anti-fascist notes of Tito's forces in Yugoslavia. The most prolific issues were those produced in Luzon, Mindanao and Negros Occidental by the Filipino resistance during the Japanese occupation (1942–5).

Guilloche French term signifying the intricate pattern of curved lines produced by the rose engine and used as a security feature in the production of banknote, cheques, stocks and share certificates.

Gun Money Emergency coinage of Ireland (1689––91) minted from gunmetal, a type of bronze used in the casting of cannon. All denominations of James II, from the sixpence to the crown, normally struck in silver, were produced in this base metal.

Gutschein German word for voucher or coupon, denoting the paper money used aboard ships of the Imperial Navy during the First World War. The last issue was made at Scapa Flow, 1918–19, during the internment of the High Seas Fleet.

Hammered Term denoting coins produce by the traditional method of striking a *flan* laid on an anvil with a hammer. A characteristic of hammered coins is their uneven shape which tended to encourage *clipping*. This abuse was gradually eliminated by the introduction of the screw press in the 15th century and the mechanisation of coining processes in the course of the 16th and 17th centuries.

"Hard Times" tokens issued by the New York and Harlem Railroad Company.

Hard Times Token Copper piece the size of the large cent, issued in the USA, 1834–44, during a shortage of coins caused by the collapse of the Bank of the United States, the panic of 1837 and the economic crisis of 1839, the landmarks in the period known as the Hard Times. Banks suspended *specie* payments and the shortage of coinage was filled by tradesmen's tokens. Many of these were more in the nature of satirical *medalets* than circulating pieces.

Hat Piece Alternative name for the *bonnet piece* of James VI of Scotland, 1591.

Hell Notes Imitation paper money used in Chinese funeral ceremonies and buried with the dead to pay for services in the next world.

Hoard Accumulation of coins concealed in times of economic or political upheaval and discovered, often centuries later. Under English common law, such hoards are subject to th law of *treasure trove* if they contain precious metal.

Hog Money Popular name for the early coinage of Bermuda, issued about 1616. The coins were minted in brass with a silver wash and circulated at various values from twopence to a shilling. They derived their name from the hog depicted on the obverse, an allusion to the pigs introduced to the island in 1515 by Juan Bermudez.

Holed Term denoting two different categories: (a) coins which have been pierced for suspension as a form of jewellery or talisman, and (b) coins which have a hole as part of their design. In the latter category come the Chinese *cash* with a square hole, and numerous issues of the 19th and 20th centuries from many countries, with the object of reducing weight and metal without sacrificing overall diameter.

Holey Dollar Spanish silver peso of 8 reales with the centre removed. The resultant ring was counter-marked "New South Wales" and dated 1813, with "Five Shillings" on the reverse, and placed into circulation during a shortage of British coin. The centre, known as a *dump*, was circulated at 15 pence.

Hub Heavy circular piece of steel on which the *die* for a coin or medal is engraved. The process of cutting the die and transferring the master die, by means of intermediary *punches*, to the die from which the coins will be struck, is known as hubbing. Soft steel is used in the preliminary process, and after the design has been transferred, the hub is hardened by chemical action.

Hybrid Alternative name for a *mule*.

Imitation Money Also known as play money or toy money, it consists of coins and notes produced for games of chance (like Monopoly), children's toy shops and post offices, as tourist souvenirs, or for political satire (e.g. the shrinking pound or dollar). See also *funeral money, hell notes, model coins* and *skit notes*.

Imprint Inscription on a paper note giving the name of the printer.

Incuse Impression which cuts into the surface of a coin or medal, as opposed to the more usual raised relief. Many of the earliest coins, especially those with a device on one side only, bear an incuse impression often in a geometric pattern. An incuse impression appears on one side of the coins, reflecting the image on the other side. Few modern coins have had an incuse design, notable examples being the American half and quarter eagle gold coins of 1908–29 designed by Bela Pratt. Incuse inscriptions on a raised rim, however, are more common, and include the British *Cartwheel* coins of 1797 and the 20p coins since 1982.

Inflation Money Coins produced as a result of inflation date back to Roman times when bronze minimi, little bigger than a pinhead, circulated as denarii. Nearer the present day inflation has had devastating effects on the coinge and banknotes of Germany (1921–3), Austria (1923), Poland (1923), Hungary (1945–6), Greece (1946) and many Latin American countries since the 1980s. Hungary holds the record for the highest value of any note ever issued — one thousand million adopengos, equivalent to 20,000,000,000,000,000,000,000,000,000,000 pengos.

Ingot Piece of precious metal, usually cast in a mould, and stamped with the weight and fineness. though mainly used as a convenient method of storing bullion, ingots have been used as currency in many countries, notably Russia and Japan.

Inlay Insertion into the surface of a coin or medal of another substance for decorative effect. e.g. Poland Amber Trade Routes 20zl (amber), Isle of Man Queen Mother centenery (pearl) and various coins incorporating rubies or diamonds.

Intaglio Form of *engraving* in which lines are cut into a steel die for the recess-printing of banknotes.

Intrinsic The net metallic value of a coin, as distinguished from the nominal or face value.

Iron Metal, chemical symbol *Fe* (from Latin *Ferrum*), used as a primitive form of currency from classical times onwards. Iron spits (obeliskoi) preceded the obol as the lowest unit of Greek coinage, a handful of six spits being worth a drachma (from *drassomai*, "I grasp"). Cast iron coins were issued in China as a substitute for copper *cash*. Many of the emergency token issues of Germany during the First World War were struck in iron. Iron coins were issued by Bulgaria in 1943. See also *Steel*.

Ithyphallic (Greek for "erect penis"). Term descriptive of coins of classical Greece showing a satyr.

Janiform Double profiles back to back, after the Roman god Janus.

Jeton (From French *jeter*, to throw). Alternative term for *counter*, and used originally on the chequerboard employed by medieval accountants. Nuremberg was the most important centre for the production of medieval jetons, often issued in lengthy portrait series. In modern parlance the term is often synonymous with *token*, though more specifically confined to pieces used in vending equipment, parking meters, laundromats, telephones and urban transport systems in many European countries. Apart from security, removing the temptation of vandals to break into the receptacles, the main advantage of such pieces is that they can be retariffed as charges increase, without any alteration in their design or composition, a method that is far cheaper than altering costly equipment to take larger coins.

Jugate (From Latin *jugum*, a yoke). Alternative to *accolated* or *conjoined* to denote overlapping profiles of rulers.

Key Date Term describing the rarest in a long-running series of coins with the dates changed at annual intervals.

Kipperzeit German term meaning the time of clipped money, denoting the period during and after the Thirty Years War (1618–48) in which debased and clipped money was in circulation.

Klippe Rectangular or square pieces of metal bearing the impression of a coin. Coins of this type were first struck in Sweden in the 16th century and were subsequently produced in many of the German states. The idea has been revived in recent years as a medium for striking commemorative pieces.

Knife Money Cast bronze pieces, with an elongated blade and a ring at one end to facilitate stringing together in bunches, were used as currency in China from the 9th century BC until the 19th century.

Kreditivsedlar (Swedish for "credit notes"). The name given to the first issue of paper money made in the western world. Paper money of this type was the brainchild of Johan Palmstruch at Riga in 1652, but nine years elapsed before it was implemented by the Stockholm Bank in Sweden. The notes were redeemable in copper *platmynt*.

Laureate Heraldic term for a laurel wreath, often framing a state emblem or shown, in the Roman fashion, as a crown on the ruler's forehead.

Leather Money Pieces of leather embossed with an official device have been used as money on several occasions, during the sieges of Faenza and Leiden and in the Isle of Man in the 15th and 16th centuries. Several towns in Austria and Germany produced leather tokens during and after the First World War.

Legal Tender Coins or paper money which are declared by law to be current money and which tradesmen and shopkeers are obliged to accept in payment for goods or services. (See *Money and the Law*).

Legend The inscription on a coin or medal.

Liberation Money Paper money prepared for use in parts of Europe and Asia, formerly under Axis occupation. Liberation notes were used in France, Belgium and the Netherlands in 1944–5, while various Japanese and Chinese notes were overprinted for use in Hong Kong when it was liberated in 1945. Indian notes overprinted for use in Burma were issued in 1945–6 when that country was freed from Japanese occupation.

Ligature (From Latin *ligatus*, bound together). Term denoting the linking of two letters in a *legend*, e.g. Æ and Œ.

Long Cross Coinage Type of coinage introduced by King Henry III in 1247, deriving its name from the reverse which bore a cross whose arms extended right to the edge to help safeguard the coins against *clipping*. This remained the style of the silver penny, its fractions and multiples, till the reign of Henry VII, and vestiges of the long cross theme can be seen in the silver coins throughout the remaining years of the Tudor period.

Love Token A coin which has been altered by smoothing one or both surfaces and engraving initials, dates, scenes, symbols of affection and messages thereon.

Lushbourne English word for base pennies of inferior silver, said to have emanated from Luxembourg, from which the name derived. These coins were first minted under John the Blind who adopted the curious spelling of his name EIWANES in the hope that illiterate English merchants might confuse it with EDWARDVS and thus be accepted as coin issued in the name of Edward III. Lushbournes were also minted by Robert of Bethune, William I of Namur and the bishops of Toul during the mid-14th century.

Lustre The sheen or bloom on the surface of an uncirculated coin resulting from the centrifugal flow of metal caused by striking.

Magnimat Trade name used by VDM (*Verein Deutscher Metallwerke*) for a high-security alloy containing copper, nickel and magnetised steel. First used for the 5 deutschemark coin of 1975, it has since been adopted for other high-value coins in Germany and other countries.

Manilla Copper, bronze or brass rings, sometimes shaped like horseshoes and sometimes open, with flattened terminals, used as currency in West Africa until recent years.

Matrix Secondary die for a coin or medal, produced from the master die by means of an intermediate punch. In this way dies can be duplicated from the original cut on the reducing machine.

Matt or Matte Finely granulated surface or overall satin finish to proof coins, a style which was briefly fashionable at the turn of the century. The Edward VII proof set of 1902 is a notable example. In more recent years many issues of the Franklin Mint have been issued in this finish.

Maundy Money Set of small silver coins, in denominations of 1, 2, 3 and 4 pence, distributed by the reigning British monarch to the poor and needy on Maundy Thursday. The custom dates back to the Middle Ages, but in its present form, of distributing pence to as many men and women as the years in the monarch's age, it dates from 1666. At first ordinary silver pennies and multiples were used but after they went out of everyday use distinctive silver coins were produced specifically for the purpose from the reign of George II (1727–60) onwards. For centuries the ceremony took place in Westminster Abbey but since 1955 other venues have been used in alternate years.

Medal (French *medaille*, Italian *medaglia*, from Latin *metallum*). A piece of metal bearing devices and legends commemorating an event or person, or given as an award. Military medals date from the 16th and 17th centuries, but were not generally awarded to all ranks till the 19th century. Commemorative medals can trace their origin back to Roman times, but in their present form they date from the Italian Renaissance when there was a fashion for large-diameter cast portrait medals.

Medalet A small medal, generally 25mm or less in diameter.

Medallion Synonym for medal, but usually confined to those with a diameter of 50mm or more.

Milling Process denoting the mechanical production of coins, as opposed to the handmade technique implied in *hammering*. It alludes to the use of watermills to drive the machinery of the screw presses and blank rollers developed in the 16th century. As the even thickness and diameter of milled coins permitted a security edge, the term milling is popularly, though erroneously, used as a synonym for *graining* or *reeding*.

Mint The place in which coins and medals are produced. Mint condition is a term sometimes used to denote pieces in an uncirculated state.

Mint Set A set of coins or medals in the package or case issued by the mint. See also *year set*.

Mintmark A device appearing on a coin to denote the place of minting. Athenian coins of classical times have been recorded with up to 40 different marks, denoting individual workshops. In the 4th century AD the Romans adopted this system to identify coins struck in provincial mints. This system was widely used in the Middle Ages and survives in France and Germany to this day. Initials and symbols are also used to identify mints, especially where the production of a coin is shared between several different mints. From 1351 onwards symbols were adopted in England to denote periods between trials of the *Pyx*, and thus assist the proper chronological sequence of coins, in an era prior to the adoption of dating. These mintmarks continued into the 17th century, but gradually died out as the use of dates became more widespread. See also *countermark* and *privy mark*.

Mionnet Scale Scale of nineteen diameters covering all sizes of coins belonging to the classical period, devised by the French numismatist, Theodore-Edme Mionnet (1770–1842) during the compilation of his fifteen-volume catalogue of the numismatic collection in the Bibliotheque Nationale in Paris.

Mirror Finish The highly polished surface of proof coins.

Misstrike A coin or medal on which the impression has been struck off-centre.

Model Coin Tiny pieces of metal, either reproducing the designs of existing coins (used as play money by children) or, more specifically, denoting patterns produced by Joseph Moore and Hyam Hyams in their attempts to promote an improved subsidiary coinage in 19th century Britain. These small coins were struck in bronze with a brass or silver centre and were designed to reduce the size of the existing cumbersome range of pence, halfpence and farthings.

Modified Effigy Any coin in which the profile on the obverse has been subtly altered. Examples include minor changes in the Victorian Young Head and Old Head effigies and the George V profile by Sir Bertram Mackennal.

Money Order Certificate for a specified amount of money, which may be transmitted by post and encashed at a money order office or post office. This system was pioneered by Britain and the United States in the early 19th century and is now virtually worldwide. The term is now confined to certificates above a certain value, the terms *postal order* and *postal note* being used for similar certificates covering small amounts.

Mule Coin whose obverse is not matched with its official or regular reverse. Mules include the erroneous combination of dies from different reigns, but in recent years such hybrids have arisen in mints where coins for several countries are struck. Examples include the Coronation Anniversary crowns combining Ascension and Isle of Man dies and the 2 cent coins with Bahamas and New Zealand dies. *Restrikes* of rare American coins have been detected in which the dated die has been paired with the wrong reverse die, e.g. the 1860 restrike of the rare 1804 large cent.

Mute An *anepigraphic* coin, identifiable only by the devices struck on it.

Nail Mark Small indentation on ancient coins. The earliest coins of Asia Minor developed from the electrum *dumps* which merchants marked with a broken nail as their personal guarantee of value, the ancient counterpart of the *chop* marks used in China and Japan.

NCLT Coins Abbreviation for "Non Circulating Legal Tender", a term devised by modern coin catalogues to denote coins which, though declared *legal tender*, are not intended for general circulation on account of their precious metal content or superior finish.

Nicked Coin Coin bearing a tiny cut or nick in its edge. Silver coins were tested by this method, especially in the reign of Henry I (1100–35) when so many base silver pennies were in circulation. Eventually people refused to accept these nicked coins a problem which was only overcome when the state decreed that all coins should have a nick in them.

Nickel Metallic element, chemical symbol Ni, a hard white metal relatively resistant to tarnish, and extensively used as a cheap substitute for silver. It was first used for the American 5 cent coin in 1866, hence its popular name which has stuck ever since, although nowadays the higher denominations are minted in an alloy of copper and nickel. Although best known as a silver substitute, nickel was widely used in Jamaica (1869–1969) for halfpence and pennies and in British West Africa for the tiny 1/10th pennies (1908–57). Pure nickel is used for French francs and German marks, but usually it is alloyed with copper or zinc to produce *cupro-nickel* or nickel brass.

Notaphily Hybrid word from Latin *nota* (note) and Greek philos (love), coined about 1970 to denote the branch of numismatics devoted to the study of paper money.

Notgeld German word meaning emergency money, applied to the *tokens*, in metals, wood,

leather and even ceramic materials, issued during the First World War when coinage disappeared from circulation. These tokens were soon superseded by low-denomination paper money issued by shops and businessmen in denominations from 10 to 50 pfennige and known as *kleine Notgeld* (small emergency money). These notes were prohibited in September 1922 but by that time some 50,000 varieties are thought to have been issued. Inflation raced out of control and the government permitted a second issue of local notes, known as *large Notgeld*, as the denominations were in thousands, and latterly millions, of marks. Some 3,600 types appeared in 1922 and over 60,000 in 1923 alone. These mementoes of the German hyperinflation ceased to circulate in 1924 when the currency was reformed.

Numismatics The study of coins, medals and other related fields, a term derived from the Latin *numisma* and Greek *nomisma* (money).

Obsidional Currency (From Latin *obsidium*, a siege). Term for *emergency money* produced by the defenders of besieged towns and cities. These usually took the form of pieces of silver plate, commandeered for the purpose, crudely marked with an official device and the value. Instances of such seige coinage have been recorded from the 12th to the 19th centuries. Paper money was issued in Venice during the Austrian siege of 1848, and by Mafeking during the Boer War.

Obverse The "heads" side of a coin or medal, generally bearing the effigy of the head of state or an allegorical figure (e.g. Liberty—Argentina, USA; Helvetia or William Tell—Switzerland; or La Semeuse—France).

Off Metal Term denoting a piece struck in a metal other than the officially authorised or issued alloy. This originally applied to *patterns* which were often struck in lead or copper instead of gold and silver as trial pieces or to test the dies; but in recent years it has applied to collectors' versions, e.g. proofs in platinum, gold or silver of coins normally issued in bronze or cupro-nickel.

Overdate One or more digits in a date altered by superimposing another figure. Alterations of this kind, by means of small hand punches, were made to dated dies so that they could be used in years other than that of the original manufacture. Coins with overdates invariably show traces of the original digit.

Overstrike Coin, token or medal produced by using a previously struck pieces as a flan. The Bank of England dollar of 1804 was overstruck on Spanish pieces of eight, and examples showing traces of the original coins are worth a good premium.

Paduan Name given to imitations of medals and bogus coins produced in Italy in the 16th century, and deriving from the city of Padua where forgeries of bronze sculpture were produced for the antique market.

Patina Oxidation forming on the surface of metallic objects. So far as coins and medals are concerned, this applies mainly to silver, brass, bronze and copper pieces which may acquire oxidation from the atmosphere, or spectacular patination from salts in the ground in which they have been buried. In extreme forms patina leads to verdigris and other forms of rust which corrode the surface, but in uncirculated coins it may be little more than a mellowing of the original *lustre*. Coins preserved in blue velvet presentation cases often acquire a subtle toning from the dyes in the material.

Pattern Piece resembling a coin or medal, prepared by the mint to the specifications or on the authorisation of the coin-issuing authority, but also applied to pieces produced by mints when tendering for coinage or medal contracts. Patterns may differ from the final coins as issued in the type of alloy used (*off metal*) but more often they differ in details of the design.

Pellet Raised circular ornament used as a spacing device between words and abbreviations in the *legend* of coins and medals. Groups of pellets were also used as ornaments in the angles of the cross on the reverse of English silver pennies.

Piece de Plaisir (French for "fancy piece"). Term given to coins struck in a superior precious metal, or to a superior finish, or on a much thicker flan than usual. See *off metal*, *piedfort* and *proof*.

A piedfort £1 coin compared to one of a normal flan.

Piedfort (Piefort) Piece struck with coinage dies on a *flan* of much more than normal thickness. This practice originated in France in the late 16th century and continues to the present day. In recent years it has been adopted by mints in Britain and other countries as a medium for collectors' pieces.

Pile Lower die incorporating the obverse motif, used in striking coins and medals. See also *trussel*.

Planchet French term used as an alternative for *blank* or *flan*.

Plaque or **Plaquette** Terms sometimes used for medals struck on a square or rectangular flan.

Plaster Cast taken from the original model for a coin or medal sculpted by an artist, and used in modern reducing machines in the manufacture of the master *die*.

Plated Coins Coins stuck in base metal but given a wash of silver or some other precious metal. This expedient was adopted in inflationary times, from the Roman Republic (91 BC) till the Tudor period. American cents of 1943 were struck in steel with a zinc coating, and more recently *clad* coins have produced similar results.

Platinum The noblest of all precious metals, platinum has a higher specific gravity than gold and a harder, brighter surface than silver. Until an industrial application was discovered in the mid-19th century, it was regarded as of little value, and was popular with counterfeiters as a cheap substitute for gold in their forgeries which, with a light gold wash, could be passed off as genuine. It was first used for circulating coins in Russia (the chief source of the metal since 1819) and 3, 6 and 12 rouble coins were mined at various times between 1828 and 1845. In recent years platinum has been a popular metal for limited-edition proof coins.

Platmynt (Swedish for "plate money"). Large copper plates bearing royal cyphers and values from half to ten dalers produced in Sweden between 1643 and 1768. They represented laudable attempts by a country rich in copper to produce a coinage in terms of its silver value, but the net result was far too cumbersome to be practical. The weight of the daler plate, for example, ranged from 766 grams to 1.1kg, and special carts had to be devised to transport them!

Plugged Coins Coins struck predominantly in one metal, but containing a small plug of another. This curious practice may be found in the farthings of Charles II (1684–85) and the halfpence or farthings of James II (1685–87), which were struck in tin, with a copper plug, to defeat forgers.

Pollard Alternative name for *crockard*.

Porcelain Money Tokens made of porcelain circulated in Thailand from the late 18th century till 1868. The Meissen pottery struck tokens in 1920–22 as a form of small *Notgeld*, using reddish-brown Bottger stoneware and white *bisque* porcelain. These ceramic tokens circulated in various towns of Saxony.

Postage Currency Small paper notes in denominations of 5, 10, 25 and 50 cents, issued by the US federal government in 1862–63, were thus inscribed and had reproductions of postage stamps engraved on them — five 5c stamps on the 25c and five 10c stamps on the

50c notes. The earliest issue even had perforations in the manner of stamps, but this unnecessary device was soon done away with. See also *stamp money*.

Postal Notes or Orders Low-value notes intended for transmission by post and encashable at post offices. Introduced by Britain in 1883, they were an extension of the earlier *money order* system, and are now issued by virtually every country.

Potin (French for pewter). Alloy of copper, tin, lead and silver used as a coinage metal by the Celtic tribes of eastern Gaul at the beginning of the Christian era.

Privy Mark Secret mark incorporated in the design of a coin or medal to identify the minter, or even the particular die used. The term is also used more loosely to denote any small symbol or initials appearing on a coin other than a *mint mark*, and is sometimes applied to the symbols associated with the trial of the *Pyx* found on English coins.

Prize Coins Coins of large size and value struck primarily as prizes in sporting contests. this principle dates from the late 5th century BC when Syracuse minted decadrachms as prizes in the Demareteian Games. The most notable example in modern times is the lengthy series of talers and five-franc coins issued by the Swiss cantons since 1842 as prizes in the annual shooting festivals, the last of which honoured the Lucerne contest of 1939.

Profile A side view of the human face, widely used as a coinage effigy.

Proof Originally a trial strike testing the *dies*, but now denoting a special collectors' version struck with dies that have been specially polished on *flans* with a mirror finish. Presses operating at a very slow speed, or multi-striking processes, are also used.

Propaganda Notes Paper money containing a political slogan or a didactic element. During the Second World War forgeries of German and Japanese notes were produced by the Allies and additionally inscribed or overprinted with slogans such as "Co-Prosperity Sphere—What is it worth?" (a reference to the Japanese occupied areas of SE Asia). Forged dollars with anti-American propaganda were airdropped over Sicily by the Germans in 1943 and counterfeit pounds with Arabic propaganda over Egypt in 1942–43. Various anti-communist organisations liberated propaganda forgeries of paper money by balloon over Eastern Europe during the Cold War period.

Provenance Mark Form of *privy mark* denoting the source of the metal used in coins. Examples include the plumes or roses on English coins

denoting silver from Welsh or West of England mines, and the elephant or elephant and castle on gold coins denoting bullion imported by the African Company. Coins inscribed VIGO (1702–03) or LIMA (1745–46) denote bullion seized from the Spaniards by Anglo-Dutch privateers and Admiral Anson respectively. Other provenance marks on English coins include the letters EIC and SSC, denoting bullion imported by the East India Company or the South Sea Company.

Pseudo Coins Derisory term coined in recent years to signify pieces of precious metal, often struck in *proof* versions only, aimed at the international investment market. Many of these pieces, though bearing a nominal face value, are not *legal tender* in the countries purporting to issue them and in many cases they go straight from the overseas mint where they are produced to coin dealers in America and western Europe, without ever appearing in the so-called country of origin. See also *NCLT coins*.

Punch or Puncheon Intermediate *die* whereby working dies can be duplicated from the master die, prior to the striking of coins and medals.

Pyx Box in which a specimen from every 15 pounds troy weight of gold and every 60 pounds of silver minted in England is kept for annual trial by weight and assay. Many of the *mintmarks* on English coins of the 14th–17th centuries were in use from one trial to the next and still exist today and can therefore be used to date them.

Reducing Machinery Equipment designed on the pantographic principle for transferring the image from a *plaster* to a *hub* and reducing it to the size of the actual coin or medal. The image is transferred by means of a stylus operating rather like a gramophone needle, but working from the centre to the outer edge.

Reeding Security edging on coins, consisting of close vertical ridges. As a rule, this appears all round the edge but some coins, e.g. New Zealand's 50c (1967) and the Isle of Man's £1 (1978) have segments of reeding alternating with a plain edge, to help blind and partially sighted persons to identify these coins.

Re-issue A coin or note issued again after an extended lapse of time.

Relief Raised parts of the *obverse* and *reverse* of coins and medals, the opposite of *incuse*.

Remainder A note from a bank or issuing authority which has never been circulated, due to inflation, political changes or bank failure. Such notes, some-times in partial or unfinished state (e.g. missing serial numbers or signatures), are generally unloaded on to the numismatic market at a nominal sum and provide a good source of inexpensive material for the beginner.

Restrike Coin, medal or token produced from *dies* subsequent to the original use. Usually restrikes are made long after the original and can often be identified by marks caused by damage, pitting or corrosion of the dies after they were taken out of service.

Retrograde Term describing inscriptions running from right to left, or with the letters in a mirror image, thought to arise from unskilled die-cutters failing to realise that inscriptions have to be engraved in negative form to achieve a positive impression. Retrograde inscriptions are common on ancient Greek coins, but also found on Roman and Byzantine coins.

Reverse The side of a coin or medal regarded as of lesser importance; in colloquial parlance, the "tails" side.

Saltire Heraldic term for a cross in the shape of an X.

Sandwich Coin *blank* consisting of thin outer layers in one alloy bonded to a core in another. See *clad coins*.

Sceat (Anglo-Saxon for "treasure", or German *Schatz*). Money of account in Kent early in the 7th century as the twelfth part of a shilling or Merovingian gold tremissis. As a silver coin, it dates from about AD 680–700 and weighed about 20 grains, putting it on par with the Merovingian denier or penny. Sceats spread to other parts of England in the 8th century but tended to decline in weight and value, but from about 760 it was gradually superseded by the silver penny minted under Offa and his successors.

Scissel The clippings of metal left after a *blank* has been cut. Occasionally one of these clippings accidentally adheres to the blank during the striking process, producing characteristic crescent-shaped flaws on the finished coin.

Scrip Paper money of restricted validity or circulation, e.g. *Bafs* and other military scrip used in canteens and post exchanges.

Scyphate (Greek *scypha*, a skiff or small boat). Byzantine coin with a concave *flan*.

Sede Vacante (Latin for "Vacant See"). Coins struck at *ecclesiastical mints* between the death of a prelate and the election of his successor are often thus inscribed. This practice originated at Rome in the 13th century and spread to every part of Europe.

Seignorage or Seigneurage Royalty or percentage paid by persons bringing *bullion* to a mint for conversion into coin, but nowadays synonymous with the royalty paid by mints in respect of the precious metal versions of coins sold direct to collectors. It arises from the medieval right of the king to a small portion of the proceeds of a mint, and amounted to a tax on moneying. It has also been applied to the money accruing to the state when the coinage is re-issued in an alloy of lesser fineness, as, for example, the debased sovereigns of Henry VIII in 20 instead of 23 carat gold, the king's treasury collecting the difference.

Series Term applied to sets of medals of a thematic character, which first became fashionable in the early 18th century. Jean Dassier pioneered the medallic series in the 1720s with his set of 72 medals portraying the rulers of France till Louis XV. The idea was developed by J. Kirk, Sir Edward Thomason, J. Mudie and A. J. Stothard in Britain, and by Moritz Fuerst and Amedee Durand in Europe. The fashion died out in the 19th century, but has been revived in America and Europe since 1964.

Serrated Having a notched or toothed edge, rather like a cogwheel. Coins of this type, struck in *electrum*, an alloy of silver and gold, are known from Carthage in the 2nd century BC, and some silver denarii of Rome in the 2nd century AD also come into this category.

Sexagesimal System Monetary system in which the principal unit is divided into 60 parts. The oldest system in the Western world was based on the gold talent of 60 minae and the mina of 60 shekels. In medieval Europe 60 groschen were worth a fine mark; in England from 1551, the silver coinage was based on the crown of 60 pence, and in the south German states till 1873 the gulden was worth 60 kreuzers.

Shin Plasters Derisory term originally applied to the Continental currency notes issued during the American War of Independence, the fractional currency of the Civil War period and also the low-denomination notes of Canada between 1870 and 1935, but often applied indiscriminately to any other low-denomination, small-format notes.

Short Cross Coinage Term for the silver coinage introduced by Henry II in 1180 and minted till 1247 at which time it was replaced by the *Long Cross* type. The termination of the arms of the cross on the reverse well within the circumference encouraged the dishonest practice of *clipping*.

Shroff Mark A *countermark* applied by Indian bankers or merchants to attest the full weight and purity of coins. See also *chop*.

Siege Money See *Obsidional Currency*

Silver Precious metal, chemical symbol *Ag*, numismatic abbreviation *Ar*, from Latin *Argentum*, widely used as a coinage metal from the 6th century BC to the present day.

Sterling silver denotes an alloy of .925 fine silver with .075 copper. Fine silver alloys used over the past 2,500 years have ranged from .880 to .960 fine, but base silver has also been all too common. British coins from 1920 to 1946 were struck in .500 fine silver, while alloys of lesser fineness are known as *billon* or *vellon*. Silver alloyed with gold produces a metal called *electrum*, used for the earliest coinage of the western world, the staters of Lydia in the 7th century BC. Since 1970 silver as a medium for circulating coinage has almost virtually disappeared, yet the volume of silver coins for sale to collectors has risen considerably in recent years.

Skit Note Piece of paper masquerading as a bankntoe. It differs from a *counterfeit* in that its design parodies that of a genuine note, often for political, satirical or advertising reasons. Others were produced as April Fools' Day jokes or a form of Valentine (e.g. the Bank of Lovers). In recent years they have been produced as advertising gimmicks, or as coupons permitting a discount off the list price of goods.

Slug Popular name for the $50 gold pieces produced by private mints in California in the mid-19th century. The term is also applied nowadays to *tokens* intended for use in gaming machines.

Spade Guinea Name given to the guineas of George III issued between 1787 and 1799 because the shield on the reverse design resembled the shape of a spade. In Victorian times the spade guinea was extensively copied in brass for gaming counters.

Spade Money Cast bronze pieces resembling miniature spades and other agricultural implements, used as money and derived from the actual implements which had previously been used in barter. Often referred to as *Pu* or *Boo* money.

Specie Financial term denoting money in the form of precious metals (silver and gold), usually struck as coin, as opposed to money in the form of paper notes and bills of exchange. It occurs in the name of some European coins (e.g. *speciedaler*, *speciestaler* and *speciesducat*) to denote the use of fine silver or gold.

Specimen Generally used to denote a single piece, but more specifically applying to a coin in a special finish, less than *proof* in quality but superior to the general circulating version. It also denotes paper notes intended for circulation between banks or for press publicity and distinguished from the generally issued version by zero serial numbers, punch holes or a security endorsement.

Spintriae Metal tokens produced in Roman imperial times, with erotic motifs, thought to have been tickets of admission to brothels.

Spit Copper or iron rod used as a primitive form of currency in the Mediterranean area. The Greek word *belos* meant a spit, dart or bolt, and from this came the word *obolos* used for a coin worth a 6th of a drachma.

Stamp Money Both postage and revenue (fiscal) stamps have circulated as money during shortages of coins, from the American Civil War onwards. *Encased postage stamps* were used in the USA, 1861–62, before they were superseded by *Postage Currency* notes, but the same expedient was adopted by many countries during and immediately after the First World War. Stamps affixed to special cards have circulated as money in Rhodesia (now Zimbabwe) in 1900, the French colonies and Turkey during the First World War, in Spain during the Civil War (1936–39) and the Philippines during the Japanese occupation (1942–45). Stamps printed on thick card, with an inscription on the reverse signifying their parity with silver coins, were issued in Russia (1917–18) and also in Armenia, the Crimea and the Ukraine (1918–20). During the Second World War Ceylon (now Sri Lanka) and several Indian states issued small money cards with contemporary stamps printed on them.

Steel Refined and tempered from *iron*, and used in chromed or stainless versions as a coinage metal in the 20th century. Zinc-coated steel cents were issued by the USA (1943) but in the form known as *acmonital* (nickel steel) it has been extensively used by Italy since 1939. Other alloys of nickel and steel have been used for coins of the Philippines (1944–45) and Roumania since 1963. Chrome steel was used by France for 5 centime coins in 1961–64. Copper-clad steel is now extensively used for subsidiary coins formerly struck in bronze.

Sterling Word of uncertain origin denoting money of a standard weight and fineness, and hence the more general meaning of recognised worth. The traditionally accepted derivation from the Easterlings, north German merchants who settled in London in the 13th century and produced silver pennies of uniform fineness, is unlikely as the term has been found in documents a century earlier. A more plausible explanation is from Old English *steorling* ("little coin with a star"), alluding to Viking pennies with this device, or even as a diminutive of *stater*. Sterling silver denotes silver of .925 fineness.

Stone Money Primitive currency in the form of large stone discs, used in West Africa in the pre-colonial period, and in the Pacific island of

Yap (now Micronesia) as recently as 1940.

Striation A pattern of alternate light and dark parallel marks or minute grooves on the surface of a coin or medal. In the latter case it is sometimes done for textural effect, but in coins it may result from faulty *annealing*. Deliberate ridging of the surface, however, was a distinctive feature of Japanese *koban* and *goryoban* coins of 1736–1862.

Styca Name given to the debased silver *sceats* of Northumbria in the 8th century.

Sutlers' Tokens Tokens issued by US Army canteen-keepers for use on military posts and redeemable in merchandise. They were mainly issued in the second half of the 19th century.

Tael Chinese unit of weight corresponding to the European ounce and sometimes referred to as a liang. It was a measure of silver varying between 32 and 39 grams. In the 19th century it served as *money of account*, 100 British or Mexican trade dollars being worth 72 tael. The term has also been loosely applied to the Chinese silver yuan, although this was worth only .72 tael, or 7 mace and 2 candareens (10 candareens = 1 mace; 10 mace = 1 tael).

Thrymsa Early Anglo-Saxon gold coin based on the Merovingian tremissis or third-solidus, current in Kent, London and York about AD 63–75.

Tical Unit of weight in Thailand, first appearing as coins in the form of crudely shaped *bullet money* current from the 14th till the late 19th centuries. When European-style coins were introduced in 1860 the word was retained as a denomination (32 solot = 16 atts = 8 peinung or sio = 4 songpy or sik = 2 fuang= 1 salung or quarter-tical. The currency was decimalised in 1909 (100 satangs = 1 tical), and the tical was superseded by the baht about 1950.

Tin Metallic element, chemical symbol *St* (from Latin *Stannum*). Because of its unstable nature and tendency to oxidise badly when exposed to the atmosphere, it is unsatisfactory as a coinage metal, but has been used on several occasions, notably in Malaya, Thailand and the East Indies. In was also used for British halfpence and farthings, 1672–92.

Token Any piece of money whose nominal value is greater than its intrinsic value is, strictly speaking, a token or promise. Thus most of the coins issued since 1964 can be regarded in this light, but numismatists reserve the term for a piece of limited validity and circulation, produced by tradesmen, chambers of commerce and other organisations during times of a shortage of government coinage. The term is also loosely applied to metal tickets of admission, such as *communion*

tokens, or *jetons* and *counters* intended for games of chance. Tokens with a nominal value may be produced for security reasons to lessen the possibility of theft from milk bottles, vending machines, telephones, parking meters and transport facilities. Tokens exchangeable for goods have been issued by co-operative societies and used in prisons and internment camps in wartime. In addition to the traditional coinage alloys, tokens have been produced in ceramics, plastics, wood, stout card, leather and even rubber, in circular, square or polygonal shapes.

Tombac Type of brass alloy with a high copper content, used in coinage requiring a rich golden colour. It is, in fact, a modern version of the *aurichalcum* used by the Romans. It was used for the Canadian 5-cent coins of 1942–43, while 5- and 10-pfennig coins of Germany have a tombac cladding on a steel core.

Touchpiece Coin kept as a lucky charm, but more specifically the medieval gold angel of England which was worn round the neck as an antidote to scrofula, otherwise known as king's evil, from the belief that the reigning monarch possessed the power of healing by touch. The ceremony of touching for king's evil involved the suspension of an angel round the victim's neck, hence the prevalence of these coins pierced for suspension.

Trade Coins Coins widely used as a medium of international trade, often far beyond the boundaries of the country issuing them. The earliest examples were the Aiginetan turtles and Athenian tetrdrachms of the classical period. In the Middle Ages the English *sterling* was widely prized on account of its silver purity. Arab dinars and Italian florins were popular as gold coins in late-medieval times, while the British gold sovereign has been the preferred gold coin of modern times. The Maria Theresa silver thaler of Austria, with its date frozen at 1782, has been minted widely down to the present time for circulation in the Near and Middle East as a trade coin. Trade dollars were minted by Britain, the USA, the Netherlands and Japan to compete with the Spanish, and later the Mexican, peso or 8-reales coins as a trading medium in the Far East.

Transport Tokens Coin-like pieces of metal, plastic or card, issued by companies and corporations to employees and exchangeable for rides on municipal transport systems, date from the mid-19th century. In more recent times similar tokens have been used in many countries to activate turnstiles in buses, trams and rapid-transit railway systems.

Treasury Note Paper money worth 10 shillings or one pound, issued by the British Treasury on the outbreak of the First World War when *specie* payments were suspended, and continuing till 1928 when the Bank of England took over responsibility for note-issuing. They were popularly known as Bradburys, from the signature of the Treasury official, Sir John Bradbury, engraved on them.

Treasure Trove Articles of precious metal concealed in times of economic or political upheaval and discovered years (often centuries) later are deemed by law to be treasure trove (from the French word *trouve*, found). For further details see *Money and the Law*.

Trial Plate Plate of the same metal as the current coinage against which the fineness and quality of the coins produced are compared and tested.

Troy Weight System of weights derived from the French town of Troyes whose standard pound was adopted in England in 1526. It continued in Britain till 1879 when it was abolished, with the exception of the troy ounce and its decimal parts and multiples, which were retained for gold, silver, platinum and precious stones. The troy ounce of 480 grains is used by numismatists for weighing coins.

Truncation Stylised cut at the base of a coinage effigy, sometimes containing a die number, engraver's initials or *mintmark*.

Trussel Reverse die in *hammered* coinage, the opposite of the *pile*.

Type Principal motif on a coin or medal, enabling numismatists to identify the issue.

Type Set A set of coins comprising one of each coin in a particular series, regardless of the actual date of issue.

Uncirculated Term used in grading coins to denote specimens in perfect condition, with original mint lustre. In recent years the term "Brilliant Uncirculated" has been adopted (abbreviated as B.Unc. or BU).

Uniface Coin, medal or token with a device on one side only.

Unique Extant in only one known example.

Variety Variation in, or modification of type, effigy, motif or inscription.

Vecture Term (mainly US) for a *transport token*.

Veld Pond (Dutch for "field pound"). Gold coin struck by the Boer guerrillas at Pilgrims Rest in 1902, in imitation of the British sovereign.

Vellon Spanish form of *billon*.

VF Abbreviation for Very Fine, used to describe the state of a coin or medal.

VG Abbreviation for Very Good.

Vignette Strictly speaking the pictorial element of a paper note shading off into the surrounding unprinted paper rather than having a clearly defined border or frame; but nowadays applied generally to the picture portion of a banknote, as opposed to portrait, armorial or numeral elements.

Vis-à-Vis (French for "face to face"). Term describing coins with double portraits of rulers, their profiles or busts facing each other. A good example is the English coinage of Philip and Mary, 1554–48.

Wampum Barter currency of the North American Indians, composed of shells of *Venus mercenaria* strung together to form belts or "fathoms" worth 5 shillings. Wampum were tariffed variously from three to six to the English penny in the American colonies till 1704.

White Gold Alternative term for *electrum*.

Wire Money Primitive currency of the Maldive Islands in the form of lengths of silver wire known as lari, from which the modern currency unit *laree* is derived. The term was also applied to English coins of the 18th century in which the numerals of value were exceptionally thin, resembling wire.

Wooden Coins Thin pieces of wood used as tokens are known from the 19th and 12th centuries in many parts of China and Africa, and as small *Notgeld* from Austria and Germany during the First World War. Wooden nickels is the somewhat contradictory name given to tokens of a commemorative nature, widely popular in the USA since 1930.

Year Set A set of coins issued annually by a mint. Such a set often contains specimens which were not generally released for circulation in that year.

Young Head Profile of Queen Victoria sculpted by William Wyon for the Guildhall Medal of 1837 and subsequently utilised for British coins struck from 1837 to 1860 (copper) and 1887 (silver and gold).

Zinc Metallic element, chemical symbol Zn, widely used, with copper, as a constituent of brass, although it was not isolated till the 18th century. Alloyed with copper to form *tombac*, it was used for Canadian 5-cent coins (1942–43) and, coated on steel, it was used for American cents (1943). Zinc was used for *emergency coinage* in Austria, Belgium, Luxembourg and Germany (1915–18) and in Germany and German-occupied countries during the Second World War. Since then alloys of copper, nickel and zinc have been used for coinage in Eastern Europe, and an alloy of zinc with titanium has been developed in the 1970s as a potential substitute for *bronze* in subsidiary coinage.

Mintmarks
of the world

The following is a list of the initials and symbols denoting mints. In many cases, notably the Royal Mint, no mintmark was used on either British coins or those struck on behalf of other countries. Conversely many countries have only used one mintmark, that of one or other of the leading private mints.

It should be noted that the mintmarks of the main private mints have been recorded on the coins of the following countries:

H (Heaton, later the Birmingham Mint):
Australia, Bolivia, British Honduras, British North Borneo, British West Africa, Bulgaria, Canada, Ceylon, Chile, Colombia, Costa Rica, Cyprus, Dominican Republic, East Africa, Ecuador, Egypt, El Salvador, Finland, French Indochina, Great Britain, Greece, Guatemala, Guernsey, Haiti, Hong Kong, Iran, Israel, Italy, Jamaica, Jersey, Liberia, Malaya and British Borneo, Mauritius, Mombasa, Mozambique, Newfoundland, Nicaragua, Poland, Roumania, Sarawak, Serbia, Siam, Straits Settlements, Uruguay and Venezuela.

FM (Franklin Mint, Philadelphia): Bahamas, Belize, British Virgin Islands, Cayman Islands, Cook Islands, Guyana, Jamaica, Liberia, Malaysia, Malta, Panama, Papua New Guinea, Philippines, Solomon Islands, Trinidad and Tobago.

PM (Pobjoy Mint, Sutton, Surrey): Ascension, Bosnia, Cook Islands, Gibraltar, Isle of Man, Liberia, Macau, Niue, Philippines, St Helena, Senegal, Seychelles, Tonga and Tristan da Cunha.

ALBANIA
L	London
R	Rome
V	Valona

ARGENTINA
BA	Buenos Aires
Bs	Buenos Aires
B.AS	Buenos Aires
JPP	Jose Policarpo Patino
M	Mendoza
PNP	Pedro Nolasco Pizarro
PP	Pedro Nolasco Pizarro
PTS	Potosi
R	Rioja
RA	Rioja
SE	Santiago del Estero
SoEo	Santiago del Estero
TN	Tucuman

AUSTRALIA
A	Perth
D	Denver
H	Heaton (1912–16)
I	Bombay (1942–43)
I	Calcutta (1916–18)
M	Melbourne
P	Perth
PL	Royal Mint, London
S	Sydney
S	San Francisco (1942–43)
Dot before and after PENNY and I on obverse	Bombay (1942–43)
Dot before and after HALFPENNY and I on obverse	Bombay (1942–43)
Dot before and after PENNY	Bombay (1942–43)
Dot after HALFPENNY	Perth
Dot before SHILLING	Perth (1946)
Dot above scroll on reverse	Sydney (1920)
Dot below scroll on reverse	Melbourne (1919–20)
Dot between designer's initials KG	Perth (1940–41)
Dot after AUSTRALIA	Perth (1952–53)

AUSTRIA
A	Vienna (1765–1872)
AH–AG	Carlsburg, Transylvania (1765–76)
AH–GS	Carlsburg (1776–80)
A–S	Hall, Tyrol (1765–74)
AS–IE	Vienna (1745)
AW	Vienna (1764, 1768)
B	Kremnitz (1765–1857)
B–L	Nagybanya (1765–71)

B–V	Nagybanya (1772–80)
C	Carlsburg (1762–64)
C	Prague (1766–1855)
C–A	Carlsburg (1746–66)
C–A	Vienna (1774–80)
CG–AK	Graz (1767–72)
CG–AR	Graz (1767)
C–K	Vienna (1765–73)
CM	Kremnitz (1779)
CVG–AK	Graz (1767–72)
CVG–AR	Graz (1767)
D	Graz (1765–72), Salzburg (1800–09)
E	Carlsburg (1765–1867)
EC–SK	Vienna (1766)
EvM–D	Kremnitz (1765–74)
EvS–AS	Prague (1765–73)
EvS–IK	Prague (1774–80)
F	Hall (1765–1807)
FH	Hall
G	Graz (1761–63)
G	Gunzburg (1764–79)
G	Nagybanya (1766–1851)
G–K	Graz (1767–72)
G–R	Graz (1746–67)
GTK	Vienna (1761)
H	Hall (1760–80)
H	Gunzburg (1765–1805)
H–A	Hall (1746–65)
H–G	Carlsburg (1765–77)
H–S	Carlsburg (1777–80)
IB–FL	Nagybanya (1765–71)
IB–IV	Nagybanya (1772–80)
IC–FA	Vienna (1774–80)
IC–IA	Vienna (1780)
IC–SK	Vienna (1765–73)
I–K	Graz (1765-67)
I–K	Vienna (1767)
IZV	Vienna (1763–65)
K	Kremnitz (1760–63)
K–B	Kremnitz (1619–1765)
K–D	Kremnitz (1765)
K–M	Kremnitz (1763–65)
M	Milan (1780–1859)
N	Nagybanya (1780)
N–B	Nagybanya (1630–1777, 1849)
O	Oravicza (1783–1816)
P	Prague (1760–63)
P–R	Prague (1746–67)
PS–IK	Prague (1774–80)
S	Hall (1765–80), Schmollnitz (1763–1816)
S–C	Gunzburg (1765–74)
SC–G	Gunzburg (1765)
S–F	Gunzburg (1775–80)
S–G	Gunzburg (1764–65)
S–IE	Vienna (1745)
SK–PD	Kremnitz (1774–80)
TS	Gunzburg (1762–88)

V	Venice (1805–66)
VC–S	Hall (1774–80)
VS–K	Prague (1774–80)
VS–S	Prague (1765–73)
W	Vienna (1748–63)
W–I	Vienna (1746–71)

BAHAMAS
FM	Franklin Mint
JP	John Pinches

BELGIUM
A	Vienna
B	Kremnitz
C	Prague
E	Carlsburg
F	Hall
G	Nagybanya
H	Gunzburg
hand	Antwerp
lion	Bruges

BELIZE (British Honduras)
FM	Franklin Mint
H	Heaton (1912–16)

BOLIVIA
H	Heaton (1892–1953)
P, PTR, PTS	Potosi

BRAZIL
A	Berlin (1913)
B	Bahia (1714–1831)
C	Cuiaba (1823–33)
G	Goias (1823–33)
M	Minas Gerais (1823–28)
P	Pernambuco
R	Rio de Janeiro (1703–1834)
RS	Rio de Janeiro (1869)
SP	Sao Paulo (1825–32)

BRITISH NORTH BORNEO (Sabah)
H	Heaton (1882–1941)

BRITISH WEST AFRICA
G	JR Gaunt, Birmingham
H	Heaton, Birmingham (1911–57)
K	King's Norton
KN	King's Norton
SA	Pretoria

BULGARIA
A	Berlin
BP	Budapest
Heaton	Heaton, Birmingham (1881–1923)
KB	Kormoczbanya
cornucopia	Paris
thunderbolt	Poissy

CANADA
C	Ottawa
H	Heaton (1871–1907)
maple leaf	Ottawa (on coins struck after the year inscribed on them)

CENTRAL AMERICAN REPUBLIC
CR	San Jose (Costa Rica)
G	Guatemala
NG	Guatemala
T	Tegucigalpa (Honduras)

CEYLON
H	Heaton (1912)

CHILE
A	Agustin de Infante y Prado (1768–72)
AJ	The above and Jose Maria de Bobadilla (1800–01)
D	Domingo Eizaguirre
DA	Domingo Eizaguirre and Agustin de Infante (1772–99)
BFF	Francisco Rodriguez Brochero
FJJF	Brochero and Jose Maria de Bobadilla (1803–17)
H	Heaton (1851)
J	Jose Larraneta (1749–67)
So	Santiago
VA	Val Distra

COLOMBIA
A	Paris
B	Bogota
BA	Bogota
B.B	Bogota
H	Heaton (1912)
M	Medellin
NR	Nuevo Reino
NoRo	Nuevo Reino
P	Popayan
PN, Pn	Popayan
SM	Santa Marta

COSTA RICA
CR	San Jose (1825–1947)
HBM	Heaton (1889–93)
S	San Domingo
SD	San Domingo

COURLAND
ICS	Justin Carl Schroder
IFS	Johan Friedrich Schmickert

CYPRUS
H	Heaton (1881–2)

DENMARK
FF	Altona
KM	Copenhagen Altona (1842)
crown	Copenhagen
heart	Copenhagen .
orb	Altona (1839–48)

Other letters are the initials of mintmasters and moneyers

DOMINICAN REPUBLIC
HH	Heaton (1888–1919)

EAST AFRICA
A	Ackroyd & Best, Morley
H	Heaton (1910–64)
I	Bombay
K	Kynoch (IMI)
KN	King's Norton
SA	Pretoria

ECUADOR
BIRM^MH	Heaton (1915)
BIRMING- HAM	Heaton (1899–1900, 1928)
D	Denver
H	Heaton (1890, 1909, 1924–5)
HEATON BIRMING- HAM	Heaton (1872–95)
HF	Le Locle
LIMA	Lima
Mo	Mexico
PHILA	Philadelphia
QUITO	Quito
SANTIAGO	Santiago de Chile

EGYPT
H	Heaton (1904–37)

EL SALVADOR
CAM	Central American Mint, San Salvador
H	Heaton (1889–1913)
Mo	Mexico
S	San Francisco

FIJI
S	San Francisco

FINLAND
H	Heaton (1921)
heart	Copenhagen (1922). Since then coins have been struck at Helsinki without a mintmark.

Initials of mintmasters:
S	August Soldan (1864–85)
L	Johan Lihr (1885–1912)
S	Isaac Sundell (1915–47)

L	V. U. Liuhto (1948)
H	Uolevi Helle (1948–58)
S	Allan Soiniemi (1958–75)
SH	Soiniemi & Heikki Halvaoja (1967–71)
K	Timo Koivuranta (1977, 1979)
KN	Koivuranta and Antti Neuvonen (1978)
KT	Koivuranta and Erja Tielinen (1982)
KM	Koivuranta and Pertti Makinen (1983)
N	Reino Nevalainen (1983)

FRANCE

A	Paris (1768)
AA	Metz (1775–98)
B	Rouen (1786–1857)
B	Beaumont le Roger (1943–58)
BB	Strasbourg (1743–1870)
C	Castelsarrasin (1914, 1942–46)
CC	Genoa (1805)
CL	Genoa (1813–14)
D	Lyons (1771–1857)
G	Geneva (1796–1805)
H	La Rochelle (1770–1837)
L	Limoges (1766–1837)
K	Bordeaux (1759–1878)
L	Bayonne (1761–1837)
M	Toulouse (1766–1837)
MA	Marseilles (1787–1857)
N	Montpellier (1766–93)
O	Riom
P	Dijon
Q	Perpignan (1777–1837)
R	Royal Mint, London (1815)
R	Orleans (1780–92)
T	Nantes (1739–1835)
U	Turin (1814)
V	Troyes
W	Lille (1759–1857)
X	Amiens (1740)
&	Aix en Provence (1775)
9	Rennes
cow	Pau (1746–93)
flag	Utrecht (1811–14)
crowned R	Rome (1811–14)
thunderbolt	Poissy (1922-24)
star	Madrid (1916)

In addition, French coins include symbols denoting the privy marks of Engravers General (Chief Engravers since 1880) and Mint Directors.

GERMANY

The first name gives the location of the mint, and the second the name of the country or state issuing the coins.

A	Amberg, Bavaria (1763–94)
A	Berlin (1850)
A	Clausthal, Hannover (1832–49)
AE	Breslau, Silesia (1743–51)

AGP	Cleve, Rhineland (1742–43)
AK	Dusseldorf, Julich-Berg (1749–66)
ALS	Berlin (1749)
B	Bayreuth, Franconia (1796–1804)
B	Breslau, Silesia (1750–1826)
B	Brunswick, Brunswick (1850–60)
B	Brunswick, Westphalia (1809–13)
B	Dresden, Saxony (1861–72)
B	Hannover, Brunswick (1860–71)
B	Hannover, East Friesland (1823–25)
B	Hannover, Hannover (1821–66)
B	Hannover, Germany (1866-78)
B	Regensburg, Regensburg (1809)
B	Vienna, Germany (1938–45)
BH	Frankfurt (1808)
B–H	Regensburg, Rhenish Confederation (1802–12)
C	Cassel, Westphalia (1810–13)
C	Clausthal, Brunswick
C	Clausthal, Westphalia (1810–11)
C	Dresden, Saxony (1779–1804)
C	Frankfurt, Germany (1866–79)
CHI	Berlin (1749–63)
CLS	Dusseldorf, Julich-Berg (1767–70)
D	Aurich, East Friesland (1750–1806)
D	Dusseldorf, Rhineland (1816–48)
D	Munich, Germany (1872)
E	Dresden, Germany (1872–87)
E	Koenigberg, East Prussia (1750–98)
E	Muldenhutte, Germany (1887–1953)
EC	Leipzig, Saxony (1753–63)
EGN	Berlin (1725–49)
F	Dresden, Saxony (1845–58)
F	Magdeburg, Lower Saxony (1740–1806)
F	Cassel, Hesse-Cassel (1803–07)
F	Stuttgart, Germany (1872)
FW	Dresden, Saxony (1734–63)
G	Dresden, Saxony (1833–44, 1850–54)
G	Glatz, Silesia (1807–09)
G	Karlsruhe, Germany (1872)
G	Stettin, Pomerania (1750–1806)
GK	Cleve (1740–55)
GN	Bamberg, Bamberg
H	Darmstadt, Germany (1872–82)
H	Dresden, Saxony (1804–12)
HK	Rostock, Rostock (1862–64)
I	Hamburg, Germany (1872)
IDB	Dresden, Prussian occupation (1756–59)
IEC	Dresden, Saxony (1779–1804)
IF	Leipzig, Saxony (1763–65)
IGG	Leipzig, Saxony (1716–34, 1813–32)
J	Hamburg, Germany (1873)
J	Paris, Westphalia (1808–09)
L	Leipzig, Saxony (1761–62)
MC	Brunswick, Brunswick (1813–14, 1820)
PM	Dusseldorf, Julich-Berg (1771–83)
PR	Dusseldorf, Julich-Berg (1783–1804)

S	Dresden, Saxony (1813–32)
S	Hannover, Hannover (1839–44)
S	Schwabach, Franconia (1792–94)
SGH	Dresden, Saxony (1804–12)
ST	Strickling, Blomberg (1820–40)

GREAT BRITAIN

A	Ashby (1645)
B	Nicolas Briot (1631–39)
B	Bridgnorth (1646)
B	Bristol (1696)
Br	Bristol (1643–45)
C	Chester (1696)
CARL	Carlisle (1644–45)
CC	Corfe Castle (1644)
CHST	Chester (1644)
CR	Chester (1644)
E	Southwark (1547–49)
E	Exeter (1696)
E	Edinburgh (1707–13)
E*	Edinburgh (1707–09)
H	Heaton, Birmingham (1874–1919)
HC	Hartlebury Castle (1646)
K	London (1547–49)
KN	King's Norton
N	Norwich (1696)
OX	Oxford (1644–45)
OXON	Oxford (1644)
PC	Pontefract (1648–49)
SC	Scarborough (1644–45)
SOHO	Birmingham (1797–1806)
T	Canterbury (1549)
TC	Bristol (1549)
WS	Bristol (1547–49)
Y	Southwark (1551)
boar	Shrewsbury (1643–44)
book	Aberystwyth (1638–42)
bow	Durham House (1548–49)
castle	Exeter (1644–45)
crown	Aberystwyth Furnace (1648–49)
plume	Shrewsbury (1642)
plume	Oxford (1642–46)
plume	Bristol (1643–46)

Other symbols and marks on the hammered coins of Great Britain are usually referred to as Initial Marks. Complete listings of these marks appear in a number of specialist publications.

GREECE

A	Paris
B	Vienna
BB	Strasbourg
H	Heaton (1921)
K	Bordeaux
KN	King's Norton
owl	Aegina (1828–32)
owl	Athens (1838–55)
thunderbolt	Poissy

GUATEMALA

CG	Guatemala City (1733-76)
G	Guatemala City (1776)
H	Heaton (1894–1901)
NG	Nueva Guatemala (1777)

GUERNSEY

H	Heaton (1855–1949)

HAITI

A	Paris
HEATON	Heaton (1863)

HONDURAS

A	Paris (1869–71)
T	Tegucigalpa (1825–62)

HONG KONG

H	Heaton (1872–1971)
KN	King's Norton

HUNGARY

A	Vienna
B	Kremnitz
BP	Budapest
CA	Vienna
G	Nagybanya
GN	Nagybanya
GYF	Carlsburg
HA	Hall
K	Kremnitz
KB	Kremnitz
NB	Nagybanya
S	Schmollnitz
WI	Vienna

INDIA

B	Bombay (1835-1947)
C	Calcutta (1835-1947)
I	Bombay (1918)
L	Lahore (1943-45)
M	Madras (1869)
P	Pretoria (1943-44)
diamond	Bombay
dot in diamond	Hyderabad
split diamond	Hyderabad
star	Hyderabad

IRAN

H	Heaton (1928–29)

IRAQ

I	Bombay

ISRAEL

H	Heaton (1951–52)
star of David	Jerusalem

ITALY AND STATES

B	Bologna
B/I	Birmingham (1893–4)
FIRENZE	Florence
H	Heaton (1866–67)
KB	Berlin
M	Milan
N	Naples
OM	Strasbourg
R	Rome
T	Turin
V	Venice
ZV	Venice
anchor	Genoa
eagle head	Turin

JAMAICA

C	Ottawa
FM	Franklin Mint
H	Heaton (1882–1916)

JERSEY

H	Heaton (1877)

KENYA

C/M	Calcutta
H	Heaton (1911–64)

LIBERIA

B	Berne
FM	Franklin Mint
H	Heaton (1896–1906)
PM	Pobjoy Mint

LIECHTENSTEIN

A	Vienna
B	Berne
M	Munich

LUXEMBOURG

A	Paris
H	Gunzburg
anchor	Paris
angel	Brussels
caduceus	Utrecht
double eagle	Brussels
sword	Utrecht

MALAYSIA

B	Bombay
FM	Franklin Mint
H	Heaton (1955–61)
I	Calcutta (1941)
I	Bombay (1945)
KN	King's Norton
W	James Watt, Birmingham

MAURITIUS

H	Heaton (1877–90)
SA	Pretoria

MEXICO

A, As	Alamos
C, CN	Culiacan
CA, CH	Chihuahua
Ce	Real del Catorce
D, Do	Durango
Eo	Tlalpam
GA	Guadalajara
GC	Guadelupe y Calvo
Go	Guanajuato
Ho	Hermosillo
M, Mo	Mexico City
Mo	Morelos
MX	Mexico City
O, OA, OKA	Oaxaca
Pi	San Luis Potosi
SLPi	San Luis Potosi
TC	Tierra Caliente
Z, Zs	Zacatecas

MONACO

A	Paris
M	Monte Carlo
clasped hands	Cabanis
thunderbolt	Poissy

MOZAMBIQUE

H	Heaton (1894)
R	Rio

NETHERLANDS AND COLONIES
Austrian Netherlands (1700-93)

H	Amsterdam
S	Utrecht
W	Vienna
hand	Antwerp
head	Brussels
lion	Bruges

Kingdom of the Netherlands

B	Brussels (1821–30)
D	Denver (1943–45)
P	Philadelphia (1941–45)
S	Utrecht (1816–36)
S	San Francisco (1944–45)
Sa	Surabaya
caduceus	Utrecht

NICARAGUA

H	Heaton (1880–1916)
NR	Leon de Nicaragua

NORWAY

hammers	Kongsberg

PANAMA

CHI	Valcambi
FM	Franklin Mint

PERU

AREQ, AREQUIPA	Arequipa
AYACUCHO	Ayacucho
CUZCO, Co	Cuzco
L, LM, LR	Lima
LIMAE	Lima
PASCO	Pasco
Paz, Po	Pasco
P	Lima (1568-70)
P	Philadelphia
S	San Francisco

PHILIPPINES

BSP	Bangko Sentral Pilipinas
D	Denver (1944–45)
FM	Franklin Mint
M, MA	Manila
PM	Pobjoy Mint
S	San Francisco (1903–47)
5 point star	Manila

POLAND

AP	Warsaw (1772–74)
CI	Cracow (1765–68)
EB	Warsaw (1774–92)
EC	Leipzig (1758–63)
FF	Stuttgart (1916–17)
FH	Warsaw (1815–27)
FS	Warsaw (1765–68)
FWoF	Dresden (1734–64)
G	Cracow (1765–72)
H	Heaton (1924)
IB	Warsaw (1811–27)
IGS	Dresden (1716–34)
IP	Warsaw (1834–43)
IS	Warsaw (1768–74)
JGG	Leipzig (1750–53)
JS	Warsaw (1810–11)
KG	Warsaw (1829–34)
MV, MW	Warsaw
arrow	Warsaw (1925–39)
Dot after date	Royal Mint (1925)
8 torches	Paris (1924)

ROUMANIA

B	Bucharest (1879–85)
C	Bucharest (1886)
H	Heaton (1867–1930)
HUGUENIN	Le Locle
J	Hamburg
KN	King's Norton
V	Vienna

W	Watt, Birmingham
thunderbolt	Poissy

RUSSIA

AM	Annensk (1762–96)
BM	Warsaw (1825–55)
bM	St Petersburg (1796)
C–M	Sestroretsk (1762–96)
CM	Souzan (1825–55)
E–M	Ekaterinburg (1762–1810)
KM	Kolpina (1810)
K–M	Kolyvan (1762–1810)
MM, M–M	Moscow (1730–96)
MMD	Moscow (1730–96)
MW	Warsaw (1842–54)
NM	Izhorsk (1811–21)
SP	St Petersburg (1798–1800)
SPB	St Petersburg (1724–1915)
SPM	St Petersburg (1825–55)
T–M	Feodosia (1762–96)

SAN MARINO

M	Milan
R	Rome

SIAM
(Thailand) H Heaton (1898)

SOUTH AFRICA

SA	Pretoria

SPAIN

B	Burgos
B, BA	Barcelona
Bo	Bilbao
C	Catalonia
C	Cuenca
C	Reus
CA	Zaragoza
G	Granada
GNA	Gerona
LD	Lerida
J, JA	Jubia
M, MD	Madrid
P	Palma de Majorca
PpP, PL, PA	Pamplona
S, S/L	Seville
Sr	Santander
T, To, Tole	Toledo
TOR:SA	Tortosa
V, VA, VAL	Valencia
crowned C	Cadiz
crowned M	Madrid
aqueduct	Segovia
crowned shield	Tarragona
pomegranate	Granada
quartered shield	Palma
scallop	Coruna

SPAIN *continued*

stars:

3 points	Segovia
4 points	Jubia
5 points	Manila
6 points	Madrid
7 points	Seville (1833)
8 points	Barcelona (1838)
wavy lines	Valladolid

SURINAM

P	Philadelphia
S	Sydney
caduceus	Utrecht

SWITZERLAND

A	Paris
AB	Strasbourg
B	Berne
B	Brussels (1874)
BA	Basle
BB	Strasbourg
S	Solothurn

URUGUAY

H	Heaton (1869)

UNITED STATES OF AMERICA

C	Charlotte, North Carolina
Cc	Carson City, Nevada
D	Dahlonega, Georgia (1838–61)
D	Denver, Colorado (1906)
O	New Orleans
P	Philadelphia
S	San Francisco
W	West Point

VENEZUELA

A	Paris
H	Heaton (1852)
HEATON	Heaton (1852–63)

YUGOSLAVIA (including former Serbia)

A	Paris	
H	Heaton (1883–84)	
KOBHNUA, A.D.		Kovnica
V	Vienna	
thunderbolt	Poissy	

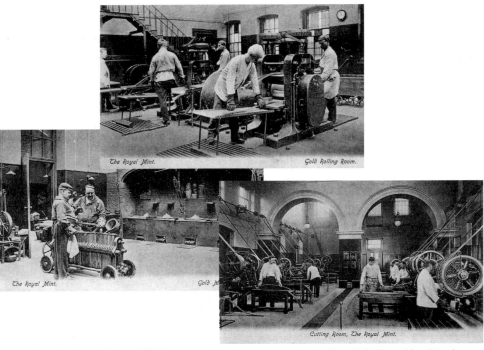

Images from the Royal Mint c. 1900 from a set of contemporary postcards. From left: The gold melting house; the gold rolling room and the cutting room.

Coin
inscriptions

This alphabetical listing is confined to inscriptions found on coins, mainly in the form of mottoes or of a commemorative nature. Names of rulers are, for the most part, excluded. Where the inscription is in a language other than English a translation is given, followed by the name of the issuing country or authority in parentheses.

A Deo et Caesare From God and the Emperor (Frankfurt).

A Domino Factum est Istud et est Mirabile in Oculis Nostris This is the Lord's doing and it is marvellous in our eyes (England, Mary).

A Solo Iehova Sapientia From God alone comes true wisdom (Wittgenstein).

Ab Inimicis Meis Libera Me Deus Free me from enemies (Burgundy).

Ad Legem Conventionis According to the law of the Convention (Furstenberg).

Ad Normam Conventionis According to the standard of the Convention (Prussia).

Ad Palmam Pressa Laeturo Resurgo Pressed to the palm I rise more joyfully (Wittgenstein).

Ad Usam Luxemburgi CC Vallati For the use of the besieged Luxembourgers (Luxembourg siege coins).

Adiuva Nos Deus Salutaris Noster Help us, O God, our Saviour (Lorraine).

Adventus Optimi Principis The coming of the noblest prince (Papacy).

Aes Usibus Aptius Auro Bronze in its uses is more suitable than gold (Brazil).

Aeternum Meditans Decus An ornament intended for all time (Alencon).

Aliis Inserviendo Consumor I spend my life devoted to others (Brunswick-Wolfenbuttel).

Alles Mit Bedacht All with reflection (Brunswick).

Amor Populi Praesidium Regis The love of the people is the king's protection (England, Charles I).

Ang Fra Dom Hib & Aquit (King) of England and France, Lord of Ireland and Aquitaine (England, Edward III).

Anno Regni Primo In the first year of the reign (Britain, edge inscription on crowns).

Apres les Tenebres la Lumiere After the shadows, the light (Geneva).

Archangelus Michael Archangel Michael (Italy, Grimoald IV).

Ardua ad Gloriam Via Struggles are the way to glory (Waldeck).

Arte Mea Bis Iustus Moneta Lud Iust By my art I am twice the just coin of King Louis (France, 1641).

Aspera Oblectant Wild places delight (Nassau-Weilburg).

Aspice Pisas Sup Omnes Specio Behold the coin of Pisa, superior to all (Pisa).

Audiatur Altera Pars Let the other part be heard (Stavelot).

Auf Gott Trawe Ich In God I trust (Brunswick).

Ausen Gefaesen der Kirchen und Burger From the vessels of the Church and citizens (Frankfurt siege, 1796).

Auspicio Regis et Senatus Angliae By authority of the king and parliament of England (East India Company).

Auxilio fortissimo Dei With the strongest help of God (Mecklenburg).

Auxilium de Sanctio Aid from the sanctuary (Papacy).

Auxilium Meum a Dno Qui Fecit Celum e Terram My help comes from God who made heaven and earth (Portugal).

Beata Tranquillatis Blessed tranquillity (Rome, Licinius II).

Beatus Qui Speravit in dom Blessed is he who has hoped in the Lord (Mansfeld).

Benedic Haereditati Tuae Blessings on your inheritance (Savoy).

Benedicta Sit Sancta Trinitas Blessed be the Holy Trinity (Albon).

Benedictio Domini Divites Facit The blessing of the Lord makes the rich (Teschen).

Benedictus Qui Venit in Nomine Domini Blessed is he who comes in the name of the Lord (Flanders).

Beschaw das Ziel Sage Nicht Viel Consider the matter but say little (Quedlinburg).

Besser Land und Lud Verloren als ein Falscher Aid Geschworn Better to lose land and wealth than swear a false oath (Hesse).

Bey Gott ist Rath und That With God is counsel and deed (Mansfeld).

Britanniarum Regina Queen of the Britains (Britain, Victoria).

Britt Omn Rex King of all the Britains (i.e. Britain and the overseas dominions) (Britain, 1902–52).

Cal et Car Com de Fugger in Zin et Norn Sen & Adm Fam Cajetan and Carl, Counts of Fugger in Zinnenberg and Nordendorf, Lords and Administrators of the Family (Empire, Fugger).

Candide et Constanter Sincerely and steadfastly (Hesse-Cassel).

Candide sed Provide Clearly but cautiously (Osterwitz).

Candore et Amore With sincerity and love (Fulda).

Candore et Constantia With sincerity and constancy (Bavaria).

Capit Cath Ecclesia Monasteriensis Chapter of the Cathedral Church of Munster (Munster).

Capit Eccle Metropolit Colon Chapter of the Metropolitan Church of Cologne (Cologne).

Capitulum Regnans Sede Vacante Chapter governing, the See being vacant (Eichstadt).

Carola Magna Ducissa Feliciter Regnante Grand Duchess Charlotte, happily reigning (Luxembourg).

Carolus a Carolo Charles (I) to Charles (II) (England).

Cedunt Prementi Fata The fates yield to him who presses (Ploen, Hese-Cassel).

Charitate et Candore With charity and sincerity (East Frisia).

Charta Magna Bavariae The Great Charter of Bavaria (Bavaria).

Christo Auspice Regno I reign under the auspices of Christ (England, Charles I).

Christus Spes Una Salutis Christ is our one hope of salvation (Cleve).

Chur Mainz Electoral Principality of Mainz (Mainz).

Circumeundo Servat et Ornat It serves and decorates by going around (Sweden).

Civibus Quorum Pietas Coniuratione Die III Mai MDCCXCI Obrutam et Deletam Libertate Polona Tueri Conabatur Respublica Resurgens To the citizens whose piety the resurgent commonwealth tried to protect Poland overturned and deprived of liberty by the conspiracy of the third day of May 1791 (Poland).

Civitas Lucemborgiensis Millesimum Ovans Expletannum Completing the celebration of a thousand years of the city of Luxembourg (Luxembourg).

Civium Industria Floret Civitas By the industry of its people the state flourishes (Festival of Britain crown, 1951).

Cluniaco Cenobio Petrus et Paulus Peter and Paul from the Abbey of Cluny (Cluny).

Comes Provincie Fili Regis Francie Court of Provence and son of the King of France (Provence).

Communitas et Senatus Bonon City and senate of Bologna (Bologna).

Concordia Fratrum The harmony of the brothers (Iever).

Concordia Patriae Nutrix Peace, the nurse of the fatherland (Waldeck).

Concordia Res Parvae Crescunt Little things increase through harmony (Batavian Republic).

Concordia Res Parvae Crescunt, Discordia Dilabuntur By harmony little things increase, by discord they fall apart (Lowenstein-Wertheim-Virneburg).

Concordia Stabili With lasting peace (Hildesheim).

Confidens Dno Non Movetur He who trusts in God is unmoved (Spanish Netherlands).

Confidentia in Deo et Vigilantia Trust in God and vigilance (Prussian Asiatic Company).

Confoederato Helvetica Swiss Confederation (Switzerland)

Conjuncto Felix Fortunate in his connections (Solms).

Conservator Urbis Suae Saviour of his city (Rome, 4th century).

Consilio et Aequitate With deliberation and justice (Fulda).

Consilio et Virtutis With deliberation and valour (Hesse-Cassel).

Constanter et Sincere Steadfastly and sincerely (Lautern).

Crescite et Multiplicamini Increase and multiply (Maryland).

Cristiana Religio Christian religion (Germany, 11th century).

Crux Benedicat May the cross bless you (Oldenburg).

Cuius Cruore Sanati Sumus By His sacrifice are we healed (Reggio).

Cultores Sui Deus Protegit God protects His followers (England, Charles I).

Cum Deo et Die (Jure) With God and the day (Wurttemberg).

Cum Deo et Jure With God and the law (Wurttemberg).

Cum Deo et Labore With God and work (Wittgenstein).

Cum His Qui Orderant Pacem Eram Pacificus With those who order peace I was peaceful (Zug).

Curie Bonthon to so Doulo Protect his servant, o Lord (Byzantine Empire).

Custos Regni Deus God is the guardian of the kingdom (Naples and Sicily).

Da Gloriam Deo et Eius Genitrici Marie Give glory to God and His mother Mary (Wurttemberg).

Da Mihi Virtutem Contra Hostes Tuos Give me valour against mine enemies (Netherlands, Charles V).

Dat Wort is Fleis Gworden The word is made flesh (Muster).

Date Caesaris Caesari et Quae Sunt Dei Deo Render unto Caesar the things that are Caesar's and unto God the things that are God's (Stralsund).

De Oficina . . . From the mint of . . . (France, medieval).

Decreto Reipublicae Nexu Confoederationis Iunctae Die V Xbris MDCCXCII Stanislao Augusto Regnante By decree of the state in conjunction with the joint federation on the fifth day of December 1792, Stanislaus Augustus ruling (Poland).

Decus et Tutamen An ornament and a safeguard (Britain, pound).

Deducet Nos Mirabiliter Dextera Tua Thy right hand will guide us miraculously (Savoy).

Denarium Terrae Mariae Penny of Maryland (Maryland).

Deo Conservatori Pacis To God, preserver of peace (Brandenburg-Ansbach).

Deo OM Auspice Suaviter et Fortiter sed Luste nec Sibi sed Suis Under the auspices of God, greatest and best, pleasantly and bravely but justly, not for himself but for his people (Speyer).

Deo Patriae et Subditio For God, fatherland and neighbourhood (Mainz).

Der Recht Glaubt In Ewig Lebt Who believes in right will live in eternity (Linange-Westerburg).

Der Rhein ist Deutschlands Strom Nicht Deutschlands Grenze The Rhine is Germany's River not Germany's Frontier.

Deum Solum Adorabis You will venerate God alone (Hesse).

Deus Constituit Regna God establishes kingdoms (Ni jmegen).

Deus Dat Qui Vult God gives to him who wishes (Hanau-Munzenberg).

Deus et Dominus God and Lord (Rome, 3rd century).

Deus in Adiutorium Meum Intende God stretch out in my assistance (France).

Deus Providebit God will provide (Lowenstein-Wertheim-Virneburg).

Deus Refugium Meum God is my refuge (Cleve).

Deus Solatium Meum God is my comfort (Sweden).

Dextera Domini Exaltavit Me The right hand of God has raised me up (Modena, Spain).

Dextra Dei Exalta Me The right hand of God exalts me (Denmark).

Dieu et Mon Droit God and my right (Britain, George IV).

Dilexit Dns Andream The Lord delights in St Andrew (Holstein).

Dilexit Dominus Decorem Iustitiae The Lord is pleased with the beauty of justice (Unterwalden).

Dirige Deus Gressus Meos O God, direct my steps (Tuscany, Britain, Una £5).

Discerne Causam Meam Distinguish my cause (Savoy).

Divina Benedictiae et Caesarea Iustitia Sacrifice of blessings and imperial justice (Coblenz).

Dn Ihs Chs Rex Regnantium Lord Jesus Christ, King of Kings (Rome, Justinian II).

Dns Ptetor Ms Z Lib'ator Ms The Lord is my protector and liberator (Scotland, David II).

Dominabitur Gentium et Ipse He himself will also be lord of the nations (Austrian Netherlands).

Domine Conserva Nos in Pace O Lord preserve us in peace (Basle, Mulhausen).

Domine Elegisti Lilium Tibi O Lord Thou hast chosen the lily for Thyself (France, Louis XIV).

Domine ne in Furore Tuo Arguas Me O Lord, rebuke me not in Thine anger (England, Edward III).

Domine Probasti Me et Congnovisti Me O Lord Thou hast tested me and recognised me (Mantua).

Domini est Regnum The Kingdom is the Lord's (Austrian Netherlands).

Dominus Deus Omnipotens Rex Lord God, almighty King (Viking coins).

Dominus Mihi Adiutor The Lord is my helper (Spanish Netherlands).

Dominus Providebit The Lord will provide (Berne).

Dominus Spes Populi Sui The Lord is the hope of his people (Lucerne).

Donum Dei ex Fodinis Vilmariens A gift of God from the Vilmar mines (Coblenz).

Duce Deo Fide et Justicia By faith and justice lead us to God (Ragusa).

Dum Praemor Amplior I increase while I die prematurely (Savoy).

Dum Spiro Spero While I live, I hope (Pontefract siege coins).

Dum Totum Compleat Orbem Until it fills the world (France, Henri II).

Dura Pati Virtus Valour endures hardships (Saxe-Lauenburg).

Durae Necessitatis Through force of necessity (Bommel siege, 1599).

Durum Telum Necessitas Hardship is a weapon of necessity (Minden).

Dux et Gubernatores Reip Genu Duke and governors of the republic of Genoa (Genoa).

E Pluribus Unum One out of more (USA).

Eccl S. Barbarae Patronae Fodin Kuttenbergensium Duo Flor Arg Puri The church of St Barbara, patron of the Kuttensberg mines, two florins of pure silver (Hungary).

Een en Ondelbaer Sterk   One and indivisible (Batavian Republic).

Eendracht Mag Macht   Unity makes strength (Belgium, South African Republic).

Einigkeit Recht und Freiheit   Union, right and freedom (Germany).

Electorus Saxoniae Administrator   Elector and administrator of Saxony (Saxony).

Elimosina   Alms (France, Pepin).

Ep Fris & Ratisb Ad Prum Pp Coad Aug   Bishop of Freising and Regensburg, administrator of Pruem, prince-provost, co-adjutant bishop of Augsburg (Trier).

Equa Libertas Deo Gratia Frat Pax in Virtute Tua et in Domino Confido   I believe in equal liberty by the grace of God, brotherly love in Thy valour and in the Lord (Burgundy).

Equitas Iudicia Tua Dom   Equity and Thy judgments O Lord (Gelderland).

Espoir Me Conforte   Hope comforts me (Mansfeld).

Espreuve Faicto Par Lexpres Commandement du Roy   Proof made by the express commandment of the King (France, piedforts).

Et in Minimis Integer   Faithful even in the smallest things (Olmutz).

Ex Auro Argentes Resurgit   From gold it arises, silver again (Sicily).

Ex Auro Sinico   From Chinese gold (Denmark).

Ex Flammis Orior   I arise from the flames (Hohenlohe-Neuenstein-Ohringen).

Ex Fodinis Bipontio Seelbergensibus   From the Seelberg mines of Zweibrucken (Pfalz-Birkenfeld).

Ex Metallo Novo   From new metal (Spain).

Ex Uno Omnis Nostra Salus   From one is all our salvation (Eichstadt, Mulhouse).

Ex Vasis Argent Cleri Mogunt Pro Aris et Focis   From the silver vessels of the clergy of Mainz for altars and for hearths (Mainz).

Ex Visceribus Fodinse Bieber   From the bowels of the Bieber mine (Hanau-Munzenberg).

Exaltabitur in Gloria   He shall be exalted in glory (England, quarter nobles).

Exemplum Probati Numismatis   An example of a proof coin (France, Louis XIII piedforts).

Exemtae Eccle Passau Episc et SRI Princ   Prince Bishop of the freed church of Passau, prince of the Holy Roman Empire (Passau).

Expectate Veni   Come, o expected one (Roman Britain, Carausius).

Extremum Subidium Campen   Kampen under extreme siege (Kampen, 1578).

Exurgat Deus et Dissipentur Inimici Eius   Let God arise and let His enemies be scattered (England, James I).

Faciam Eos in Gentem Unam   I will make them one nation (England, unites and laurels).

Faith and Truth I will Bear unto You   (UK £5, 1993).

Fata Consiliis Potiora   The fates are more powerful than councils (Hesse-Cassel).

Fata Viam Invenient   The fates will find a way (Gelderland).

Fecit Potentiam in Brachio Suo   He put power in your forearm (Lorraine).

Fecunditas   Fertility (Naples and Sicily).

Fel Temp Reparatio   The restoration of lucky times (Rome, AD 348).

Felicitas Perpetua   Everlasting good fortune (Rome, Constantius II).

Felix coniunctio   Happy Union (Brandenburg-Ansbach).

Fiat Misericordia Tua Dne   Let Thy mercy be O Lord (Gelderland).

Fiat Voluntas Domini Perpetuo   Let the goodwill of the Lord last for ever (Fulda).

Fidei Defensor   Defender of the Faith (Britain).

Fidelitate et Fortitudine   With fidelity and fortitude (Batthanyi).

Fideliter et Constanter   Faithfully and steadfastly (Saxe-Coburg-Gotha).

Fidem Servando Patriam Tuendo   By keeping faith and protecting the fatherland (Savoy).

Filius Augustorum   Son of emperors (Rome, 4th century).

Fisci Iudaici Calumnia Sublata   The false accusation of the Jewish tax lifted (Rome, Nerva).

Florent Concordia Regna   Through harmony kingdoms flourish (England, Charles I and II).

Fortitudo et Laus Mea Dominu   Fortitude and my praise in the Lord (Sardinia).

Free Trade to Africa by Act of Parliment *(Sic)* (Gold Coast).

Friedt Ernehrt Unfriedt Verzehrt   Peace nourishes, unrest wastes (Brunswick).

Fulgent Sic Littora Rheni   Thus shine the banks of the Rhine (Mannheim).

Fundator Pacis   Founder of peace (Rome, Severus).

Gaudium Populi Romani   The joy of the Roman people (Rome, 4th century).

Gen C Mar VI Dim Col USC & RAMAI Cons & S Conf M   General field marshal, colonel of the only dragoon regiment, present privy councillor of both their sacred imperial and royal apostolic majesties, and state conference minister (Batthanyi).

Gerecht und Beharrlich   Just and steadfast (Bavaria).

Germ Hun Boh Rex AAD Loth Ven Sal   King of Germany, Hungary and Bohemia, Archduke of Austria, Duke of Lorraine, Venice and Salzburg (Austria).

Germ Jero Rex Loth Bar Mag Het Dux   King of Germany, Jerusalem, Lorraine and Bar, Grand Duke of Tuscany (Austrian Netherlands).

Germania Voti Compos   Germany sharing the vows (Brandenburg-Ansbach).

Gloria ex Amore Patriae   Glory from love of country (Denmark).

Gloria in Excelsis Deo   Glory to God in the highest (France, Sweden).

Gloria Novi Saeculi   The glory of a new century (Rome, Gratian).

God With Us   (England, Commonwealth).

Godt Met Ons   God with us (Oudewater).

Gottes Freundt der Pfaffen Feindt   God's friend, the Pope's enemy (Brunswick, Christian).

Gratia Dei Sum Id Quod Sum   By the grace of God, I am what I am (Navarre).

Gratia Di Rex   By the grace of God, king (France, 8th century).

Gratitudo Concivibus Exemplum Posteritati   Gratitude to fellow Citizens, an example to posterity (Poland).

Gud och Folket   God and the people (Sweden).

Hac Nitimur Hanc Tuemur   With this we strive, this we shall defend (Batavian Republic).

Hac Sub Tutela   Under this protection (Eichstadt).

Haec Sunt Munera Minerae S Antony Eremitae   These are the rewards of the mine of St Antony the hermit (Hildesheim).

Hanc Deus Dedit   God has given this (Pontefract siege coins).

Hanc Tuemur Hac Nitimur   This we defend, by this we strive (Batavian Republic).

Has Nisi Periturus Mihi Adimat Nemo   Let no one remove these (Letters) from me under penalty of death (Commonwealth, edge inscription).

Henricus Rosas Regna Jacobus   Henry (united) the roses, James the kingdoms (England and Scotland, James VI and I).

Herculeo Vincta Nodo   Bound by a Herculean fetter (Savoy).

Herr Nach Deinem Willen   O Lord Thy will be done (Palatinate, Erbach).

Herre Gott Verleich Uns Gnade   Lord God grant us grace (Brunswick).

Hic Est Qui Multum Orat Pro Populo   Here is he who prays a lot for the people (Paderborn).

Hir Steid te Biscop   Here is represented the bishop (Gittelde).

His Ventis Vela Levantur   By these winds the sails are raised up (Hesse-Cassel).

Hispaniarum Infans   Infante of Spain and its dominions (Spain).

Hispaniarum et Ind Rex   King of Spain and the Indies.

Hispaniarum Rex   King of Spain (Spain).

Hoc Signo Victor Eris   With this sign you will be victor (Rome, Vetranio).

Honeste et Decenter   Honestly and decently (Nassau-Idstein).

Honi Soit Qui Mal y Pense   Evil to him who evil thinks (Britain, George III).

Honni Soit Qui Mal y Pense   (Hesse-Cassel).

Hospitalis et S Sepul Hierusal   Hospital and Holy Sepulchre of Jerusalem (Malta).

Hun Boh Gal Rex AA Lo Wi et in Fr Dux   King of Hungary, Bohemia and Galicia, Archduke of Austria, Dalmatia, Lodomeria, Wurzburg and Duke in Franconia (Austria).

Hung Boh Lomb et Ven Gal Lod III Rex Aa   King of Hungary, Bohemia, Lombardo-Venezia, Galicia, Lodomeria and Illyria, Archduke of Austria (Austria).

Ich Dien   I serve (Aberystwyth 2d, UK 2p).

Ich Getrawe Got in Aller Noth   I trust in God in all my needs (Hesse-Marburg).

Ich Habe Nur Ein Vaterland und das Heisst Deutschland   I have only one fatherland and that is called Germany (Germany).

Ielithes Penniae   Penny of Gittelde (Gittelde, 11th century).

Iesus Autem Transiens Per Medium Illorum Ibat   But Jesus, passing through the midst of them, went His way (England, Scotland, Anglo-Gallic).

Iesus Rex Noster et Deus Noster   Jesus is our king and our God (Florence).

Ihs Xs Rex Regnantium   Jesus Christ, King of Kings (Byzantine Empire).

Ihsus Xristus Basileu Baslie   Jesus Christ, King of Kings (Byzantine Empire).

Imago Sanch Regis Illustris Castelle Legionis e Toleto   The image of Sancho the illustrious king of Castile, Leon and Toledo.

In Casus Per Vigil Omnes   In all seasons through vigil (Wertheim).

In Deo Meo Transgrediar Murum   In my God I shall pass through walls (Teschen).

In Deo Spes Mea   In God is my hope (Gelderland).

In Domino Fiducia Nostra   In the Lord is our trust (Iever).

In Equitate Tua Vivificasti Me   In thy equity Thou hast vivified me (Gelderland).

In God We Trust   (USA).

In Hoc Signo Vinces   In this sign shalt thou conquer (Portugal).

In Honore Sci Mavrici Marti   In honour of the martyr St Maurice (St Maurice, 8th century).

In Manibus Domini sortes Meae   In the hands of the Lord are my fates (Mainz siege, 1688–9).

In Memor Vindicatae Libere ac Relig   In memory of the establishment of freedom and religion (Sweden).

In Memoriam Conjunctionis Utriusque Burgraviatus Norice   In memory of the union of both burgraviates in peace (Brandenburg-Ansbach).

In Memorian Connub Feliciaes Inter Princ Her Frider Carol et Dub Sax August Louis Frider Rodas D 28 Nov 1780 Celebrati   In memory of the most happy marriage between the hereditary prince Friedrich Karl and the Duchess of Saxony Augusta Louisa Frederika, celebrated on 28 Nov 1780 (Schwarzburg-Rudolstadt).

In Memorian Felicisssimi Matrimonii   In memory of the most happy marriage (Wied).

In Memoriam Pacis Teschinensis   Commemorating the Treaty of Teschen (Brandenburg-Ansbach).

In Nomine Domini Amen   In the name of the Lord amen (Zaltbommel).

In Omnem Terram Sonus Eorum   In to all the land their shall go sound (Chateau Renault, Papal States).

In Silencio et Spe Fortitudo Mea   In silence and hope is my fortitude (Brandenburg-Kustrin).

In Spe et Silentio Fortitudo Mea   In hope and silence is my fortitude (Vianen).

In Te Domine Confido   In you O Lord I place my trust (Hesse).

In Te Domine Speravi   In You, O Lord, I have hoped (Gurk).

In Terra Pax   Peace in the land (Papacy).

In Via Virtuti Nulla Via   There is no way for virtue on the way. (Veldenz).

Ind Imp, Indiae Imperator, Imperatrix   Emperor (Empress) of India (Britain).

India Tibi Cessit   India has yielded to thee (Portuguese India).

Infestus Infestis   Hostile to the troublesome (Savoy).

Inimicos Eius Induam Confusione   As for his enemies, I shall clothe them in shame (Sardinia, England, Edward VI).

Insignia Capituli Brixensis   The badge of the chapter of Brixen (Brixen).

Isti Sunt Patres Tui Verique Pastores   These are your fathers and true shepherds (Papacy).

Iudicium Melius Posteritatis Erit   Posterity's judgment will be better (Paderborn).

Iure et Tempore   By right and time (Groningen).

Iusques a Sa Plenitude   As far as your plenitude (France, Henri II).

Iuste et Constanter   Justly and constantly (Paderborn).

Iustirt   Adjusted (Hesse-Cassel).

Iustitia et Concordia   Justice and harmony (Zurich).

Iustitia et Mansuetudine   By justice and mildness (Bavaria, Cologne).

Iustitia Regnorum Fundamentum   Justice is the foundation of kingdoms (Austria).

Iustitia Thronum Firmat   Justice strengthens the throne (England, Charles I).

Iustus Non Derelinquitur   The just person is not deserted (Brandenburg-Calenberg).

Iustus Ut Palma Florebit   The just will flourish like the palm (Portugal).

L Mun Planco Rauracorum Illustratori Vetustissimo   To L Municius Plancus the most ancient and celebrated of the Rauraci (Basle).

Landgr in Cleggov Com in Sulz Dux Crum   Landgrave of Klettgau, count of Sulz, duke of Krumlau (Schwarzburg-Sonderhausen).

Latina Emeri Munita   Latin money of Merida (Suevi).

Lege et Fide   By law and faith (Austria).

Lex Tua Veritas   Thy law is the truth (Tuscany).

Liberta Eguaglianza   Freedom and equality (Venice)

Libertad en la Ley   Freedom within the law (Mexico).

Libertas Carior Auro   Freedom is dearer than gold (St Gall).

Libertas Vita Carior   Freedom is dearer than life (Kulenberg).

Libertas Xpo Firmata   Freedom strengthened by Christ (Genoa).

Liberte, Egalite, Fraternite   Liberty, equality, fraternity (France).

Lucerna Pedibus Meis Verbum Est   Thy word is a lamp unto mine feet (England, Edward VI).

Lumen ad Revelationem Gentium   Light to enlighten the nations (Papacy).

L'Union Fait la Force   The union makes strength (Belgium).

Macula Non Est in Te   There is no sin in Thee (Essen).

Magnus ab Integro Saeculorum Nascitur Ordo   The great order of the centuries is born anew (Bavaria).

Mandavit Dominus Palatie hanc Monetam Fiert   The lord of the Palatine ordained this coin to be made (Balath).

Manibus Ne Laedar Avaris   Lest I be injured by greedy hands (Sweden).

Mar Bran Sac Rom Imp Arcam et Elec Sup Dux Siles   Margrave of Brandenburg, archchamberlain of the Holy Roman Empire and elector, senior duke of Silesia (Prussia).

Maria Mater Domini Xpi   Mary mother of Christ the Lord (Teutonic Knights).

Maria Unxit Pedes Xpisti   Mary washes the feet of Christ (France, Rene d'Anjou).

Mater Castrorum   Mother of fortresses (Rome, Marcus Aurelius).

Matrimonio Conjuncti   Joined in wedlock (Austria).

Me Coniunctio Servat Dum Scinditur Frangor   The relationship serves me while I am being torn to pieces (Lowenstein-Wertheim).

Mediolani Dux   Duke of Milan (Milan).

Mediolani et Man   Duke of Mantua and Milan (Milan).

Memor Ero Tui Iustina Virgo   I shall remember you, o maiden Justina (Venice).

Merces Laborum   Wages of work (Wurzburg).

Mirabilia Fecit   He wrought marvels (Viking coinage).

Misericordia Di Rex   King by the mercy of God (France, Louis II).

Mo Arg Ord Foe Belg D Gel & CZ   Silver coin of the order of the Belgian Federation, duchy of Guelder-land, county of Zutphen

(Guelderland).

Moneta Abbatis   Coin of the abbey (German ecclesiastical coins, 13th–14th centuries).

Moneta Argentiae Ord Foed Belgii Holl   Silver coin of the federated union of Belgium and Holland (Batavian Republic).

Mo No Arg Con Foe Belg Pro Hol   New silver coin of the Belgian Federation, province of Holland (Holland).

Mo No Arg Pro Confoe Belg Trai Holl   New silver coin of the confederated Belgian provinces, Utrecht and Holland (Batavian Republic).

Mon Lib Reip Bremens   Coin of the free state of Bremen (Bremen).

Mon Nova Arg Duc Curl Ad Norma Tal Alb   New silver coin of the duchy of Courland, according to the standard of the Albert thaler (Courland).

Mon Nov Castri Imp   New coin of the Imperial free city of . . . (Friedberg).

Moneta Bipont   Coin of Zweibrucken (Pfalz-Birkenfeld-Zweibrucken).

Monet Capit Cathedr Fuld Sede Vacante   Coin of the cathedral chapter of Fulda, the see being vacant (Fulda).

Moneta in Obsidione Tornacensi Cusa   Coin struck during the siege of Tournai (Tournai, 1709).

Moneta Livosesthonica   Coin of Livonia (Estonia).

Moneta Nov Arg Regis Daniae   New silver coin of the king of Denmark (Denmark).

Moneta Nova Ad Norman Conventionis   New coin according to the Convention standard (Orsini-Rosenberg).

Moneta Nova Domini Imperatoris   New coin of the lord emperor (Brunswick, 13th century).

Moneta Nova Lubecensis   New coin of Lubeck.

Moneta Nova Reipublicae Halae Suevicae   New coin of the republic of Hall in Swabia.

Moneta Reipublicae Ratisbonensis   Coin of the republic of Regensburg.

Nach Alt Reichs Schrot und Korn   According to the old empire's grits and grain (Hesse).

Nach dem Conventions Fusse   According to the Convention's basis (German Conventionsthalers).

Nach dem Frankf Schlus   According to the Frankfurt standard (Solms).

Nach dem Schlus der V Staend   According to the standard of the union (Hesse).

Navigare Necesse Est   It is necessary to navigate (Germany).

Nec Aspera Terrent   Nor do difficulties terrify (Brunswick).

Nec Cito Nec Temere   Neither hastily nor rashlly (Cambrai).

Nec Numina Desunt   Nor is the divine will absent (Savoy).

Nec Temere Nec Timide   Neither rashly nor timidly (Danzig, Lippe).

Necessitas Legem Non Habet   Necessity has no law (Magdeburg).

Nemo Me Impune Lacessit   No one touches me with impunity (UK, Scottish pound edge inscription).

Nihil Restat Reliqui   No relic remains (Ypres).

Nil Ultra Aras   Nothing beyond the rocks (Franque-mont).

No Nobis Dne Sed Noi Tuo Da Gloriam   Not to us, o Lord but to Thy name be glory given (France, Francis I).

Nobilissimum Dom Ac Com in Lipp & St   Most noble lord and count in Lippe and Sternberg (Schaumburg-Lippe).

Nomen Domini Turris Fortissima   The name of the Lord is the strongest tower (Frankfurt).

Non Aes Sed Fides   Not bronze but trust (Malta).

Non Est Mortale Quod Opto   What I desire is not mortal. (Mecklenburg).

Non Mihi Sed Populo   Not to me but to the people (Bavaria).

Non Relinquam Vos Orphanos   I shall not leave you as orphans (Papacy).

Non Surrexit Major   None greater has arisen (Genoa, Malta).

Nullum Simulatum Diuturnum Tandem   Nothing that is feigned lasts long (Wittgenstein).

Nummorum Famulus   The servant of the coinage (England, tin halfpence and farthings).

Nunquam Retrorsum   Never backwards (Brunswick-Wolfenbuttel).

O Crux Ave Spes Unica   Hail, o Cross, our only hope (England half-angels, France, Rene d'Anjou).

O Maria Ora Pro Me   O Mary pray for me (Bavaria).

Ob Cives Servatos   On account of the rescued citizens (Rome, Augustus).

Oculi Domini Super Iustos   The eyes of the Lord look down on the just (Neuchatel).

Omnia Auxiliante Maria   Mary helping everything (Schwyz).

Omnia Cum Deo   Everything with God (Reuss-Greiz).

Omnia cum Deo et Nihil Sine Eo   Everthing with God and nothing without Him (Erbach).

Omnis Potestas a Deo Est   All power comes from God (Sweden).

Opp & Carn Dux Comm Rittb SCM Cons Int & Compi Mareschal   Duke of Troppau and Carniola, count of Rietberg, privy councillor of his sacred imperial majesty, field marshal (Liechtenstein).

Opp & Carn . . . Aur Velleris Eques   Duke of Troppau . . . knight of the Golden Fleece (Liechtenstein).

Opportune   Conveniently (Savoy).

Optimus Princeps   Best prince (Rome, Trajan).

Opulentia Salerno   Wealthy Salerno (Siculo-Norman kingdom).

Pace et Iustitia With peace and justice (Spanish Netherlands).

Pacator Orbis Pacifier of the world (Rome, Aurelian).

Palma Sub Pondere Crescit The palm grows under its weight (Waldeck).

Pater Noster Our Father (Flanders, 14th century).

Pater Patriae Farther of his country (Rome, Caligula).

Patria Si Dreptul Meu The country and my right (Roumania).

Patrimon Henr Frid Sorte Divisum The heritage of Heinrich Friedrich divided by lot (Hohenlohe-Langenberg).

Patrimonia Beati Petri The inheritance of the blessed Peter (Papacy).

Patrona Franconiae Patron of Franconia (Wurzburg).

Pax Aeterna Eternal peace (Rome, Marcus Aurelius).

Pax et Abundantia Peace and plenty (Burgundy, Gelderland).

Pax Missa Per Orbem Peace sent throughout the world (England, Anne).

Pax Petrus Peace Peter (Trier, 10th century).

Pax Praevalet Armis May peace prevail by force of arms (Mainz).

Pax Quaeritur Bello Peace is sought by war (Commonwealth, Cromwell).

Pecunia Totum Circumit Orbem Money goes round the whole world (Brazil).

Per Aspera Ad Astra Through difficulties to the stars (Mecklenburg-Schwerin).

Per Angusta ad Augusta Through precarious times to the majestic (Solms-Roedelheim, a pun on the name of the ruler Johan August).

Per Crucem Tuam Salva Nos Christe Redemptor By Thy cross save us, O Christ our Redeemer (England, angels).

Per Crucem Tuam Salva Nos Xpe Redemt By Thy cross save us, O Christ our Redeemer (Portugal, 15th century).

Perdam Babillonis Nomen May the name of Babylon perish (Naples).

Perennitati Iustissimi Regis For the duration of the most just king (France, Louis XIII).

Perennitati Principis Galliae Restitutionis For the duration of the restoration of the prince of the Gauls (France, Henri IV).

Perfer et Obdura Bruxella Carry on and stick it out, Brussels (Brussels siege, 1579–80).

Perpetuus in Nemet Vivar Hereditary count in Nemt-Ujvar (Batthanyi).

Pietate et Constantia By piety and constancy (Fulda).

Pietate et Iustitia By piety and justice (Denmark).

Plebei Urbanae Frumento Constituto Free distribu-tion of grain to the urban working-class established (Rome, Nerva).

Pleidio Wyf Im Gwlad True am I to my country (UK, Welsh pound edge inscription).

Plus Ultra Beyond (the Pillars of Hercules) (Spanish America).

Point du Couronne sans Peine Point of the crown without penalty (Coburg).

Pons Civit Castellana The bridge of the town of Castellana (Papacy).

Populus et Senatus Bonon The people and senate of Bologna (Bologna).

Post Mortem Patris Pro Filio For the son after his father's death (Pontefract siege coins).

Post Tenebras Lux After darkness light (Geneva).

Post Tenebras Spero Lucem After darkness I hope for light (Geneva).

Posui Deum Adiutorem Meum I have made God my helper (England, Ireland, 1351–1603).

Praesidium et Decus Protection and ornament (Bologna).

Prima Sedes Galliarum First see of the Gauls (Lyon).

Primitiae Fodin Kuttenb ab Aerari Iterum Susceptarum First results dug from the Kuttenberg mines in a renewed undertaking (Austria).

Princps Iuventutis Prince of youth (Roman Empire).

Pro Defensione Urbis et Patriae For the defence of city and country (France, Louis XIV).

Pro Deo et Patria For God and the fatherland (Fulda).

Pro Deo et Populo For God and the people (Bavaria).

Pro Ecclesia et Pro Patria For the church and the fatherland (Constance).

Pro Fausio PP Reitur VS For happy returns of the princes of the Two Sicilies (Naples and Sicily).

Pro Lege et Grege For law and the flock (Fulda).

Pro maximo Dei Gloria et Bono Publico For the greatest glory of God and the good of the people (Wurttemberg).

Pro Patria For the fatherland (Wurzburg).

Propitio Deo Secura Ago With God's favour I lead a secure life. (Saxe-Lauenburg).

Protector Literis Literae Nummis Corona et Salus A protection to the letters (on the face of the coin), the letters (on the edge) are a garland and a safeguard to the coinage (Commonwealth, Cromwell broad).

Protege Virgo Pisas Protect Pisa, O Virgin (Pisa).

Provide et Constanter Wisely and firmly (Wurttem-berg).

Providentia et Pactis Through foresight and pacts (Brandenburg-Ansbach).

Providentia Optimi Principis With the foresight of the best prince (Naples and Sicily).

Proxima Fisica Finis Nearest to natural end (Orciano).

Proxima Soli Nearest to the sun (Modena).

Pulcra Virtutis Imago The beautiful image of virtue (Genoa).

Pupillum et Viduam Suscipiat May he support the orphan and the widow (Savoy).

Quae Deus Conjunxit Nemo Separet What God hath joined let no man put asunder (England, James I).

Quem Quadragesies et Semel Patriae Natum Esse Gratulamur Whom we congratulate for the forty-first time for being born for the fatherland (Lippe-Detmold).

Qui Dat Pauperi Non Indigebit Who gives to the poor will never be in need (Munster).

Quid Non Cogit Necessitas To what does Necessity not drive. (Ypres).

Quin Matrimonii Lustrum Celebrant They celebrate their silver wedding (Austria, 1879).

Quocunque Gesseris (Jeceris) Stabit Whichever way you throw it it will stand (Isle of Man).

Quod Deus Vult Hoc Semper Fit What God wishes always occurs. (Saxe-Weimar).

Reconduntur non Retonduntur They are laid up in store, not thundered back (Savoy).

Recta Tueri Defend the right (Austria).

Recte Constanter et Fortiter Rightly, constantly and bravely (Bavaria).

Recte Faciendo Neminem Timeas May you fear no one in doing right. (Solms-Laubach).

Rector Orbis Ruler of the world (Rome, Didius Julianus).

Rectus et Immotus Right and immovable (Hesse).

Redde Cuique Quod Suum Est Render to each that which is his own (England, Henry VIII).

Redeunt antiqui Gaudia Moris There return the joys of ancient custom (Regensburg).

Reg Pr Pol et Lith Saxon Dux Royal prince of Poland and Lithuania and duke of Saxony (Trier).

Regia Boruss Societas Asiat Embdae Royal Prussian Asiatic Society of Emden (Prussia).

Regier Mich Her Nach Deinen Wort Govern me here according to Thy word (Palatinate).

Regnans Capitulum Ecclesiae Cathedralis Ratisbonensis Sede Vacante Administering the chapter of the cathedral church at Regensburg, the see being vacant (Regensburg).

Regni Utr Sic et Hier Of the kingdom of the Two Sicilies and of Jerusalem (Naples and Sicily).

Religio Protestantium Leges Angliae Libertas Parliamenti The religion of the Protestants, the laws of England and the freedom of Parliament (England, Royalists, 1642).

Relinquo Vos Liberos ab Utroque Homine I leave you as children of each man (San Marino).

Restauracao da Independencia Restoration of inde-pendence (Portugal, 1990).

Restitutor Exercitus Restorer of the army (Rome, Aurelian).

Restitutor Galliarum Restorer of the Gauls (Rome, Gallienus).

Restitutor Generis Humani Restorer of mankind (Rome, Valerian).

Restitutor Libertatis Restorer of freedom (Rome, Constantine).

Restitutor Orbis Restorer of the world (Rome, Valerian).

Restitutor Orientis Restorer of the east (Rome, Valerian).

Restitutor Saeculi Restorer of the century (Rome, Valerian).

Restitutor Urbis Restorer of the city (Rome, Severus).

Rosa Americana Utile Dulci The American rose, useful and sweet (American colonies).

Rosa Sine Spina A rose without a thorn (England, Tudor coins).

Rutilans Rosa Sine Spina A dazzling rose without a thorn (England, Tudor gold coins).

S Annae Fundgruben Ausb Tha in N Oe Mining thaler of the St Anne mine in Lower Austria (Austria).

S Ap S Leg Nat Germ Primas Legate of the Holy Apostolic See, born Primate of Germany (Salzburg).

S Carolus Magnus Fundator Charlemagne founder (Munster).

S. Gertrudis Virgo Prudens Niviella St Gertrude the wise virgin of Nivelles (Nivelles).

SI Aul Reg Her & P Ge H Post Mag General hereditary postmaster, supreme of the imperial court of the hereditary kingdom and provinces (Paar).

S. Ian Bapt F. Zachari St John the Baptist, son of Zachary (Florence).

S. Kilianus Cum Sociis Francorum Apostoli St Kilian and his companions, apostles to the Franks (Wurzburg).

S. Lambertus Patronus Leodiensis St Lambert, patron of Liege (Liege).

Sac Nupt Celeb Berol For the holy matrimony celebrated at Berlin (Brandenburg-Ansbach).

Sac Rom Imp Holy Roman Empire (German states).

Sac Rom Imp Provisor Iterum Administrator of the Holy Roman Empire for the second time (Saxony).

Salus Generis Humani Safety of mankind (Rome, Vindex).

Salus Patriae Safety of the fatherland (Italy).

Salus Populi The safety of the people (Spain).

Salus Provinciarum Safety of the provinces (Rome, Postumus).

Salus Publica Salus Mea Public safety is my safety (Sweden).

Salus Reipublicae The safety of the republic (Rome, Theodosius II).

Salus Reipublicae Suprema Lex The safety of the republic is the supreme law (Poland).

Salvam Fac Rempublicam Tuam Make your state safe (San Marino).

Sanctus Iohannes Innoce St John the harmless (Gandersheim).

Sans Changer Without changing (Isle of Man).

Sans Eclat Without pomp (Bouchain siege, 1711).

Sapiente Diffidentia   Wise distrust (Teschen).

Scutum Fidei Proteget Eum / Eam   The shield of faith shall protect him / her (England, Edward VI and Elizabeth I).

Secundum Voluntatem Tuam Domine   Your favourable will o Lord (Hesse).

Securitati Publicae   For the public safety (Brandenburg-Ansbach).

Sede Vacante   The see being vacant (Papal states, Vatican and ecclesiastical coinage).

Sena Vetus Alpha et W Principum et Finis   Old Siena alpha and omega, the beginning and the end (Siena).

Senatus Populus QR   Senate and people of Rome (Rome, 1188).

Si Deus Nobiscum Quis Contra Nos   If God is with us who can oppose us (Hesse).

Si Deus Pro Nobis Quis Contra Nos   If God is for us who can oppose us (Roemhild).

Sieh Deine Seeligkeit Steht Fest Ins Vaters Liebe   Behold thy salvation stands surely in thy Father's love (Gotha).

Signis Receptis   When the standards had been recovered (Rome, Augustus).

Signum Crucis   The sign of the cross (Groningen).

Sincere et Constanter   Truthfully and steadfastly (Hesse-Darmstadt).

Sit Nomen Domini Benedictum   Blessed be the name of the Lord (Burgundy, Strasbourg).

St T X Adiuto Reg Iste Domba   Let it be to you, o Christ, the assistant to the king of Dombes (Dombes).

Sit Tibi Xpe Dat q'tu Regis Iste Ducat   May this duchy which Thou rulest be given to Thee, O Christ (Venice, ducat).

Sit Unio Haec Perennis   May this union last for ever (Hohenlohe-Langenberg).

Sola Bona Quae Honesta   The only good things are those which are honest (Brunswick).

Sola Facta Deum Sequor   Through deeds alone I strive to follow God (Milan).

Soli Deo Honor et Gloria   To God alone be honour and glory (Nassau).

Soli Reduci   To him, the only one restored (Naples and Sicily).

Solius Virtutis Flos Perpetuus   The flower of Virtue alone is perpetual (Strasbourg).

Spes Confisa Deo Nunquam Confusa Recedit   Hope entrusted in God never retreats in a disorderly fashion (Lippe).

Spes Nr Deus   God is our hope (Oudenarde siege, 1582).

Spes Rei Publicae   The hope of the republic (Rome, Valens).

Strena ex Argyrocopeo Vallis S Christoph   A New Year's gift from the silver-bearing valley of St Christopher (Wurttemberg, 1625).

Sub His Secura Spes Clupeus Omnibus in Te Sperantibus   Under these hope is safe, a shield for all who reside hope in Thee (Bavaria).

Sub Pondere   Under weight (Fulda).

Sub Protectione Caesarea   Under imperial protection (Soragna).

Sub Tuum Praesidium Confug   We flee to Thy protection (Salzburg).

Sub Umbra Alarum Tuarum   Under the shadow of Thy wings (Iever, Scotland, James V).

Subditorum Salus Felicitas Summa   The safety of the subjects is the highest happiness (Lubeck).

Sufficit Mihi Gratia Tua Domine   Sufficient to me is Thy grace, o Lord (Ploen).

Supra Firmam Petram   Upon a firm rock (Papacy).

Susceptor Noster Deus   God is our defence (Tuscany).

Sydera Favent Industriae   The stars favour industry (Furstenberg).

Sylvarum Culturae Praemium   Prize for the culture of the forest (Brandenburg-Ansbach).

Tali Dicata Signo Mens Fluctuari Nequit   Consecrated by such a sign the mind cannot waver (England, Henry VIII George noble).

Tandem Bona Caus Triumphat   A good cause eventually triumphs (Dillenburg).

Tandem Fortuna Obstetrice   With good luck ultimately as the midwife (Wittgenstein).

Te Stante Virebo   With you at my side I shall be strong (Moravia).

Tene Mensuram et Respice Finem   Hold the measure and look to the end (Burgundy).

Tert Ducat Secular   Tercentenary of the duchy (Wurttemberg).

Thu Recht Schev Niemand   Go with right and fear no one (Saxe-Lauenburg).

Tibi Laus et Gloria   To Thee be praise and glory (Venice).

Timor Domini Fons Vitae   The fear of the Lord is a fountain of life (England, Edward VI shillings).

Tout Avec Dieu   Everything with God (Brunswick, 1626).

Traiectum ad Mosam   The crossing of the Maas (Maastricht).

Transvolat Nubila Virtus   Marriageable virtue soon flies past (Grueyeres).

Travail, Famille, Patrie   Work, family, country (Vichy France).

Triumphator Gent Barb   Victor over the barbarian people (Byzantine Empire, Arcadius).

Tueatur Unita Deus   May God guard these united (Kingdoms) (England, James I; Britain, 1847).

Turck Blegert Wien   Vienna besieged by the Turks (Vienna, 1531).

Tut Mar Gab Pr Vid de Lobk Nat Pr Sab Car et Aug Pr de Lobk   Regency of Maria Gabriela, widow of the prince of Lobkowitz, born princess of Savoy-Carignan, and August prince of Lobkowitz (Lobkowitz).

Tutela Italiae   The guardianship of Italy (Rome, Nerva).

Ubi Vult Spirat   He breathes where he will (Papacy).

Ubique Pax   Peace everywhere (Rome, Gallienus).

Union et Force   Union and strength (France).

Urbe Obsessa   The city under siege (Maastricht).

Urbem Virgo Tuam Serva   Protects thy city o virgin (Mary) (Strasbourg).

USC & RAM Cons Int Gen C Mar & Nob Praet H Turmae Capit   Privy councillor of both their holy imperial and royal apostolic majesties, general field marshal and captain of the noble praetorian Hungarian squadrons (Eszterhazy).

Vculis Aulae Argenteis Patriae Indigenti Ministravit Auxilia   With the silver vessels of the court aid was brought to the needy fatherland (Eichstadt, 1796).

Vehiculatione Italiae Remissa   Postal tax of Italy remitted (Rome, Nerva).

Veni Luumen Cordium   Come light of hearts (Vatican).

Veni Sancte Spiritus   Come Holy Ghost (Vatican).

Verbum Domini Manet in Aeternum   The word of the Lord abides forever (Hesse-Darmstadt, Veldenz).

Veritas Lex Tua   The truth is your law (Salzburg).

Veritas Temporis Filia   Truth is the daughter of time (England and Ireland, Mary Tudor).

Veritate et Labore   By truth and work (Wittgenstein).

Veritate et Iustitia   By truth and justice (German states).

Victoria Principum   The victory of princes (Ostrogoths).

Videant Pauperes et Laetentur   Let the poor see and rejoice (Tuscany).

Virgo Maria Protege Civitatem Savonae   Virgin Mary Protect the city of Savona (Savona).

Viribus Unitis   With united strength (Austria).

Virtute et Fidelitate   By virtue and faithfulness (Hesse-Cassel).

Virtute et Prudentia   With virtue and prudence (Auersperg).

Virtute Viam Dimetiar   I shall mark the way with valour (Waldeck).

Virtutis Gloria Merces   Glory is the reward of valour (Holstein-Gottorp).

Vis Unita Concordia Fratrum Fortior   United power is the stronger harmony of brothers (Mansfeld).

Visitavit Nos Oriens ex Alto   He has visited us arising on high (Luneburg).

Vivit Post Funera   He lives after death (Bremen).

Von Gottes Gn Iohan Bischof Zu Strasburg Landtgraf in Elsass   By God's grace John, Bishop of Strasbourg, Landgrave in Alsace (Strasbourg).

Vota Optata Romae Fel   Vows taken for the luck of Rome (Rome, Maxentius).

Vox de Throno   A voice from the throne (Papacy).

Was Got Beschert Bleibet Unerwert   What God hath endowed leave undisturbed

Wider macht und List Mein Fels Gott Ist   Against might and trickery God is my rock (Hesse-Cassel).

Xpc Vincit Xpc Regnat   Christ conquers, Christ reigns (Scotland, Spain).

Xpc Vivet Xpc Regnat Xpc Impat   Christ lives, Christ reigns, Christ commands (Cambrai).

Xpe Resurescit   Christ lives again (Venice).

Xpistiana Religio   Christian religion (Carolingian Empire).

Xps Ihs Elegit me Regem Populo   Jesus Christ chose me as king to the people (Norway).

Zelator Fidei Usque ad Montem   An upholder of the faith through and through (Portugal).

Zum Besten des Vaterlands   To the best of the fatherland (Bamberg).

Care
of coins

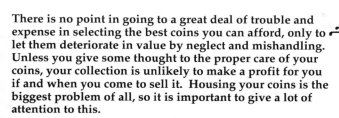

There is no point in going to a great deal of trouble and expense in selecting the best coins you can afford, only to let them deteriorate in value by neglect and mishandling. Unless you give some thought to the proper care of your coins, your collection is unlikely to make a profit for you if and when you come to sell it. Housing your coins is the biggest problem of all, so it is important to give a lot of attention to this.

Storage

The ideal, but admittedly the most expensive, method is the coin cabinet, constructed of air-dried mahogany, walnut or rosewood (*never* oak, cedar or any highly resinous timber likely to cause chemical tarnish). These cabinets have banks of shallow drawers containing trays made of the same wood, with half-drilled holes of various sizes to accommodate the different denominations of coins. Such cabinets are handsome pieces of furniture but, being largely handmade, tend to be rather expensive. Occasionally good specimens can be picked up in secondhand furniture shops, or at the dispersal of house contents by auction, but the best bet is still to purchase a new cabinet, tailored to your own requirements.

Peter Nichols of 3 Norman Road, St Leonards-on-Sea, East Sussex TN37 6NH (telephone 01424 436682) is a specialist manufacturer of display and storage systems who has also been producing coin and medal cabinets to suit every need for more than a quarter of a century. He can produce a cabinet to fit into a wall safe or some other form of security box. He can match existing work, and thus replicate cabinets which you may already be using, or even produce designs to suit your specific requirements. The only proviso is that the cabinets are made in only one timber—Brazilian mahogany, for reason of chemical balance. A nice touch is that all the products in the Nichols repertoire take their names from Elizabethan mint-marks.

Nichols also offers a custom drilling service for coin trays, either all of the same diameter or in mixed sizes, depending on what you require. Drilling templates are also available on request. Apart from coin cabinets, Peter Nichols manufactures *medal* cabinets in two basic types, the seven-tray Pheon and the fourteen-tray Crozier.

The cases for these cabinets are similar in all respects to the coin cabinets, but medal trays are twice the thickness of coin trays. Each tray is made up from solid mahogany mouldings, base and polished mahogany front edges and trimmed with two turned brass knobs. The base of each tray is trimmed with a red felt pad.

Nichols produces a wide range of cabinets from

The 4-tray Martlet—the smallest in an extensive range from Peter Nichols.

The Crozier—a cabinet for the connoisseur.

The Mini-Porter, smallest of Abafil's plush Diplomat range.

the seven-tray Pheon all the way up to the massive 40-tray specials designed for the British Museum. All cabinets are fitted with double doors. Nichols also produces the glass-topped Crown display case and the Sceptre display case, fitted with a glazed lid and containing a single tray. The Orb range of display cases are intended for wall mounting and are ideal for a display of campaign medals and decorations.

Prices start at around £30 for a four-tray Martlet coin cabinet and go all the way to the Coronet thirty-tray version at about £300. They are not cheap, but you have the satisfaction of acquiring exquisite examples of the cabinetmaker's craft which would be an elegant addition to any lounge or study.

An excellent compromise is provided by firms such as Abafil of Italy and Lindner of Germany who manufacture coin trays in durable, felt-lined materials with shallow compartments to suit the various sizes of coins. These trays interlock so that they build up into a cabinet of the desired size, and there are also versions designed as carrying cases, which are ideal for transporting coins.

Collectors Gallery of Castle Hall, Castle Gate, Shrewsbury, SY1 2AD (telephone: 01743 272140, fax: 01743 366041) is the UK agent and distributor for the Abafil series manufactured in Milan. These cases are of stout wooden construction covered with simulated leather and lined with red plush. The Diplomat range is designed primarily for secure transportation, but the Mini-diplomat, at around £40, makes a good static cabinet, and can take up to three standard trays holding a maximum of 241 coins, while the Custom case holds 14 de luxe or 20 standard trays and will house up to 1,500 coins. Even cheaper is the Mignon case holding up to 105 coins, ideally suited for carrying in a briefcase or travel bag.

Lindner Publications of 13 Fore Street, Hayle, Cornwall TR27 4DX (telephone 01726 751914) are well-known for their wide range of philatelic and numismatic accessories, but these include a full array of coin boxes, capsules, carrying cases and trays. The basic Lindner coin box is, in fact, a shallow tray available in a standard version or a smoked glass version. These trays have a crystal clear frame, red felt inserts and holes for various diameters of coins and medals. A novel feature of these trays is the rounded insert which facilitates the removal of coins from their spaces with the minimum of handling. These boxes are designed in such a manner that they interlock and can be built up into banks of trays, each fitted with a draw-handle and sliding in and out easily. Various types of chemically inert plastic capsules and envelopes have been designed for use in combination with plain shallow trays, without holes drilled. Lindner also manufacture a range of luxury cases lined in velvet and Atlas silk with padded covers and gold embossing on the spines, producing a most tasteful and elegant appearance.

Safe Albums of 16 Falcon Business Park, Hogwood Lane, Finchampstead, Berkshire RG11 4QW (telephone 01734 328976) are the UK agents for the German Stapel-Element, a drawer-stacking system with clear plasticiser-free trays that fit into standard bookshelves. The sliding coin compartments, lined with blue velvet, can be angled for display to best advantage. Stackable drawers cost around £12 each, and can be built up to any height desired. A wide range of drawer sizes is available, with compartments suitable for the smallest coins right up to four-compartment trays designed for very large artefacts such as card-cases or cigarette cases. The Mobel-Element cabinet is a superb specialised cabinet constructed of the finest timber with a steel frame and steel grip bars which can be securely locked. It thus combines elegance with security and is the ideal medium for the most valuable coins and medals.

There are also various storage systems, such as Coindex, which operate on the principle of narrow

Adding on to the stacking Lindner range is easy.

drawers in which the coins are stored in envelopes of chemically-inert plastic. A strip across the top holds a little slip giving a brief description, catalogue number and the price of each coin.

Kwikseal of the USA produce cards with a plastic window: these cards are especially suitable for slabbing coins. The traditional method used by many collectors was to house coins in small, air-dried manila envelopes that could be stored upright in narrow wooden or stout card boxes—knife-boxes were highly regarded as being the right width and depth. The Sydney Museum in Australia, for example, keeps its coins in manila envelopes stored in plastic lunch-boxes which seemed to do the job pretty well!

Albums can be carried around easily

Safe's cabinet combines elegance with security.

Coin Albums

When coin collecting became a popular hobby in the 1960s, several firms marketed ranges of coin albums. They had clear plastic sleeves divided into tiny compartments of various sizes and had the merit of being cheap and taking up little room on a bookshelf.

They had several drawbacks, however, not the least being the tendency of the pages to sag with the weight of the coins, or even, in extreme cases, to pull away from the pegs or rings holding them on to the spine. They required very careful handling as the coins could easily fall out of the top row as the pages were turned. The more expensive albums had little flaps that folded over the top of the coin to overcome this problem.

Arguably the worst aspect of these albums was the use of polyvinyl chloride (PVC) in the construction of the sleeves. Collectors soon discovered to their horror that this reacted chemically with their coins, especially those made of silver, causing a rather disgusting yellow slime to adhere to the coins' surface. I shudder to think how many fine collections were ruined as a result,

or of the countless coins that required highly expert treatment in a bid to restore them to as near the original condition as possible.

Fortunately the lesson has been learned and the coin albums now on the market are quite safe. Lindner offer a wide range of albums designed to house coins, medals or banknotes. The old problem about sagging pages is overcome by the use of a multi-ring binding welded to a very stout spine, while the sleeves contain neither Styrol nor PVC and will not affect any metals at all. In addition to pages with pockets of uniform size, the Karat range of albums operates on a slide principle which enables the user to insert vertical strips of different sizes on the same page, so that the coins of one country or series, or perhaps a thematic display of coins from different countries, can be displayed side by side.

Safe Albums offer a wide range of albums in the Coinholder System and Coin-Combi ranges. These, too, offer the choice of fixed pages with uniform-sized pockets, or interchangeable sliding inserts for different sizes side by side.

Cleaning Coins

This is like matrimony—it should not be embarked on lightly. Indeed, the advice given by the magazine *Punch* in regard to marriage is equally sound in this case—don't do it! It is far better to have a dirty coin than an irretrievably damaged one. Every dealer has horror stories of handling coins that previous owners have cleaned, to their detriment. The worst example I ever saw was a display of coins found by a metal detectorist who "improved" his finds by abrading them in the kind of rotary drum used by lapidarists to polish gemstones. If you really must remove the dirt and grease from coins, it is advisable to practise on coins of little value.

Warm water containing a mild household detergent or washing-up liquid will work wonders in removing surface dirt and grease from most coins, but silver is best washed in a weak solution of ammonia and warm water—one part ammonia to ten parts water. Gold coins can be cleaned with diluted citric acid, such as lemon juice. Copper or bronze coins present more of a problem, but patches of verdigris can usually be removed by careful washing in a 20 per cent solution of sodium sesquicarbonate. Wartime coins made of tin, zinc, iron or steel can be cleaned in a 5 per cent solution of caustic soda containing some aluminium or zinc foil or filings, but they must be rinsed afterwards in clean water and carefully dried. Cotton buds are ideal for gently prising dirt out of coin legends and crevices in the designs. Soft brushes (with animal bristles—*never* nylon or other artificial bristles) designed for cleaning silver are most suitable for gently cleaning coins.

Coins recovered from the soil or the sea bed present special problems, due to chemical reaction between the metals and the salts in the earth or sea water. In such cases, the best advice is to take them to the nearest museum and let the professional experts decide on what can or should be done.

Both Lindner and Safe Albums offer a range of coin-cleaning kits and materials suitable for gold, silver, copper and other base alloys respectively. Safe (living up to their name) also provide a stern warning that rubber gloves should be worn and care taken to avoid breathing fumes or getting splashes of liquid in your eyes or on your skin. Obviously, the whole business of cleaning is a matter that should not be entered into without the utmost care and forethought.

POLISHING: A WARNING

If cleaning should only be approached with the greatest trepidation, polishing is definitely *out!* Beginners sometimes fall into the appalling error of thinking that a smart rub with metal polish might improve the appearance of their coins. Short of actually punching a hole through it, there can hardly be a more destructive act. Polishing a coin may improve its superficial appearance for a few days, but such abrasive action will destroy the patina and reduce the fineness of the high points of the surface. Even if a coin is only polished once, it will never be quite the same again, and an expert can tell this a mile off.

Celtic
coinage of Britain

Celtic coins were the first coins made in Britain. They were issued for a century and a half before the Roman invasion, and possibly a little later in some areas. They were issued by 11 tribal groups or administrative authorities situated southeast of a line from the Humber to the Severn. In this short article Celtic specialist CHRIS RUDD introduces this increasingly popular area.

The earliest coins were uninscribed and often abstract in design. Later ones carried the names of local leaders and tribal centres, and in the southeast became increasingly Roman in style, sometimes copying classical images quite closely.

Most Celtic coins were struck between two dies on flans of gold, silver, billion and bronze. Some were cast in strip moulds in tin-rich bronze alloy called "potin".

Because the Celts wrote no books and left no written records of their activities, little is known about the people and places behind their coins. Who made them? When? Where? And why? These are questions that are still largely unanswered, except in the very vaguest terms. Celtic cataloguers talk about gold quarters, silver units and silver minims. But the truth is we don't even know what the Celts themselves called their coins.

British Celtic coins are among the most fascinating ever fashioned and perhaps the least familiar to the average collector because of their rarity. Like the Celts themselves, Celtic coin designs are wild, free flowing, flamboyant and full of fun. Yes, Celtic moneyers had a great sense of humour!

Celtic coins bear a vast variety of gods and goddesses, armed warriors, chariot wheels, hidden faces, decapitated heads, suns, moons, stars, thunderbolts, floral motifs, magic signs and phallic symbols. Plus a menagerie of antelopes, bears, boars, bulls, cocks, crabs, cranes, dogs, dolphins, ducks, eagles, hares, all kinds of horses (some with wings, some with human heads, many with three tails, a few breathing fire), goats, lions, lizards, owls, rams, rats, ravens, snakes, stags, starfish, worms and wolves. Not to mention dragons, griffins, hippocamps, sphinxes and ram-horned serpents.

Ask any metal detectorist how many Celtic coins he or she has found and you will immediately realise they are rarer than Roman coins in this country—at least a thousand times rarer on average. This is because far fewer Celtic coins were minted, in smaller runs, over a much shorter time span. Though some may have been made as early as 80 BC, the majority of British Celtic coins were struck from 54 BC to AD 43; barely 100 years of production, and most of that seems to have been sporadic.

However, the greater rarity of Celtic coins doesn't mean they are necessarily more costly than other ancient coins: in fact, they are often cheaper. You see, in the coin market, demand determines price. The more collectors that want a coin, the higher its price.

A recent survey revealed "worldwide there may be no more than 150 regular private collectors

Method that may have been used for striking Celtic coins (drawing by Simon Pressey).

of Celtic coins, buying on average one or more coins per month". Whereas there are literally thousands of people collecting the other major series of ancient and medieval coins. That is why Celtic coins are still comparatively less costly than Greek, Anglo-Saxon and English hammered coins. The Celtic market is smaller, though expanding. For example a very fine Celtic gold stater typically costs half the price of a Greek gold stater or an English gold noble of comparable quality and

rarity. The price differential can be even more dramatic at major international auctions. But the disparity is diminishing as more and more collectors are beginning to appreciate the hitherto unrecognised beauty, scarcity and good value of British Celtic coins. So now could be a good time to start collecting Celtic coins, before their prices begin climbing more steeply.

Thirty years ago collecting British Celtic coins was a rich man's hobby and understanding them

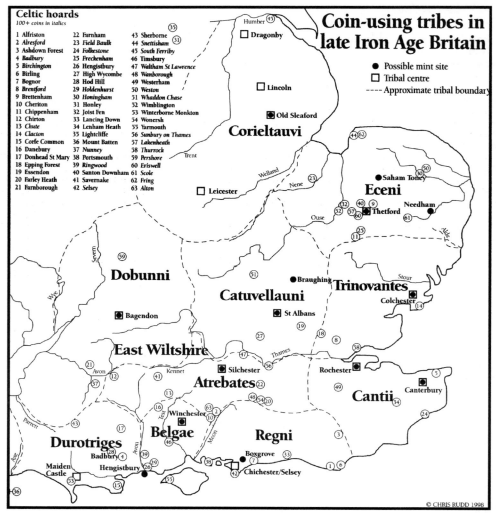

Eleven tribal groups minted coins in late Iron Age Britain, c. 80 BC–AD 45. The boundaries shown here are guesstimates, not actual, and often follow rivers, many of which are still known by their Celtic names.

Silver unit attributed to King Prasutagus of the Eceni, whose death resulted in the revolt of Queen Boudica, AD 60 (drawn four times actual size by Susan White).

was the lonely pursuit of a few scholarly numismatists. Today, thanks to the popularity of metal detecting, Celtic coins are more plentiful and almost everyone can afford to collect them. Most ancient coin dealers sell Celtic coins, some for as little as £20 each, and you will always find a few trays of them at every coin fair.

British Celtic coins are also easier to study today, thanks to the publication of some excellent books on the subject. The Celtic collector's bible is *Celtic Coinage of Britain* by Robert D. Van Arsdell (Spink, 1989)—well researched, well written, well illustrated, always quoted in dealers' catalogues, often controversial when dates are discussed and hopefully to be republished soon in a revised edition. For the dedicated Celtic devotee *British Iron Age Coins in the British Museum* by Richard Hobbs (British Museum Press, 1996) is an invaluable companion volume to Van Arsdell— more cautious, less speculative.

By far the best introductory book is *Celtic Coinage in Britain* by Dr Philip de Jersey (Shire Archaeology, 1996) who manages the Celtic Coin Index, a photographic record of over 23,000 British coins at the Institute of Archaeology, Oxford. In plain language Dr Philip de Jersey explains how Celtic coins and the images they carry can reveal information on the political, economic and social life of the Celts. *Celtic Coinage in Britain* contains clear twice-size photos of over a hundred Celtic coins, some of them rarely seen before. It gives the names, addresses and phone numbers of the museums in England, Scotland and Wales with the best and most accessible collections of Celtic coins.

In short, if you want to know more about British Celtic coins, *Celtic Coinage in Britain* is where you start reading and keep reading. This is the best little book ever written about British Celtic coins and outstanding value for money at £4.99.

How should you start collecting British Celtic coins? First, get a few of the commoner uninscribed types from each of the 11 tribal areas, aiming for the highest grade you can comfortably afford. Then you may wish to get an inscribed coin of each of the main rulers. You would also be well advised to acquire some Gaulish coins at the same time, because many British coins were influenced by Gallic prototypes.

How much do British Celtic coins cost? Very little, considering how scarce they are. Types with legends usually cost more than those without and top quality bronze is frequently more pricey than top quality silver (which may surprise you) because silver is commoner and generally survives better after two-thousand years underground.

Chris Rudd is a well-known dealer who specialises in Celtic coins.

Collecting
Ancient coins

Ancient coins differ from most other series which are collected in Britain in that every piece has spent the major part of the last two thousand years in the ground.

As JOHN CUMMINGS, dealer in ancient coins and antiquities explains here, the effect that burial has had on the surface of the coin determines more than anything else the value of a particular piece. With more modern coins, the only things which affect price are rarity and grade. There may be a premium for coins exhibiting particularly fine tone, or with outstanding pedigrees, but an 1887 crown in "extremely fine" condition has virtually the same value as every other piece with the same grade and of the same date. With ancient coins the story is very different.

A large number of different criteria affect the price of an ancient coin. Factors affecting prices can be broken down into several categories:

Condition

The most important factor by far in determining price. Ancient coins were struck by hand and can exhibit striking faults. Value suffers if the coin is struck with the designs off-centre, is weakly struck, or if the flan is irregular in shape. Many of the Celtic tribes issued coins of varying fineness and those made from low quality gold or silver are worth less than similar specimens where the metal quality is better. Conversely, coins on exceptional flans, particularly well struck, or with fine patinas command a premium.

Many ancient coins have suffered during their stay in the ground. It must be borne in mind that the prices given in the price guide are for uncorroded, undamaged examples. A Roman denarius should be graded using the same criteria as those used for grading modern coins. The surfaces must be good, and the coin intact. The fact that the coin is 2,000 years old is irrelevant as far as grading is concerned. Coins which are not perfectly preserved are not without value but the value for a given grade decreases with the degree of fault.

Rarity

As with all other series, rare coins usually command higher prices than common ones although this is not written in stone. A unique variety of a small fourth century Roman bronze coin, even in perfect condition, can be worth much less than a more worn and common piece from an earlier part of the empire. In the Celtic series, there is an almost infinite variety of minor types and a unique variety of an uninscribed type will rarely outbid an inscribed issue of a known king.

Historical and local significance

Types which have historical or local interest can command a price far above their scarcity value. Denarii of the emperor Tiberius are believed to have been referred to in the New Testament and command a far higher price than a less interesting piece of similar rarity. Similarly, pieces which have British reverse types such as the "VICT BRIT" reverse of the third century AD are more expensive than their scarcity would indicate. The 12 Caesars are ever popular especially in the American market and this affects prices throughout the world. In the Celtic series, coins of Cunobelin or Boudicca are far more popular than pieces which have no historical interest but which are far scarcer.

Reverse types

All Roman emperors who survived for a reasonable time issued coins with many different reverse types. The most common of these usually show various Roman gods. When a coin has an unusual reverse it always enhances the value.

Particularly popular are architectural scenes, animals, references to Judaism, and legionary types.

Artistic merit

Most Celtic tribes issued several distinct series which generally speaking, improved in style up to the time of the Roman invasion. Later issues which exhibit fine "Celtic" style are usually more popular than the more stylised, earlier types.

Typical of the former would be the beautiful gold staters of Tasciovanus and Cunobelin. The Roman coinage is blessed with a large number of bust varieties and these can have a startling effect on price. A common coin with the bust left instead of right can be worth several times the price of a normal example. The coinage of Hadrian has a large number of bust varieties some of which are extremely artistic and these can command a premium.

The coinage used in Britain from the time of the invasion in AD 43 was the same as that introduced throughout the Empire by the emperor Augustus around 20 BC. The simple divisions of 2 asses equal to one dupondius, 2 dupondii equal to 1 sestertius, 4 sestertii equal to one denarius and 25 denarii equal to one aureus continued in use until the reformation of the coinage by Caracalla in AD 214.

Aureus (gold)

Denarius (silver)

Sestertius (bronze)

Dupondius (copper)

As (copper)

Introducing
Hammered coinage

The hammered currency of medieval Britain is among some of the most interesting coinage in the world. The turbulent history of these islands is reflected in the fascinating changes in size, design, fineness and workmanship, culminating in the many strange examples that emanated from the strife of the Civil War.

The Norman Conquest of England in 1066 and succeeding years had far-reaching effects on all aspects of life. Surprisingly, however, it had little impact on the coinage. William the Conqueror was anxious to emphasise the continuity of his reign, so far as the ordinary people were concerned, and therefore he retained the fabric, size and general design pattern of the silver penny. Almost 70 mints were in operation during this reign, but by the middle of the 12th century the number was reduced to 55 and under Henry II (1154–89) it fell to 30 and latterly to only eleven. By the early 14th century the production of coins had been centralised on London and Canterbury, together with the ecclesiastical mints at York and Canterbury. The silver penny was the principal denomination throughout the Norman period, pieces cut along the lines of the cross on the reverse continuing to serve as halfpence and farthings.

Eight types of penny were struck under William I and five under his son William Rufus, both profiles (left and right) and facing portraits being used in both reigns allied to crosses of various types. Fifteen types were minted under Henry I (1100–35), portraiture having now degenerated to crude caricature, the lines engraved on the coinage dies being built up by means of various punches. Halfpence modelled on the same pattern were also struck, but very sparingly and are very rare.

On Henry's death the succession was contested by his daughter Matilda and his nephew Stephen of Blois. Civil war broke out in 1138 and continued till 1153. Stephen controlled London and its mint, but Matilda and her supporters occupied the West Country and struck their own coins at Bristol. Several of the powerful barons struck their own coins, and there were distinct regional variants of the regal coinage. Of particular interest are the coins struck

Silver pennies of, from left to right, William I, William Rufus, Henry I and Stephen.

from obverse dies with Stephen's portrait erased or defaced, believed to date from 1148 when the usurper was under papal interdict.

Peace was restored in 1153 when it was agreed that Matilda's son Henry should succeed Stephen. On the latter's death the following year, Henry II ascended the throne. Coins of Stephen's last type continued to be minted till 1158, but Henry then took the opportunity to overhaul the coinage which had become irregular and sub-standard during the civil war. The new "Cross Crosslet" coins, usually known as the Tealby coinage (from the hoard of over 5,000 pennies found at Tealby, Lincolnshire in 1807), were produced at 30 mints, but when the recoinage was completed this number was reduced to a dozen. The design of Henry's coins remained virtually the same throughout more than two decades, apart from minor variants. Then, in 1180, a new type, known as the Short Cross coinage, was introduced. This was a vast improvement over the poorly struck Cross Crosslet coins and continued without alteration, not only to the end of the reign of Henry II in 1189, but throughout the reigns of his sons Richard (1189–99) and John (1199–1216) and the first half of the reign of his grandson Henry III (1216–46). Throughout that 66 year period, however, there were minor variations in portraits and lettering which enable numismatists to attribute the HENRICUS coins to specific reigns and periods.

"Tealby" type penny, left, and "Short Cross" penny of Henry II.

The style and workmanship of the Short Cross coinage deteriorated in the reign of Henry III. By the 1220s coin production was confined to the regal mints at London and Canterbury, the sole exception being the ecclesiastical mint maintained by the Abbot of Bury St Edmunds.

Halfpence and farthings were briefly struck in 1221–30, though halfpence are now extremely rare and so far only a solitary farthing has been discovered.

By the middle of this reign the coinage was in a deplorable state, being poorly struck, badly worn and often ruthlessly clipped. In 1247 Henry ordered a new coinage and in this the arms of the cross on the reverse were extended to the rim as a safeguard against clipping. This established a pattern of facing portrait and long cross on obverse and reverse respectively that was to continue till the beginning of the 16th century. Several provincial mints were re-activated to assist with the recoinage but they were all closed down again by 1250, only the regal mints at London and Canterbury and the ecclesiastical mints at Durham and Bury St Edmunds remaining active.

"Long Cross" pennies of Henry III, left, and Edward I.

In 1257 Henry tentatively introduced a gold penny (worth 20 silver pence and twice the weight of a silver penny). The coin was undervalued and soon disappeared from circulation.

The Long Cross coinage of Henry III continued under Edward I till 1279 when the king introduced a new coinage in his own name. The penny continued the style of its predecessors, though much better designed and executed; but new denominations were now added. Henceforward halfpence and farthings became a regular issue and, at the same time, a fourpenny coin known as the groat (from French *gros*) was briefly introduced (minting ceased in 1282 and was not revived till 1351). Due to the centralisation of coin production the name of the moneyer was now generally dropped, although it lingered on a few years at Bury St Edmunds. The provincial mints were again revived in 1299–1302 to recoin the lightweight foreign imitations of pennies which had flooded in from the Continent.

The coinage of Edward II (1307–27) differed only in minor respects from that of his father, and a similar pattern prevailed in the first years of Edward III. In 1335 halfpence and farthings below the sterling fineness were struck. More importantly, further attempts were made to introduce gold coins. In 1344 the florin or double

Pre-Treaty Noble of Edward III which contained reference to France in the legend.

leopard of six shillings was introduced, along with its half and quarter. This coinage was not successful and was soon replaced by a heavier series based on the noble of 80 pence (6s. 8d.), half a mark or one third of a pound. The noble originally weighed 138.5 grains but it was successively reduced to 120 grains, at which weight it continued from 1351. During this reign the protracted conflict with France known as the Hundred Years' War erupted. Edward III, through his mother, claimed the French throne and inscribed this title on his coins. By the Treaty of Bretigny (1361) Edward temporarily gave up his claim and the reference to France

Noble of Edward IV, issued before he was forced to abandon the throne of England.

was dropped from the coins, but when war was renewed in 1369 the title was resumed, and remained on many English coins until the end of the 18th century. The silver coinage followed the pattern of the previous reign, but in 1351 the groat was re-introduced and with it came the twopence or half-groat. Another innovation was the use of mintmarks at the beginning of the inscriptions. Seven types of cross and one crown were employed from 1334 onwards and their sequence enables numismatists to date coins fairly accurately.

The full range of gold (noble, half-noble and quarter-noble) and silver (groat, half-groat, penny, halfpenny and farthing) continued under Richard II (1377–99). Little attempt was made to alter the facing portrait on the silver coins, by now little more than a stylised caricature anyway.

Noble of Henry IV which was reduced in weight due to the shortage of gold.

Under Henry IV (1399–1413) the pattern of previous reigns prevailed, but in 1412 the weights of the coinage were reduced due to a shortage of bullion. The noble was reduced to 108 grains and its sub-divisions lightened proportionately. The penny was reduced by 3 grains, and its multiples and sub-divisions correspondingly reduced. One interesting change was the reduction of the fleur de lis of France from four to three in the heraldic shield on the reverse of the noble; this change corresponded with the alteration in the arms used in France itself. The Calais mint, opened by Edward III in 1363, was closed in 1411. There was no change in the designs used for the coins of Henry V (1413–22) but greater use was now made of mintmarks to distinguish the various periods of production. Coins were by now produced mainly at London, although the episcopal mints at Durham and York were permitted to strike pennies.

The supply of gold dwindled early in the reign of Henry VI and few nobles were struck after 1426. The Calais mint was re-opened in 1424 and struck a large amount of gold before closing finally in 1440. A regal mint briefly operated at York in 1423–24. Mintmarks were now much more widely used and tended to correspond more closely to the annual trials of the Pyx. The series of civil upheavals known as the Wars of the Roses erupted in this period.

In 1461 Henry VI was deposed by the Yorkist Earl of March after he defeated the Lancastrians at Mortimer's Cross. The Yorkists advanced on London where the victor was crowned Edward IV. At first he continued the gold series of his predecessor, issuing nobles and quarter-nobles, but in 1464 the weight of the penny was reduced

Groat of Richard III (1483–85).

to 12 grains and the value of the noble was raised to 100 pence (8s. 4d.).The ryal or rose-noble of 120 grains, together with its half and quarter, was introduced in 1465 and tariffed at ten shillings or half a pound. The need for a coin worth a third of a pound, however, led to the issue of the angel of 80 grains, worth 6s. 8d., but this was initially unsucessful and very few examples are now extant. The angel derived its name from the figure of the Archangel Michael on the obverse; a cross surmounting a shield appeared on the reverse.

In 1470 Edward was forced to flee to Holland and Henry VI was briefly restored. During this brief period (to April 1471) the ryal was discontinued but a substantial issue of angels and half-angels was made both at London and Bristol. Silver coins were struck at York as well as London and Bristol, the issues of the provincial mints being identified by the initials B or E (Eboracum, Latin for York). Edward defeated

the Lancastrians at Tewkesbury and deposed the luckless Henry once more. In his second reign Edward struck only angels and half-angels as well as silver from the groat to halfpenny. In addition to the three existing mints, silver coins were struck at Canterbury, Durham and the archiepiscopal mint at York. Mintmarks were now much more frequent and varied. Coins with a mark of a halved sun and rose are usually assigned to the reign of Edward IV, but they were probably also struck in the nominal reign of Edward V, the twelve-year-old prince held in the Tower of London under the protection of his uncle Richard, Duke of Gloucester. Coins with this mark on the reverse had an obverse mark of a boar's head, Richard's personal emblem. The brief reign of Richard III (1483–5) came to an end with his defeat at Bosworth and the relatively scarce coins of this period followed the pattern of the previous reigns, distinguished by the sequence of mint marks and the inscription RICAD or RICARD.

In the early years of Henry VII's reign the coinage likewise followed the previous patterns, but in 1489 the first of several radical changes was effected, with the introduction of the gold sovereign of 20 shillings showing a full-length portrait of the monarch seated on an elaborate throne. For reverse, this coin depicted a Tudor rose surmounted by a heraldic shield. A similar reverse appeared on the ryal of 10 shillings, but the angel and angelet retained previous motifs. The silver coins at first adhered to the medieval pattern, with the stylised facing portrait and long cross, but at the beginning of the 16th century a large silver coin, the testoon or shilling of 12 pence, was introduced and adopted a realistic profile of the king, allied to a reverse showing a cross surmounted by the royal arms.

First coinage Angel of Henry VIII which retained the traditional 23.5 carat fineness.

The same design was also used for the later issue of groat and half groat.

This established a pattern which was to continue till the reign of Charles I. In the reign of Henry VIII, however, the coinage was subject to considerable debasement. This led to the eventual introduction of 22 carat (.916 fine) gold for the crown while the traditional 23 ½ carat gold was retained for the angel and ryal. This dual system continued until the angel was discontinued at the outset of the Civil War in 1642; latterly it had been associated with the ceremony of touching for "King's Evil" or scrofula, a ritual used by the early Stuart monarchs to bolster their belief in the divine right of kings.

Under the Tudors and Stuarts the range and complexity of the gold coinage increased, but it was not until the reign of Edward VI that the silver series was expanded. In 1551 he introduced the silver crown of five shillings, the first English coin to bear a clear date on the obverse. Under Mary dates were extended to the shilling and sixpence.

The mixture of dated and undated coins continued under Elizabeth I, a reign remarkable for the range of denominations—nine gold and eight silver. The latter included the sixpence, threepence, threehalfpence and threefarthings, distinguished by the rose which appeared behind the Queen's head.

The coinage of James I was even more complex, reflecting the king's attempts to unite his dominions. The first issue bore the legend ANG: SCO (England and Scotland), but from 1604 this was altered to MAG: BRIT (Great Britain). This period witnessed new denominations, such as the rose-ryal and spur-ryal, the unite, the Britain crown and the thistle crown, and finally the laurel of 20 shillings and its sub-divisions.

In the reign of Elizabeth experiments began with milled coinage under Eloi Mestrell. These continued sporadically in the 17th century, culminating in the beautiful coins struck by Nicholas Briot (1631–39). A branch mint was established at Aberystwyth in 1637 to refine and coin silver from the Welsh mines. Relations between King and Parliament deteriorated in the reign of Charles I and led to the Civil War (1642). Parliament controlled London but continued to strike coins in the King's name. The Royalists struck coins, both in pre-war and new types, at Shrewsbury, Oxford, Bristol, Worcester, Exeter, Chester, Hereford and other Royalist strongholds, while curious siege pieces were pressed into service at Newark, Pontefract and Scarborough.

After the execution of Charles I in 1649 the Commonwealth was proclaimed under Oliver Cromwell. Gold and silver coins were now inscribed in English instead of Latin. Patterns portraying Cromwell and a crowned shield restored Latin in 1656. Plans for milled coinage were already being considered before the Restoration of the monarchy in 1660. Hammered coinage appeared initially, resuming the style of coins under Charles I, but in 1662 the hand-hammering of coins was abandoned in favour of coins struck on the mill and screw press. The hammered coins of 1660–62 were undated and bore a crown mintmark, the last vestiges of medievalism in British coinage.

The magnificent Rose-Ryal of James I.

COIN grading

CONDITION is the secret to the value of virtually anything, whether it be antiques, jewellery, horses or second-hand cars—and coins are *certainly* no exception. When collecting coins it is vital to understand the recognised standard British system of grading, i.e. accurately assessing a coin's condition or state of wear. Grading is an art which can only be learned by experience and so often it remains one person's opinion against another's, therefore it is important for the beginner or inexperienced collector to seek assistance from a reputable dealer or knowledgeable numismatist when making major purchases.

The standard grades as used in this Price Guide are as follows:

UNC **Uncirculated**
A coin that has never been in circulation, although it may show signs of contact with other coins during the minting process.

EF **Extremely Fine**
A coin in this grade may appear uncirculated to the naked eye but on closer examination will show signs of minor friction on the highest surface.

VF **Very Fine**
A coin that has had very little use, but shows signs of wear on the high surfaces.

F **Fine**
A coin that has been in circulation and shows general signs of wear, but with all legends and date clearly visible.

Other grades used in the normal grading system are:

BU **Brilliant Uncirculated**
As the name implies, a coin retaining its mint lustre.

Fair A coin extensively worn but still quite recognisable and legends readable.

Poor A coin very worn and only just recognisable.

Other abbreviations used in the Price Guide are:

Obv **Obverse**

Rev **Reverse**

Other abbreviations, mintmarks, etc. can be identified under the appropriate section of this Yearbook.

Coins illustrated in the following listings are indicated with an asterisk (*)

A SIMPLIFIED PRICE GUIDE
TO
ANCIENT COINS USED IN BRITAIN

PART I
CELTIC

The prices given in this section are those that you would expect to pay from a reputable dealer and not the prices at which you could expect to sell coins.

The list below contains most of the commonly available types: a full comprehensive guide is beyond the scope of this book. Prices are for coins with good surfaces which are not weakly struck or struck from worn dies. Examples which are struck from worn or damaged dies can be worth considerably less. Particularly attractive examples of bronze Celtic coins command a very high premium. Where a price is given for an issue of which there are many varieties, the price is for the most common type.

The illustrations are representative examples only and are indicated by an asterisk (*) in the listings.

	F	VF	EF
UNINSCRIBED COINAGE			
GOLD STATERS			
Gallo-Belgic A	£600	£1,350	£5,000
Gallo-Belgic E (Ambiani)	£135	£250	£375
Chute type	£145	£265	£375
Cheriton type			
normally rather "brassy" metal	£200	£400	£800
Corieltauvi (various types)	£150	£300	£500
Norfolk "wolf" type			
fine gold	£200	£400	£750
brassy gold	£125	£250	£420
very debased	£75	£150	£350
*Whaddon Chase types	£200	£400	£800
Wonersh type	£200	£400	£700
Eceni (various types)	£250	£450	£800
Remic type	£200	£350	£550
Dobunni	£250	£450	£800
GOLD QUARTER STATERS			
North Thames types	£155	£245	£400
North Kent types	£155	£235	£400
Eceni	£145	£200	£350
Sussex types	£100	£175	£300
Dobunni	£150	£250	£500
SILVER COINAGE			
North Thames types	£85	£150	£300
South Thames types	£85	£150	£300
Durotriges full stater			
fine silver	£50	£145	£265
*base silver	£35	£75	£180

Uninscribed Whaddon Chase type gold stater

Uninscribed Durotriges base silver stater

115

	F	VF	EF
Durotriges small silver	£30	£75	£150
Dobunni	£40	£90	£200
(Note—Most examples are base in appearance. Prices for examples with fine surfaces are appreciably higher)			
Corieltauvi	£40	£100	£200
Eceni ("crescent" types)	£30	£65	£125
Eceni ("Norfolk god" types)	£50	£100	£250
Armorican Billon staters	£75	£150	£400

POTIN COINAGE

Kent	£20	£50	£100

BRONZE COINAGE

Durotriges debased stater	£25	£45	£85
*Durotriges cast bronzes	£60	£120	£200
North Thames types. Various issues from:	£40	£90	£400

Durotriges cast bronze

INSCRIBED CELTIC COINAGE

ATTREBATES & REGNI

*Commios			
stater	£550	£1,250	£2,650
Tincomarus			
stater	£420	£850	£1,850
quarter stater	£145	£250	£435
silver unit	£75	£140	£275
silver minim	£155	£285	£525
Eppillus			
quarter stater	£145	£235	£425
silver unit	£75	£145	£300
bronze			Rare
Verica			
stater	£255	£550	£1,000
quarter stater	£155	£275	£420
silver unit	£55	£100	£220
Epaticcus			
stater	£1,000	£2,000	£4,000
*silver unit	£50	£100	£265
silver minim	£55	£110	£275
Caratacos			
silver unit	£165	£320	£465
silver minim	£110	£220	£310

Commios stater

CANTII

Dubnovellaunos			
stater	£280	£565	£900
silver unit	£130	£210	£500
bronze unit	£55	£150	£350
Vosenos			
stater	£1,000	£2,500	£4,500
quarter stater	£265	£565	£1,100
silver unit	£135	£285	£650
bronze unit	£110	£215	£550
Eppillus			
stater	£1,000	£2,000	£4,000
quarter stater	£145	£255	£500
silver unit	£65	£145	£350
bronze unit	£55	£125	£450
Amminus			
silver unit	£155	£320	£650
silver minim	£110	£215	£450
bronze unit	£80	£155	£500

Epaticcus silver unit

DUROTRIGES	F	VF	EF
Crab			
silver	£155	£320	£650
silver minim	£100	£250	£400

TRINOVANTES			
Addedomaros			
stater	£265	£500	£800
quarter stater	£155	£320	£550

Dubnovellaunos			
stater	£255	£455	£775
quarter stater	£155	£310	£550
*bronze unit	£55	£130	£450

Dubnovellaunos bronze unit

CATUVELLAUNI			
Tasciovanos			
*stater	£225	£425	£1,000
quarter stater	£130	£235	£450
silver unit	£80	£165	£375
bronze unit	£55	£135	£350
bronze half unit	£55	£135	£275
Andoco			
stater	£510	£1,250	£2,750
quarter stater	£210	£420	£755
silver unit	£155	£400	£750
bronze	£85	£215	£355
Cunobelin			
*stater	£200	£455	£1,000
quarter stater	£145	£265	£420
silver unit	£85	£165	£360
bronze unit	£65	£145	£320

DOBUNNI			
Anted			
stater	£310	£650	£1,250
silver unit	£55	£120	£300
Eisu			
stater	£450	£750	£1,500
silver unit	£55	£125	£320
Catti			
stater	£255	£520	£1,000
Comux			
stater	£800	£1,650	£3,150
Corio			
stater	£265	£525	£1,000
quarter stater	£200	£355	£625
Boduoc			
stater	£1,000	£2,000	£3,500
silver unit	£200	£500	£850

Tasciovanos stater

ECENI			
Duro			
silver unit	£110	£265	£550
Anted			
stater	£425	£1,000	£2,500
silver unit	£35	£65	£185
silver half unit	£45	£95	£165
Ecen			
silver unit	£35	£65	£185
silver half unit	£45	£95	£185
Saemu			
silver unit	£60	£125	£285
Aesu			
silver unit	£60	£125	£285

Cunobelin stater

	F	VF	EF
Prasutagus			
silver unit	£420	£1,000	£1,850
Ale Sca			
silver unit	£355	£765	£1,550
CORIELTAUVI			
Aunt Cost			
stater	£255	£565	£1,000
silver unit	£85	£185	£315
silver half unit	£85	£160	£300
Esup Asu			
stater	£330	£675	£1,250
silver unit	£155	£310	£550
Vep Corf			
stater	£410	£1,000	£2,150
*silver unit	£80	£185	£300
silver half unit	£100	£215	£450
Dumno Tigir Seno			
stater	£755	£1,850	£3,150
silver unit	£100	£185	£500
Volisios Dumnocoveros			
*stater	£310	£725	£1,550
silver unit	£100	£185	£475
silver half unit	£100	£185	£450
Volisios Dumnovellaunos			
stater	£300	£675	£1,250
silver half unit	£150	£335	£655
Volisios Cartivel			
silver half unit	£300	£620	£1,150
Iat Iso			
silver unit	£155	£420	£1,150

Vep Corf silver unit

Volisios Dumnocoveros stater

Illustrations by courtesy of Chris Rudd.

A SIMPLIFIED PRICE GUIDE
TO
ANCIENT COINS USED IN BRITAIN

PART II
ROMAN BRITAIN

In certain cases, especially with large bronze coins, the price for coins in extremely fine condition are _much_ higher than the price for the same coin in very fine condition as early bronze coins are seldom found in hoards and perfect undamaged examples are rarely available.

The illustrations provided are a representative guide to assist with identification only and are indicated by an asterisk (*) in the listings.

	F	VF	EF
Julius Caesar			
aureus	£1,000	£2,600	£4,250
denarius ("elephant" type)	£120	£265	£450
denarius (with portrait)	£300	£850	£2,500
Mark Anthony			
denarius ("Galley" type)	£65	£125	£375
denarius (with portrait)	£150	£400	£1,850
Augustus			
aureus	£675	£1,850	£3,500
denarius (Caius & Lucius Caesars)	£55	£145	£400
*other types	£65	£185	£650
as	£65	£150	£500
Livia			
Ae as	£95	£285	£850
Tiberius			
aureus	£455	£1,350	£2,600
*denarius	£85	£175	£475
Drusus			
as	£65	£155	£475
Germanicus			
*as	£65	£155	£475
Caligula			
denarius	£365	£685	£1,850
*as	£85	£255	£850
Claudius			
aureus ("DE BRITANN" type)	£950	£2,250	£5,500
denarius similar	£350	£1,000	£2,200
sestertius	£135	£450	£1,650
as	£55	£120	£300
Nero			
aureus	£500	£1,350	£2,850
sestertius	£200	£355	£2,200
as	£65	£150	£550

Augustus

Germanicus

Caligula

	F	VF	EF
Galba			
denarius	£95	£355	£1,000
*sestertius	£185	£425	£3,250
as	£75	£175	£700
Otho			
denarius	£225	£520	£1,850
Vitellius			
denarius	£125	£325	£950
sestertius	£265	£755	£4,250
as	£120	£325	£1,800
Vespasian			
aureus	£675	£1,850	£2,850
sestertius	£120	£285	£655
as	£55	£155	£455
Titus			
aureus	£650	£1,750	£2,850
denarius	£65	£155	£350
as	£75	£185	£450
Domitian			
aureus	£650	£1,550	£3,350
denarius	£50	£65	£225
*sestertius	£90	£325	£1,900
as	£55	£110	£455
Nerva			
aureus	£655	£1,850	£3,850
denarius	£65	£150	£400
as	£65	£175	£585
Trajan			
aureus	£520	£1,365	£2,850
denarius	£50	£75	£200
sestertius	£75	£195	£565
as	£45	£80	£365
Hadrian			
aureus	£575	£1,365	£2,850
denarius	£55	£85	£200
as	£60	£125	£330
Sabina			
denarius	£55	£95	£300
*sestertius	£85	£220	£825
as	£50	£155	£385
Aelius			
denarius	£70	£155	£380
sestertius	£110	£265	£1,000
as	£50	£155	£615
Antoninus Pius			
denarius	£26	£55	£155
sestertius	£48	£120	£475
as	£38	£70	£285
Faustina Senior			
denarius	£32	£65	£155
sestertius	£38	£115	£565
as	£32	£75	£285
Marcus Aurelius			
*denarius	£30	£55	£155
sestertius	£55	£135	£565
as	£35	£75	£275
Faustina Junior			
*denarius	£30	£55	£150
sestertius	£45	£120	£535
as	£30	£65	£275
Lucius Verus			
denarius	£30	£75	£185
sestertius	£55	£160	£750
as	£50	£145	£365

Galba

Domitian

Sabina

Marcus Aurelius

Faustina Junior

	F	VF	EF
Lucilla			
denarius	£35	£80	£275
sestertius	£45	£140	£565
as	£34	£70	£275
Commodus			
denarius	£28	£60	£155
*sestertius	£42	£155	£675
as	£34	£78	£325
Crispina			
denarius	£38	£85	£255
Pertinax			
*denarius	£215	£625	£1,650
Didius Julianus			
denarius	£455	£1,000	£2,150
Clodius Albinus			
denarius	£65	£185	£425
sestertius	£85	£315	£1,300
Septimius Severus			
denarius	£25	£45	£115
denarius (VICT BRIT)	£48	£100	£195
sestertius	£70	£225	£650
as	£55	£135	£350
Julia Domna			
denarius	£22	£50	£90
sestertius	£80	£265	£900
as	£48	£135	£465
Caracalla			
*denarius	£28	£50	£100
denarius (VICT BRIT)	£48	£95	£200
sestertius	£85	£215	£750
as	£46	£95	£375
Plautilla			
denarius	£48	£95	£225
Geta			
denarius	£28	£55	£125
denarius (VICT BRIT)	£55	£125	£235
sestertius	£65	£225	£655
as	£55	£135	£375
Macrinus			
denarius	£60	£145	£285
*sestertius	£115	£300	£850
Diadumenian			
*denarius	£125	£250	£475
Elagabalus			
antoninianus	£50	£120	£225
denarius	£30	£55	£125
Julia Paula			
denarius	£60	£150	£300
Aquilla Severa			
denarius	£145	£265	£550
Julia Soaemias			
denarius	£28	£65	£135
Julia Maesa			
denarius	£28	£55	£125
Severus Alexander			
*denarius	£26	£55	£120
sestertius	£32	£75	£245
as	£30	£55	£175
Orblana			
denarius	£120	£235	£550
Julia Mamaea			
denarius	£30	£55	£150

Commodus

Pertinax

Caracalla

Macrinus

Diadumenian

Severus Alexander

	F	VF	EF
Maximinus I			
denarius	£28	£50	£100
*sestertius	£42	£80	£300
as	£42	£80	£250
Maximus			
denarius	£135	£265	£475
sestertius	£75	£150	£420
Balbinus			
denarius	£125	£255	£475
Papienus			
denarius	£125	£255	£475
Gordian III			
antoninianus	£20	£30	£60
denarius	£22	£40	£85
sestertius	£22	£60	£150
Philip I			
antoninianus	£20	£30	£60
*sestertius	£22	£75	£185
Otacilla Severa			
antoniniaus	£20	£30	£60
sestertius	£35	£80	£265
Philip II			
antoninianus	£20	£28	£65
Trajan Decius			
antoninianus	£20	£28	£65
Herennius Etruscus			
antoninianus	£22	£55	£135
Hostilian			
antoninianus	£50	£115	£265
Trebonianus Gallus			
antoninianus	£20	£28	£65
Volusian			
antoninianus	£20	£32	£80
Aemillan			
*antoninianus	£55	£135	£255
Valerian I			
antoninianus	£20	£28	£60
Gallienus			
*silver antoninianus	£15	£28	£48
Ae antoninianus	£12	£20	£40
Salonina			
Ae antoninianus	£12	£20	£40
Valerian II			
billon antoninianus	£18	£32	£100
Saloninus			
antoninianus	£18	£38	£125
Macrianus			
billon antoninianus	£38	£85	£175
Quietus			
billon antoninianus	£38	£85	£175
Postumus			
silver antoninianus	£12	£24	£55
*Ae antoninianus	£10	£18	£30
Laelianus			
antoninianus	£155	£285	£500
Marius			
antoninianus	£42	£90	£185
Victorinus			
Ae antoninianus	£10	£20	£35
Claudius II Gothicus			
Ae antoninianus	£10	£20	£35
Tetricus I			
Ae antoninianus	£10	£20	£35

Maximinus

Philip I

Aemillian

Gallienus

Postumus

	F	VF	EF
Tetricus II			
Ae antoninianus	£8	£20	£45
Quintillus			
*Ae antoninianus	£10	£22	£75
Aurelian			
Ae antoninianus	£8	£20	£50
Severina			
*Ae antoninianus	£12	£28	£70
Tacitus			
Ae antoninianus	£10	£25	£65
Florian			
Ae antoninianus	£42	£85	£175
Probus			
Ae antoninianus	£8	£18	£40
Carus			
Ae antoninianus	£15	£28	£75
Numerian			
Ae antoninianus	£15	£28	£75
Carinus			
Ae antoninianus	£15	£28	£75
Diocletian			
Ae follis (London mint)	£20	£40	£85
Ae follis (other mints)	£15	£28	£65
Maximianus			
Ae follis (London mint)	£20	£40	£85
*Ae follis (other mints)	£15	£28	£65
Carausius			
denarius	£255	£775	£1,550
antoninianus	£30	£70	£225
Allectus			
antoninianus	£30	£80	£275
quinarius	£25	£65	£200
Constantius I.			
Ae follis (London mint)	£25	£60	£125
Ae follis (other mints)	£15	£27	£55
Galerius			
Ae follis (London mint)	£20	£40	£85
Ae follis (other mints)	£15	£27	£50
Galeria Valeria			
follis	£35	£75	£200
Severus II			
Ae follis (London mint)	£65	£135	£275
*Ae follis (other mints)	£35	£85	£200
Maximinus II			
Ae follis (London mint)	£25	£55	£115
*Ae follis (other mints)	£15	£28	£55
Maxentius			
follis	£12	£22	£50
Licinius I			
follis	£12	£20	£45
Ae 3	£8	£15	£40
Licinius II			
Ae 3	£10	£20	£50
Constantine I			
follis (London mint)	£15	£28	£60
follis (other mints)	£8	£16	£40
Ae 3	£8	£15	£40
Fausta			
Ae 3 (London mint)	£100	£180	£325
Ae 3 (other mints)	£18	£50	£115
Helena			
*Ae 3 (London mint)	£115	£185	£350
Ae 3 (other mints)	£20	£50	£115

Quintillus

Severina

Maximianus

Severus II

Maximinus II

Helena

	F	VF	EF
Theodora			
Ae 4	£12	£20	£55
Crispus			
*Ae 3	£10	£18	£50
Deimatius			
Ae 3/4	£15	£28	£75
Hanniballianus			
Ae 4	£130	£250	£450
Constantine II			
Ae 3	£10	£18	£45
Ae 4	£8	£15	£35
Constans			
*centenionalis	£15	£25	£65
Ae 4	£8	£15	£25
Constantius II			
*siliqua	£30	£60	£150
centenionalis	£12	£20	£50
Ae 4	£8	£15	£25
Magnentius			
double centenionalis	£35	£70	£160
centenionalis	£18	£28	£85
Decentius			
double centenionalis	£45	£95	£250
centenionalis	£20	£40	£125
Constantius Gallus			
centenionalis	£12	£28	£65
Julian II			
*siliqua	£25	£55	£125
Ae 1	£65	£150	£355
Ae 3 (helmeted bust)	£18	£45	£115
Jovian			
Ae 1	£50	£120	£275
Ae 3	£18	£45	£115
Valentinian I			
gold solidus	£155	£300	£575
siliqua	£30	£60	£135
Ae 3	£10	£20	£50
Valens			
gold solidus	£155	£300	£575
*siliqua	£25	£65	£135
Ae 3	£10	£20	£50
Gratian			
*siliqua	£28	£65	£145
Ae 3	£10	£20	£50
Valentinian II			
siliqua	£28	£65	£144
Ae 2	£15	£30	£75
Ae 4	£10	£18	£35
Theodosius I			
siliqua	£28	£75	£145
Magnus Maximus			
solidus	£755	£1,850	£4,250
siliqua	£45	£115	£185
*Ae 2	£25	£80	£145

Crispus

Constans

Constantius II

Julian II

Valens

Gratian

Magnus Maximus

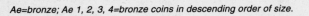

Ae=bronze; Ae 1, 2, 3, 4=bronze coins in descending order of size.

Illustrations by courtesy of Classical Numismatic Group/Seaby Coins.

A SIMPLIFIED PRICE GUIDE
TO
ENGLISH HAMMERED COINS
1066–1663

PART I
1066–1485

INTRODUCTION

In this section we give an approximate price guide that one could expect to pay for the more commonly-located hammered coins in gold and silver. Although coins were struck in England for up to 1,000 years before the Norman Conquest, 1066–1663 provides a useful historical period with which most new collectors can associate.

PRICING

The prices given in the following pages are intended to be used as a "Pocket book guide" to the values of the *most common* coins within any denomination of any one reign. The price quoted is what a collector may expect to pay for such a piece in the condition indicated. For more detailed information we recommend the reader to one of the many specialist publications.

GRADING

The prices quoted are for three different grades of condition: Fine (F), Very Fine (VF) and Extremely Fine (EF). A "Fine" coin is assumed to be a fairly worn, circulated, piece but with all or most of the main features and lettering still clear. "Very Fine" is a middle grade with a small amount of wear and most details fairly clear. For this edition we have included the prices for coins in Extremely Fine condition where appropriate, although very few hammered coins actually turn up in this grade (i.e. nearly mint state with hardly any wear). In some instances the prices quoted are theoretically based and are only included to provide a guide. It is important to note that on all hammered coins the very nature of striking, i.e. individually, by hand, means hammered coinage is rarely a straight grade and when listed by a dealer the overall condition will often be qualified by terms such as: *weak in parts, struck off-centre, cracked or chipped flan, double struck*, etc. When applicable the price should be adjusted accordingly.

HISTORY

Below the heading for each monarch we have given a few historical notes as and when they apply to significant changes in the coinage.

WILLIAM I
(1066–87)

The Norman Conquest had very little immediate effect on the coinage of England. The Anglo-Saxon standard of minting silver pennies was very high and the practise of the moneyer putting his name and mint town on the reverse continued as before, except with William's portrait of course. It is worth noting here that non-realistic, stylised portraits were used until the reign of Henry VII.

There are eight major types of William I penny of which the last, the PAXS type, is by far the commonest.

	F	VF	EF
William I, Penny	£100	£200	£350

WILLIAM II
(1087–1100)

Very little change from his father's reign except that five new types were issued, most of which were much more crudely designed than previous, all are scarce.

	F	VF	EF
William II, Penny	£300	£650	—

HENRY I
(1100–35)

There are fifteen different types of penny for this reign of which the last two are the most common. Most issues are of a very poor standard both in workmanship and metal, the prices reflect a poor quality of issue.

	F	VF	EF
Henry I, Penny	£100	£250	—

STEPHEN
(1135–54)

This is historically a very complicated time for the coinage, mainly due to civil war and a consequential lack of central control in the country which resulted in very poor quality and deliberately damaged pieces. Coins were struck not only in the name of Stephen and his main rival claimant Matilda but also by their supporters. The commonest issue is the "Watford" type; so named, as are many issues, after the area in which a hoard was found.

	F	VF	EF
Stephen, Penny	£130	£300	—

HENRY II
(1154–89)

There were two distinct issues struck during this reign. The first, Cross and Crosslets or "Tealby" coinage (named after Tealby in Lincolnshire), continued to be very poorly made and lasted 20 years. However, in 1180 the new and superior "Short Cross" issue commenced, being issued from only twelve major towns.

	F	VF	EF
Henry II, Penny, Tealby	£60	£140	—

	F	VF	EF
Henry II, Penny, Short Cross	£35	£80	£200

RICHARD I
(1189–1199)

There were no major changes during this reign, in fact pennies continued to be struck with his father Henry's name throughout the reign. The coins struck under Richard tend to be rather crude in style.

	F	VF	EF
Richard I, Penny	£40	£120	£300

JOHN
(1199–1216)

As with his brother before him, there were no major changes during the reign of King John, and pennies with his father's name were struck throughout the reign, although they tended to be somewhat neater in style than those struck during the reign of Richard I.

	F	VF	EF
John, Penny	£30	£65	£135

HENRY III
(1216–72)

The coinage during Henry III's reign continued as before with the short cross issue. However, in 1247 a new long cross design was introduced to prevent clipping. This design was to last in one form or another for many centuries.

	F	VF	EF
Henry III, Penny, Short Cross	£15	£40	£100
Henry III, Penny, Long Cross	£15	£30	£70

EDWARD I
(1272–1307)

After a few years of issuing similar pieces to his father, in 1279 Edward I ordered a major re-coinage. This consisted of well-made pennies, halfpennies and farthings in relatively large quantities, and for a brief period a groat (four pence) was produced. The pennies are amongst the most common of all hammered coins.

	F	VF	EF
Edward I (and Edward II)			
Groat (often damaged)	£950	£3,250	—
Penny	£15	£30	£60
Halfpenny	£20	£45	£135
Farthing	£15	£30	£110

Edward I halfpenny

EDWARD II
(1307–1327)

The coinage of Edward II differs in only a very few minor details from that of Edward I and are of similar value.

EDWARD III
(1327–77)

This was a long reign which saw major changes in the coinage, the most significant being the introduction of a gold coinage (based on the Noble, valued at 6s 8d, and its fractions) and a regular issue of a large silver groat (and half groat). The mints were limited to a few episcopal cities but coins of English type were also struck in the newly-acquired Calais.

	F	VF	EF
Gold			
Noble	£350	£700	£1,350
Half Noble	£250	£500	£950
Quarter Noble	£150	£300	£550
Silver			
Groat	£40	£100	£275
Half Groat	£20	£50	£150
Penny	£15	£35	£115
Half Penny	£15	£35	£100
Farthing	£30	£60	£140

Gold Noble

RICHARD II
(1377–1399)

The denominations continued during this reign much as before. However, coins are quite rare mainly due to the lack of bullion gold and silver going into the mints, mainly because of an inbalance with European weights and fineness.

	F	VF	EF
Gold			
Noble	£500	£1,000	£2,400
Half Noble	£600	£1,200	—
Quarter Noble	£275	£525	£850
Silver			
Groat	£220	£575	—
Half Groat	£160	£400	—
Penny	£50	£140	—
Half Penny	£25	£75	—
Farthing	£900	£200	—

Groat

HENRY IV
(1399–1413)

Because of the continuing problems with the scarcity of gold and silver the coinage was reduced in weight in 1412, towards the end of the reign. All coins of this reign are quite scarce.

	F	VF
Gold		
Noble	£900	£2,000
Half Noble	£2,150	£5,000
Quarter Noble	£385	£800
Silver		
Groat	£1,300	£3,450
Half Groat	£425	£925
Penny	£165	£525
Half Penny	£135	£300
Farthing	£475	£1000

Noble

HENRY V
(1413–22)

Monetary reform introduced towards the end of his father's reign in 1412 improved the supply of bullion and hence coins of Henry V are far more common. All of the main denominations continued as before.

	F	VF	EF
Gold			
Noble	£400	£800	£1,600
Half Noble	£375	£775	—
Quarter Noble	£225	£500	£800
Silver			
Groat	£85	£185	—
Half Groat	£70	£175	—
Penny	£25	£70	—
Half Penny	£20	£50	—
Farthing	£115	£300	—

Half Groat

HENRY VI
(1422–61 and again 1470–71)

Although there were no new denominations during these reigns (see Edward IV below), Henry's first reign saw eleven different issues, each for a few years and distinguished by privy marks, i.e. crosses, pellets, annulets, etc.

HENRY VI *continued*

Gold

	F	VF	EF
First reign—			
Noble	£375	£750	£1,500
Half Noble	£240	£500	£1000
Quarter Noble	£160	£300	£550
2nd reign—			
Angel	£700	£1,750	£2,750
Half Angel	£1,500	£3,500	—

Silver

	F	VF	EF
Groat	£30	£60	£150
Half Groat	£25	£45	£120
Penny	£20	£50	£110
Half Penny	£15	£35	£90
Farthing	£85	£200	—

Groat

EDWARD IV
(1461–70 and again 1471–83)

The significant changes during these reigns were the replacement of the noble by the rose Ryal (and revalued at 10s) and the introduction of the angel at the old noble value. We also start to see mint-marks or initial marks appearing, usually at the top of the coin, they were used to denote the period of issue for dating purposes and often lasted for 2–3 years.

Gold

	F	VF	EF
Ryal	£350	£750	£1,350
Half Ryal	£280	£600	£100
Quarter Ryal	£200	£440	£750
Angel	£280	£600	£1,200
Half Angel	£265	£525	£1,000

Silver

	F	VF	EF
Groat	£35	£90	£225
Half Groat	£30	£70	£185
Penny	£20	£60	£150
Half Penny	£20	£60	—
Farthing	£350	£550	—

Gold Ryal

RICHARD III
(1483–85)

The close of the Yorkist Plantagenet and the beginning of the Medieval period come together at this time. There are no new significant numismatic changes but most coins of Richard whilst not really rare, continue to be very popular and priced quite high.

Gold

	F	VF	EF
Angel	£1000	£2,250	—
Half Angel	£2,350	£5,500	—

Silver

	F	VF	EF
Groat	£300	£600	£1,350
Half Groat	£450	£925	—
Penny	£150	£400	—
Half Penny	£110	£285	—
Farthing	£725	£1,850	—

Groat

PART II: 1485–1663

Among the more significant features of the post-Renaissance period as it affected coinage is the introduction of realistic portraiture during the reign of Henry VII. We also have a much wider and varied number of new and revised denominations, for example eleven different gold denominations of Henry VIII and the same number of silver for Elizabeth I. Here we only mention the introduction or changes in the main denominations, giving a value for all of them, once again listing the commonest type.

HENRY VII
(1485–1509)

The gold sovereign of 20 shillings makes its first appearance in 1489 as does the testoon (later shilling) in about 1500. The silver penny was re-designed to a rather crude likeness of the sovereign.

	F	VF	EF
Gold			
Sovereign	£6,750	£14,500	—
Ryal	£7,000	£18,000	—
Angel	£300	£600	£1100
Half Angel	£225	£475	£950
Silver			
Testoon 1/-	£5,000	£9,500	—
Groat	£45	£125	£350
Half Groat	£25	£60	£200
Penny	£25	£65	£150
Half Penny	£20	£55	—
Farthing	£125	£350	—

Profile Groat

Sovereign-style penny

HENRY VIII
(1509–47)

After a long initial period of very little change in the coinage, in 1526 there were many, with an attempt to bring the gold/silver ratio in line with the continental currencies. Some gold coins only lasted a short time and are very rare. The crown (in gold) makes its first appearance. Towards the end of the reign we see large issues of debased silver coins (with a high copper content) bearing the well-known facing portrait of the ageing King. These tend to turn up in poor condition.

Gold			
Sovereign	£1,700	£3,800	—
Half Sovereign	£300	£675	—
Angel	£275	£575	£1000
Half Angel	£225	£500	£900
Quarter Angel	£260	£550	—
George Noble	£3,000	£7,000	—
Half George Noble	Rare	Rare	—
Crown of the rose	Rare	Rare	—
Crown of the double rose	£275	£550	£1000
Half Crown of the double rose	£300	£650	—
Silver			
Testoon 1/-	£500	£1,600	—
Groat	£50	£130	£325
Half Groat	£30	£85	£200
Penny	£30	£80	£150
Half Penny	£25	£60	—
Farthing	£250	£600	—

Facing Groat

Crown of the double rose

EDWARD VI
(1547–53)

Some of the coins struck in the first few years of this short reign could really be called Henry VIII posthumous issues as there is continuity in both name and style from his father's last issue. However, overlapping this period are portrait issues of the boy King, particularly shillings (usually poor quality coins). This period also sees the first dated English coin (shown in Roman numerals). In 1551 however, a new coinage was introduced with a restored silver quality from the Crown (dated 1551) down to the new sixpence and threepence.

	F	VF	EF
Gold			
Sovereign (30s)	£2,000	£4,500	—
Half Sovereign	£600	£1,350	—
Crown	£775	£1,750	—
Half Crown	£750	£1,650	—
Angel	£3,250	£8,500	—
Half Angel	—	—	—
Sovereign (20s)	£1,250	£3,000	—
Silver			
Crown	£350	£800	—
Half Crown	£300	£650	—
Shilling	£70	£200	£500
Sixpence	£80	£250	—
Groat	£500	£1,300	—
Threepence	£130	£425	—
Half Groat	£200	£500	—
Penny	£45	£150	—
Half Penny	£150	£425	—
Farthing	£600	2000	—

Base Shilling, obverse

Fine Shilling

MARY
(1553–54)

The early coins of Mary's sole reign are limited and continue to use the same denominations as Edward, except that the gold Ryal was reintroduced.

	F	VF
Gold		
Sovereign (30s)	£2,200	£5,500
Ryal	£7,500	—
Angel	£675	£1,500
Half Angel	£1,800	£4,500
Silver		
Groat	£75	£240
Half Groat	£550	£1,400
Penny	£375	£1000

Groat

PHILIP & MARY
(1554–58)

After a very short reign alone, Mary married Philip of Spain and they technically ruled jointly (although not for very long in practise) until her death. After her marriage we see both her and Philip on the shillings and sixpences.

	F	VF
Gold		
Angel	£1,750	£4,000
Half Angel	£4,500	—
Silver		
Shilling	£185	£650
Sixpence	£200	£675
Groat	£80	£275
Half Groat	£275	£700
Penny	£60	£185

Shilling

ELIZABETH I
(1558–1603)

As might be expected with a long reign there are a number of significant changes in the coinage which include several new denominations—so many in silver that every value from the shilling downwards was marked and dated to distinguish them. Early on we have old base Edward VI shillings countermarked to a new reduced value (not priced here). Also due to a lack of small change and the expense of making a miniscule farthing we have a new threehalfpence and threefarthings. Finally we see the beginnings of a milled (machine produced) coinage for a brief period from 1561–71.

	F	VF	EF
Gold			
Sovereign (30s)	£1,750	£4,000	—
Ryal (15s)	£3,250	£8,250	—
Angel	£350	£750	—
Half Angel	£350	£700	—
Quarter Angel	£300	£625	—
Pound (20s)	£775	£1,800	£3,500
Half Pound	£500	£1100	—
Crown	£500	£1000	—
Half Crown	£475	£950	—
Silver			
Crown	£575	£1,300	£3,500
Half Crown	£325	£800	—
Shilling	£60	£180	£500
Sixpence	£40	£110	£275
Groat	£40	£125	£200
Threepence	£30	£90	£170
Half Groat	£20	£50	—
Threehalfpence	£25	£85	—
Penny	£20	£60	£135
Threefarthings	£50	£135	—
Half Penny	£20	£50	£90

Shilling

Milled Sixpence

JAMES I
(1603–25)

Although the size of the gold coinage remains much the same as Elizabeth's reign, the name and weight or value of the denominations have several changes, i.e. Pound = Sovereign = Unite = Laurel. A new four shilling gold coin (thistle crown) was introduced. A number of the silver coins now have their value in Roman numerals on the coin. Relatively few angels were made from this period onwards and they are usually found pierced.

	F	VF	EF
Gold			
Sovereign (20s)	£700	£1,700	—
Unite	£300	£575	£1,200
Double crown/half unite	£325	£475	£950
Crown	£140	£300	£650
Thistle Crown	£160	£350	£650
Half Crown	£140	£260	—
Rose Ryal (30s)	£955	£2,250	—
Spur Ryal (15s)	£1,800	£4,750	—
Angel (pierced)	£300	£625	—
Half Angel (Unpierced)	£1,300	£3,500	—
Laurel	£240	£475	£1100
Half Laurel	£200	£425	£900
Quarter Laurel	£140	£260	£500
Silver			
Crown	£256	£650	—
Half Crown	£125	£325	—
Shilling	£50	£175	—
Sixpence	£50	£165	—
Half Groat	£20	£50	£80
Penny	£20	£40	£70
Half Penny	£15	£30	£50

Half Groat

Shilling

CHARLES I
(1625–49)

This reign is probably the most difficult to simplify as there are so many different issues and whole books have been produced on this period alone. From the beginning of the King's reign and throughout the Civil War, a number of mints operated for varying lengths of time, producing both regular and irregular issues. The Tower mint was taken over by Parliament in 1642 but before this a small quantity of milled coinage was produced alongside the regular hammered issues. The Court then moved to Oxford from where, for the next three years, large quantities of gold and silver were struck (including rare triple unites and large silver pounds). The most prolific of the provincial mints were those situated at Aberystwyth, York, Oxford, Shrewsbury, Bristol, Exeter, Truro, Chester and Worcester as well as some smaller mints mainly situated in the West Country. Among the more interesting coins of the period are the pieces struck on unusually-shaped flans at Newark and Pontefract whilst those towns were under siege. As many of the coins struck during the Civil War were crudely struck on hastily gathered bullion and plate, they provide a fascinating area of study. The prices indicated below are the minimum for the commonest examples of each denomination irrespective of town of origin.

	F	VF	EF
Gold			
Triple Unite (£3)	£2,200	£6,000	—
Unite	£260	£575	—
Double crown/Half unite	£235	£500	—
Crown	£140	£300	—
Angel (pierced)	£400	£875	—
Silver			
Pound (20 shillings)	£950	£2,300	—
Half Pound	£400	£900	—
Crown	£235	£500	—
Half Crown	£40	£120	—
Shilling	£30	£90	£350
Sixpence	£30	£115	£300
Groat	£40	£90	£180
Threepence	£40	£75	£165
Half Groat	£15	£35	£85
Penny	£12	£28	£75
Half Penny	£12	£25	£50

Many of the coins of Charles' reign, particularly those produced during the Civil War, are poorly struck. However, the sixpence shown above is a superb example with a good portrait.

The siege coins of Newark, Pontefract and Scarborough are keenly sought.

THE COMMONWEALTH
(1649–60)

After the execution of Charles I, Parliament changed the design of the coinage. They are simple non portrait pieces with an English legend.

	F	VF	EF
Gold			
Unite	£450	£925	£1,800
Double crown/Half unite	£375	£750	£1,500
Crown	£350	£650	£1,250
Silver			
Crown	£350	£675	£1,400
Half Crown	£125	£325	£800
Shilling	£80	£185	£450
Sixpence	£75	£175	£425
Half Groat	£25	£60	£125
Penny	£25	£50	£120
Half Penny	£25	£50	£95

Unite

CHARLES II
(1660–85)

Although milled coins had been produced for Oliver Cromwell in 1656–58, after the Restoration of the monarchy hammered coins continued to be produced until 1663, when the machinery was ready to manufacture large quantities of good milled pieces.

	F	VF	EF
Gold			
Unite	£675	£1,600	—
Double crown/Half unite	£525	£1300	—
Crown	£550	£1,400	—
Silver			
Half Crown	£115	£375	—
Shilling	£80	£250	—
Sixpence	£75	£225	—
Fourpence	£25	£65	£90
Threepence	£25	£60	£90
Twopence	£20	£40	£55
Penny	£25	£50	£90

Halfcrown

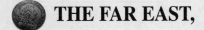

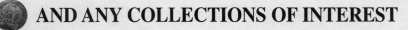

A COMPREHENSIVE PRICE GUIDE
TO THE COINS OF

THE
UNITED KINGDOM
1656–1999

including

ENGLAND
SCOTLAND
ISLE OF MAN
GUERNSEY, JERSEY, ALDERNEY

and

IRELAND

When referring to this price guide one must bear a number of important points in mind. The points listed here have been taken into consideration during the preparation of this guide and we hope that the prices given will provide a true reflection of the market at the time of going to press. Nevertheless, the publishers can accept no liability for the accuracy of the prices quoted.

1. "As struck" examples with flaws will be worth less than the indicated price.
2. Any coin in superb state will command a higher price.
3. These prices refer strictly to the British market, and do not reflect outside opinions.
4. Some prices given for coins not seen in recent years are estimates based on a knowledge of   the market.
5. In the case of coins of high rarity, prices are not generally given.
6. In the listing, "—" indicates, where applicable, one of the following:
     a. Metal or bullion value only
     b. Not usually found in this grade
     c. Not collected in this condition
7. Proof coins are listed in FDC under the UNC column.
8. All prices are quoted in £ sterling, exclusive of VAT (where applicable).

FIVE GUINEAS

	F	VF	EF

CHARLES II (1660–85)

	F	VF	EF
1668 First bust	£1000	£2000	£7000
1668 — Elephant	£1000	£2000	£7500
1669 —	£1000	£2100	—
1669 — Elephant	£1600	—	—
*1670 —	£1000	£2000	£7000
1671 —	£1000	£2100	—
1672 —	£1000	£2000	£7000
1673 —	£1000	£2000	£7000
1674 —	£1000	£2000	£7500
1675 —	£1000	£2000	£7000
1675 — Elephant	£1600		
1675 — Elephant & Castle		Extremely rare	
1676 —	£1050	£1100	—
1676 — Elephant & Castle	£1000	£2100	—
1677 —	£1000	£2100	—
1677/5 —		Extremely rare	
1677 — Elephant & Castle	£1050	£2100	—
1678 —	£1000	£2000	£6500
1678 — Elephant & Castle	£1200	£2300	—
1678 Second bust	£1200	£2300	—
1679 —	£1000	£2000	£6500
1680 —	£1000	£2000	£7000
1680 — Elephant & Castle		Extremely rare	
1681 —	£1000	£2000	£6500
1681 — Elephant & Castle	£1200	£2300	—
1682 —	£1000	£2000	£6500
1682 — Elephant & Castle	£1000	£2000	—
1683 —	£1000	£2000	£6500
1683 — Elephant & Castle	£1200	£2300	—
1684 —	£1000	£2000	£6500

JAMES II (1685–88)

	F	VF	EF
1686	£1000	£1950	£6000
1687	£1150	£2100	£6500
1687 Elephant & Castle	£1000	£1850	£6000
1688	£1150	£2100	£6500
1688 Elephant & Castle	£1150	£2100	£6500

WILLIAM AND MARY (1688–94)

	F	VF	EF
*1691	£1000	£1950	£5000
1691 Elephant & Castle	£1100	£2000	£5250
1692	£1000	£1950	£5000
1692 Elephant & Castle	£1250	£2100	£5500
1693	£1000	£1950	£5000
1693 Elephant & Castle	£1250	£2100	£5750
1694	£1000	£1950	£5000
1694 Elephant & Castle	£1250	£2000	£5500

WILLIAM III (1694–1702)

	F	VF	EF
1699 First bust	£1000	£1950	£4500
1699 — Elephant & Castle	£1100	£2000	£4500
1700 —	£1000	£1950	£4500
1701 Second bust "fine work"	£1200	£2300	£5000

ANNE (1702–14)

Pre-Union with Scotland

	F	VF	EF
1703 VIGO below bust		Extremely rare	

	F	VF	EF
*1705	£1250	£2500	£6750
1706	£1250	£2350	£6500
Post-Union altered shields			
1706	£1000	£1700	£5000
1709 Broader shields	£1050	£1850	£5500
1711 Broader bust	£1000	£1700	£5000
1713 —	£1050	£1800	£5500
1714 —	£1000	£1700	£5000

GEORGE I (1714–27)

	F	VF	EF
1716	£1250	£2600	£7000
1717	£1250	£2800	£7500
1720	£1250	£2600	£7000
1726	£1250	£2600	£7000

GEORGE II (1727–60)

	F	VF	EF
1729 Young head	£1000	£1700	£4200
1729 — E.I.C. below head	£1000	£1700	£4200
1731 —	£1050	£1750	£4600
1735 —	£1050	£1750	£4600
1738 —	£1000	£1700	£4400
1741 —	£950	£1700	£4200
1746 Old head, LIMA	£1050	£1800	£4600
1748 —	£950	£1700	£4200
1753 —	£950	£1700	£4200

GEORGE III (1760–1820)

	F	VF	EF
1770 Patterns	—	—	£35000
1773	—	—	£35000
1777	—	—	£35000

TWO GUINEAS

	F	VF	EF

CHARLES II (1660–85)

	F	VF	EF
1664 First bust	£450	£1400	—
*1664 — Elephant	£400	£900	£4500
1665 —		Extremely rare	
1669 —		Extremely rare	
1671 —	£500	£1700	—
1675 Second bust	£450	£1500	—
1676 —	£450	£1300	—
1676 — Elephant & Castle	£450	£1300	—
1677 —	£450	£1100	£4500
1677 — Elephant & Castle		Extremely rare	
1678 —	£450	£1100	—
1678 — Elephant		Extremely rare	
1678 — Elephant & Castle	£475	£1350	—
1679 —	£450	£1300	—
1680 —	£550	£1800	—
1681 —	£450	£1250	£4000
1682 — Elephant & Castle	£450	£1300	—
1683 —	£425	£1350	£4000
1683 — Elephant & Castle	£750	—	—
1684 —	£450	£1350	—
1684 — Elephant & Castle	£600	£1700	—

JAMES II (1685–88)

	F	VF	EF
1687	£500	£1150	£4000
*1688/7	£525	£1400	£4500

WILLIAM AND MARY (1688–94)

	F	VF	EF
1691 Elephant & Castle		Extremely rare	
1693	£475	£1200	£3500
1693 Elephant & Castle	£525	£1300	£4000
1694	£475	£1200	£3500
1694 Elephant & Castle	£525	£1375	£3850

WILLIAM III (1694–1702)

	F	VF	EF
1701 "fine work"	£575	£1800	£4500

ANNE (1702–14)

	F	VF	EF
1709	£450	£1050	£3500
1711	£450	£1050	£3000
1713	£450	£1050	£3500
1714	£450	£1150	£3800

GEORGE I (1714–27)

	F	VF	EF
1717	£450	£1200	£4000
1720	£475	£1250	£4500
*1726	£450	£1200	£4000

	F	VF	EF

GEORGE II (1727–60)

	F	VF	EF
1734 Young head	£750	£2000	—
1735 —	£350	£750	£2500
*1738 —	£300	£650	£1700
1739 —	£300	£700	£1750
1739 Intermediate head	£300	£600	£1500
1740 —	£300	£650	£1800
1748 Old head	£325	£750	£2100
1753 —	£500	£1400	—

GEORGE III (1760–1820)

	F	VF	EF
1768 Patterns only	—	—	£12000
1773 Patterns only	—	—	£12000
1777 Patterns only	—	—	£12000

GUINEAS

CHARLES II (1660–85)

	F	VF	EF
1663 First bust	£550	£1600	—
1663 — Elephant below	£550	£1600	—
1664 Second bust	£400	£1200	—
1664 — Elephant		Extremely rare	
1664 Third bust	£300	£825	£3250
1664 — Elephant	£325	£1000	£3950
1665 —	£300	£725	£3250
1665 — Elephant	£350	£1000	£4000
1666 —	£275	£850	£3250
1667 —	£300	£825	£3250
1668 —	£300	£800	£3250
1668 — Elephant		Extremely rare	
1669 —	£350	£1100	—
*1670 —	£300	£800	£3250
1671 —	£300	£800	£3250
1672 —	£350	£1100	—
1672 Fourth bust	£240	£675	£3000
1673 Third bust	£400	£1400	—
1673 Fourth bust	£300	£750	£3000
1674 —	£300	£1100	—
1674 — Elephant & Castle	£2500	—	—
1675 —	£275	£750	£3250
*1675 — Elephant & Castle	£350	£1250	—
1676 —	£250	£675	£2750
1676 — Elephant & Castle	£325	£1000	£3000
1677 —	£220	£650	£2800
1677 — Elephant		Extremely rare	
1677 — Elephant & Castle	£325	£1000	£3250
1678 —	£200	£650	£2800
1678 — Elephant	£2500	—	—
1678 — Elephant & Castle	£425	£1300	—
1679 —	£200	£550	£2800

Charles II, third bust

Charles II, fourth bust, elephant & castle below

	F	VF	EF
1679 — Elephant & Castle	£350	£1250	—
1680 —	£200	£650	£2800
1680 — Elephant & Castle	£500	£1300	—
1681 —	£275	£750	£3000
1681 — Elephant & Castle	£325	£1150	—
1682 —	£275	£750	£3000
1682 — Elephant & Castle	£325	£1150	£2800
1683 —	£250	£650	£2800
1683 — Elephant & Castle	£500	£1350	£3250
1684 —	£275	£750	£3300
1684 — Elephant & Castle	£325	£850	£3250

James II, first bust, elephant & castle below

JAMES II (1685–1688)

	F	VF	EF
1685 First bust	£240	£550	£2500
*1685 — Elephant & Castle	£270	£625	£2750
1686 —	£275	£600	£3000
1686 — Elephant & Castle		Extremely rare	
1686 Second bust	£240	£600	£2500
1686 — Elephant & Castle	£350	£850	£3000
1687 —	£250	£600	£2500
1687 —Elephant & Castle	£300	£625	£2500
*1688 —	£250	£600	£2500
1688 — Elephant & Castle	£300	£625	£2500

James II second bust

WILLIAM AND MARY (1688–94)

	F	VF	EF
1689	£250	£625	£2500
1689 Elephant & Castle	£275	£625	£2500
1690	£300	£650	£2500
1690 Elephant & Castle	£5000	£900	£3250
1691	£325	£700	£2750
1691 Elephant & Castle	£350	£750	£2800
1692	£375	£700	£2750
1692 Elephant	£500	£1100	£3500
1692 Elephant & Castle	£400	£850	£2800
1693	£325	£700	£2800
1693 Elephant		Extremely rare	
1693 Elephant & Castle		Extremely rare	
1694	£275	£625	£2500
1694 Elephant & Castle	£400	£850	£2750

WILLIAM III (1694–1702)

	F	VF	EF
1695 First bust	£200	£475	£2000
1695 — Elephant & Castle	£350	£650	£2500
1696 —	£220	£475	£2000
1696 — Elephant & Castle		Extremely rare	
1697 —	£220	£475	£2000
1697 Second bust	£220	£475	£2000
1697 — Elephant & Castle	£650	£1500	—
1698 —	£220	£475	£2000
1698 — Elephant & Castle	£350	£650	£2500
1699 —	£300	£600	£2250
1699 — Elephant & Castle		Extremely rare	
1700 —	£200	£460	£2000
1700 — Elephant & Castle	£700	£1600	—
1701 —	£220	£475	£2000
1701 — Elephant & Castle		Extremely rare	
1701 Third bust "fine work"	£450	£1100	£2600

	F	VF	EF

ANNE (1702–1714)

	F	VF	EF
1702 (Pre-Union) First bust	£275	£750	£2750
1703 — VIGO below	£4000	£8000	—
1705 —	£275	£750	£2750
1706 —	£275	£750	£2750
1707 —	£275	£750	£2750
1707 — (Post-Union)	£200	£525	£2000
1707 — Elephant & Castle	£850	£1500	—
1707 Second bust	£650	—	—
1708 First bust		Extremely rare	
1708 Second bust	£200	£450	£1650
1708 — Elephant & Castle	£700	£1250	£3250
1709 —	£200	£450	£1750
1709 — Elephant & Castle	£700	£1250	£3250
1710 Third bust	£175	£375	£1600
1711 —	£175	£375	£1600
1712 —	£175	£375	£1600
*1713 —	£175	£375	£1600
1714 —	£175	£375	£1600

GEORGE I (1714–27)

	F	VF	EF
1714 First bust (Prince Elector)	£600	£1000	£3000
1715 Second bust	£200	£375	£1750
1715 Third bust	£200	£375	£1750
1716 —	£200	£375	£1750
1716 Fourth bust	£200	£375	£1750
1717 —	£200	£375	£1750
1718 —		Extremely rare	
1719 —	£200	£375	£1750
1720 —	£200	£375	£1750
1721 —	£200	£375	£1750
1721 — Elephant & Castle		Extremely rare	
1722 —	£200	£375	£1750
1722 — Elephant & Castle		Extremely rare	
1723 —	£200	£375	£1850
1723 Fifth bust	£200	£375	£1850
1724 —	£200	£375	£1850
1725 —	£200	£375	£1850
1726 —	£200	£375	£1750
1726 — Elephant & Castle	£600	£1500	—
1727 —	£270	£525	£2000

GEORGE II (1727–60)

	F	VF	EF
1727 First young head, early large shield	£500	£900	£2500
1727 — Larger lettering, early small shield	£350	£700	£2000
1728 — —	£350	£600	£2000
1729 2nd young head E.I.C. below	£330	£650	£2400
1730 —	£200	£475	£2000
1731 —	£190	£400	£2000
1731 — E.I.C. below	£300	£475	£2500
1732 —	£200	£400	£2000
1732 — E.I.C. below	£275	£450	£2400
1732 — Larger lettering obverse	£225	£600	£1600
1732 — — E.I.C. below	£325	£950	£2600
1733 — —	£200	£350	£1750
1734 — —	£200	£350	£1750
1735 — —	£200	£350	£1750
1736 — —	£200	£350	£1750
1737 — —	£200	£350	£1750
1738 — —	£200	£350	£1500

	F	VF	EF
1739 Intermediate head	£200	£400	£1600
1739 — E.I.C. below	£225	£475	£2400
1740 —	£200	£350	£1600
1741/39 —		Extremely rare	
1743 —		Extremely rare	
1745 — (GEORGIUS) Larger lettering obv.	£220	£400	£2000
1745 — LIMA below	£400	£1250	£3250
1746 — (GEORGIVS) Larger lettering obv.	£200	£350	£1500
1747 Old head, large lettering	£200	£350	£1250
1748 —	£200	£350	£1250
1749 —	£200	£350	£1250
1750 —	£200	£350	£1250
1751 — small lettering	£200	£350	£1250
1753 —	£200	£350	£1250
1755 —	£200	£350	£1250
1756 —	£200	£350	£1250
1758 —	£200	£350	£1250
1759 —	£200	£350	£1250
1760 —	£200	£350	£1250

GEORGE III (1760–1820)

	F	VF	EF
1761 First head	£375	£850	£2400
1763 Second head	£325	£750	£2000
1764 —	£220	£500	£1500
1765 Third head	£170	£375	£875
1766 —	£140	£325	£750
1767 —	£175	£400	£900
1768 —	£140	£325	£750
1769 —	£140	£325	£750
1770 —	£175	£400	£900
*1771 —	£140	£325	£750
1772 —	£140	£325	£750
1773 —	£140	£300	£675
1774 Fourth head	£95	£160	£400
1775 —	£95	£160	£400
1776 —	£95	£160	£400
1777 —	£95	£160	£400
1778 —	£95	£180	£500
1779 —	£100	£180	£450
1781 —	£100	£170	£400
1782 —	£100	£170	£400
1783 —	£100	£170	£400
1784 —	£100	£170	£400
1785 —	£100	£170	£400
1786 —	£100	£170	£400
1787 Fifth head, "Spade" reverse	£80	£125	£200
1788 —	£85	£125	£250
1789 —	£85	£125	£250
1790 —	£85	£125	£250
1791 —	£85	£125	£250
1792 —	£85	£125	£250
1793 —	£85	£125	£250
1794 —	£85	£125	£250
1795 —	£100	£175	£350
1796 —	£120	£200	£500
1797 —	£100	£140	£300
*1798 —	£80	£110	£225
1799 —	£95	£180	£400
*1813 Sixth head, "Military" reverse	£160	£425	£900

(Beware of counterfeits of this series—many dangerous copies exist)

HALF GUINEAS

	F	VF	EF

CHARLES II (1660–85)

	F	VF	EF
1669 First bust	£260	£525	£2500
*1670 —	£180	£450	£2000
1671 —	£350	£900	—
1672 —	£350	£900	—
1672 Second bust	£180	£475	£2000
1673 —	£400	£1100	—
1674 —	£400	£1100	—
1675 —		Extremely rare	
1676 —	£190	£500	—
1676 — Elephant & Castle		Extremely rare	
1677 —	£200	£450	£1750
1677 — Elephant & Castle	£400	£1100	—
1678 —	£200	£500	£2000
1678 — Elephant & Castle	£350	£900	—
1679 —	£190	£425	£1750
1680 —	£400	£1100	—
1680 — Elephant & Castle		Extremely rare	
1681 —	£400	£1100	—
1682 —	£275	£650	£2200
1682 — Elephant & Castle	£450	£1350	—
1683 — —		Extremely rare	
1684 —	£190	£375	£1800
1684 — Elephant & Castle	£350	£700	£2750

JAMES II (1685–88)

	F	VF	EF
1686	£250	£550	£2500
1686 Elephant & Castle	£450	£1500	£4000
1687	£325	£600	£2750
1688	£275	£600	£2500

WILLIAM AND MARY (1688–94)

	F	VF	EF
1689 First busts	£300	£600	£2000
1690 Second busts	£350	£650	£2000
1691 —	£400	£750	£2000
1691 — Elephant & Castle	£300	£650	£2000
1692 —	£325	£620	£2250
*1692 — Elephant		Extremely rare	
1692 — Elephant & Castle	£300	£600	£2000
1693 —		Extremely rare	
1694 —	£250	£600	£1850

WILLIAM III (1694–1702)

	F	VF	EF
1695	£150	£400	£1750
1695 Elephant & Castle	£400	£800	£2250
1696 —	£220	£525	£2000
1697 Larger Harp rev.	£250	£600	£2000
1698	£150	£400	£1500
1698 Elephant & Castle	£350	£700	£2250
*1699		Extremely rare	
1700	£150	£425	£1850
1701	£150	£425	£1850

	F	VF	EF

ANNE (1702–14)

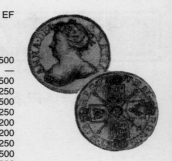

	F	VF	EF
1702 (Pre-Union)	£250	£600	£2500
1703 VIGO below bust	£2200	£5000	—
1705	£250	£600	£2500
1707 (Post-Union)	£160	£350	£1250
1708	£180	£375	£1500
1709	£160	£350	£1250
1710	£160	£280	£1200
*1711	£160	£280	£1200
1712	£160	£300	£1250
1713	£160	£300	£1500
1714	£160	£300	£1500

GEORGE I (1714–27)

	F	VF	EF
1715 First bust	£160	£320	£1100
*1718 —	£150	£300	£1000
1719 —	£150	£300	£1000
1720 —	£250	£600	—
1721 —		Extremely rare	
1721 — Elephant & Castle		Extremely rare	
1722 —	£150	£325	£1350
1723 —		Extremely rare	
1724 —	£250	£500	£1850
1725 Second bust	£150	£300	£1000
1726 —	£150	£300	£1000
1727 —	£175	£375	£1000

GEORGE II (1727–60)

	F	VF	EF
1728 Young head	£180	£400	£1500
1729 —	£180	£400	£1500
1729 — E.I.C.	£275	£600	—
1730 —		Extremely rare	
1730 — E.I.C.	£350	£850	—
1731 —	£220	£450	£1750
1731 — E.I.C.		Extremely rare	
1732 —	£180	£400	£1500
1732 — E.I.C.		Extremely rare	
1733 —		Extremely rare	
1734 —	£175	£374	£1500
1735 —		Extremely rare	
1736 —	£175	£375	£1500
*1737 —		Extremely rare	
1738 —	£160	£350	£1500
1739 —	£160	£325	£1500
1739 — E.I.C.		Extremely rare	
1740 Intermediate head	£180	£400	£1500
1743 —		Extremely rare	
1745 —	£180	£400	£1500
1745 — LIMA	£600	£1500	—
1746 —	£160	£325	£1250
1747 Old head	£250	£500	£1250
1748 —	£140	£320	£1000
1749 —		Extremely rare	
*1750 —	£150	£350	£1000
1751 —	£150	£350	£1000
1752 —	£150	£350	£1000
1753 —	£140	£275	£850
1755 —	£140	£275	£850

George II, young head

George II, old head

	F	VF	EF
1756 —	£140	£270	£850
1758 —	£140	£270	£850
1759 —	£125	£220	£850
1760 —	£125	£220	£85
0			

George III, second head

GEORGE III (1760–1820)

	F	VF	EF
1762 First head	£220	£400	£1100
1763 —	£300	£600	£1500
1764 Second head	£150	£275	£500
1765 —	£250	£500	£1250
1766 —	£175	£300	£750
1768 —	£175	£300	£750
*1769 —	£150	£280	£600
1772 —		Extremely rare	
1773 —	£175	£300	£750
1774 —	£250	£500	£1500
1774 Third head		Extremely rare	
1775 —	£275	£500	£1500
1775 Fourth head	£75	£135	£300
1776 —	£75	£140	£300
1777 —	£75	£140	£300
1778 —	£90	£150	£350
1779 —	£100	£200	£425
1781 —	£90	£150	£350
1783 —	£300	£750	—
1784 —	£75	£135	£300
1785 —	£70	£155	£300
1786 —	£70	£155	£300
1787 Fifth head, "Spade" rev.	£60	£110	£225
1788 —	£60	£110	£225
1789 —	£60	£110	£225
1790 —	£60	£110	£225
1791 —	£60	£110	£225
1792 —		Extremely Rare	
1793 —	£60	£110	£225
1794 —	£60	£100	£225
1795 —	£75	£140	£325
*1796 —	£60	£110	£225
1797 —	£60	£110	£225
1798 —	£60	£110	£225
1800 —	£125	£300	£750
*1801 Sixth head, Shield in Garter rev.	£55	£95	£180
1802 —	£55	£95	£180
1803 —	£55	£95	£180
1804 Seventh head	£55	£95	£180
1805		Extremely Rare	
1806 —	£55	£95	£180
1808 —	£55	£95	£180
1899 —	£55	£95	£180
1810 —	£55	£95	£180
1811 —	£80	£140	£300
1813 —	£70	£125	£275

George III, fifth head, "spade" reverse

George III, sixth head

THIRD GUINEAS

GEORGE III (1760–1820)

DATE	F	VF	EF
*1797 First head, date in legend	£40	£65	£140
1798 — —	£40	£65	£140
1799 — —	£65	£100	£210
1800 — —	£40	£65	£140
1801 Date under crown	£40	£65	£140
1802 —	£40	£65	£140
1803 —	£40	£65	£140
1804 Second head	£40	£65	£150
1806 —	£40	£65	£150
1808 —	£40	£65	£150
1809 —	£40	£65	£150
*1810 —	£40	£65	£150
1811 —	£110	£350	£700
1813 —	£55	£110	£200

George III, date in legend

George III, date under crown

QUARTER GUINEAS

GEORGE I (1714–27)

	F	VF	EF
1718	£60	£110	£230

GEORGE III (1760–1820)

	F	VF	EF
*1762	£45	£100	£230

FIVE POUNDS

DATE	Mintage	F	VF	EF	UNC

GEORGE III (1760–1820)

1820 (pattern only)	—		Extremely rare		

GEORGE IV (1820–30)

*1826 proof only	—	—	—	£6,000	£10,000

VICTORIA (1837–1901)

1839 Proof Only	—	—	—	£16,000	£20,000
1887	53,844	£325	£450	£650	£850
1887 Proof	797	—	—	—	£2,000
1887 S on ground on rev. (Sydney Mint)			Excessively rare		
1893	20,405	£400	£575	£800	£1,250
1893 Proof	773	—	—	—	£2,500

EDWARD VII (1902–10)

1902	34,910	—	£400	£550	£750
1902 Matt proof	8,066	—	—	—	£750

DATE	MINTAGE	F	VF	EF	UNC

GEORGE V (1911–36)

| 1911 Proof only .... | 2,812 | — | — | — | £1,500 |

GEORGE VI (1937–52)

| *1937 Proof only .... | 5,501 | — | — | — | £750 |

Later issues are listed in the Decimal section.

TWO POUNDS

GEORGE III (1760–1820)

| 1820 (pattern only) .... | — | — | — | Extremely rare |

GEORGE IV (1820–30)

| 1823 St George reverse .... | — | £200 | £375 | £750 | £1550 |
| 1826 Proof only, shield reverse | — | — | — | £2750 | £4000 |

WILLIAM IV (1830–37)

| 1831 Proof only .... | 225 | — | — | £2800 | £5000 |

VICTORIA (1837–1901)

1887	91,345	£160	£225	£350	£450
1887 Proof	797	—	—	—	£850
1887 S on ground of rev. (Sydney Mint)				Excessively rare	
1893	52,212	£220	£325	£480	£650
1893 Proof	773	—	—	—	£1000

EDWARD VII (1902–10)

| 1902 .... | 45,807 | £140 | £175 | £260 | £350 |
| 1902 Matt proof .... | 8,066 | — | — | — | £350 |

GEORGE V (1911–36)

| 1911 Proof only .... | 2,812 | — | — | — | £650 |

GEORGE VI (1937–52)

| *1937 Proof only .... | 5,501 | — | — | — | £360 |

Later issues are listed in the Decimal section.

SOVEREIGNS

DATE	MINTAGE	F	VF	EF	UNC

GEORGE III (1760–1820)

DATE	MINTAGE	F	VF	EF	UNC
1817	3,235,239	£90	£175	£450	£650
1818	2,347,230	£90	£175	£405	£650
1819	3,574		Exceedingly rare		
1820	931,994	£90	£165	£450	£700

GEORGE IV (1820–30)

DATE	MINTAGE	F	VF	EF	UNC
1821 First bust, St George reverse	9,405,114	£95	£170	£450	£850
1821 — Proof	incl. above	—	—	£1500	£2500
1822 —	5,356,787	£90	£170	£450	£850
1823 —	616,770	£125	£350	£1200	—
1824 —	3,767,904	£90	£170	£450	£850
1825 —	4,200,343	£160	£400	£1200	—
1825 Second bust, shield reverse	incl. above	£90	£150	£425	£750
1826 —	5,724,046	£90	£150	£425	£750
*1826 — Proof	—	—	—	£1500	£2500
1827 —	2,266,629	£90	£150	£425	£750
1828 —	386,182	£500	£1250	£2500	—
1829 —	2,444,652	£90	£150	£425	£750
1830 —	2,387,881	£90	£150	£425	£750

WILLIAM IV (1830–37)

DATE	MINTAGE	F	VF	EF	UNC
1831	598,547	£100	£175	£475	£900
*1831 Proof	—	—	—	£1750	£2750
1832	3,737,065	£100	£160	£450	£850
1833	1,225,269	£100	£170	£450	£800
1835	723,441	£100	£170	£450	£850
1836	1,714,349	£100	£170	£450	£850
1837	1,172,984	£100	£160	£450	£800

VICTORIA (1837–1901)

Many of the gold coins struck at the colonial mints found their way into circulation in Britain, for the sake of completeness these coins are listed here. These can easily be identified by a tiny initial letter for the appropriate mint which can be found below the base of the reverse shield or, in the case of the St George reverse, below the bust on the obverse of the Young Head issues, or on the "ground" below the horse's hoof on the later issues.

YOUNG HEAD ISSUES

Shield reverse
(Note—Shield back sovereigns in Fine/VF condition, common dates, are normally traded as bullion + a percentage)

DATE	MINTAGE	F	VF	EF	UNC
1838	2,718,994	£60	£100	£225	£600
1839	503,695	£100	£350	£850	£2000
*1839 Proof	—	—	—	—	£2000
1841	124,054	£525	£1100	£2200	—
1842	4,865,375	—	£70	£140	£240
1843	5,981,968	—	£70	£140	£240
1843 "Narrow shield" variety	incl. above	£275	£600	£1500	—
1844	3,000,445	—	£70	£140	£240
1845	3,800,845	—	£70	£140	£240
1846	3,802,947	—	£70	£140	£270

DATE	MINTAGE	F	VF	EF	UNC
1847	4,667,126	£55	£70	£140	£240
1848	2,246,701	£55	£70	£150	£325
1849	1,755,399	£55	£70	£150	£325
1850	1,402,039	£55	£70	£140	£275
1851	4,013,624	£55	£70	£140	£240
1852	8,053,435	£55	£70	£140	£240
1853	10,597,993	£55	£70	£140	£240
1853 Proof	—	£55	—	—	£3500
1854	3,589,611	£55	£70	£140	£240
1855	8,448,482	£55	£70	£140	£240
1856	4,806,160	£55	£70	£140	£240
1857	4,495,748	£55	£70	£140	£240
1858	803,234	£55	£80	£175	£450
1859	1,547,603	£55	£70	£140	£300
1859 "Ansell" (additional line on lower part of hair ribbon)	—	£160	£320	£1200	—
1860	2,555,958	£55	£70	£200	£500
1861	7,624,736	£55	£70	£140	£240
1862	7,836,413	—	£70	£140	£240
1863	5,921,669	—	£70	£140	£240
1863 with Die number	*incl. above*	£55	£70	£125	£220
1864 —	8,656,352	£55	£70	£125	£220
1865 —	1,450,238	£55	£70	£125	£220
1866 —	4,047,288	£55	£70	£125	£220
1868 —	1,653,384	£55	£70	£125	£220
1869 —	6,441,322	£55	£70	£125	£220
1870 —	2,189,960	£55	£70	£125	£220
1871 —	8,767,250	£55	£70	£125	£220
1872 —	8,767,250	£55	£70	£140	£240
1872 no Die number	*incl. above*	£55	£70	£140	£240
1873 with Die number	2,368,215	£55	£70	£130	£240
1874 —	520,713	£800	—	—	—

M below (Melbourne Mint)

1872	748,180	£55	£75	£175	£325
1873	—	Extremely rare			
1874	1,373,298	£55	£75	£150	£300
1879		Extremely rare			
1880	3,053,454	£200	£600	£1500	£3000
1881	2,325,303	£75	£125	£375	£650
1882	2,465,781	£55	£75	£175	£325
1883	2,050,450	£100	£200	£600	—
1884	2,942,630	£55	£75	£150	£300
1885	2,967,143	£55	£75	£150	£300
1886	2,902,131	£500	£1300	£3000	—
1887	1,916,424	£300	£700	£1800	£3000

"S" below the shield indicates that the coin was struck at the Sydney Mint

S below (Sydney Mint)

1871	2,814,000	£55	£65	£140	—
1872	1,815,000	£55	£65	£140	—
1873	1,478,000	£55	£65	£140	—
1875	2,122,000	£55	£65	£140	—
1877	1,590,000	£55	£65	£140	—
1878	1,259,000	£55	£75	£150	—
1879	1,366,000	£55	£65	£140	—
1880	1,459,000	£55	£65	£140	—
1881	1,360,000	£55	£75	£170	—
1882	1,298,000	£55	£65	£140	—
1883	1,108,000	£55	£75	£170	—
1884	1,595,000	£55	£65	£140	—
1885	1,486,000	£55	£65	£140	—
1886	1,667,000	£55	£65	£140	—
1887	1,000,000	£55	£75	£170	£325

DATE	MINTAGE	F	VF	EF	UNC
St George & Dragon reverse					
1871	incl. above	—	£60	£85	£160
1872	incl. above	—	£60	£85	£160
1873	incl. above	—	£60	£85	£160
1874	incl. above	—	£60	£85	£160
1876	3,318,866	—	£60	£85	£160
1878	1,091,275	—	£60	£85	£200
1879	20,013	£100	£300	£600	—
1880	3,650,080	—	£60	£85	£160
1884	1,769,635	—	£60	£85	£160
1885	717,723	—	£60	£85	£160
M below (Melbourne Mint)					
1872	incl. above	—	£60	£100	£160
1873	752,199	—	£60	£100	£150
1874	incl. above	—	£60	£100	£150
1875	incl. above	—	£60	£100	£150
1876	2,124,445	—	£60	£100	£160
1877	1,487,316	—	£60	£100	£150
1878	2,171,457	—	£60	£100	£150
1879	2,740,594	—	£60	£100	£150
1880	incl. above	—	£60	£100	£150
1881	incl. above	—	£60	£100	£150
1882	incl. above	—	£60	£100	£150
1883	incl. above	—	£60	£100	£150
1884	incl. above	—	£60	£100	£150
1885	incl. above	—	£60	£100	£150
1886	incl. above	—	£60	£100	£150
1887	incl. above	—	£60	£100	£150
S below (Sydney Mint)					
1871	incl. above	—	£60	£110	£175
1872	incl. above	—	£60	£110	£175
1873	incl. above	—	£60	£110	£175
1874	1,899,000	—	£60	£100	£150
1875	inc above	—	£60	£100	£150
1876	1,613,000	—	£60	£100	£150
1877	—		Extremely rare		
1879	incl. above	—	£60	£100	£150
1880	incl. above	—	£60	£100	£150
1881	incl. above	—	£60	£100	£150
1882	incl. above	—	£60	£100	£150
1883	incl. above	—	£60	£100	£150
1884	incl. above	—	£60	£100	£150
1885	incl. above	—	£60	£100	£150
1886	incl. above	—	£60	£100	£150
1887	incl. above	—	£60	£100	£150
JUBILEE HEAD ISSUES					
*1887	1,111,280	—	—	£70	£90
1887 Proof	797	—	—	—	£700
1888	2,717,424	—	—	£60	£90
1889	7,257,455	—	—	£60	£90
1890	6,529.887	—	—	£60	£90
1891	6,329,476	—	—	£60	£90
1892	7,104,720	—	—	£60	£90
M below (Melbourne Mint)					
1887	940,000	£70	£100	£200	—
1888	2,830,612	£55	£70	£110	—
1889	2,732,590	£55	£70	£110	—
1890	2,473,537	£55	£70	£110	—
1891	2,749,592	£55	£70	£110	—
1892	3,488,750	£55	£70	£110	—
1893	1,649,352	£55	£70	£110	—

"M" below the horse's hoof above the date indicates that the coin was struck at the Melbourne Mint

DATE	MINTAGE	F	VF	EF	UNC
S below (Sydney Mint)					
1887	1,002,000	£55	£100	£125	£175
1888	2,187,000	—	£75	£100	—
1889	3,262,000	—	£75	£100	—
1890	2,808,000	—	£75	£100	—
1891	2,596,000	—	£75	£100	—
1892	2,837,000	—	£75	£100	—
1893	1,498,000	—	£75	£100	—

OLD HEAD ISSUES

DATE	MINTAGE	F	VF	EF	UNC
*1893	6,898,260	—	—	£65	£85
1893 Proof	773	—	—	—	£650
1894	3,782,611	—	—	£65	£85
1895	2,285,317	—	—	£65	£85
1896	3,334,065	—	—	£65	£85
1898	4,361,347	—	—	£65	£85
1899	7,515,978	—	—	£65	£85
1900	10,846,741	—	—	£65	£85
1901	1,578,948	—	—	£65	£85
M below (Melbourne Mint)					
1893	1,914,000	—	—	£90	£100
1894	4,166,874	—	—	£90	£100
1895	4,165,869	—	—	£90	£100
1896	4,456,932	—	—	£90	£100
1897	5,130,565	—	—	£90	£100
1898	5,509,138	—	—	£90	£100
1899	5,579,157	—	—	£90	£100
1900	4,305,904	—	—	£90	£100
1901	3,987,701	—	—	£90	£100
P below (Perth Mint)					
1899	690,992	—	£75	£150	£225
1900	1,886,089	—	—	£90	£130
1901	2,889,333	—	—	£90	£130
S below (Sydney Mint)					
1893	1,346,000	—	—	£75	£100
1894	3,067,000	—	—	£75	£100
1895	2,758,000	—	—	£75	£100
1896	2,544,000	—	—	£100	£140
1897	2,532,000	—	—	£75	£100
1898	2,548,000	—	—	£75	£100
1899	3,259,000	—	—	£75	£100
1900	3,586,000	—	—	£75	£100
1901	3,012,000	—	—	£75	£100

EDWARD VII (1902–10)

DATE	MINTAGE	F	VF	EF	UNC
*1902	4,737,796	—	—	£60	£75
1902 Matt proof	15,123	—	—	£60	£150
1903	8,888,627	—	—	£60	£75
1904	10,041,369	—	—	£60	£75
1905	5,910,403	—	—	£60	£75
1906	10,466,981	—	—	£60	£75
1907	18,458,663	—	—	£60	£75
1908	11,729,006	—	—	£60	£75
1909	12,157,099	—	—	£60	£75
1910	22,379,624	—	—	£60	£75
C below (Ottawa Mint)					
1908 Satin finish Proof only	636		Extremely rare		
1909	16,273	—	£80	£220	—
1910	28,012	—	£80	£220	—

DATE	MINTAGE	F	VF	EF	UNC
M below (Melbourne Mint)					
1902	4,267,157	—	—	£80	£120
1903	3,521,780	—	—	£80	£120
1904	3,743,897	—	—	£80	£120
1905	3,633,838	—	—	£80	£120
1906	3,657,853	—	—	£80	£120
1907	3,332,691	—	—	£80	£120
1908	3,080,148	—	—	£80	£120
1909	3,029,538	—	—	£80	£120
1910	3,054,547	—	—	£80	£120
P below (Perth Mint)					
1902	3,289,122	—	—	£80	£120
1903	4,674,783	—	—	£80	£120
1904	4,506,756	—	—	£80	£120
1905	4,876,193	—	—	£80	£120
1906	4,829,817	—	—	£80	£120
1907	4,972,289	—	—	£80	£120
1908	4,875,617	—	—	£80	£120
1909	4,524,241	—	—	£80	£120
1910	4,690,625	—	—	£80	£120
S below (Sydney Mint)					
1902	2,813,000	—	—	£80	£120
1902 Proof	*incl. above*			Extremely rare	
1903	2,806,000	—	—	£80	£120
1904	2,986,000	—	—	£80	£120
1905	2,778,000	—	—	£80	£120
1906	2,792,000	—	—	£80	£120
1907	2,539,000	—	—	£80	£120
1908	2,017,000	—	—	£80	£120
1909	2,057,000	—	—	£80	£120
1910	2,135,000	—	—	£80	£120

GEORGE V (1911–36)

(Extra care should be exercised when purchasing as good quality forgeries exist of virtually all dates and mintmarks)

DATE	MINTAGE	F	VF	EF	UNC
1911	30,044,105	—	—	£60	£70
1911 Proof	3,764	—	—	—	£275
1912	30,317,921	—	—	£60	£70
1913	24,539,672	—	—	£60	£70
1914	11,501,117	—	—	£60	£70
1915	20,295,280	—	—	£60	£70
1916	1,554,120	—	—	£60	£75
1917	1,014,714	£2500	£3250	£4000	—
1925	4,406,431	—	—	£60	£70
C below (Ottawa Mint)					
1911	256,946	—	£70	£100	£150
1913	3,715	£100	£120	£500	—
1914	14,891	£100	£180	£300	—
1916	6,111			Extremely rare	
1917	58,845	—	£70	£110	£125
1918	106,516	—	£70	£110	£125
1919	135,889	—	£70	£110	£125
I below (Bombay Mint)					
1918	1,295,372	—	—	£75	—
M below (Melbourne Mint)					
1911	2,851,451	—	—	£75	£100
1912	2,469,257	—	—	£75	£100
1913	2,323,180	—	—	£75	£100
1914	2,012,029	—	—	£75	£100
1915	1,637,839	—	—	£75	£100

DATE	MINTAGE	F	VF	EF	UNC
1916	1,273,643	—	—	£75	£100
1917	934,469	—	—	£75	£100
1918	4,969,493	—	—	£75	£100
1919	514,257	—	—	£90	£125
1920	530,266	£200	£600	£1000	—
1921	240,121	—	—	£4000	—
1922	608,306	£300	£800	£3000	—
1923	510,870	—	—	£100	£140
1924	278,140	—	—	£100	£140
1925	3,311,622	—	—	£75	£100
1926	211,107	—	—	£75	£100
1928	413,208	£200	£500	£750	—
1929	436,719	£100	£300	£1000	—
1930	77,547	—	£75	£150	—
1931	57,779	£70	£110	£275	—

P below (Perth Mint)

DATE	MINTAGE	F	VF	EF	UNC
1911	4,373,165	—	—	£75	£100
1912	4,278,144	—	—	£75	£100
1913	4,635,287	—	—	£75	£100
1914	4,815,996	—	—	£75	£100
1915	4,373,596	—	—	£75	£100
1916	4,096,771	—	—	£75	£100
1917	4,110,286	—	—	£75	£100
1918	3,812,884	—	—	£75	£100
1919	2,995,216	—	—	£75	£100
1920	2,421,196	—	—	£75	£100
1921	2,134,360	—	—	£75	£100
1922	2,298,884	—	—	£75	£100
1923	2,124,154	—	—	£75	£100
1924	1,464,416	—	—	£75	£100
1925	1,837,901	—	—	£75	£120
1926	1,313,578	—	—	£100	£200
1927	1,383,544	F	—	£90	£200
1928	1,333,417	—	—	£100	£140
1929	1,606,625	—	—	£75	£100
1930	1,915,352	—	—	£75	£100
1931	1,173,568	—	—	£75	£100

S below (Sydney Mint)

DATE	MINTAGE	F	VF	EF	UNC
1911	2,519,000	—	—	£70	£90
1912	2,227,000	—	—	£70	£90
1913	2,249,000	—	—	£70	£90
1914	1,774,000	—	—	£70	£90
1915	1,346,000	—	—	£70	£90
1916	1,242,000	—	—	£70	£90
1917	1,666,000	—	—	£70	£90
1918	3,716,000	—	—	£70	£90
1919	1,835,000	—	—	£70	£90
1920	—		Excessively rare		
1921	839,000	—	£500	£1200	—
1922	578,000		Extremely rare		
1923	416,000		Extremely rare		
1924	394,000	—	£400	£800	£1250
1925	5,632,000	—	—	£75	£100
1926	1,031,050		Extremely rare		

SA below (Pretoria Mint)

DATE	MINTAGE	F	VF	EF	UNC
1923	719		Extremely rare		
1923 Proof	655		Extremely rare		
1924	3,184		Extremely rare		
1925	6,086,264	—	£60	£80	£95
1926	11,107,611	—	£60	£80	£95
1927	16,379,704	—	£60	£80	£95
1928	18,235,057	—	£60	£80	£95

DATE	MINTAGE	F	VF	EF	UNC
1929	12,024,107	—	—	£80	£95
1930	10,027,756	—	—	£80	£95
1931	8,511,792	—	—	£80	£95
1932	1,066,680	—	—	£90	£110

GEORGE VI (1937–52)

*1937 Proof only	5,501	—	—	£275	£350

ELIZABETH II (1952–   )

Pre Decimal Issues

1957	2,072,000	—	—	—	£65
1958	8,700,140	—	—	—	£60
1959	1,358,228	—	—	—	£65
1962	3,000,000	—	—	—	£60
1963	7,400,000	—	—	—	£60
1964	3,000,000	—	—	—	£60
1965	3,800,000	—	—	—	£60
1966	7,050,000	—	—	—	£60
1967	5,000,000	—	—	—	£60
1968	4,203,000	—	—	—	£60

Later issues are included in the Decimal section.

HALF SOVEREIGNS

GEORGE III (1760–1820)

1817	2,080,197	£55	£85	£175	£325
1818	1,030,286	£55	£85	£175	£350
1820	35,043	£55	£85	£175	£350

GEORGE IV (1820–30)

1821 First bust, ornate shield reverse	231,288	£160	£450	£1500	£2250
1821 — Proof	*unrecorded*	—	—	£2000	£3000
1823 First bust, Plain shield rev.	224,280	£70	£150	£400	£675
1824 —	591,538	£70	£150	£425	£675
1825 —	761,150	£70	£150	£425	£675
1826 bare head, shield with full legend reverse	344,830	£65	£130	£400	£600
1826 — Proof	*unrecorded*	—	—	£750	£1000
1827 —	492,014	£70	£150	£400	£650
1828 —	1,224,754	£65	£130	£400	£675

WILLIAM IV (1830–37)

1831 Proof only	*uncrecorded*	—	—	£750	£1250
1834	133,899	£80	£160	£450	£800
1835	772,554	£70	£130	£400	£775
1836	146,865	£85	£160	£450	£850
1836 obverse from 6d die	*incl. above*	£500	£1000	£2500	—
1837	160,207	£70	£140	£400	£750

DATE	MINTAGE	F	VF	EF	UNC

VICTORIA (1837–1901)

YOUNG HEAD ISSUES
Shield reverse

DATE	MINTAGE	F	VF	EF	UNC
1838	273,341	£60	£80	£225	£450
1839 Proof only	1,230	—	—	—	£900
1841	508,835	£60	£80	£250	£500
1842	2,223,352	—	£65	£200	£320
1843	1,251,762	£60	£75	£250	£500
1844	1,127,007	£60	£70	£200	£320
1845	887,526	£65	£175	£400	£600
1846	1,063,928	£60	£70	£200	£350
1847	982,636	£60	£70	£200	£350
1848	410,595	£60	£70	£200	£350
1849	845,112	—	£70	£180	£325
1850	179,595	£60	£175	£400	£700
1851	773,573	—	£70	£200	£350
1852	1,377,671	—	£70	£200	£350
1853	2,708,796	—	£70	£180	£300
1853 Proof	unrecorded	—	—	—	£2750
1854	1,125,144			Extremely rare	
1855	1,120,362	—	£70	£180	£325
1856	2,391,909	—	£70	£180	£325
1857	728,223	—	£70	£180	£325
1858	855,578	—	£70	£180	£325
1859	2,203,813	—	£65	£180	£325
1860	1,131,500	—	£65	£180	£325
1861	1,130,867	—	£65	£180	£325
1862	unrecorded			Extremely rare	
1863	1,571,574	—	£65	£180	£325
1863 with Die number	incl. above	—	£65	£180	£325
1864 —	1,758,490	—	£65	£180	£325
1865 —	1,834,750	—	£65	£180	£325
1866 —	2,058,776	—	£65	£180	£325
1867 —	992,795	—	£65	£180	£325
1869 —	1,861,764	—	£60	£180	£325
1870 —	1,159,544	—	£65	£175	£250
1871 —	2,062,970	—	£60	£130	£250
1872 —	3,248,627	—	£60	£130	£240
1873 —	1,927,050	—	£60	£130	£250
1874 —	1,884,432	—	£55	£140	£240
1875 —	516,240	—	£55	£140	£250
1876 —	2,785,187	—	£55	£140	£250
1877 —	2,197,482	—	£55	£120	£250
1878 —	2,081,941	—	£55	£120	£250
1879 —	35,201	—	£55	£120	£250
1880 —	1,009,049	—	£55	£120	£250
1880 no Die number	incl. above	—	£55	£130	£240
1883 —	2,870,457	—	£55	£120	£225
1884 —	1,113,756	—	£55	£120	£225
1885 —	4,468,871	—	£55	£120	£225

M below (Melbourne Mint)

DATE	MINTAGE	F	VF	EF	UNC
1873	165,034	£50	£110	£350	—
1877	80,016	£50	£110	£350	—
1881	42,009	£70	£175	£450	—
1882	107,522	£70	£100	£400	—
1884	48,009	£70	£100	£350	—
1885	11,003	£75	£200	£800	—
1886	38,008	£70	£110	£450	—
1887	64,013	£800	£250	£800	—

S below (Sydney Mint)

DATE	MINTAGE	F	VF	EF	UNC
1871	unrecorded	£60	£95	£400	—
1872	356,000	£65	£110	£400	—

Date	Mintage	F	VF	EF	UNC
1875	*unrecorded*	£70	£120	£400	—
1879	94,000	£70	£120	£400	—
1880	80,000	£70	£120	£400	—
1881	62,000	£100	£175	£700	—
1882	52,000	£150	£250	£1000	—
1883	220,000	£65	£100	£400	—
1886	82,000	£65	£100	£350	—
1887	134,000	£65	£100	£350	—

JUBILEE HEAD ISSUES

1887	871,770	—	—	£60	£80
1887 Proof	797	—	—	—	£400
1890	2.266,023	—	—	£60	£95
1891	1,079,286	—	—	£60	£95
1892	13,680,486	—	—	£60	£90
1893	4,426,625	—	—	£65	£120

M below (Melbourne Mint)

1887	*incl. above*	£50	£90	£250	£450
1893	110,024	£60	£100	£325	—

S below (Sydney Mint)

1887	*incl. above*	£50	£90	£225	£400
1889	64,000	£60	£100	£300	—
1891	154,000	£60	£110	£325	—

OLD HEAD ISSUES

1893	*incl. above*	—	£42	£55	£85
1893 Proof	773	—	—	—	£500
1894	3,794,591	—	£42	£60	£85
1895	2,869,183	—	£42	£60	£85
1896	2,946,605	—	£42	£60	£85
1897	3,568,156	—	£42	£60	£85
1898	2,868,527	—	£42	£60	£85
1899	3,361,881	—	£42	£60	£85
1900	4,307,372	—	£42	£60	£85
1901	2,037,664	—	£42	£60	£85

M below (Melbourne Mint)

1893	*unrecorded*		Extremely rare		
1896	218,946	£50	£90	£300	—
1899	97,221	£50	£90	£300	—
1900	112,920	£50	£90	£300	—

P below (Perth Mint)

1899			Extremely rare		
1900	119,376	£100	£250	£450	—

S below (Sydney Mint)

1893	250,000	£55	£100	£300	—
1897	*unrecorded*	£50	£90	£300	—
1900	260,00	£50	£90	£300	—

EDWARD VII (1902–10)

1902	4,244,457	—	—	£45	£55
1902 Matt proof	15,123	—	—	—	£100
1903	2,522,057	—	—	£45	£55
1904	1,717,440	—	—	£45	£55
1905	3,023,993	—	—	£45	£55
1906	4,245,437	—	—	£45	£55
1907	4,233,421	—	—	£45	£55
1908	3,996,992	—	—	£45	£55
1909	4,010,715	—	—	£45	£55
1910	5,023,881	—	—	£45	£55

DATE		F	VF	EF	UNC
M below (Melbourne Mint)					
1906	82,042	—	£40	£80	£165
1907	405,034	—	£40	£80	£165
1908	incl. above	—	£40	£80	£165
1909	186,094	—	£40	£80	£165
P below (Perth Mint)					
1904	60,030	£100	£150	£550	—
1908	24,668	£100	£150	£550	—
1909	44,022	£70	£130	£350	—
S below (Sydney Mint)					
1902	84,000	—	£45	£100	£175
1903	231,000	—	£45	£100	£175
1906	308,00	—	£45	£100	£175
1908	538,000	—	£45	£100	£175
1910	474,000	—	£45	£100	£175

GEORGE V (1911–36)

DATE		F	VF	EF	UNC
1911	6,104,106	—	£40	£60	£80
1911 Proof	3,764	—	—	—	£175
1912	6,224,316	—	£40	£60	£80
1913	6,094,290	—	£40	£60	£80
1914	7,251,124	—	£40	£60	£80
1915	2,042,747	—	£40	£60	£80
M below (Melbourne Mint)					
1915	125,664	—	—	£70	£120
P below (Perth Mint)					
1911	130,373	—	—	£70	£100
1915	136,219	—	—	£70	£100
1918	unrecorded	£175	£375	£700	—
S below (Sydney Mint)					
1911	252,000	—	—	£70	£110
1912	278,000	—	—	£70	£110
1914	322,000	—	—	£70	£110
1915	892,000	—	—	£70	£110
1916	448,000	—	—	£70	£110
SA below (Pretoria Mint)					
1923 Proof only	655	—	—	—	£450
1925	946,615	—	—	£65	£100
1926	806,540	—	—	£65	£100

GEORGE VI (1937–52)

DATE		F	VF	EF	UNC
1937 Proof only	5,501	—	—	—	£165

Later issues are included in the Decimal section.

CROWNS

DATE	F	VF	EF	UNC

OLIVER CROMWELL

	F	VF	EF	UNC
1658 8 over 7 (always)	£550	£925	£2000	—
1658 Dutch Copy			Extremely rare	
1658 Patterns. In Various Metals			Extremely rare	

CHARLES II (1660–85)

	F	VF	EF	UNC
1662 First bust, rose (2 varieties)	£65	£250	£2000	—
1662 — no rose (2 varieties)	£65	£250	£2000	—
1663 —	£65	£250	£2000	—
1664 Second bust	£65	£300	£2500	—
1665 —	£150	£450	—	—
*1666 —	£75	£325	£2500	—
1666 — error RE.X for REX			Extremely rare	
1666 — Elephant below bust	£175	£500	£3500	—
1667 —	£65	£250	£2000	—
1668/7 — 8 over 7	£80	£275	—	—
1668 —	£65	£250	£2000	—
1669/8 — 9 over 8	£175	—	—	—
1669 —	£125	£300	£2250	—
1670/69 — 70 over 69	£100	£400	—	—
1670 —	£65	£250	£1850	—
1671 —	£65	£250	£1850	—
1671 Third bust	£65	£250	£1750	—
1672 —	£65	£250	£1750	—
1673 —	£65	£250	£1750	—
1674 —			Extremely rare	
1675 —	£175	—	—	—
1675/3 —	£175	£600	—	—
1676 —	£65	£250	£1700	—
1677 —	£65	£240	£1700	—
1677/6 — 7 over 6	£100	£400	—	—
1678/7 —	£75	£300	—	—
1678/7 — 8 over 7	£100	—	—	—
1679 —	£65	£250	£1700	—
1679 Fourth bust	£65	£250	£1800	—
1680 Third bust	£65	£250	£1850	—
1680/79 — 80 over 79	£100	—	—	—
1680 Fourth bust	£65	£250	£1850	—
1680/79 — 80 over 79	£100	—	—	—
1681 —	£65	£250	£1850	—
1681 — Elephant & Castle below bust	£500	£1000	—	—
1682/1 —	£70	£300	£1850	—
1682 — edge error QVRRTO for QVARTO	£175	—	—	—
1683 —	£75	£350	£2000	—
1684 —	£110	£500	—	—

JAMES II (1685–88)

	F	VF	EF	UNC
1686 First bust	£85	£340	£1300	—
1686 — No stops on obv	£100	£340	—	—
1687 Second bust	£75	£300	£900	—
1688/7 — 8 over 7	£100	£350	—	—
*1688 —	£75	£300	£900	—

WILLIAM AND MARY (1688–94)

	F	VF	EF	UNC
1691	£175	£475	£1850	—
1692	£175	£460	£1850	—
1692 2 over upside down 2	£175	£450	£1850	—

DATE	F	VF	EF	UNC

WILLIAM III (1694–1702)

	F	VF	EF	UNC
1695 First bust	£50	£160	£500	—
1696 — no stops on obv.	£150	—	—	—
1996 — no stops obv./rev.	£250	—	—	—
1696 — GEI for DEI	£80	£250	—	—
1696 —	£50	£160	£500	—
1696 Second bust				Unique
1696 Third bust	£50	£160	£550	—
1697 —	£200	£750	£1000	—
1700 Third bust variety edge year DUODECIMO	£80	£200	£650	—
1700 — edge year Duodecimo Tertio	£80	£200	£650	—

ANNE (1702–14)

	F	VF	EF	UNC
1703 First bust, VIGO	£130	£380	£1200	—
1705 — Plumes in angles on rev.	£250	£600	£2000	—
1706 — Roses & Plumes in angles on rev.	£140	£350	£950	—
1707 — Roses & Plumes in angles on rev.	£140	£350	£950	—
1707 Second bust, E below	£80	£230	£725	—
1707 — Plain	£80	£250	£750	—
1708 — E below	£80	£250	£725	—
1708/7 — 8 over 7	£110	£400	—	—
1708 — Plain	£80	£225	£750	—
1708 — — error BR for BRI		Extremely rare		
1708 — Plumes in angles on rev.	£125	£350	£1100	—
*1713 Third bust, Roses & Plumes rev.	£150	£420	£1100	—

GEORGE I (1714–27)

	F	VF	EF	UNC
1716	£240	£475	£1400	—
1718 8 over 6	£240	£475	£1550	—
1720 20 over 18	£240	£475	£1550	—
1723 SSC in angles on rev(South Sea Co.)	£280	£475	£1300	—
1726	£250	£550	£1800	—

GEORGE II (1727–60)

	F	VF	EF	UNC
1732 Young head, Plain Proof	—	—	£3000	—
1732 — Roses & Plumes in angles on rev .	£150	£325	£800	—
1734 —	£150	£325	£800	—
1735 —	£150	£325	£800	—
1736 —	£165	£350	£900	—
1739 — Roses in angles on rev	£150	£325	£675	—
1741 —	£150	£325	£675	—
1743 Old head, Roses in angles on rev	£125	£300	£700	—
*1746 — LIMA below bust	£125	£300	£700	—
1746 — Plain Proof	—	—	£1750	—
1750 — Plain	£190	£370	£900	—
1751 —	£225	£475	£1100	—

GEORGE III (1760–1820)

	F	VF	EF	UNC
Dollar with oval counterstamp	£80	£180	£400	—
Dollar with octagonal counterstamp	£100	£200	£450	—
1804 Bank of England Dollar, Britannia rev.	£70	£120	£300	—
1818 LVIII	£20	£60	£225	£450
1818 LIX	£20	£60	£225	£450
1819 LIX 9 over 8	£25	£90	£250	—
1819 no stops on edge	£50	£120	£250	£550
1819 LIX	£20	£60	£225	£450
1819 LX	£20	£60	£225	£450
1820 LX	£20	£60	£225	£450
1820 LX 20 over 19	£30	£75	£250	—

DATE	MINTAGE	F	VF	EF	UNC

GEORGE IV (1820–30)

	MINTAGE	F	VF	EF	UNC
1821 First bust, St George rev.					
SECUNDO on edge		£20	£70	£270	£650
1821 — — Proof	—	—	—	£2000
1821 — — Proof TERTIO (error edge)	—	—	—	£3000
1822 — — SECUNDO		£20	£80	£350	£900
1822 — — TERTIO		£20	£70	£320	£750
1823 — — Proof only		Extremely rare			
1826 Second bust, shield rev, SEPTIMO					
Proof only	—	—	£1750	£2250	

WILLIAM IV (1830–37)

	MINTAGE	F	VF	EF	UNC
1831 Proof only W.W. on truncation		—	—	£2500	£4500
1831 Proof only W. WYON on truncation ...		—	—	£3000	£5250
1834 Proof only		—	—	—	—

VICTORIA (1837–1901)

YOUNG HEAD ISSUES

	MINTAGE	F	VF	EF	UNC
1839 Proof only	—	—	—	—	£2500
1844 Star stops on edge	94,248	£30	£140	£600	£1800
1844 Cinquefoil stops on edge ...	*incl. above*	£30	£140	£600	£1800
1845 Star stops on edge	159,192	£30	£140	£600	£1800
1845 Cinquefoil stops on edge ...	*incl. above*	£30	£140	£600	£1800
1847	140,976	£35	£150	£625	£2000
1847 "Gothic" Proof only UNDECIMO					
edge	8,000	£250	£450	£650	£1500
1847 Plain edge, Proof only	—	—	—	£800	£1800
1853 D. SEPTIMO edge, Proof only	460	—	—	—	£5000
1853 Plain edge, Proof only	—	—	—	—	£5000

JUBILEE HEAD ISSUES

	MINTAGE	F	VF	EF	UNC
*1887	173,581	£10	£22	£45	£70
1887 Proof	1,084	—	—	—	£300
1888 Narrow date	131,899	£12	£25	£60	£120
1888 Wide date		£15	£30	£80	£140
1889	1,807,224	£10	£20	£40	£75
1890	997,862	£12	£25	£60	£100
1891	556,394	£12	£25	£60	£100
1892	451,334	£12	£25	£60	£110

OLD HEAD ISSUES (Regnal date on edge in Roman numerals)

	MINTAGE	F	VF	EF	UNC
1893 LVI	497,845	£12	£24	£70	£150
1893 LVII	*incl. above*	£14	£35	£150	£350
1893 Proof	1,312	—	—	—	£350
1894 LVII	144,906	£14	£40	£85	£160
1894 LVIII	*incl. above*	£14	£40	£85	£160
1895 LVIII	252,862	£12	£32	£85	£150
1895 LIX	*incl. above*	£12	£32	£85	£150
1896 LIX	317,599	£14	£32	£125	£300
1896 LX	*incl. above*	£12	£32	£80	£150
1897 LX	262,118	£12	£32	£80	£150
1897 LXI	*incl. above*	£12	£32	£80	£150
1898 LXI	166,150	£14	£35	£90	£200
1898 LXII	*incl. above*	£12	£32	£80	£160
1899 LXII	166,300	£12	£32	£80	£160
1899 LXIII	*incl. above*	£12	£32	£80	£160
1900 LXIII	353,356	£12	£32	£70	£150
1900 LXIV	*incl. above*	£12	£32	£70	£145

EDWARD VII (1901–10)

	MINTAGE	F	VF	EF	UNC
1902	256,020	£20	£40	£85	£120
1902 "Matt Proof"	15,123	—	—	—	£110

Victoria, young head

Victoria, Jubilee head

DATE	MINTAGE	F	VF	EF	UNC

GEORGE V (1910–36)

DATE	MINTAGE	F	VF	EF	UNC
1927 Proof only	15,030	—	£55	£85	£125
1928	9,034	£45	£65	£110	£150
1929	4,994	£45	£65	£110	£155
1930	4,847	£45	£65	£120	£170
1931	4,056	£45	£65	£110	£150
1932	2,395	£80	£130	£210	£340
1933	7,132	£45	£65	£110	£150
*1934	932	£325	£525	£1000	£1500
1935 Jubilee issue	714,769	£8	£12	£16	£25
1935 Specimen in box	—	—	—	—	£35
1935 Proof. Raised Edge inscription	2,500	—	—	£150	£200
1936	2,473	£70	£140	£225	£340

GEORGE VI (1936–52)

DATE	MINTAGE	F	VF	EF	UNC
1937 Coronation	418,699	£9	£14	£20	£30
1937 Proof	26,402	—	—	—	£30
1951 Festival of Britain, Proof-like	1,983,540	—	—	£3	£5

ELIZABETH II (1952–   )

DATE	MINTAGE	F	VF	EF	UNC
Pre-Decimal issues (Five Shillings)					
*1953	5,962,621	—	—	£3	£6
1953 Proof	40,000	—	—	—	£15
1960	1,024,038	—	—	£3	£6
1960 Polished dies	70,000	—	—	—	£8
1965	19,640,000	—	—	—	£1

Later issues are listed in the Decimal section.

DOUBLE FLORINS

VICTORIA (1837–1901)

DATE	MINTAGE	F	VF	EF	UNC
1887 Roman I	483,347	£9	£20	£40	£60
1887 Roman I Proof	incl. above	—	—	—	£210
1887 Arabic 1	incl. above	£9	£20	£40	£60
1887 Arabic 1 Proof	incl. above	—	—	—	£175
1888	243,340	£11	£27	£55	£80
1888 Second I in VICTORIA an inverted 1	incl. above	£20	£35	£65	£150
1889	1,185,111	£15	£23	£37	£65
1889 inverted 1	incl. above	£15	£33	£65	£150
1890	782,146	£11	£33	£55	£105

Patterns were also produced in 1911, 1914 and 1950 and are all extremely rare.

HALFCROWNS

DATE	MINTAGE	F	VF	EF	UNC

OLIVER CROMWELL

DATE	MINTAGE	F	VF	EF	UNC
1656				Extremely rare	
1658	£300	£525	£925	—	
1658 Proof in Gold				Extremely rare	

CHARLES II (1660–1685)

DATE	MINTAGE	F	VF	EF	UNC
1663 First bust	£60	£300	£1250	—	
1663 — no stops on obv.	£100	£400	—	—	
1664 Second bust	£65	£360	£1750	—	
1666 Third bust	£300	—	—	—	
1666 — Elephant	£175	£450	£2500	—	
1667/4 — 7 over 4			Extremely rare		
1668/4 — 8 over 4	£75	—	—	—	
1669 —	£120	£425	—	—	
1669/4 — 9 over 4	£150	—	—	—	
1670 —	£45	£150	£850	—	
1670 — MRG for MAG	£275	—	—	—	
1671 —	£45	£150	£850	—	
1671/0 — 1 over 0	£45	£150	£850	—	
1672 —	£45	£150	£850	—	
1672 Fourth bust	£50	£175	£1000	—	
1673 —	£45	£150	£850	—	
1673 — Plumes both sides			Extremely rare		
1673 — Plume below bust	£800	—	—	—	
1674 —	£65	£200	—	—	
1675 —	£50	£150	£850	—	
1676 —	£50	£150	£800	—	
1676 — inverted 1 in date	£60	£160	£850	—	
1677 —	£40	£130	£750	—	
1678 —	£100	£300	—	—	
1679 — GRATTA error			Extremely rare		
1679 —	£50	£150	£800	—	
1680 —	£100	£270	—	—	
1681/0 — 1 over 0	£100	—	—	—	
1681 —	£65	£160	£875	—	
1681 — Elephant & Castle	£600	—	—	—	
1682 —	£75	£190	£1350	—	
1683 —	£75	£170	£900	—	
1683 — Plume below bust			Extremely rare		
1684/3 — 4 over 3	£100	£300	£1500	—	

JAMES II (1685–1688)

DATE	MINTAGE	F	VF	EF	UNC
1685 First bust	£70	£180	£650	—	
1686 —	£70	£180	£650	—	
1686/5 — 6 over 5	£100	£350	—	—	
1686 — V over S	£175	£450	—	—	
1687 —	£75	£180	£700	—	
1687/6 — 7 over 6	£100	£350	—	—	
1687 Second bust	£70	£180	£725	—	
1688 —	£70	£180	£725	—	

WILLIAM AND MARY (1688–1694)

DATE	MINTAGE	F	VF	EF	UNC
1689 First busts; first shield	£55	£130	£425	—	
1689 — — no pearls in crown	£55	£130	£425	—	
1689 — — FRA for FR	£100	£200	£650	—	
1689 — — No stop on obv.	£55	£130	£425	—	
1689 — Second shield	£55	£130	£425	—	

DATE	MINTAGE	F	VF	EF	UNC
1689 — — no pearls in crown		£55	£250	£550	—
1690 — —		£60	£175	£575	—
1690 — — error GRETIA for GRATIA		£110	£350	£1000	—
1691 Second busts		£75	£175	£500	—
1692 —		£75	£175	£500	—
1693 —		£75	£175	£500	—
1693 — 3 over inverted 3		£100	£225	—	—

WILLIAM III (1694–1702)

		F	VF	EF	UNC
1696 First bust, large shields, early harp		£30	£80	£275	—
1696 — — — B (Bristol) below bust		£35	£120	£375	—
1696 — — — C (Chester)		£35	£120	£400	—
1696 — — — E (Exeter)		£35	£120	£450	—
1696 — — — N (Norwich)		£60	£170	—	—
1696 — — — Y (York)		£40	£130	£350	—
1696 — — — — Scottish arms at date			Extremely rare		
1696 — — ordinary harp		£65	£180	—	—
1696 — — — C		£65	£200	—	—
1696 — — — E		£65	£200	—	—
1696 — — — N		£75	£285	—	—
1696 — Small shields, ordinary harp		£30	£110	£275	—
1696 — — — B		£35	£140	£475	—
1696 — — — C		£40	£160	£525	—
1696 — — — E		£60	£170	—	—
1696 — — — N		£35	£140	£475	—
1696 — — — y		£35	£140	£475	—
1696 Second bust			Only one known		
1697 First bust, large shields, ordinary harp		£30	£100	£275	—
1697 — — — GRR for GRA			Extremely rare		
1697 — — — B		£32	£120	£350	—
1697 — — — C		£35	£120	£375	—
1697 — — — E		£35	£130	£350	—
1697 — — — N		£35	£130	£375	—
1697 — — — y		£35	£130	£350	—
1698 — —		£40	£120	£300	—
1698/7 — — 8 over 7			Extremely rare		
1699 — —		£60	£170	£475	—
1699 — — Scottish arms at date			Extremely rare		
1700 — —		£50	£130	£375	—
1701 — —		£60	£140	£400	—
1701 — — No stops on rev		£80	£220	—	—
1701 — — Elephant & Castle below			Extremely rare		
1701 — — Plumes in angles on rev.		£70	£230	£600	—

ANNE (1702–1714)

		F	VF	EF	UNC
1703 Plain (pre-Union)		£110	£375	—	—
1703 VIGO below bust		£55	£130	£425	—
1704 Plumes in angles on rev.		£80	£150	£500	—
1705 —		£45	£150	£500	—
1706 Roses & Plumes in angles on rev.		£45	£130	£400	—
*1707 —		£40	£130	£375	—
1707 Plain (post-Union)		£40	£110	£300	—
1707 E below bust		£40	£110	£375	—
1707 — SEPTIMO edge			Extremely rare		
1708 Plain		£35	£100	£260	—
1708 E below bust		£35	£100	£360	—
1708 Plumes in angles on rev.		£35	£110	£400	—
1709 Plain		£35	£110	£300	—
1709 E below bust		£65	£150	—	—
1710 Roses & Plumes in angles on rev.		£40	£120	£375	—
1712 —		£40	£120	£375	—
1713 Plain		£40	£120	£425	—
1713 Roses & Plumes in angles on rev.		£40	£120	£375	—
1714 —		£40	£120	£375	—
1714/3 4 over 3		£100	—	—	—

DATE	MINTAGE	F	VF	EF	UNC

GEORGE I (1714–1727)

DATE	MINTAGE	F	VF	EF	UNC
1715 Roses & Plumes in angles on rev.		£140	£350	£800	—
1715 Plain edge			Extremely rare		
1717 —		£140	£350	£800	—
*1720 —		£140	£350	£800	—
1720/17 20 over 17		£140	£375	—	—
1723 SSC in angles on rev.		£140	£350	£725	—
1726 Small Roses & Plumes in angles on rev..		£800	£1800	—	—

GEORGE II (1727–1760)

DATE	MINTAGE	F	VF	EF	UNC
1731 Young head, Plain, proof only		—	—	£1850	—
1731 — Roses & Plumes in angles on rev.		£60	£140	£400	—
1732 — —		£60	£140	£400	—
1734 — —		£60	£140	£400	—
1735 — —		£60	£150	£400	—
1736 — —		£60	£150	£400	—
1739 — Roses in angles on rev.		£55	£135	£350	—
1741/39 — — 41 over 39		£80	£175	—	—
1741 — —		£55	£135	£350	—
1743 Old head, Roses in angles on rev.		£35	£70	£220	—
1745 — —		£35	£70	£220	—
1745 — LIMA below bust		£30	£60	£175	—
1746 — —		£30	£60	£175	—
1746/5 — — 6 over 5		£40	£100	£275	—
1746 — Plain, Proof		—	—	£750	—
1750 — —		£55	£200	£500	—
1751 — —		£65	£220	£625	—

GEORGE III (1760–1820)

DATE	MINTAGE	F	VF	EF	UNC
1816 "Bull head"	—	£10	£35	£100	£165
1817 —	8,092,656	£10	£35	£100	£170
1817 "Small head"	incl. above	£10	£35	£100	£185
1818 —	2,905,056	£10	£35	£100	£185
1819/8 — 9 over 8	incl. above		Extremely rare		
1819 —	4,790,016	£10	£35	£100	£185
1820 —	2,396,592	£14	£45	£130	£260

GEORGE IV (1820–30)

DATE	MINTAGE	F	VF	EF	UNC
1820 First bust, first reverse	incl. above	£12	£35	£125	£240
1821 — —	1,435,104	£12	£35	£125	£240
1821 — — Proof	incl. above	—	—	—	£650
1823 — —	2,003,760	£250	£500	£1750	—
1823 — Second reverse	incl. above	£14	£40	£125	£240
1824 — —	465,696	£16	£45	£150	£260
1824 Second bust, third reverse .	incl. above		Extremely rare		
*1825 — —	2,258,784	£14	£35	£100	£225
1826 — —	2,189,088	£14	£35	£100	£225
1826 — — Proof	incl. above	—	—	£325	£450
1828 — —	49,890	£40	£70	£175	£375
1829 — —	508,464	£35	£70	£175	£325

WILLIAM IV (1830–37)

DATE	MINTAGE	F	VF	EF	UNC
1831	—		Extremely rare		
1831 Proof (W.W. in script & block)	—	—	—	£350	£600
1834 W.W. in block	993,168	£12	£45	£150	£275
1834 W.W. in script	incl. above	£12	£45	£150	£275
1835	281,952	£12	£45	£150	£275
*1836	1,588,752	£12	£35	£130	£260
1836/5 6 over 5	incl. above	£20	£60	£250	—
1837	150,526	£12	£50	£170	£300

DATE	MINTAGE	F	VF	EF	UNC

VICTORIA (1837–1901)

YOUNG HEAD ISSUES

DATE	MINTAGE	F	VF	EF	UNC
1839 (two varieties)	—	£400	£800	£2000	—
1839 Proof	—	—	—	—	£1000
1840	386,496	£30	£100	£200	£350
1841	42,768	£300	£600	£1500	£2200
1842	486,288	£30	£70	£200	£350
1843	454,608	£60	£150	£600	£900
*1844	1,999,008	£20	£50	£160	£300
1845	2,231,856	£20	£50	£160	£300
1846	1,539,668	£20	£50	£175	£325
1848 Plain 8	367,488	£45	£100	£400	£700
1848/6	incl. above	£35	£90	£300	£600
1849	261,360	£35	£75	£250	£500
1849 Small date	incl. above	£50	£100	£400	£600
1850	484,613	£30	£70	£250	£400
1853 Proof only	—	—	—	—	£1800
1874	2,188,599	£15	£35	£90	£175
1875	1,113,483	£15	£35	£90	£175
1876	633,221	£15	£35	£90	£175
1876/5 6 over 5	incl. above	£20	£50	£175	£375
1877	447,059	£15	£35	£90	£175
1878	1,466,323	£15	£35	£90	£175
1879	901,356	£20	£40	£130	£240
1880	1,346,350	£15	£35	£90	£150
1881	2,301,495	£15	£35	£90	£150
1882	808,227	£15	£35	£90	£150
1883	2,982,779	£15	£35	£90	£150
1884	1,569,175	£15	£35	£90	£150
1885	1,628,438	£15	£35	£90	£150
1886	891,767	£15	£35	£90	£150
1887	1,438,046	£15	£35	£90	£150

JUBILEE HEAD ISSUES

DATE	MINTAGE	F	VF	EF	UNC
1887	incl. above	£5	£8	£15	£35
1887 Proof	1,084	—	—	—	£125
1888	1,428,787	£8	£14	£35	£60
1889	4,811,954	£8	£14	£35	£60
1890	3,228,111	£8	£14	£45	£65
1891	2,284,632	£8	£15	£45	£75
1892	1,710,946	£8	£14	£45	£70

OLD HEAD ISSUES

DATE	MINTAGE	F	VF	EF	UNC
1893	1,792,600	£6	£14	£35	£60
1893 Proof	1,312	—	—	—	135
1894	1,524,960	£10	£24	£50	£85
1895	1,772,662	£8	£18	£45	£70
1896	2,148,505	£7	£15	£40	£70
1897	1,678,643	£7	£15	£40	£65
1898	1,870,055	£7	£15	£40	£65
1899	2,865,872	£7	£15	£40	£65
1900	4,479,128	£7	£15	£40	£65
1901	1,516,570	£7	£15	£40	£65

EDWARD VII (1901–10)

DATE	MINTAGE	F	VF	EF	UNC
1902	1,316,008	£6	£18	£50	£65
1902 "Matt Proof"	15,123	—	—	—	£60
*1903	274,840	£50	£120	£400	£850
1904	709,652	£50	£120	£350	£600
1905	166,008	£150	£350	£750	£1400
1906	2,886,206	£8	£30	£90	£160
1907	3,693,930	£8	£30	£90	£175
1908	1,758,889	£12	£40	£160	£400
1909	3,051,592	£8	£30	£100	£275
1910	2,557,685	£8	£25	£70	£140

GEORGE V (1910–36)

First issue

DATE	MINTAGE	F	VF	EF	UNC
1911	2,914,573	£6	£18	£35	£70
1911 Proof	6,007	—	—	—	£75
1912	4,700,789	£5	£12	£35	£65

George V first type reverse

DATE	MINTAGE	F	VF	EF	UNC
1913	4,090,169	£5	£12	£40	£80
1914	18,333,003	£3	£8	£22	£35
1915	32,433,066	£3	£8	£18	£35
1916	29,530,020	£3	£8	£18	£35
1917	11,172,052	£3	£8	£20	£40
1918	29,079,592	£3	£8	£18	£35
1919	10,266,737	£4	£10	£22	£45

Second issue—*debased silver*

1920	17,982,077	£2	£7	£15	£40
1921	23,677,889	£2	£7	£16	£40
1922	16,396,724	£2	£7	£16	£40
1923	26,308,526	£6	£7	£15	£28
1924	5,866,294	£6	£12	£40	£70
1925	1,413,461	£8	£25	£100	£200
1926	4,473,516	£4	£12	£35	£70

Third issue—*Modified effigy*

1926	incl. above	£4	£10	£25	£60
1927	6,837,872	£3	£8	£24	£40

Fourth issue—*New shield reverse*

1927 Proof	15,000	—	—	—	£35
1928	18,762,727	£2	£5	£12	£25
1929	17,632,636	£2	£5	£12	£25
1930	809,051	£5	£35	£90	£180
1931	11,264,468	£2	£5	£15	£25
1932	4,793,643	£2	£5	£18	£55
1933	10,311,494	£2	£5	£15	£35
1934	2,422,399	£3	£8	£35	£70
1935	7,022,216	£2	£5	£12	£16
*1936	7,039,423	£2	£5	£10	£15

George V, fourth issue, new shield reverse

GEORGE VI (1936–52)

1937	9,106,440	—	£2	£4	£10
1937 Proof	26,402	—	—	—	£12
1938	6,426,478	£1	£3	£10	£17
1939	15,478,635	—	£1	£3	£8
1940	17,948,439	—	£1	£3	£6
1941	15,773,984	—	£1	£3	£6
1942	31,220,090	—	£1	£3	£6
1943	15,462,875	—	£1	£3	£6
*1944	15,255,165	—	£1	£3	£6
1945	19,849,242	—	£1	£3	£6
1946	22,724,873	—	£1	£3	£6

Cupro-nickel

1947	21,911,484	—	£1	£2	£4
1948	71,164,703	—	£1	£2	£4
1949	28,272,512	—	£1	£2	£6
1950	28,335,500	—	£1	£2	£6
1950 Proof	17,513	—	£1	£2	£9
1951	9,003,520	—	£1	£2	£6
1951 Proof	20,000	—	—	—	£9
1952			Only one known		

ELIZABETH II (1952–   )

1953	4,333,214	—	—	£1	£3
1953 Proof	40,000	—	—	—	£5
1954	11,614,953	£1	£3	£15	
1955	23,628,726	—	£1	£4	
1956	33,934,909	—	£1	£4	
1957	34,200,563	—	£1	£4	
1958	15,745,668	—	£1	£3	£15
1959	9,028,844	—	£1	£5	£18
1960	19,929,191	—	£1	£2	
1961	25,887,897	—	—	£1	
1961 Polished dies	incl. above	—	—	£1	£2
1962	24,013,312	—	—	£1	
1963	17,625,200	—	—	£1	
1964	5,973,600	—	—	£1	
1965	9,778,440	—	—	£1	
1966	13,375,200	—	—	£1	
1967	33,058,400	—	—	—	

FLORINS

DATE	MINTAGE	F	VF	EF	UNC

VICTORIA (1837–1901)

YOUNG (CROWNED) HEAD ISSUES
"Godless" type (without D.G.—"Dei Gratia")

1848 "Godless" Pattern only plain edge	—			Very rare	
1848 "Godless" Pattern only milled edge	—			Extremely rare	
*1849	413,820	£10	£26	£75	£150

"Gothic" type i.e. date in Roman numerals in obverse legend
"brit." in legend. No die no.

1851 mdcccli Proof	1,540			Extremely rare	
1852 mdccclii	1,014,552	£15	£40	£100	£200
1853 mdcccliii	3,919,950	£15	£40	£100	£200
1853 — Proof	incl. above	—	—	—	£1200
1854 mdcccliv	550,413	£500	—	—	—
1855 mdccclv	831,017	£15	£40	£100	£200
1856 mdccclvi	2,201,760	£15	£40	£100	£200
1857 mdccclvii	1,671,120	£15	£40	£100	£200
1858 mdccclviii	2,239,380	£15	£40	£100	£200
1859 mdccclix	2,568,060	£15	£40	£100	£200
1860 mdccclx	1,475,100	£18	£45	£135	£300
1862 mdccclxii	594,000	£70	£180	£500	£1000
1863 mdccclxiii	938,520	£175	£350	£1000	£1500

"brit" in legend. Die no. below bust

1864 mdccclxiv	1,861,200	£15	£40	£100	£200
1864 Gothic Piedfort flan	incl. above			Extremely rare	
1865 mdccclxv	1,580,044	£15	£40	£100	£200
1866 mdccclxvi	914,760	£15	£40	£100	£200
*1867 mdccclxvii	423,720	£22	£70	£225	£425
1867—only 42 arcs in border	incl. above			Extremely rare	

"britt" in legend. Die no. below bust

1868 mdccclxviii	896,940	£15	£40	£100	£200
1869 mdccclxix	297,000	£20	£45	£140	£275
1870 mdccclxx	1,080,648	£15	£38	£100	£180
1871 mdccclxxi	3,425,605	£15	£38	£100	£175
1872 mdccclxxii	7,199,690	£12	£38	£100	£175
1873 mdccclxxiii	5,921,839	£12	£38	£100	£175
1874 mdccclxxiv	1,642,630	£12	£38	£100	£175
1874 — iv over iii in date	incl. above	£25	£60	£140	£220
1875 mdccclxxv	1,117,030	£12	£38	£100	£175
1876 mdccclxxvi	580,034	£12	£38	£100	£200
1877 mdccclxxvii	682,292	£12	£38	£100	£175
1877 — 48 arcs in border no W.W.	incl. above	£15	£45	£125	£240
1877 — 42 arcs	incl. above	£15	£45	£125	£240
1877 — — no die number	incl. above			Extremely rare	
1878 mdccclxxviii with die number	1,786,680	£14	£40	£120	£200
1879 mdcccixxix no die no	1,512,247			Extremely rare	
1879 — 48 arcs in border	incl. above	£12	£35	£120	£200
1879 — no die number	incl. above			Extremely rare	
1879 — 38 arcs, no W.W...	incl. above	£12	£45	£125	£220
1880 mdccclxxx Younger portrait	—			Extremely rare	
1880 — 34 arcs, Older portrait	2,167,170	£12	£40	£100	£200
1881 mdccclxxxi — —	2,570,337	£12	£40	£100	£160
1881 — xxⲅi broken puncheon ...	incl. above	£20	£60	£140	£220
1883 mdccclxxxiii — —	3,555,667	£12	£40	£100	£175
1884 mdccclxxxiv — —	1,447,379	£12	£40	£100	£175
1885 mdccclxxxv — —	1,758,210	£12	£40	£100	£175
1886 mdccclxxxvi — —	591,773	£12	£40	£90	£150
1887 mdccclxxxvii — —	1,776,903	£18	£60	£175	£320
1887 — 46 arcs	incl. above	£20	£65	£200	£360

"Godless" florin

"Gothic" florin

DATE	MINTAGE	F	VF	EF	UNC
JUBILEE HEAD ISSUES					
1887	*incl. above*	£3	£7	£16	£30
1887 Proof	1,084	—	—	—	£90
1888	1,547,540	£4	£8	£30	£50
1889	2,973,561	£4	£10	£30	£50
1890	1,684,737	£7	£20	£60	£120
1891	836,438	£12	£40	£100	£185
1892	283,401	£20	£55	£150	£320
VICTORIA—OLD HEAD ISSUES					
1893	1,666,103	£4	£12	£30	£50
1893 Proof	1,312	—	—	—	£100
1894	1,952,842	£8	£22	£50	£100
1895	2,182,968	£6	£20	£50	£85
1896	2,944,416	£5	£16	£40	£65
1897	1,699,921	£5	£16	£40	£65
1898	3,061,343	£5	£16	£40	£65
1899	3,966,953	£5	£16	£40	£65
*1900	5,528,630	£5	£16	£40	£65
1901	2,648,870	£5	£16	£40	£65

EDWARD VII (1901–10)

DATE	MINTAGE	F	VF	EF	UNC
*1902	2,189,575	£5	£12	£35	£65
1902 "Matt Proof"	15,123	—	—	—	£50
1903	1,995,298	£10	£30	£75	£200
1904	2,769,932	£10	£30	£75	£200
1905	1,187,596	£25	£60	£250	£550
1906	6,910,128	£9	£30	£75	£175
1907	5,947,895	£11	£30	£75	£175
1908	3,280,010	£10	£38	£120	£275
1909	3,482,829	£9	£32	£110	£200
1910	5,650,713	£7	£24	£65	£110

GEORGE V (1910–36)

DATE	MINTAGE	F	VF	EF	UNC
First issue					
1911	5,951,284	£3	£8	£25	£55
1911 Proof	6,007	—	—	—	£60
1912	8,571,731	£3	£11	£30	£65
1913	4,545,278	£5	£16	£35	£75
1914	21,252,701	£3	£14	£22	£40
1915	12,367,939	£3	£14	£22	£40
1916	21,064,337	£3	£14	£22	£40
1917	11,181,617	£3	£14	£22	£45
1918	29,211,792	£3	£14	£22	£40
1919	9,469,292	£3	£15	£30	£55
Second issue —*debased silver*					
1920	15,387,833	£2	£12	£32	£55
1921	34,863,895	£2	£12	£30	£45
1922	23,861,044	£2	£12	£30	£45
1923	21,546,533	£2	£10	£25	£40
1924	4,582,372	£4	£14	£45	£80
1925	1,404,136	£10	£32	£100	£175
1926	5,125,410	£5	£15	£40	£70
Fourth issue—*new reverse*					
1927 Proof only	101,497	—	—	—	£35
1928	11,087,186	£2	£4	£12	£25
1929	16,397,279	£2	£4	£12	£25
1930	5,753,568	£2	£5	£15	£35
1931	6,556,331	£2	£5	£12	£28
1932	717,041	£7	£16	£80	£175
1933	8,685,303	£2	£5	£14	£32
1935	7,540,546	£2	£5	£10	£20
*1936	9,897,448	£2	£4	£9	£16

DATE	MINTAGE	F	VF	EF	UNC

GEORGE VI (1936–52)

DATE	MINTAGE	F	VF	EF	UNC
1937	13,006,781	—	£1	£3	£6
1937 Proof	26,402	—	—	—	£8
1938	7,909,388	£1	£2	£8	£16
1939	20,850,607	£1	£2	£3	£5
1940	18,700,338	£1	£2	£3	£5
1941	24,451,079	£1	£2	£3	£5
1942	39,895,243	£1	£2	£3	£5
1943	26,711,987	£1	£2	£3	£5
*1944	27,560,005	£1	£2	£3	£5
1945	25,858,049	£1	£2	£3	£5
1946	22,300,254	£1	£2	£3	£5
1947	22,910,085	—	—	£1	£3
1948	67,553,636	—	—	£1	£3
1949	28,614,939	—	—	£1	£5
1950	24,357,490	—	—	£2	£7
1950 Proof	17,513	—	—	£1	£8
1951	27,411,747	—	—	£2	£8
1951 Proof	20,000	—	—	—	£8

ELIZABETH II (1952–   )

DATE	MINTAGE	F	VF	EF	UNC
1953	11,958,710	—	—	—	£2
1953 Proof	40,000	—	—	—	£5
1954	13,085,422	—	—	£5	£15
1955	25,887,253	—	—	£1	£3
1956	47,824,500	—	—	£1	£3
1957	33,071,282	—	—	£4	£15
1958	9,564,580	—	—	£3	£14
1959	14,080,319	—	—	£4	£15
1960	13,831,782	—	—	£1	£3
1961	37,735,315	—	—	£1	£2
1962	35,147,903	—	—	£1	£2
1963	26,471,000	—	—	£1	£2
1964	16,539,000	—	—	£1	£2
1965	48,163,000	—	—	—	£1.50
1966	83,999,000	—	—	—	£1.50
1967	39,718,000	—	—	—	£1.50

SHILLINGS

OLIVER CROMWELL

		F	VF	EF	UNC
1658		£275	£450	£850	—
1658 Dutch Copy				Extremely rare	

CHARLES II (1660–85)

		F	VF	EF	UNC
*1663 First bust		£50	£130	£425	—
1663 — GARTIA error				Extremely rare	
1663 — Irish & Scottish shields transposed		£125	£450	—	—
1666 — Elephant below bust		£200	£550	£1500	—
1666 "Guinea" head, elephant		£500	£950	—	—
1666 Second bust				Extremely rare	
1668 —		£50	£130	£425	—
1668/7 — 8 over 7		£55	£125	—	—
1669/6 First bust variety				Extremely rare	
1669 Second bust				Extremely rare	
1670 —		£65	£220	£550	—
1671 —		£80	£250	£725	—
1671 — Plume below, plume in centre rev.		£160	£350	£1100	—
1672 —		£55	£150	£475	—
1673 —		£75	£250	£675	—
1673 — Plume below, plume in centre rev.		£170	£350	£1150	—
1673/2 — 3 over 2		£100	£350	—	—

DATE	F	VF	EF	UNC
1674/3 — 4 over 3	£100	£350	—	—
1674 —	£75	£250	£675	—
1674 — Plume below bust, plume in centre rev.	£170	£370	£1100	—
1674 — Plume rev. only	£170	£375	£1100	—
1674 Third bust	£225	£575	—	—
1675 Second bust	£90	£275	—	—
1675/4 — 5 over 4	£140	£450	—	—
1675 — Plume below bust, plume in centre rev.	£170	£375	£1100	—
1675 Third bust	£175	£450	—	—
1675/3 — 5 over 3	£200	£500	—	—
1676 Second bust	£55	£160	£425	—
1676/5 — 6 over 5	£80	£270	—	—
1676 — Plume below bust, plume in centre rev.	£170	£360	£1050	—
1677 —	£65	£160	£500	—
1677 — Plume below bust	£180	£400	£1200	—
1678 —	£70	£220	£650	—
1678/7 — 8 over 7	£80	£300	—	—
1679 —	£60	£170	£500	—
1679 — Plume below bust, plume in centre rev.	£180	£400	£1100	—
1679 — Plume below bust	£180	£400	£1100	—
1679 — 9 over 7	£80	£300	—	—
1680 —	£225	—	—	—
1680 — Plume below bust, plume in centre rev.	£180	£425	£1100	—
1680/79 — — 80 over 79	£300	£800	—	—
1681 —	£80	£275	£800	—
1681/0 — 1 over 0	£80	£275	£800	—
1681/0 — — Elephant & Castle below bust	£750	—	—	—
1682/1 — 2 over 1	£200	£600	—	—
1683 —	£600	—	—	—
1683 Fourth bust	£120	£350	£850	—
1684 —	£120	£335	£850	—

William III First bust

JAMES II (1685–88)

1685	£80	£200	£500	—
1685 Plume in centre rev. rev		Extremely rare		
1685 No stops on rev.	£125	£400	—	—
1686	£80	£200	£500	—
1686/5 6 over 5	£80	£200	£500	—
1687	£85	£220	£525	—
1687/6 7 over 6	£85	£220	£525	—
1688	£85	£235	£550	—
1688/7 last 8 over 7	£90	£250	—	—

William III Second bust

WILLIAM & MARY (1688–94)

1692	£80	£230	£575	—
1692 inverted 1	£90	£250	£600	—
1693	£80	£230	£575	—

William III Third bust

WILLIAM III (1694–1702)

Provincially produced shillings carry privy marks or initials below the bust:
B: Bristol. C: Chester. E: Exeter. N: Norwich. Y or y: York.

1695 First bust	£25	£60	£175	—
1696 —	£20	£55	£160	—
1696 — no stops on rev.	£30	£85	£270	—
1696 — MAB for MAG		Extremely rare		
1696 — 1669 error		Extremely rare		
1696 — 1669 various GVLELMVS errors		Extremely rare		
1696 — B below bust	£30	£70	£225	—
1696 — C	£30	£70	£240	—
1696 — E	£30	£75	£240	—
1696 — N	£30	£75	£260	—
1696 — y	£30	£80	£260	—

William III Fourth bust

William III Fifth bust

DATE	F	VF	EF	UNC
1696 — Y	£25	£85	£280	—
1696 Second bust		Only one known		
1696 Third bust C below	£75	£175	£500	—
1696 — Y	£300	—	—	—
1697 First bust	£24	£60	£175	—
1697 — GRI for GRA error		Extremely rare		
1697 — Scottish & Irish shields transposed		Extremely rare		
1697 — Irish arms at date		Extremely rare		
1697 — no stops on rev	£30	£80	£200	—
1697 — GVLELMVS error		Extremely rare		
1697 — B	£30	£70	£260	—
1697 — C	£30	£70	£260	—
1697 — E	£30	£70	£260	—
1697 — N	£30	£70	£260	—
1697 — — no stops on obv.		Extremely rare		
1697 — y	£30	£70	£260	—
1697 — — arms of France & Ireland transposed		Extremely rare		
1697 — Y	£30	£75	£275	—
1697 Third bust	£24	£75	£160	—
1697 — B	£30	£75	£275	—
1697 — C	£30	£75	£275	—
1697 — — Fr.a error	£40	£100	—	—
1697 — — no stops on rev.	£60	£125	—	—
1697 — — arms of Scotland at date		Extremely rare		
1697 — E	£30	£75	£275	—
1697 — N	£30	£75	£275	—
1697 — y	£30	£75	£275	—
1697 Third bust variety	£24	£60	£175	—
1697 — B	£30	£75	£275	—
1697 — C	£50	£175	—	—
1698 —	£40	£100	£300	—
1698 — Plumes in angles of rev.	£60	£250	£600	—
1698 Fourth bust "Flaming hair"	£80	£250	£750	—
1699 —	£80	£250	£750	—
1699 Fifth bust	£60	£120	£440	—
1699 — Plumes in angles on rev.	£60	£180	£500	—
1699 — Roses in angles on rev.	£60	£180	£550	—
1700 —	£35	£75	£200	—
1700 — Small round oo in date	£35	£75	£200	—
1700 — no stop after DEI		Extremely rare		
1700 — Plume below bust	£800	—	—	—
1701 —	£50	£115	£275	—
1701 — Plumes in angles on rev.	£70	£175	£450	—

Anne, VIGO below bust

ANNE (1702–14)

	F	VF	EF	UNC
1702 First bust (pre-Union with Scotland)	£35	£80	£250	—
1702 — Plumes in angles on rev.	£35	£90	£275	—
*1702 — VIGO below bust	£35	£80	£240	—
1702 — — colon before ANNA		Extremely rare		
1703 Second bust, VIGO below	£35	£80	£240	—
1704 — Plain	£200	—	—	—
1704 — Plumes in angles on rev.	£40	£120	£375	—
1705 — Plain	£40	£120	£340	—
1705 — Plumes in angles on rev.	£35	£110	£325	—
1705 — Roses & Plumes in angles on rev.	£35	£110	£325	—
1707 — —	£30	£110	£325	—
1707 Second bust (post-Union) E below bust	£25	£55	£220	—
1707 — E* below bust	£60	£140	£400	—
1707 Third bust, Plain	£25	£60	£140	—
1707 — Plumes in angles on rev.	£35	£90	£375	—
1707 — E below bust	£25	£60	£220	—
1707 "Edinburgh" bust, E* below		Extremely rare		
1708 Second bust, E below	£25	£60	£250	—
1708 — E below bust	£30	£100	£300	—
1708/7 — — 8 over 7		Extremely rare		
1708 — Roses & Plumes in angles on rev.	£70	£200	£425	—
1708 Third bust, Plain	£25	£55	£160	—
1708 — Plumes in angles on rev.	£35	£90	£250	—

Anne, E below bust

DATE	MINTAGE	F	VF	EF	UNC
1708 Third bust, E below bust		£35	£110	£260	—
1708/7 — — 8 over 7		£60	£150	—	—
1708 — Roses & Plumes in angles on rev.		£30	£90	£275	—
1708 "Edinburgh" bust, E* below		£35	£100	£300	—
1709 Third bust, Plain		£25	£60	£170	—
1709 "Edinburgh" bust, E* below		£35	£100	£300	—
1709 — E no star (filled in die?)		£60	£150	£300	—
1710 Third bust, Roses & Plumes in angles		£35	£80	£250	—
1710 Fourth bust, Roses & Plumes in angles ...		£35	£100	£260	—
1711 Third bust, Plain		£60	£120	£325	—
1711 Fourth bust, Plain		£20	£40	£125	—
1712 — Roses & Plumes in angles on rev.		£30	£65	£190	—
1713 — —		£30	£65	£190	—
1713/2 — 3 over 2		£40	£125	—	—
1714 — —		£30	£65	£190	—
1714/3 — —				Extremely rare	

GEORGE I (1714–27)

DATE	MINTAGE	F	VF	EF	UNC
*1715 First bust, Roses & Plumes in angles on rev.		£35	£80	£260	—
1716 — —		£60	£150	£400	—
1717 — —		£35	£90	£260	—
1718 — —		£30	£70	£210	—
1719 — —		£70	£150	£550	—
1720 — —		£30	£75	£200	—
1720/18 — —		£40	£85	£250	—
1720 — Plain		£22	£65	£200	—
1721 — Roses & Plumes in angles on rev.		£40	£100	£350	—
1721/0 — — 1 over 0		£40	£100	£350	—
1721 — Plain		£100	£225	£700	—
172170 — — 1 over 0		£100	£225	£700	—
1721/19 — — 21 over 19		£125	£250		—
1722 — Roses & Plumes in angles on rev.		£50	£150	£500	—
1723 — —		£50	£150	£425	—
1723 — SSC in angles of rev.		£15	£35	£120	—
1723 — SSC rev., Arms of France at date		£60	£120	£425	—
1723 Second bust, SSC in angles on rev.		£25	£70	£260	—
1723 Second bust, Roses & Plumes in angles .		£40	£120	£400	—
1723 — WCC (Welsh Copper Co) below bust ..		£220	£500	£1800	—
1724 — Roses & Plumes in angles on rev.		£35	£90	£260	—
1724 — WCC below bust		£220	£500	£2000	—
1725 — Roses & Plumes in angles on rev.		£35	£100	£280	—
1725 — — no stops on obv.		£50	£130	£320	—
1725 — WCC below bust		£220	£500	£2000	—
1726 — —.		£220	£500	£2000	—
1726 — Roses & Plumes in angles on rev.		£200	£700		—
1727 — —				Extremely rare	
1727 — — no stops on obv.				Extremely rare	

GEORGE II (1727–60)

DATE	MINTAGE	F	VF	EF	UNC
1727 Young head, Plumes in angles on rev.		£35	£110	£320	—
1727 — Roses & Plumes in angles on rev.		£35	£100	£260	—
1728 — —		£35	£100	£320	—
1728 — Plain		£38	£110	£350	—
1729 — Roses & Plumes in angles on rev.		£35	£100	£275	—
1731 — —		£35	£80	£190	—
1731 — Plumes in angles on rev.		£40	£125	£375	—
1732 — Roses & Plumes in angles on rev.		£35	£80	£200	—
1734 — —		£35	£80	£200	—
1735 — —		£35	£80	£200	—
1736 — —		£35	£80	£200	—
1736/5 — — 6 over 5		£40	£85	£220	—
1737 — —		£35	£80	£200	—
*1739 — Roses in angles on rev.		£28	£65	£175	—
1739/7 — — 9 over 7				Extremely rare	
1741 — —		£28	£65	£175	—
1741/39 — — 41 over 39				Extremely rare	
1743 Old head, Roses in angles on rev.		£18	£45	£140	—
1745 — —		£18	£45	£140	—
1745 — — LIMA beow bust		£15	£40	£120	—
1745/3 — — — 5 over 3		£25	£60	£220	—
1746 — — —		£30	£100	£350	—

George II Young head

DATE	MINTAGE	F	VF	EF	UNC
1746/5 — — 6 over 5		£50	£125	—	—
1746 — Plain, Proof	—	—	£425	—
*1747 — Roses in angles on rev.		£18	£50	£150	—
1750 — Plain		£18	£50	£160	—
1750/6 — — 0 over 6		£30	£80	£220	—
1751 — —		£25	£65	£185	—
1758 — —		£8	£25	£75	—

GEORGE III (1760–1820)

	MINTAGE	F	VF	EF	UNC
*1763 "Northumberland" bust		£150	£300	£500	—
1787 rev. no semée of hearts in 4th shield		£7	£16	£50	—
1787 — No stop over head		£7	£16	£50	—
1787 — No stop at date		£7	£16	£50	—
1787 — No stops on obv		£15	£30	£70	—
1787 rev. with semée of hearts in shield		£7	£16	£50	—
1798 "Dorrien Magens" bust		—	—	£3500	—

NEW COINAGE—shield in garter reverse

	MINTAGE	F	VF	EF	UNC
1816		£5	£14	£40	£75
1817	3,031,360	£5	£14	£40	£75
1817 GEOE for GEOR	*incl. above*	£70	£160	£300	—
1818	1,342,440	£6	£16	£55	£100
1819	7,595,280	£5	£14	£35	£75
1819/8 9 over 8	*incl. above*	£8	£25	£60	—
1820	7,975,440	£5	£14	£35	£75

George II Old head

GEORGE IV (1820–30)

	MINTAGE	F	VF	EF	UNC
1821 First bust, first reverse	2,463,120	£8	£25	£85	£160
1821 — — Proof	*incl. above*	—	—	—	£400
1823 — Second reverse	693,000	£20	£50	£150	£225
1824 — —	4,158,000	£8	£25	£80	£150
1825 — —	2,459,160	£15	£30	£70	£150
1825/3 — — 5 over 3	*incl. above*			Extremely rare	
1825 Second bust, third reverse .	*incl. above*	£3	£12	£45	£95
1825 — — Roman I	*incl. above*			Extremely rare	
1826 — —	6,351,840	£3	£12	£45	£95
1826 — — Proof	*incl. above*	—	—	—	£175
1827 — —	574,200	£20	£45	£110	£220
1829 — —	879,120	£165	£35	£90	£180

WILLIAM IV (1830–37)

	MINTAGE	F	VF	EF	UNC
1831 Proof only	—	—	—	£140	£245
1834	3,223,440	£6	£20	£70	£150
1835	1,449,360	£6	£20	£70	£150
1836	3,567,960	£6	£20	£60	£140
1837	478,160	£8	£24	£90	£220

George III "Northumberland" shilling

VICTORIA (1837–1901)

YOUNG HEAD ISSUES
First head

	MINTAGE	F	VF	EF	UNC
1838 WW on truncation	1,956,240	£6	£20	£65	£130
1839 —	5,666,760	£6	£20	£65	£130

Second head

	MINTAGE	F	VF	EF	UNC
1839 WW on truncation, Proof only	*incl. above*	—	—	—	£250
1839 no WW	*incl. above*	£6	£22	£70	£130
1840	1,639,440	£7	£22	£80	£180
1841	875,160	£6	£22	£80	£170
1842	2,094,840	£6	£22	£60	£130
1843	1,465,200	£6	£24	£80	£150
1844	4,466,880	£6	£22	£70	£120
1845	4,082,760	£6	£22	£70	£130
1846	4,031,280	£6	£22	£60	£130
1848 last 8 of date over 6	1,041,480	£25	£45	£135	£300
1849	845,480	£8	£30	£80	£160
1850	685,080	£175	£350	£900	£1500
1851	470,071	£25	£100	£250	£400

177

DATE	MINTAGE	F	VF	EF	UNC
1851/49 51 over 49	incl. above	£125	£350	—	—
1852	1,306,574	£6	£22	£65	£130
1853	4,256,188	£6	£22	£65	£130
1853 Proof	incl. above	—	—	—	£400
1854	552,414	£60	£130	£270	£550
1854/1 4 over 1	incl. above	£125	£350	—	—
1855	1,368,400	£6	£22	£72	£130
1856	3,168,000	£6	£22	£70	£130
1857	2,562,120	£6	£22	£70	£130
1857 error F:G with inverted G ..	incl. above	£100	£250	—	—
1858	3,108,600	£6	£22	£70	£130
1859	4,561,920	£6	£22	£70	£120
1860	1,671,120	£6	£22	£65	£140
1861	1,382,040	£7	£25	£80	£160
1862	954,360	£40	£90	£200	£400
1863	859,320	£70	£140	£275	£550
1863/1 3 over 1			Extremely rare		
Die no. added above date up to 1879					
1864	4,518,360	£6	£22	£55	£100
1865	5,619,240	£6	£22	£55	£100
1866	4,984,600	£6	£22	£55	£100
1866 error BBITANNIAR	incl. above	£70	£140	—	—
1867	2,166,120	£6	£22	£55	£100
Third head—with die no					
1867	incl. above	£20	£50	£125	£200
1868	3,330,360	£6	£20	£50	£85
1869	736,560	£6	£20	£50	£100
1870	1,467,471	£6	£20	£50	£100
1871	4,910,010	£6	£18	£50	£90
1872	8,897,781	£6	£18	£50	£90
1873	6,489,598	£6	£18	£50	£90
1874	5,503,747	£6	£18	£50	£90
1875	4,353,983	£6	£18	£50	£90
1876	1,057,487	£6	£18	£50	£95
1877	2,989,703	£6	£18	£45	£90
1878	3,127,131	£6	£18	£45	£90
1879	3,611,507	£7	£30	£70	£140
Fourth head—no die no					
1879 no Die no.	incl. above	£5	£15	£50	£100
1880	4,842,786	£5	£16	£45	£80
1881	5,255,332	£5	£16	£45	£80
1882	1,611,786	£7	£22	£90	£175
1883	7,281,450	£4	£16	£45	£75
1884	3,923,993	£4	£16	£45	£75
1885	3,336,526	£4	£16	£45	£75
1886	2,086,819	£4	£16	£45	£75
1887	4,034,133	£5	£15	£50	£100
JUBILEE HEAD ISSUES					
1887	incl. above	£2	£4	£9	£18
1887 Proof	1,084	—	—	—	£60
1888	4,526,856	£2	£8	£16	£40
1889	7,039,628	£12	£40	£150	—
1889 Large bust (until 1892)	incl. above	£3	£7	£32	£60
1890	8,794,042	£3	£7	£32	£60
*1891	5,665,348	£3	£7	£32	£60
1892	4,591,622	£3	£7	£32	£60
OLD HEAD ISSUES					
1893	7,039,074	£3	£7	£18	£40
1893 small lettering	incl. above	£3	£7	£18	£40
1893 Proof	1,312	—	—	—	£75
1894	5,953,152	£6	£15	£40	£80
1895	8,880,651	£5	£14	£35	£70
1896	9,264,551	£5	£11	£30	£55
1897	6,270,364	£4	£10	£30	£45
*1898	9,768,703	£4	£10	£30	£45
1899	10,965,382	£4	£10	£30	£50
1900	10,937,590	£4	£10	£30	£42
1901	3,426,294	£4	£10	£30	£42

Victoria Small Jubilee head

Victoria Large Jubilee head

Victoria Old or Veiled head

DATE	MINTAGE	F	VF	EF	UNC

EDWARD VII (1901–10)

DATE	MINTAGE	F	VF	EF	UNC
1902	7,809,481	£3	£6	£15	£35
1902 Proof matt	13,123	—	—	—	£30
1903	2,061,823	£5	£25	£70	£200
1904	2,040,161	£5	£25	£70	£200
1905	488,390	£35	£120	£400	£900
1906	10,791,025	£3	£9	£32	£60
1907	14,083,418	£3	£10	£40	£75
1908	3,806,969	£5	£20	£75	£175
1909	5,664,982	£3	£14	£55	£120
*1910	26,547,236	£2	£5	£20	£38

GEORGE V (1910–36)

First issue

DATE	MINTAGE	F	VF	EF	UNC
1911	20,065,901	£2	£6	£16	£35
1911 Proof	6,007	—	—	—	£35
*1912	15,594,009	£2	£7	£22	£45
1913	9,011,509	£3	£8	£25	£60
1914	23,415,843	£1	£4	£16	£32
1915	39,279,024	£1	£4	£16	£32
1916	35,862,015	£1	£4	£16	£32
1917	22,202,608	£1	£4	£16	£32
1918	34,915,934	£1	£4	£16	£32
1919	10,823,824	£1	£5	£16	£32

Second issue —debased silver

DATE	MINTAGE	F	VF	EF	UNC
1920	22,825,142	—	£2	£15	£35
1921	22,648,763	—	£2	£15	£35
1922	27,215,738	—	£2	£15	£35
1923	14,575,243	—	£2	£15	£30
1924	9,250,095	£2	£5	£26	£60
1925	5,418,764	£2	£5	£25	£65
1926	22,516,453	—	£4	£18	£40

Third issue—Modified bust

DATE	MINTAGE	F	VF	EF	UNC
1926	incl. above	—	£3	£18	£30
1927 —	9,247,344	£1	£3	£18	£30

George V First obverse

Fourth issue —large lion and crown on rev., date in legend

DATE	MINTAGE	F	VF	EF	UNC
1927	incl. above	£1	£2	£15	£32
1927 Proof	15,000	—	—	—	£25
1928	18,136,778	—	£2	£10	£25
1929	19,343,006	—	£2	£12	£25
1930	3,172,092	—	£2	£15	£35
1931	6,993,926	—	£2	£10	£25
1932	12,168,101	—	£2	£10	£25
1933	11,511,624	—	£2	£10	£25
*1934	6,138,463	—	£2	£12	£35
1935	9,183,462	—	£2	£6	£15
1936	11,910,613	—	£2	£4	£10

George V Second obverse

GEORGE VI (1936–52)

E = England rev. (lion standing on large crown). S = Scotland rev. (lion seated on small crown holding sword and mace)

DATE	MINTAGE	F	VF	EF	UNC
1937 E	8,359,122	—	£1	£2	£5
1937 E Proof	26,402	—	—	—	£8
1937 S	6,748,875	—	£1	£2	£5
1937 S Proof	26,402	—	—	—	£8
1938 E	4,833,436	—	£1	£7	£14
1938 S	4,797,852	—	£1	£7	£14
1939 E	11,052,677	—	£1	£2	£5
1939 S	10,263,892	—	£1	£2	£5
1940 E	11,099,126	—	—	£2	£5
1940 S	9,913,089	—	—	£2	£5

DATE	MINTAGE	F	VF	EF	UNC
1941 E	11,391,883	—	—	£2	£5
1941 S	8,086,030	—	—	£2	£5
1942 E	17,453,643	—	—	£2	£4
1942 S	13,676,759	—	—	£2	£4
1943 E	11,404,213	—	—	£2	£4
1943 S	9,824,214	—	—	£2	£4
*1944 E	11,586,751	—	—	£2	£4
*1944 S	10,990,167	—	—	£2	£4
1945 E	15,143,404	—	—	£2	£5
1945 S	15,106,270	—	—	£2	£5
1946 E	16,663,797	—	—	£2	£5
1946 S	16,381,501	—	—	£2	£5
1947 E	12,120,611	—	—	—	£2
1947 S	12,283,223	—	—	—	£2
1948 E	45,576,923	—	—	—	£2
1948 S	45,351,937	—	—	—	£2
1949 E	19,328,405	—	—	—	£4
1949 S	21,243,074	—	—	—	£4
1950 E	19,243,872	—	—	—	£4
1950 E Proof	17,513	—	—	—	£8
1950 S	14,299,601	—	—	—	£4
1950 S Proof	17,513	—	—	—	£8
1951 E	9,956,930	—	—	—	£4
1951 E Proof	20,000	—	—	—	£8
1951 S	10,961,174	—	—	—	£4
1951 S Proof	20,000	—	—	—	£8

English reverse

Scottish reverse

ELIZABETH II (1952–)

E = England rev. (shield with three lions). S = Scotland rev. (shield with one lion).

1953 E	41,942,894	—	—	—	£1
1953 E Proof	40,000	—	—	—	£3
1953 S	20,663,528	—	—	—	£1
1953 S Proof	40,000	—	—	—	£3
*1954 E	30,262,032	—	—	—	£2
*1954 S	26,771,735	—	—	—	£2
1955 E	45,259,908	—	—	—	£2
1955 S	27,950,906	—	—	—	£2
1956 E	44,907,008	—	—	—	£8
1956 S	42,853,639	—	—	—	£8
1957 E	42,774,217	—	—	—	£1
1957 S	17,959,988	—	—	—	£9
1958 E	14,392,305	—	—	—	£9
1958 S	40,822,557	—	—	—	£1
1959 E	19,442,778	—	—	—	£1
1959 S	1,012,988	£1	£2	£4	£15
1960 E	27,027,914	—	—	—	£1
1960 S	14,376,932	—	—	—	£1
1961 E	39,816,907	—	—	—	£1
1961 S	2,762,558	—	—	—	£3
1962 E	36,704,379	—	—	—	£1
1962 S	17,475,310	—	—	—	£1
1963 E	49,433,607	—	—	—	£1
1963 S	32,300,000	—	—	—	£1
1964 E	8,590,900	—	—	—	£1
1964 S	5,239,100	—	—	—	£1
1965 E	9,216,000	—	—	—	£1
1965 S	2,774,000	—	—	—	£2
1966 E	15,002,000	—	—	—	£1
1966 S	15,604,000	—	—	—	£1

English reverse

Scottish reverse

SIXPENCES

DATE	F	VF	EF	UNC

OLIVER CROMWELL

1658 Patterns by Thos. Simon & Tanner
All are very Rare 4 Varieties .... Extremely Rare

CHARLES II (1660–85)

	F	VF	EF	UNC
1674	£45	£100	£300	—
1675	£45	£100	£300	—
1675/4 5 over 4	£60	£120	£300	—
1676	£50	£100	£300	—
1676/5 6 over 5	£70	£140	£350	—
*1677	£45	£100	£300	—
1678/7	£45	£100	£300	—
1679	£45	£100	£300	—
1680	£55	£125	£400	—
1681	£40	£100	£300	—
1682/1	£45	£100	£300	—
1682	£50	£100	£300	—
1683	£45	£100	£300	—
1684	£55	£130	£325	—

JAMES II (1685–88)

	F	VF	EF	UNC
1686 Early shields	£75	£170	£450	—
1687/6 — 7 over 6	£75	£170	£450	—
1687 Late shields	£70	£170	£425	—
1687/6 — 7 over 6	£70	£170	£425	—
1688 —	£70	£160	£450	—

WILLIAM & MARY (1688–94)

	F	VF	EF	UNC
*1693	£80	£175	£450	—
1693 error inverted 3	£80	£200	£500	—
1694	£80	£180	£475	—

WILLIAM III (1694–1702)

Provincially produced sixpences carry privy marks or initials below the bust:
B: Bristol. C: Chester. E: Exeter. N: Norwich. Y or y: York.

	F	VF	EF	UNC
1695 First bust, early harp in 4th shield on rev.	£16	£55	£150	—
1696 — —	£15	£40	£110	—
1696 — — French arms at date		Extremely rare		
1696 — — Scottish arms at date		Extremely rare		
1696 — — DFI for DEI		Extremely rare		
1696 — — No stops on obv.	£20	£60	£175	—
1696 — — B	£22	£55	£175	—
1696 — — — B over E		Extremely rare		
1696 — — C	£22	£55	£185	—
1696 — — E	£22	£55	£200	—
1696 — — N	£22	£55	£180	—
1696 — — y	£22	£55	£180	—
1696 — — Y	£25	£70	£240	—
1696 — Later harp	£35	£100	£325	—
1696 — — B	£30	£110	£285	—
1696 — — — no stops on obv	£35	£120	£300	—
1696 — — C	£45	£160	—	—
1696 — — N	£40	£150	—	—
1696 Second bust	£175	£400	—	—
1697 First bust, later harp	£20	£40	£120	—
1697 — — Arms of France & Ireland transposed		Extremely rare		

DATE	MINTAGE	F	VF	EF	UNC
1697 — — B		£25	£60	£200	—
1697 — — C		£25	£60	£200	—
1697 — — Irish shield at date		Extremely rare			
1697 — — E		£25	£60	£200	—
1697 — — N		£25	£60	£200	—
1697 — — error GVLIEMVS		Extremely rare			
1697 — — y		£25	£60	£200	—
1697 — — Irish shield at date		Extremely rare			
1697 Second bust		£70	£175	£600	—
1697 Third bust		£15	£40	£110	—
1697 — error GVLIEIMVS		Extremely rare			
1697 — B		£22	£70	£200	—
1697 — IRA for FRA		Extremely rare			
1697 — C		£22	£90	£285	—
1697 — E		£25	£90	£240	—
1697 — Y		£30	£90	£250	—
1698 —		£30	£90	£225	—
1698 — Plumes in angles on rev.		£35	£90	£300	—
1699 —		£40	£120	£375	—
1699 — Plumes in angles on rev.		£40	£120	£300	—
1699 — Roses in angles on rev.		£45	£125	£320	—
1699 — — error G LIELMVS		Extremely rare			
1700 —		£25	£60	£175	—
1700 — Plume below bust		£600	—	—	—
1701 —		£30	£75	£240	—

ANNE (1702–14)

	MINTAGE	F	VF	EF	UNC
1703 VIGO below bust Before Union with Scotland	£25	£60	£160	—	
1705 Plain		£40	£100	£250	—
*1705 Plumes in angles on rev.		£25	£65	£190	—
1705 Roses & Plumes in angles on rev.		£25	£65	£180	—
1707 Roses & Plumes in angles on rev.		£25	£65	£175	—
1707 (Post-Union), Plain		£20	£40	£140	—
1707 E (Edinburgh) below bust		£20	£45	£150	—
1707 Plumes in angles on rev.		£20	£50	£160	—
1708 Plain		£20	£40	£130	—
1708 E below bust		£18	£45	£150	—
1708 E* below bust		£25	£60	£180	—
1708 "Edinburgh" bust E* below		£25	£75	£200	—
1708 Plumes in angles on rev.		£25	£60	£175	—
1710 Roses & Plumes in angles on rev.		£25	£60	£200	—
1711 Plain		£15	£32	£100	—

GEORGE I (1714–27)

	MINTAGE	F	VF	EF	UNC
*1717 Roses & Plumes in angles on rev.		£50	£110	£275	—
1717 Plain edge		Extremely rare			
1720 —		£40	£100	£275	—
1723 SSC in angles on rev.		£12	£40	£115	—
1723 Larger lettering		£12	£40	£115	—
1726 Small Roses & Plumes in angles on rev.		£70	£170	£450	—

GEORGE II (1727–60)

	MINTAGE	F	VF	EF	UNC
1728 Young head, Plain		£40	£100	£325	—
1728 — Proof		—	—	£1250	—
1728 — Plumes in angles on rev.		£30	£80	£250	—
1728 — Roses & Plumes in angles on rev.		£25	£70	£175	—
1731 — —		£25	£55	£160	—
*1732 — —		£25	£55	£160	—
1734 — —		£25	£60	£170	—
1735 — —		£25	£55	£160	—
1735/4 5 over 4		£30	£70	£180	—
1736 — —		£25	£55	£160	—
1739 — Roses in angles on rev.		£20	£50	£125	—
1741 —		£18	£50	£125	—

DATE	MINTAGE	F	VF	EF	UNC
1743 Old head, Roses in angles on rev.		£12	£40	£100	—
1745 — —		£12	£35	£100	—
1745 — — 5 over 3		£15	£45	£120	—
1745 — Plain, LIMA below bust		£12	£35	£85	—
1746 — —		£12	£35	£85	—
1746 — — Proof		—	—	£350	—
1750 — —		£16	£35	£100	—
1751 — —		£18	£40	£120	—
1757 — —		£10	£20	£50	—
1758 — —		£10	£20	£50	—

GEORGE III (1760–1820)

1787 rev. no semée of hearts on 4th shield		£8	£18	£35	—
1787 rev. with semée of hearts		£8	£18	£35	—

NEW COINAGE

1816	—	£5	£12	£35	£60
1817	10,921,680	£5	£12	£35	£60
1818	4,284,720	£6	£16	£50	£90
1819	4,712,400	£5	£12	£35	£6
1819 very small 8 in date	*incl. above*	£5	£12	£35	£6
1820	1,488,960	£5	£12	£35	£60

GEORGE IV (1820–30)

*1821 First bust, first reverse	863,280	£8	£25	£70	£135
1821 — — Proof	*incl. above*	—	—	—	£350
1824 — Second (garter) reverse	633,600	£8	£25	£75	£135
1825 —	483,120	£8	£25	£75	£135
1826 — —	689,040	£15	£45	£110	£225
1826 Second bust, third (lion on crown) reverse	*incl. above*	£6	£22	£60	£110
1826 — — Proof	*incl. above*	—	—	—	£125
1827 — —	166,320	£15	£35	£100	£175
1828 — —	15,840	£12	£28	£90	£140
1829 — —	403,290	£10	£25	£90	£130

WILLIAM IV (1830–37)

1821 error BBRITANNIAR		£50	£150	£500	—
1831	1,340,195	£8	£22	£65	£110
1831 Proof	*incl. above*	—	—	£90	£175
*1834	5,892,480	£8	£22	£65	£130
1835	1,552,320	£8	£22	£65	£130
1836	1,987,920	£10	£30	£100	£170
1837	506,880	£10	£32	£110	£180

VICTORIA (1837–1901)

YOUNG HEAD ISSUES
First head

1838	1,607,760	£7	£20	£45	£90
1839	3,310,560	£7	£20	£45	£90
1839 Proof	*incl. above*	—	—	—	£150
1840	2,098,800	£7	£20	£45	£120
1841	1,386,000	£7	£22	£50	£130
1842	601,920	£7	£20	£70	£120
1843	3,160,080	£7	£22	£50	£120
1844	3,975,840	£7	£20	£45	£110
1844 Large 44 in date	*incl. above*	£8	£25	£80	£150
1845	3,714,480	£7	£22	£50	£120
1846	4,226,880	£7	£22	£50	£10
1848	586,080	£20	£50	£125	£300
1848/6 final 8 over 6	*incl. above*	£25	£65	£170	—
1850	498,960	£7	£24	£50	£120
1850/3 0 over 3	*incl. above*	£14	£25	£70	£175

183

DATE	MINTAGE	F	VF	EF	UNC
1851	2,288,107	£7	£24	£50	£120
1852	904,586	£7	£24	£50	£120
1853	3,837,930	£7	£24	£50	£120
1853 Proof	incl above	—	—	—	£300
1854	840,116	£45	£110	£250	£375
1855	1,129,684	£7	£20	£50	£110
1855/3 last 5 over 3	incl. above	£10	£30	£60	£140
1856	2,779,920	£7	£20	£50	£120
1857	2,233,440	£7	£20	£50	£120
1858	1,932,480	£7	£20	£50	£120
1859	4,688,640	£7	£20	£50	£120
1859/8 9 over 8	incl. above	£10	£30	£60	£140
1860	1,100,880	£8	£22	£55	£130
1862	990,000	£25	£60	£150	£325
1863	491,040	£25	£60	£150	£325

Die no. added above date from 1864 to 1879

1864	4,253,040	£7	£22	£50	£110
1865	1,631,520	£7	£22	£50	£110
1866	4,140,080	£7	£22	£50	£110
1866 no Die no.	incl. above	£15	£60	£150	£220

Second head

1867	1,362,240	£7	£20	£50	£100
1868	1,069,200	£7	£20	£50	£100
1869	388,080	£7	£20	£50	£110
1870	479,613	£7	£20	£50	£100
1871	3,662,684	£6	£20	£45	£80
1871 no Die no.	incl. above	£6	£20	£45	£85
1872	3,382,048	£6	£20	£45	£85
1873	4,594,733	£6	£20	£45	£85
1874	4,225,726	£6	£20	£45	£85
1875	3,256,545	£6	£20	£45	£85
1876	841,435	£6	£20	£50	£85
1877	4,066,486	£6	£20	£50	£85
1877 no Die no	incl. above	£6	£20	£50	£85
1878	2,624,525	£6	£20	£50	£85
1878 Dritanniar Error	incl. above	£60	£175	—	—
1879	3,326,313	£6	£18	£50	£80
1879 no Die no	incl. above	£5	£18	£50	£80
1880 no Die no	3,892,501	£5	£18	£50	£85

Third head

1880	incl above	£4	£18	£40	£60
1881	6,239,447	£4	£18	£40	£60
1882	759,809	£5	£18	£60	£120
1883	4,986,558	£4	£16	£35	£55
1884	3,422,565	£4	£16	£35	£55
1885	4,652,771	£4	£16	£35	£55
1886	2,728,249	£4	£16	£35	£55
1887	3,675,607	£4	£16	£35	£60

JUBILEE HEAD ISSUES

*1887 Shield reverse	incl. above	£3	£5	£9	£18
1887 — Proof	incl. above	—	—	—	£50
1887 Six Pence in wreath reverse	incl. above	£2	£4	£9	£18
1888 —	4,197,698	£3	£7	£20	£35
*1889 —	8,738,928	£3	£7	£25	£40
1890 —	9,386,955	£3	£7	£25	£40
1891 —	7,022,734	£3	£7	£25	£40
1892 —	6,245,746	£3	£8	£28	£50
1893 —	7,350,619	£175	£325	£1000	£1500

OLD HEAD ISSUES

1893	incl. above	£3	£7	£18	£32
1893 Proof	1,312	—	—	—	£60
1894	3,467,704	£6	£14	£40	£70
1895	7,024,631	£5	£12	£35	£55
1896	6,651,699	£4	£8	£30	£45
1897	5,031,498	£4	£8	£30	£45
1898	5,914,100	£4	£8	£30	£45
1899	7,996,80	£4	£8	£30	£45
1900	8,984,354	£4	£8	£30	£45
1901	5,108,757	£4	£8	£25	£40

Jubilee head, shield reverse

Jubilee head, wreath reverse

DATE	MINTAGE	F	VF	EF	UNC

EDWARD VII (1901–10)

DATE	MINTAGE	F	VF	EF	UNC
1902	6,367,378	£1	£4	£20	£32
1902 "Matt Proof"	15,123	—	—	—	£25
1903	5,410,096	£3	£10	£35	£80
1904	4,487,098	£6	£22	£55	£130
1905	4,235,556	£5	£15	£40	£100
1906	7,641,146	£3	£8	£30	£65
1907	8,733,673	£3	£8	£30	£65
*1908	6,739,491	£5	£18	£40	£100
1909	6,584,017	£3	£10	£35	£65
1910	12,490,724	£1	£5	£18	£35

Edward VII

GEORGE V (1910–36)

First issue

DATE	MINTAGE	F	VF	EF	UNC
1911	9,155,310	£1	£3	£10	£25
1911 Proof	6,007	—	—	—	£30
1912	10,984,129	£1	£3	£20	£35
1913	7,499,833	£1	£6	£22	£45
1914	22,714,602	£1	£2	£10	£24
*1915	15,694,597	£1	£3	£12	£30
1916	22,207,178	£1	£2	£8	£25
1917	7,725,475	£2	£7	£25	£55
1918	27,553,743	£1	£2	£12	£25
1919	13,375,447	£1	£3	£12	£30
1920	14,136,287	£1	£3	£10	£25

George V, first reverse above and second reverse below

Second issue—*debased silver*

DATE	MINTAGE	F	VF	EF	UNC
1920	incl. above	£1	£3	£10	£25
1921	30,339,741	£1	£3	£10	£25
1922	16,878,890	£1	£2	£10	£25
1923	6,382,793	£2	£6	£25	£50
1924	17,444,218	£1	£5	£10	£20
1925	12,720,558	£1	£2	£10	£20
1925 Broad rim	incl. above	£1	£2	£10	£22
1926 —	21,809,621	£1	£2	£10	£22

Third issue—*Modified bust*

DATE	MINTAGE	F	VF	EF	UNC
1926	incl. above	£1	£2	£10	£25
1927	8,924,873	—	£1	£8	£25

Fourth issue—*New design (oakleaves)*

DATE	MINTAGE	F	VF	EF	UNC
1927 Proof only	15,000	—	—	—	£20
1928	23,123,384	—	£1	£7	£18
1929	28,319,326	—	£1	£7	£18
1930	16,990,289	—	£1	£7	£18
1931	16,873,268	—	£1	£7	£18
1932	9,406,117	—	£1	£7	£18
1933	22,185,083	—	£1	£7	£18
1934	9,304,009	£1	£2	£9	£22
1935	13,995,621	—	£1	£5	£10
*1936	24,380,171	—	£1	£5	£10

GEORGE VI (1936–52)

First type

DATE	MINTAGE	F	VF	EF	UNC
1937	22,302,524	—	—	£1	£4
1937 Proof	26,402	—	—	—	£5
1938	13,402,701	—	£1	£3	£11
1939	28,670,304	—	—	£1	£5
1940	20,875,196	—	—	£1	£5
1941	23,086,616	—	—	£1	£5
1942	44,942,785	—	—	£1	£4
1943	46,927,111	—	—	£1	£4
1944	36,952,600	—	—	£1	£4
1945	39,939,259	—	—	£1	£3
1946	43,466,407	—	—	£1	£3

George VI first reverse

Cupro-nickel

DATE	MINTAGE	F	VF	EF	UNC
1947	29,993,263	—	—	£1	£3
1948	88,323,540	—	—	£1	£3

Second type—*new cypher on rev.*

DATE	MINTAGE	F	VF	EF	UNC
1949	41,335,515	—	—	£1	£3

George VI second reverse

185

Date	Mintage				
1950	32,741,955	—	—	£1	£3
1950 Proof	17,513	—	—	—	£5
1951	40,399,491	—	—	£1	£3
1951 Proof	20,000	—	—	—	£5
1952	1,013,477	£2.50	£8	£15	£30

ELIZABETH II (1952–   )

1953	70,323,876	—	—	—	£2
1953 Proof	40,000	—	—	—	£4
1954	105,241,150	—	—	—	£3
1955	109,929,554	—	—	—	£1
1956	109,841,555	—	—	—	£1
1957	105,654,290	—	—	—	£1
1958	123,518,527	—	—	—	£3
1959	93,089,441	—	—	—	£1
1960	103,283,346	—	—	—	£3
1961	115,052,017	—	—	—	£3
1962	166,483,637	—	—	—	25p
1963	120,056,000	—	—	—	25p
1964	152,336,000	—	—	—	25p
1965	129,644,000	—	—	—	25p
1966	175,676,000	—	—	—	25p
1967	240,788,000	—	—	—	25p

GROATS OR FOURPENCES

DATE	MINTAGE	F	VF	EF	UNC

The earlier fourpences are included in the Maundy oddments section.

WILLIAM IV (1831–37)

*1836	—	£5	£12	£28	£50
1837	962,280	£5	£12	£28	£50

VICTORIA (1838–1901)

1837	Extremely Rare Proofs or Patterns only				
1837 Last 8 over 8 on its side		£10	£18	£50	£80
1838	2,150,280	£5	£12	£30	£55
1839	1,461,240	£6	£14	£32	£55
1839 Proof	incl. above	—	—	—	£125
1840	1,496,880	£6	£12	£30	£55
1840 Small 0 in date	incl. above	£6	£12	£30	£55
1841	344,520	£6	£14	£35	£55
1842/1 2 over 1	incl. above	£6	£14	£35	£55
1842	724,680	£6	£14	£35	£55
1843	1,817640	£6	£14	£35	£55
1843 4 over 5	incl. above	£6	£14	£35	£55
1844	855,360	£6	£14	£35	£60
1845	914,760	£6	£14	£35	£55
1846	1,366,200	£6	£14	£35	£55
1847 7 over 6	225,720	£10	£25	£100	—
1848	712,800	£6	£14	£30	£50
1848/6 8 over 6	incl. above	£20	£100	—	—
1848/7 8 over 7	incl. above	£8	£20	£50	£80
1849	380,160	£6	£14	£30	£50
1849/8 9 over 8	incl. above	£8	£20	£50	£80
*1851	594,000	£18	£50	£160	£220
1852	31,300	£30	£85	£240	—
1853	11,880	£35	£100	£325	—
1853 Proof	incl. above	—	—	—	£300
1854	1,096,613	£6	£14	£35	£55
1855	646,041	£6	£14	£35	£55
1888 Jubilee Head	—	£6	£14	£35	£60

THREEPENCES

DATE	MINTAGE	F	VF	EF	UNC

The earlier threepences are included in the Maundy oddments section.

WILLIAM IV (1830–37)

(issued for use in the West Indies)

DATE	MINTAGE	F	VF	EF	UNC
1834		£6	£12	£35	£60
1835		£6	£12	£35	£60
1836		£6	£12	£35	£60
1837		£6	£12	£38	£65

VICTORIA (1837–1901)

YOUNG HEAD ISSUES

Victoria first type

DATE	MINTAGE	F	VF	EF	UNC
1838 BRITANNIAB error				Extremely rare	
1838	—	£6	£18	£40	£60
1839	—	£6	£18	£45	£70
1940	—	£6	£18	£45	£70
1841	—	£6	£18	£50	£75
1842	—	£6	£18	£50	£75
1843	—	£6	£18	£35	£55
1844	—	£6	£18	£60	£80
*1845	1,314,720	£7	£18	£35	£60
1846	47,520	£7	£22	£70	£110
1849	126,720	£7	£20	£55	£90
1850	950,400	£7	£18	£40	£60
1851	479,065	£6	£18	£45	£60
1851 5 over 8	incl. above	£10	£20	£80	—
1853	31,680	£15	£40	£80	£125
1854	1,467,246	£6	£18	£45	£65
1855	383,350	£6	£18	£45	£70
1856	1,013,760	£6	£18	£50	£70
1857	1,758,240	£6	£18	£50	£70
1858	1,441,440	£6	£18	£50	£60
1858 BRITANNIAB error	incl. above			Extremely rare	
1858/6 final 8 over 6	incl. above	£8	£25	£80	—
1858/5 final 8 over 5	incl. above	£8	£25	£80	—
1859	3,579,840	£6	£18	£45	£60
1860	3,405,600	£6	£18	£45	£60
1861	3,294,720	£6	£18	£45	£60
1862	1,156,320	£6	£18	£45	£65
1863	950,400	£6	£18	£45	£75
1864	1,330,560	£6	£18	£45	£65
1865	1,742,400	£6	£18	£45	£80
1866	1,900,800	£6	£18	£45	£60
1867	712,800	£6	£18	£45	£70
1868	1,457,280	£6	£18	£45	£65
1868 RRITANNIAR error	incl. above	£50	£100	£225	—
1869	—	£25	£50	£125	£175
1870	1,283,218	£5	£16	£40	£55
1871	999,633	£5	£16	£35	£55
1872	1,293,271	£5	£16	£35	£55
1873	4,055,550	£5	£16	£35	£55
1874	4,427,031	£5	£16	£35	£55
1875	3,306,500	£5	£16	£35	£55
1876	1,834,389	£5	£16	£35	£55
1877	2,622,393	£5	£16	£35	£55
1878	2,419,975	£5	£16	£35	£55
1879	3,140,265	£5	£16	£35	£55
1880	1,610,069	£5	£16	£35	£55
1881	3,248,265	£5	£16	£35	£55
1882	472,965	£6	£20	£55	£100
1883	4,369,971	£5	£10	£28	£40
1884	3,322,424	£5	£10	£28	£40
1885	5,183,653	£5	£10	£28	£40
1886	6,152,669	£5	£10	£25	£40
1887	2,780,761	£5	£10	£25	£40

DATE	MINTAGE	F	VF	EF	UNC
JUBILEE HEAD ISSUES					
1887	incl. above	£1	£3	£9	£18
1887 Proof	incl. above	—	—	—	£35
1888	518,199	£2	£5	£18	£35
*1889	4,587,010	£2	£5	£18	£35
1890	4,465,834	£2	£5	£18	£35
1891	6,323,027	£2	£5	£18	£35
1892	2,578,226	£2	£5	£18	£35
1893	3,067,243	£8	£24	£100	£140
OLD HEAD ISSUES					
1893	incl. above	£1	£3	£15	£25
1893 Proof	incl. above	—	—	—	£40
1894	1,608,603	£2	£6	£24	£40
1895	4,788,609	£1	£5	£22	£40
1896	4,598,442	£1	£5	£18	£30
1897	4,541,294	£1	£5	£18	£30
1898	4,567,177	£1	£5	£18	£30
*1899	6,246,281	£1	£5	£18	£30
1900	10,644,480	£1	£5	£18	£30
1901	6,098,400	£1	£5	£14	£28

Victoria Jubilee head

Victoria Old or Veiled head

EDWARD VII (1901–10)

DATE	MINTAGE	F	VF	EF	UNC
1902	8,268,480	£1	£2	£7	£15
1902 "Matt Proof"	incl. above	—	—	—	£15
1903	5,227,200	£1	£4	£20	£35
1904	3,627,360	£2	£7	£35	£70
1905	3,548,160	£1	£4	£25	£50
1906	3,152,160	£1	£4	£20	£45
1907	4,831,200	£1	£4	£20	£45
1908	8,157,600	£1	£3	£20	£45
1909	4,055,040	£1	£4	£20	£40
*1910	4,563,380	£1	£3	£15	£30

GEORGE V (1910–36)

DATE	MINTAGE	F	VF	EF	UNC
First issue					
1911	5,841,084	—	—	£3	£10
1911 Proof	incl. above	—	—	—	£20
1912	8,932,825	—	—	£3	£10
1913	7,143,242	—	—	£3	£10
1914	6,733,584	—	—	£3	£10
1915	5,450,617	—	—	£3	£10
1916	18,555,201	—	—	£3	£8
1917	21,662,490	—	—	£3	£8
7918	20,630,909	—	—	£3	£8
1919	16,845,687	—	—	£3	£8
1920	16,703,597	—	—	£3	£8
Second issue—*debased silver*					
1920	incl. above	—	—	£3	£8
1921	8,749,301	—	—	£3	£8
1922	7,979,998	—	—	£3	£8
1925	3,731,859	—	—	£5	£20
1926	4,107,910	—	—	£7	£20
Third issue—*Modified bust*					
1926	incl. above	—	—	£7	£18
Fourth issue—*new design (oakleaves)*					
1927 Proof only	15,022	—	—	—	£38
1928	1,302,106	£2	£6	£18	£40
1930	1,319,412	£1	£3	£8	£20
1931	6,251,936	—	—	£2	£6
*1932	5,887,325	—	—	£2	£6
1933	5,578,541	—	—	£2	£6
1934	7,405,954	—	—	£2	£6
1935	7,027,654	—	—	£2	£6
1936	3,328,670	—	—	£2	£6

George V, fourth issue oak leaves design reverse

GEORGE VI (1936–52)

DATE	MINTAGE	F	VF	EF	UNC
Silver					
*1937	8,148,156	—	—	£1	£3
1937 Proof	26,402	—	—	—	£5
1938	6,402,473	—	—	£1	£3

DATE	MINTAGE	F	VF	EF	UNC
1939	1,355,860	—	—	£2	£7
1940	7,914,401	—	—	£1	£3
1941	7,979,411	—	—	£1	£3
1942	4,144,051	£2	£5	£12	£30
1943	1,397,220	£2	£5	£12	£30
1944	2,005,553	£4	£12	£35	£70
1945	Only one known				

Brass—lareger size, 12 sided, "Thrift" design

1937	45,707,957	—	—	£1	£3
1937 Proof	26,402	—	—	—	£3
1938	14,532,332	—	—	£1	£10
1939	5,603,021	—	—	£2	£16
1940	12,636,018	—	—	£1	£6
1941	60,239,489	—	—	£1	£4
1942	103,214,400	—	—	£1	£5
1943	101,702,400	—	—	£1	£5
1944	69,760,000	—	—	£1	£6
1945	33,942,466	—	—	£1	£4
1946	620,734	£2	£10	£70	£160
1948	4,230,400	—	—	—	£7
1949	464,000	£3	£8	£80	£185
1950	1,600,000	—	£1	£7	£20
1950 Proof	17,513	—	—	—	£5
1951	1,184,000	—	£1	£7	£25
1951 Proof	20,000	—	—	—	£5
1952	25,494,400	—	—	—	£5

George VI "Thrift" design of the brass 3d

ELIZABETH II (1952–   )

1953	30,618,000	—	—	—	£1
1953 Proof	40,000	—	—	—	£5
1954	41,720,000	—	—	—	£4
1955	41,075,200	—	—	—	£4
1956	36,801,600	—	—	—	£4
1957	24,294,500	—	—	—	£3
1958	20,504,000	—	—	—	£6
1959	28,499,200	—	—	—	£3
1960	83,078,400	—	—	—	£2
1961	41,102,400	—	—	—	£1
1962	51,545,600	—	—	—	£1
1963	39,482,866	—	—	—	£1
1964	44,867,200	—	—	—	—
1965	27,160,000	—	—	—	—
1966	53,160,000	—	—	—	—
1967	151,780,800	—	—	—	—

TWO PENCE

It is generally accepted that earlier issues of the small silver twopences were only produced for inclusion with the Maundy sets, q.v., except for those listed below

GEORGE III (1760–1820)

1797 "Cartwheel"	£18	£37	£175	£500
1797 Copper Proof	—	—	—	£500

Proofs also exist in various other metals

VICTORIA (1837–1901)

For use in the Colonies

1838	£4	£10	£18	£30
1848	£4	£12	£20	£35

THREE-HALFPENCE

DATE		F	VF	EF	UNC

WILLIAM IV (1830–37)

For use in the Colonies

		F	VF	EF	UNC
1834		£6	£16	£30	£70
1835 over 4		£6	£16	£30	£70
1836		£8	£18	£35	£75
1837		£12	£35	£100	£175

VICTORIA (1837–1901)

For use in the Colonies

		F	VF	EF	UNC
1838		£6	£15	£30	£60
1839		£6	£15	£30	£60
1840		£7	£18	£40	£75
1841		£6	£15	£30	£60
1842		£6	£18	£35	£70
1843		£6	£15	£30	£55
1860		£9	£20	£60	£100
1862		£9	£20	£60	£100

PENNIES

DATE	MINTAGE	F	VF	EF	UNC

The earlier small silver pennies are included in the Maundy oddments section.

GEORGE III (1760–1820)

	MINTAGE	F	VF	EF	UNC
*1797 "Cartwheel", 10 laurel leaves	8,601,600	£15	£30	£125	£350
1797 — 11 laurel leaves	*incl. above*	£15	£30	£125	£350
1806 Third type	—	£5	£11	£55	£120
1807	—	£5	£11	£55	£125
1808					Unique

GEORGE IV (1820–30)

	MINTAGE	F	VF	EF	UNC
1825	1,075,200	£9	£32	£90	£220
*1826 (varieties)	5,913,600	£9	£32	£90	£220
1826 Proof	—	—	—	£90	£150
1827	1,451,520	£60	£150	£650	£1400

WILLIAM IV (1830–37)

	MINTAGE	F	VF	EF	UNC
1831(varieties)	806,400	£12	£32	£120	£250
1831 Proof	—	—	—	£100	£180
1834	322,560	£12	£35	£125	£275
1837	174,720	£12	£35	£125	£275

VICTORIA (1837–1901)

YOUNG HEAD ISSUES

Copper

	MINTAGE	F	VF	EF	UNC
1839 Proof	unrecorded	—	—	—	£175
*1841	913,920	£6	£14	£45	£100
1841 No colon after REG	*incl. above*	£6	£14	£45	£100
1843	483,840	£24	£75	£200	£375
1844	215,040	£7	£16	£50	£120
1845	322,560	£7	£18	£75	£125

"Cartwheel" penny

DATE	MINTAGE	F	VF	EF	UNC
1846	483,840	£8	£18	£75	£125
1846 FID: DEF colon spaced	incl. above	£8	£18	£75	£125
1846 FID:DEF colon close	incl. above	£8	£18	£75	£125
1847	430,080	£6	£15	£70	£120
1848	161,280	£6	£15	£60	£100
1848/7 final 8 over 7	incl. above	£6	£15	£60	£100
1848/6 final 8 over 6	incl. above	£10	£20	£80	—
1849	268,800	£35	£140	£320	£550
1851	268,800	£8	£20	£80	£160
1853	1,021,440	£4	£10	£40	£70
1853 Proof	—	—	—	—	£300
1854	6,720,000	£4	£10	£40	£70
1854/3 4 over 3	incl. above	£8	£20	£70	—
1855	5,273,856	£4	£10	£40	£70
1856	1,212,288	£12	£40	£100	£180
1857 Plain trident	752,640	£4	£14	£40	£85
1857 Ornamental trident	incl. above	£4	£14	£40	£85
1858/7 final 8 over 7	incl. above	£4	£14	£40	£85
1858/3 final 8 over 3	incl. above	£20	£60	£150	—
1858	1,599,040	£4	£12	£40	£80
1859	1,075,200	£5	£20	£55	£125
1860/59	32,256	£300	£475	£1200	—
Bronze					
1860 Beaded border	5,053,440	£4	£9	£40	£70
1860 Toothed border	incl. above	£4	£10	£45	£90
1860 — Piedfort flan	—		Extremely rare		
1861	36,449,280	£3	£8	£35	£60
1862	50,534,400	£3	£7	£35	£65
1862 8 over 6	incl. above		Extremely rare		
1863	28,062,720	£3	£7	£35	£65
1863 Die no below date	incl. above		Extremely rare		
1864 Plain 4	3,440,640	£8	£35	£200	£300
1864 Crosslet 4	incl. above	£8	£35	£200	£300
1865	8,601,600	£4	£12	£35	£75
1865/3 5 over 3	incl. above	£10	£50	£150	—
1866	9,999,360	£4	£12	£35	£75
1867	5,483,520	£4	£12	£35	£75
*1868	1,182,720	£8	£32	£100	£175
1869	2,580,480	£40	£120	£375	£625
1870	5,695,022	£6	£20	£80	£150
1871	1,290,318	£25	£90	£190	£450
1872	8,494,572	£5	£15	£40	£75
1873	8,494,200	£5	£15	£40	£75
1874	5,621,865	£5	£15	£40	£75
1874 H	6,666,240	£5	£15	£40	£75
1874 Later (older) bust	incl. above	£8	£22	£50	£100
1875	10,691,040	£5	£15	£40	£75
1875 H	752,640	£25	£80	£225	£450
1876 H	11,074,560	£5	£12	£45	£80
1877	9,624,747	£5	£14	£45	£80
1878	2,764,470	£5	£14	£45	£75
1879	7,666,476	£3	£12	£40	£70
1880	3,000,831	£4	£12	£35	£65
1881	2,302,362	£5	£12	£40	£70
1881 H	3,763,200	£5	£12	£35	£65
1882 H	7,526,400	£5	£12	£35	£60
1882 no H	—		Extremely Rare		
1883	6,237,438	£5	£12	£35	£65
1884	11,702,802	£5	£12	£35	£75
1885	7,145,862	£4	£11	£40	£65
1886	6,087,759	£4	£11	£40	£65
1887	5,315,085	£4	£11	£40	£65

Victoria copper penny

Victoria bronze penny

DATE	MINTAGE	F	VF	EF	UNC
1888	5,125,020	£4	£11	£40	£65
1889	12,559,737	£4	£11	£40	£65
1890	15,330,840	£4	£11	£40	£65
1891	17,885,961	£4	£11	£40	£65
1892	10,501,671	£4	£11	£40	£65
1893	8,161,737	£4	£11	£40	£65
1894	3,883,452	£7	£20	£55	£100

OLD HEAD ISSUES

DATE	MINTAGE	F	VF	EF	UNC
1895 Trident 2mm from P(ENNY)	5,395,830	£4	£18	£70	£200
1895 Trident 1mm from P	*incl. above*	—	£2	£15	£35
1896	24,147,156	—	£2	£15	£33
*1897	20,756,620	—	£2	£15	£33
1898	14,296,836	—	£2	£16	£35
1899	26,441,069	—	£2	£14	£35
1900	31,778,109	—	£2	£13	£25
1901	22,205,568	—	£2	£7	£15

EDWARD VII (1901–10)

DATE	MINTAGE	F	VF	EF	UNC
1902	26,976,768	—	£1	£8	£22
1902 "Low tide" to sea line	*incl. above*	—	£5	£20	£50
1903	21,415,296	—	£3	£14	£50
1904	12,913,152	—	£3	£14	£40
1905	17,783,808	—	£3	£14	£40
1906	37,989,504	—	£3	£14	£40
1907	47,322,240	—	£3	£14	£40
*1908	31,506,048	—	£3	£14	£45
1909	19,617,024	—	£3	£15	£45
1910	29,549,184	—	£3	£14	£38

GEORGE V (1910–36)

DATE	MINTAGE	F	VF	EF	UNC
1911	23,079,168	—	£3	£12	£32
1912	48,306,048	—	£3	£12	£32
*1912 H	16,800,000	—	£3	£25	£70
1913	65,497,812	—	£3	£12	£40
1914	50,820,997	—	£3	£12	£40
1915	47,310,807	—	£3	£12	£40
1916	86,411,165	—	£3	£12	£40
1917	107,905,436	—	£3	£12	£40
1918	84,227,372	—	£3	£12	£40
1918 H	3,660,800	£1	£8	£80	£240
1918 KN	*incl. above*	£7	£50	£250	£750
1919	113,761,090	—	£2	£12	£40
1919 H	5,209,600	£1	£10	£70	£240
1919 KN	*incl. above*	£8	£60	£250	£750
1920	124,693,485	—	£2	£12	£25
1921	129,717,693	—	£2	£12	£25
1922	16,346,711	—	£2	£12	£35
1926	4,498,519	—	£6	£20	£70
1926 Modified effigy	incl above	£7	£25	£300	£500
1927	60,989,561	—	£2	£8	£25
1928	50,178,00	—	£2	£8	£25
1929	49,132,800	—	£2	£8	£25
1930	29,097,600	—	£2	£15	£40
1931	19,843,200	—	£2	£8	£30
1932	8,277,600	—	£2	£10	£32
1933			Only 7 examples known		
1934	13,965,600	—	£2	£8	£32
1935	56,070,000	—	—	£2	£9
1936	154,296,000	—	—	£2	£8

DATE	MINTAGE	F	VF	EF	UNC

GEORGE VI (1936–52)

DATE	MINTAGE	F	VF	EF	UNC
1937	88,896,000	—	—	—	£3
1937 Proof	26,402	—	—	—	£5
1938	121,560,00	—	—	—	£3
1939	55,560,000	—	—	—	£4
1940	42,284,400	—	—	—	£6
1944	42,600,000	—	—	—	£6
1945	79,531,200	—	—	—	£5
1946	66,855,600	—	—	—	£3
1947	52,220,400	—	—	—	£3
1948	63,961,200	—	—	—	£3
1949	14,324,400	—	—	—	£3
1950	240,000	£3	£7	£14	£20
1950 Proof	17,513	—	—	—	£14
1951	120,000	£5	£9	£18	£26
1951 Proof	20,000	—	—	—	—

ELIZABETH II (1952–   )

DATE	MINTAGE	F	VF	EF	UNC
*1953	1,308,400	—	—	£1	£4
1953 Proof	40,000	—	—	—	£6
1954				Only one known	
1961	48,313,400	—	—	—	£1
1962	143,308,600	—	—	—	50p
1963	125,235,600	—	—	—	50p
1964	153,294,000	—	—	—	50p
1965	121,310,400	—	—	—	50p
1966	165,739,200	—	—	—	50p
1967	654,564,000	—	—	—	—

Later issues are included in the Decimal section.

HALFPENNIES

DATE		F	VF	EF	UNC

CHARLES II (1660–85)

	F	VF	EF	UNC
1672	£35	£125	£475	—
1672 CRAOLVS error		Extremely rare		
1673	£35	£125	£475	—
1673 CRAOLVS error		Extremely rare		
1673 No rev. stop	£70	£250	—	—
1673 No stops on obv.		Extremely rare		
1675	£35	£90	£450	—
1675 No stops on obv.	£50	£175	—	—

JAMES II (1685–88)

	F	VF	EF	UNC
1685 (tin)	£100	£220	£1000	—
1686 (tin)	£110	£240	£1000	—
1687 (tin)	£100	£220	£1000	—

WILLIAM & MARY (1688–94)

Tin

	F	VF	EF	UNC
1689 Small draped busts, edge dated	£300	—	—	—
1690 Large cuirassed busts, edge dated	£110	£265	£1000	—
1691 — date on edge and in exergue	£110	£265	£1000	—
1692 — —	£110	£265	£1000	—

DATE	F	VF	EF	UNC

Copper

*1694 Large cuirassed busts, date in exergue	£30	£85	£650	—
1694 — — GVLIEMVS error	Extremely rare			
1694 — — MΛRIΛ error	Extremely rare			
1694 — — No stops on rev.	Extremely rare			

WILLIAM III (1694–1702)

1695 First issue (date in exergue)	£28	£80	£425	—
1695 — No stop after GVLIEMVS on obv.	£50	£100	—	—
1695 — No stop after BRITANNIA on rev.	£50	£100	—	—
1696 —	£28	£90	£475	—
1696 — TERTVS error	Extremely rare			
1697 —	£28	£80	£450	—
1697 — No stop after TERTIVS on obv.	£50	£100	—	—
1698 —	£28	£80	£525	—
1698 Second issue (date in legend)	£30	£120	—	—
1698 — No stop after date	£45	£100	—	—
1699 —	£28	£80	£450	—
1699 — No stop after date	£45	£100	—	—
1699 Third issue (date in exergue) (Britannia with right hand on knee)	£28	£80	£450	—
1699 — No stop after date	Extremely rare			
1699 — BRITΛNNIΛ error	£70	£140	—	—
1699 — TERTVS error	Extremely rare			
1699 — No stop on rev.	Extremely rare			
1699 — No stops on obv.	£70	£140	—	—
1700 —	£28	£80	£425	—
1700 — No stops on obv.	£75	£150	—	—
1700 — No stops after GVLIELMUS	£75	£150	—	—
1700 — BRITVANNIA error	Extremely rare			
1700 — GVIELMS error	£75	£150	—	—
1700 — GVLIEEMVS error	£50	£140	—	—
*1701 —	£28	£80	£425	—
1701 — BRITΛNNIΛ error	£50	£140	—	—
1701 — No stops on obv.	Extremely rare			
1701 — inverted As for Vs	£50	£140	—	—

GEORGE I (1714–27)

*1717 "Dump" issue	£40	£110	£375	—
1718 —	£25	£60	£275	—
1719 Second issue	£22	£60	£275	—
1720 —	£22	£60	£275	—
1721 —	£22	£60	£275	—
1721 — Stop after date	£35	£80	—	—
1722 —	£22	£60	£275	—
1722 —inverted A for V on obv.	£40	£125	—	—
1723 —	£22	£60	£275	—
1723 —No stop on rev.	£30	£80	—	—
1724 —	£22	£60	£275	—

GEORGE II (1727–60)

1729 Young head	£20	£50	£160	—
1729 — No stop on rev.	£25	£60	£180	—
1730 —	£15	£45	£150	—
1730 — GEOGIVS error	£25	£70	£200	—
1730 — Stop after date	£25	£70	£180	—
1730 — No stop after REX on obv.	£30	£80	£200	—
1731 —	£15	£45	£150	—
1731 — No rev. stop	£25	£70	£180	—
1732 —	£15	£45	£150	—
1732 — No rev. stop	£25	£70	£180	—
1733 —	£15	£45	£150	—

DATE	MINTAGE	F	VF	EF	UNC
1734 —		£15	£45	£150	—
1734/3 — 4 over 3		£25	£100	—	—
1734 — No stop on obv.		£30	£100	—	—
1735 —		£15	£35	£150	—
1736 —		£15	£35	£135	—
1737 —		£15	£35	£135	—
1738 —		£15	£35	£135	—
1739 —		£15	£35	£135	—
1740 Old head		£10	£35	£135	—
1742 —		£10	£35	£135	—
1742/0 — 2 over 0		£20	£75	£200	—
1743 —		£10	£35	£135	—
1744 —		£10	£35	£135	—
1745 —		£10	£35	£135	—
1746 —		£10	£35	£135	—
1747 —		£10	£35	£135	—
1748 —		£10	£35	£135	—
1749 —		£10	£35	£135	—
1750 —		£10	£35	£135	—
*1751 —		£10	£35	£135	—
1752 —		£10	£35	£135	—
1753 —		£10	£35	£135	—
1754 —		£10	£30	£135	—

George II old head

GEORGE III (1760–1820)

First type—Royal Mint

		F	VF	EF	UNC
1770		£10	£28	£130	—
1770 No stop on rev.		£20	£55	£140	—
1771		£8	£25	£120	—
1771 No stop on rev.		£20	£55	£140	—
1772 Error GEORIVS		£35	£80	£300	—
1772		£8	£25	£120	—
1772 No stop on rev		£20	£60	£140	—
1773		£8	£25	£120	—
1773 No stop after REX		£25	£60	—	—
1773 No stop on rev.		£20	£40	£130	—
1774		£8	£25	£120	—
*1775		£10	£28	£130	—

George III first type

Second type—Soho Mint

	F	VF	EF	UNC
*1799	£2	£6	£30	£65

Third type

	F	VF	EF	UNC
1806	£2	£6	£30	£65
1807	£2	£6	£30	£66

GEORGE IV (1820–30)

	MINTAGE	F	VF	EF	UNC
1825	215,040	£8	£28	£70	£125
1826 (varieties)	9,031,630	£7	£25	£50	£100
1826 Proof	—	—	—	£80	£110
1827	5,376,000	£8	£25	£65	£110

WILLIAM IV (1830–37)

	MINTAGE	F	VF	EF	UNC
1831	806,400	£7	£22	£65	£120
1831 Proof	—	—	—	—	£125
1834	537,600	£7	£22	£65	£120
1837	349,440	£7	£22	£66	£120

VICTORIA (1837–1901)

YOUNG HEAD ISSUES

Copper

	MINTAGE	F	VF	EF	UNC
1838	456,960	£4	£14	£40	£70

George III second type

DATE	MINTAGE	F	VF	EF	UNC
1839 Proof	268,800	—	—	—	£120
1841	1,0745,200	£4	£14	£40	£70
1843	967,680	£12	£35	£75	£160
1844	1,075,200	£4	£15	£40	£70
1845	1,075,200	£25	£70	£250	£400
1846	860,160	£6	£15	£35	£70
1847	725,640	£6	£15	£35	£70
1848	322,560	£6	£15	£35	£70
1848/7 final 8 OVER 7	incl. above	£7	£15	£40	£80
1851	215,040	£5	£12	£35	£60
1852	637,056	£5	£12	£35	£60
1853	1,559,040	£4	£7	£20	£50
1853/2 3 over 2	incl. above	£10	£20	£40	£100
1853 Proof	—	—	—	—	£200
1854	12,354,048	£4	£8	£30	£50
1855	1,455,837	£4	£8	£30	£50
1856	1,942,080	£6	£14	£40	£75
1857	1,82,720	£5	£12	£30	£60
1858	2,472,960	£4	£10	£30	£55
1858/7 final 8 over 7	incl. above	£4	£10	£30	£55
1858/6 final 8 over 6	incl. above	£4	£10	£30	£55
1859	1,290,240	£5	£15	£35	£75
1859/8 9 over 8	incl. above	£4	£10	£30	£55
1860	unrecorded		£600	£1750	—

Victoria copper halfpenny

Bronze

1860 Beaded border	6,630,400	£3	£9	£30	£50
1860 Toothed border		£4	£12	£40	£70
1861	54,118,400	£3	£9	£30	£50
1862 Die letter A, B or C to left of lighthouse				Extremely rare	
1862	61,107,200	£3	£9	£30	£50
1863	15,948,800	£3	£9	£30	£50
1864	537,600	£3	£10	£40	£75
1865	8,064,000	£4	£15	£50	£85
1865/3 5 over 3	incl. above	£15	£30	£75	—
1866	2,508,800	£5	£15	£45	£85
1867	2,508,800	£5	£15	£45	£85
1868	3,046,400	£4	£10	£40	£100
1869	3,225,600	£7	£30	£60	£150
1870	4,350,739	£5	£15	£50	£90
1871	1,075,280	£25	£70	£140	£300
1872	4,659,410	£4	£10	£35	£70
1873	3,404,880	£4	£10	£35	£70
1874	1,347,655	£5	£20	£60	£125
1874 H	5,017,600	£3	£10	£30	£60
1875	5,430,815	£3	£8	£30	£65
1875 H	1,254,400	£4	£10	£35	£75
1876 H	5,809,600	£4	£10	£35	£65
1877	5,209,505	£3	£10	£30	£65
1878	1,425,535	£5	£20	£50	£100
1879	3,582,545	£3	£10	£30	£55
1880	2,423,465	£4	£12	£40	£75
1881	2,007,515	£4	£12	£35	£70
1881 H	1,792,000	£3	£10	£30	£50
1882 H	4,480,000	£3	£10	£30	£05
1883	3,000,725	£3	£10	£30	£45
1884	6,989,580	£3	£10	£30	£45
1885	8,600,574	£3	£10	£30	£45
1886	8,586,155	£3	£10	£25	£45
1887	10,701,305	£3	£10	£25	£45
1888	6,814,670	£3	£10	£25	£45
1889	7,748,234	£3	£10	£25	£45
1889/8 9 over 8	incl. above	£10	£30	£75	—

Victoria bronze halfpenny

DATE	MINTAGE	F	VF	EF	UNC
1890	11,254,235	£3	£10	£25	£45
1891	13,192,260	£3	£10	£25	£45
1892	2,478,335	£3	£10	£25	£55
1893	7,229,344	£3	£10	£25	£45
1894	1,767,635	£5	£12	£30	£75

OLD HEAD ISSUES

1895	3,032,154	£1	£4	£15	£35
1896	9,142,500	£1	£4	£10	£30
1897	8,690,315	£1	£4	£10	£30
1898	8,595,180	£1	£4	£10	£30
1899	12,108,001	£1	£4	£10	£30
1900	13,805,190	£1	£4	£10	£25
1901	11,127,360	£1	£2	£6	£12

EDWARD VII (1901–10)

1902	13,672,960	£2	£4	£8	£20
1902 "Low tide"	incl. above	£5	£12	£40	£80
*1903	11,450,880	£2	£5	£18	£35
1904	8,131,200	£2	£5	£18	£35
1905	10,124,800	£2	£5	£18	£35
1906	16,849,280	£2	£5	£18	£35
1907	16,849,280	£2	£5	£18	£35
1908	16,620,800	£2	£5	£18	£35
1909	8,279,040	£2	£5	£18	£35
1910	10,769,920	£2	£5	£18	£35

GEORGE V (1910–36)

1911	12,570,880	—	£3	£12	£30
1912	21,185,920	—	£2	£12	£30
1913	17,476,480	—	£2	£14	£35
1914	20,289,111	—	£2	£12	£30
1915	21,563,040	£1	£3	£14	£35
1916	39,386,143	—	£2	£12	£30
1917	38,245,436	—	£2	£12	£30
1918	22,321,072	—	£2	£12	£30
1919	28,104,001	—	£2	£12	£30
1920	35,146,793	—	£2	£12	£30
1921	28,027,293	—	£2	£12	£30
*1922	10,734,964	—	£2	£14	£35
1923	12,266,282	—	£2	£12	£30
1924	13,971,038	—	£2	£10	£30
1925	12,216,123	—	£2	£10	£30
1925 Modified effigy	incl. above	£2	£5	£18	£40
1926	6,172,306	—	£2	£10	£30
1927	15,589,622	—	£2	£10	£30
1928	20,935,200	—	£2	£8	£18
1929	25,680,000	—	£2	£8	£25
1930	12,532,800	—	£2	£8	£25
1931	16,137,600	—	£2	£8	£25
1932	14,448,000	—	£2	£8	£25
1933	10,560,000	—	£2	£8	£25
1934	7,704,000	—	£2	£12	£30
1935	12,180,000	—	£1	£6	£15
1936	23,008,800	—	£1	£5	£8

GEORGE VI (1936–52)

1937	24,504,000	—	—	£1	£2
1937 Proof	26,402	—	—	£1	£5
1938	40,320,000	—	—	£1	£4

1939	28,924,800	—	—	£1	£4
1940	32,162,400	—	—	£1	£5
1941	45,120,000	—	—	£1	£5
1942	71,908,800	—	—	£1	£3
1943	76,200,000	—	—	£1	£3
1944	81,840,000	—	—	£1	£3
1945	57,000,000	—	—	£1	£3
1946	22,725,600	—	—	£1	£5
1947	21,266,400	—	—	£1	£3
1948	26,947,200	—	—	£1	£2
*1949	24,744,000	—	—	£1	£2
1950	24,153,600	—	—	£1	£4
1950 Proof	17,513	—	—	£1	£5
1951	14,868,000	—	—	£1	£5
1951 Proof	20,000	—	—	£1	£5
1952	33,78,400	—	—	£1	£2

ELIZABETH II (1952–)

1953	8,926,366	—	—	—	£1
1953 Proof	40,000	—	—	—	£3
*1954	19,375,000	—	—	—	£3
1955	18,799,200	—	—	—	£3
1956	21,799,200	—	—	—	£3
1957	43,684,800	—	—	—	£1
1958	62,318,400	—	—	—	£1
1959	79,176,000	—	—	—	£1
1960	41,340,000	—	—	—	£1
1962	41,779,200	—	—	—	£1
1963	45,036,000	—	—	—	20p
1964	78,583,200	—	—	—	20p
1965	98,083,200	—	—	—	20p
1966	95,289,600	—	—	—	20p
1967	146,491,200	—	—	—	10p

Later issues are included in the Decimal section.

FARTHINGS

DATE	F	VF	EF	UNC

OLIVER CROMWELL

Undated (copper) Draped bust, shield rev. Variations   Extremely rare

CHARLES II (1660–85)

Copper

	F	VF	EF	UNC
1672	£22	£50	£250	—
*1673	£22	£50	£250	—
1673 CAROLA for CAROLO error	£70	£250	—	—
1673 No stops on obv.			Extremely rare	
1673 No stop on rev.			Extremely rare	
1674	£22	£50	£250	—
1675	£22	£60	£250	—
1675 No stop after CAROLVS			Extremely rare	
1679	£25	£55	£270	—
1679 No stop on rev.	£60	£180	—	—
Tin				
1684 with date on edge	£150	£375	—	—
1685 —	£300	—	—	—

DATE	F	VF	EF	UNC

JAMES II (1685–88)

	F	VF	EF	UNC
1684 (tin) Cuirassed bust	£60	£220	£800	—
1685 (tin) —	£70	£220	£750	—
1686 (tin) —	£75	£220	£800	—
1687 (tin) —		Extremely rare		
1687 (tin) Draped bust	£150	£350	—	—

WILLIAM & MARY (1688–94)

	F	VF	EF	UNC
1689 (tin) Small draped busts	£300	—	—	—
1689 (tin) — with edge date 1690		Extremely rare		
1690 (tin) Large cuirassed busts	£100	£225	£850	—
1690 (tin) — with edge date 1689	£200	—	—	—
1691 (tin) —	£125	£325	—	—
1692 (tin) —	£100	£225	£900	—
1694 (copper) —	£30	£75	£500	—
1694 No stop after MARIΛ		Extremely rare		
1694 No stop on obv.		Extremely rare		
1694 No stop on rev.		Extremely rare		
1694 Unbarred As in BRITANNIA		Extremely rare		

WILLIAM III (1694–1702)

	F	VF	EF	UNC
1695 First issue (date in exergue)	£25	£80	£400	—
1695 — GVLIELMV error		Extremely rare		
1696 —	£25	£80	£400	—
1697 —	£25	£80	£400	—
1697 — GVLIELMS error		Extremely rare		
1698 —	£60	£150	—	—
1698 Second issue (date in legend)	£28	£95	£500	—
1699 First issue	£28	£90	£450	—
1699 Second issue	£28	£80	£475	—
1699 — No stop after date	£40	£100	—	—
1700 First issue	£28	£85	£450	—
1700 — error RRITANNIA		Extremely rare		

ANNE (1702–14)

	F	VF	EF	UNC
*1714	£90	£240	£400	—

GEORGE I (1714–27)

	F	VF	EF	UNC
*1717 First small "Dump" issue	£35	£115	£420	—
1719 Second issue	£20	£60	£225	—
1719 — No stop on rev.	£40	£130	—	—
1719 — No stops on obv.	£40	£130	—	—
1720 —	£20	£60	£225	—
*1721 —	£20	£60	£225	—
1721/0 — Last 1 over 0	£40	£130	—	—
1722 —	£20	£60	£225	—
1723 —	£20	£60	£225	—
1723 — R over sideways R in REX		Extremely rare		
1724 —	£20	£60	£225	—

George I, first type

GEORGE II (1727–60)

	F	VF	EF	UNC
1730 Young head	£14	£40	£160	—
1731 —	£14	£40	£160	—
1732 —	£14	£40	£160	—
1733 —	£14	£40	£160	—
1734 —	£11	£30	£150	—
1734 — No stop on obv.	£20	£80	£200	—

George I second type

DATE	MINTAGE	F	VF	EF	UNC
1735 —		£11	£30	£140	—
1735 — 3 over 5		£20	£30	£200	—
1736 —		£11	£30	£150	—
1737 —		£11	£30	£150	—
1739 —		£11	£30	£140	—
1741 Old Head		£11	£30	£130	—
1744 —		£10	£30	£130	—
1746 —		£10	£30	£130	—
1746 — V over LL in GEORGIVS			Extremely rare		
1749 —		£10	£30	£130	—
1750 —		£9	£22	£130	—
1754 —		£8	£20	£120	—
1754 — 4 over 0		£10	£30	£175	—

George III, third (Soho Mint) issue

GEORGE III (1760–1820)

	MINTAGE	F	VF	EF	UNC
1771 First (London) issue		£18	£40	£160	—
1773 —		£11	£25	£90	—
1773 — No stop on rev.		£18	£40	£90	—
1773 — No stop after REX		£20	£60	£125	
1774 —		£8	£25	£100	—
1775 —		£8	£25	£110	—
1797 Second (Soho Mint) issue			Patterns only		
*1799 Third (Soho Mint) issue		£2	£7	£30	£65
*1806 Fourth (Soho Mint) issue		£2	£7	£30	£60
1807 —		£2	£7	£30	£60

George III, fourth (Soho Mint) issue

GEORGE IV (1820–30)

	MINTAGE	F	VF	EF	UNC
1821 First bust (laureate, draped), first reverse (date in exergue) .	2,688,000	£2	£8	£35	£70
*1822 —	5,924,350	£2	£8	£35	£70
1823 —	2,365,440	£2	£8	£35	£70
1823 I for 1 in date	*incl. above*	£10	£50	£125	—
1825 —	4,300.800	£2	£8	£35	£70
1826 —	6,666,240	£2	£8	£35	£70
1826 Second bust (couped, date below), second reverse (ornament in exergue)	*incl. above*	£2	£8	£35	£75
1826 — Proof	—	—	—	£70	£120
1827 —	2,365,440	£2	£9	£35	£80
1828 —	2,365,440	£2	£9	£35	£80
1829 —	1,505,280	£2	£10	£40	£90
1830 —	2,365,440	£2	£8	£35	£80

WILLIAM IV (1830–37)

	MINTAGE	F	VF	EF	UNC
1831	2,688,000	£5	£12	£35	£80
1831 Proof	—	—	—	—	£100
1834	1,935,360	£5	£12	£35	£80
1835	1,720,320	£5	£12	£30	£75
1836	1,290.240	£5	£12	£40	£80
1837	3.010,560	£5	£12	£35	£80

VICTORIA (1837–1901)

FIRST YOUNG HEAD (COPPER) ISSUES

	MINTAGE	F	VF	EF	UNC
1838	591,360	£4	£12	£35	£60
1839	4,300,800	£4	£12	£35	£60
1839 Proof	—	—	—	—	£140
1840	3,010,560	£4	£12	£35	£50
1841	1,720,320	£4	£12	£35	£50
1842	1,290,240	£6	£18	£40	£90

DATE	MINTAGE	F	VF	EF	UNC
1843	4,085,760	£4	£10	£35	£55
1843 I for 1 in date		£45	£150	—	—
1844	430,080	£35	£80	£200	£450
1845	3,225,600	£4	£10	£35	£60
1846	2,580,480	£5	£16	£40	£75
*1847	3,879,720	£4	£10	£35	£60
1848	1,290,240	£4	£10	£35	£60
1849	645,120	£15	£40	£90	£200
1850	430,080	£4	£10	£35	£55
1851	1,935,360	£5	£15	£45	£75
1851 D over sideways D in DEI ..	incl. above	£25	£50	£100	—
1852	822,528	£6	£15	£45	£80
1853	1,028,628	£3	£7	£30	£45
1853 Proof	—	—	—	—	£250
1854	6,504,960	£3	£8	£30	£45
1855	3,440,640	£3	£8	£30	£45
1856	1,771,392	£7	£14	£50	£90
1856 R over E in VICTORIA	incl. above	£20	£50	£100	—
1857	1,075,200	£3	£10	£35	£50
1858	1,720,320	£3	£8	£35	£45
1859	1,290,240	£8	£25	£60	£125
1860	unrecorded	£750	£1800	—	—

Victoria Young Head first (copper) issue

SECOND YOUNG OR "BUN" HEAD (BRONZE) ISSUES

DATE	MINTAGE	F	VF	EF	UNC
1860 Toothed border	2,867,200	£1	£5	£20	£40
1860 Beaded border	incl. above	£3	£7	£24	£45
1860 Toothed/Beaded border mule	incl. above		Extremely rare		
1861	8,601,600	£1	£5	£20	£40
1862	14,336,000	£1	£5	£20	£40
1862 Large 8 in date	incl. above		Extremely rare		
1863	1,433,600	£20	£50	£130	£220
1864	2,508,800	£1	£5	£20	£40
1865	4,659,200	£1	£5	£20	£40
1866	3,584,000	£1	£5	£20	£40
1867	5,017,600	£1	£5	£20	£40
1868	4,851,210	£1	£5	£20	£40
1869	3,225,600	£1	£7	£28	£55
1872	2,150,400	£1	£5	£20	£40
1873	3,225,620	£1	£5	£20	£40
1874 H	3,584,000	£1	£5	£20	£40
1874 H both Gs over sideways G	incl. above	£70	£150	£300	—
1875	712,760	£2	£8	£32	£60
1875 H	6,092,800	£1	£5	£20	£50
1876 H	1,175,200	£2	£9	£28	£65
*1878	4,008,540	£1	£4	£18	£40
1879	3,977,180	£1	£4	£18	£40
1880	1,842,710	£1	£4	£18	£40
1881	3,494,670	£1	£4	£18	£40
1881 H	1,792,000	£1	£4	£18	£35
1882 H	1,792,000	£1	£5	£18	£35
1883	1,128,680	£3	£12	£35	£60
1884	5,782,000	£1	£4	£16	£30
1885	5,442,308	£1	£4	£16	£30
1886	7.707,790	£1	£4	£16	£30
1887	1,340,800	£1	£4	£16	£30
1888	1,887,250	£1	£4	£16	£30
1890	2,133,070	£1	£4	£16	£30
1891	4,959,690	£1	£4	£16	£30
1892	887,240	£1	£7	£28	£50
1893	3,904,320	£1	£4	£16	£30
1894	2,396,770	£1	£4	£16	£30

Victoria Young Head second (bronze) issue

DATE	MINTAGE	F	VF	EF	UNC
1895	2,852,852	£10	£25	£60	£110

OLD HEAD ISSUES

1895 Bright finish	incl. above	£1	£2	£12	£18
1896 —	3,668,610	£1	£2	£12	£18
1897 —	4,579,800	£1	£2	£12	£18
1897 Dark finish	incl. above	£1	£2	£12	£18
1898 —	4,010,080	£1	£2	£12	£18
1899 —	3,864,616	£1	£2	£12	£18
1900 —	5,969,317	£1	£2	£12	£18
*1901 —	8,016,460	£1	£2	£6	£12

EDWARD VII (1901–10)

1902	5,125,120	50p	£1	£7	£12
1903	5,331,200	50p	£1	£7	£14
1904	3,628,800	£1	£2	£10	£20
1905	4,076,800	50p	£1	£7	£19
1906	5,340,160	50p	£1	£7	£14
*1907	4,399,360	50p	£1	£7	£14
1908	4,264,960	50p	£1	£7	£14
1909	8,852,480	50p	£1	£7	£14
1910	2,298,400	£1	£6	£14	£40

GEORGE V (1910–36)

1911	5,196,800	25p	50p	£4	£11
1912	7,669,760	25p	50p	£4	£10
1913	4,184,320	25p	50p	£4	£11
1914	6,126,988	25p	50p	£4	£10
1915	7,129,255	25p	50p	£4	£10
1916	10,993,325	25p	50p	£4	£10
*1917	21,434,844	25p	50p	£4	£10
1918	19,362,818	25p	50p	£4	£10
1919	15,089,425	25p	50p	£4	£10
1920	11,480,536	25p	50p	£4	£8
1921	9,469,097	25p	50p	£4	£8
1922	9,956,983	25p	50p	£4	£8
1923	8,034,457	25p	50p	£4	£8
1924	8,733,414	25p	50p	£4	£8
1925	12,634,697	25p	50p	£4	£8
1926 Modified effigy	9,792,397	25p	50p	£4	£8
1927	7,868,355	25p	50p	£4	£8
1928	11,625,600	25p	50p	£4	£8
1929	8,419,200	25p	50p	£4	£8
1930	4,195,200	25p	50p	£4	£8
1931	6,595,200	25p	50p	£4	£8
1932	9,292,800	25p	50p	£4	£8
1933	4,560,000	25p	50p	£4	£8
1934	3,052,800	25p	50p	£4	£8
1935	2.227,200	£1	£2	£8	£20
1936	9,734,400	25p	50p	£3	£6

GEORGE VI (1936–52)

1937	8,131,200	—	—	50p	£1
1937 Proof	26,402	—	—	£1	£4
1938	7,449,600	—	—	£1	£5
1939	31,440,000	—	—	50p	£1
1940	18,360,000	—	—	50p	£1
1941	27,312,000	—	—	50p	£1
1942	28,857,600	—	—	50p	£1
1943	33,345,600	—	—	50p	£1
1944	25,137,600	—	—	50p	£1

DATE	MINTAGE	F	VF	EF	UNC
1945	23,736,000	—	—	50p	£1
1946	24,364,800	—	—	50p	£1
1947	14,745,600	—	—	50p	£1
1948	16,622,400	—	—	50p	£1
*1949	8,424,000	—	—	50p	£1
1950	10,324,800	—	—	50p	£1
1950 Proof	17,513	—	—	50p	£3
1951	14,016,000	—	—	50p	£1
1951 Proof	20,000	—	—	50p	£3
1952	5,251,200	—	—	50p	£1

ELIZABETH II (1952–   )

DATE	MINTAGE	F	VF	EF	UNC
1953	6,131,037	—	—	—	£1
1953 Proof	40,000	—	—	—	£2
*1954	6,566,400	—	—	—	£1
1955	5,779,200	—	—	—	£1
1956	1,996,800	—	£0.50	£1	£2

HALF FARTHINGS

DATE	MINTAGE	F	VF	EF	UNC

GEORGE IV (1820–30)

DATE	MINTAGE	F	VF	EF	UNC
1828 (two different obverses) (issued for Ceylon)	7,680,000	£8	£16	£35	£65
1830 (large or small date) (issued for Ceylon)	8,766,320	£7	£15	£35	£65

WILLIAM IV (1830–37)

DATE	MINTAGE	F	VF	EF	UNC
1837 (issued for Ceylon)	1,935,360	£15	£45	£100	£160

VICTORIA (1837–1901)

DATE	MINTAGE	F	VF	EF	UNC
1839	2,042,880	£5	£10	£25	£55
1842	unrecorded	£4	£7	£20	£45
1843	3,440,640	£3	£6	£16	£40
1844	6,451,200	£3	£6	£15	£40
1844 E over N in REGINA	incl. above	£8	£40	£100	—
1847	3,010,560	£6	£12	£30	£55
1851	unrecorded	£4	£12	£32	£55
1852	989,184	£4	£12	£40	£65
1853	955,224	£4	£12	£40	£75
1853 Proof	incl. above	—	—	—	£150
1854	677,376	£8	£24	£70	£125
1856	913,920	£8	£24	£70	£125

THIRD FARTHINGS

DATE	MINTAGE	F	VF	EF	UNC

GEORGE IV (1820–30)

DATE	MINTAGE	F	VF	EF	UNC
1827 (issued for Malta)	*unrecorded*	£5	£12	£30	£55

WILLIAM IV (1830–37)

DATE	MINTAGE	F	VF	EF	UNC
1835 (issued for Malta)	*unrecorded*	£7	£16	£35	£70

VICTORIA (1837–1901)

DATE	MINTAGE	F	VF	EF	UNC
1844 (issued for Malta)	1,301,040	£8	£20	£60	£110
1844 RE for REG	*incl. above*	£30	£60	£225	—
1866	576,000	£6	£14	£30	£55
1868	144,000	£6	£14	£30	£55
1876	162,000	£6	£14	£30	£55
1878	288,000	£6	£14	£30	£55
1881	144,000	£6	£14	£30	£50
1884	144,000	£6	£14	£30	£50
1885	288,000	£6	£14	£30	£50

EDWARD VII (1902–10)

DATE	MINTAGE	F	VF	EF	UNC
1902 (issued for Malta)	288,000	£3	£7	£20	£30

GEORGE V (1911–36)

DATE	MINTAGE	F	VF	EF	UNC
1913 (issued for Malta)	288,000	£3	£7	£20	£30

QUARTER FARTHINGS

DATE	MINTAGE	F	VF	EF	UNC

VICTORIA (1837–1901)

DATE	MINTAGE	F	VF	EF	UNC
1839 (issued for Ceylon)	3,840,000	£10	£25	£50	£100
1851 (issued for Ceylon)	2,215,680	£10	£25	£50	£100
1852 (issued for Ceylon)	*incl. above*	£10	£25	£50	£100
1853 (issued for Ceylon)	*incl. above*	£10	£25	£50	£100
1853 Proof	—	—	—	—	£240

EMERGENCY ISSUES

DATE		F	VF	EF	UNC

GEORGE III (1760–1820)

To alleviate the shortage of circulating coinage during the Napoleonic Wars the Bank of England firstly authorised the countermarking of other countries' coins, enabling them to pass as English currency. The coins, countermarked with punches depicting the head of George III, were mostly Spanish American 8 reales of Charles III. Although this had limited success it was later decided to completely overstrike the coins with a new English design on both sides— specimens that still show traces of the original host coin's date are avidly sought after by collectors. This overstriking continued for a number of years although all the known coins are dated 1804. Finally, in 1811 the Bank of England issued silver tokens which continued up to 1816 when a completely new regal coinage was introduced.

DOLLAR
Oval countermark of George III

	F	VF	EF	UNC
On "Pillar" type 8 reales	£165	£650	£1000	—
*On "Portrait" type	£150	£300	£650	—

Octagonal countermark of George III

	F	VF	EF	UNC
On "Portrait" type	£200	£600	£850	—

HALF DOLLAR
Oval countermark of George III

	F	VF	EF	UNC
On "Portrait" type 4 reales .	£185	£375	£750	—

FIVE SHILLINGS OR ONE DOLLAR
These coins were overstruck on Spanish-American coins

	F	VF	EF	UNC
*1804	£95	£200	£400	—

— With details of original coin still visible add from 10%.

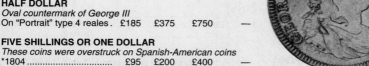

BANK OF ENGLAND TOKENS

THREE SHILLINGS

	F	VF	EF	UNC
1811 Draped bust	£35	£45	£85	—
1812 —	£35	£50	£120	—
1812 Laureate bust	£35	£45	£85	—
1813 —	£35	£45	£85	—
1814 —	£35	£45	£85	—
1815 —	£35	£45	£85	—
1816 —	£120	£225	£750	—

ONE SHILLING AND SIXPENCE

	F	VF	EF	UNC
1811 Draped bust	£20	£35	£65	£125
1812 —	£20	£35	£65	£125
*1812 Laureate bust	£20	£35	£65	£125
1812 Proof in platinum				Unique
1813 —	£20	£35	£65	£125
1813 Proof in platinum				Unique
1814 —	£20	£35	£65	£125
1815 —	£20	£35	£65	£125
1816 —	£20	£35	£65	£125

NINEPENCE

	F	VF	EF	UNC
1812 Pattern only	—	—	—	£1500

MAUNDY SETS

CHARLES II (1660–85)

DATE	F	VF	EF	UNC
Undated	£75	£130	£350	—
1670	£75	£120	£300	—
1671	£70	£100	£270	—
1672	£70	£100	£270	—
1673	£70	£100	£270	—
1674	£75	£110	£280	—
1675	£70	£100	£270	—
1676	£75	£110	£290	—
1677	£70	£100	£270	—
1678	£110	£160	£350	—
1679	£80	£120	£280	—
1680	£70	£100	£270	—
1681	£90	£130	£300	—
1682	£75	£105	£280	—
1683	£75	£110	£280	—
1684	£120	£180	£350	—

JAMES II (1685–88)

DATE	F	VF	EF	UNC
1686	£75	£120	£300	—
1687	£70	£130	£300	—
1688	£120	£150	£350	—

WILLIAM & MARY (1688–94)

DATE	F	VF	EF	UNC
1689	£325	£500	£750	—
1691	£150	£225	£400	—
1692	£165	£250	£450	—
1693	£140	£225	£400	—
1694	£125	£215	£325	—

WILLIAM III (1694–1702)

DATE	F	VF	EF	UNC
1698	£100	£170	£350	—
1699	£150	£225	£450	—
1700	£110	£185	£375	—
1701	£100	£175	£350	—

ANNE (1702–14)

DATE	F	VF	EF	UNC
1703	£90	£170	£350	—
1705	£85	£150	£345	—
1706	£80	£145	£325	—
1708	£160	£225	£400	—
1709	£95	£170	£350	—
1710	£115	£180	£370	—
1713	£90	£170	£355	—

GEORGE I (1714–27)

DATE	F	VF	EF	UNC
1723	£90	£160	£325	—
1727	£85	£150	£315	—

GEORGE II (1727–60)

DATE	F	VF	EF	UNC
1729	£75	£115	£270	—
1731	£75	£115	£270	—
1732	£60	£100	£225	—
1735	£60	£100	£225	—
1737	£60	£100	£225	—
1739	£60	£100	£225	—
1740	£60	£100	£225	—
1743	£75	£120	£250	—
1746	£60	£100	£225	—
1760	£65	£105	£230	—

GEORGE III (1760–1820)

DATE	MINTAGE	F	VF	EF	UNC
1763		£60	£85	£180	—
1766		£60	£85	£180	—
1772		£60	£90	£185	—
1780		£60	£85	£180	—
1784		£60	£85	£180	—
1786		£60	£90	£190	—
1792 Wire		£125	£180	£300	—
1795		£55	£75	£125	—
1800		£55	£75	£110	—
New Coinage					
1817		£60	£70	£115	£200
1818		£50	£70	£110	£180
1820		£50	£70	£115	£200

GEORGE IV (1820–30)

DATE	F	VF	EF	UNC
1822	—	£70	£125	£190
1823	—	£70	£125	£190
1824	—	£70	£125	£190
1825	—	£65	£125	£175
1826	—	£65	£125	£175
1827	—	£65	£125	£175
1828	—	£65	£125	£175
1829	—	£65	£125	£175
1830	—	£65	£125	£175

WILLIAM IV (1830–37)

DATE	F	VF	EF	UNC
1831	—	£70	£125	£180
1831 Proof	—	—	—	£350
1832	—	£70	£125	£180
1833	—	£70	£125	£180
1834	—	£70	£125	£180
1835	—	£70	£125	£180
1836	—	£70	£125	£180

VICTORIA (1837–1901)

YOUNG HEAD ISSUES

DATE	MINTAGE	F	VF	EF	UNC
1838	4,158	—	—	£85	£135
1839	4,125	—	—	£90	£145
1839 Proof	unrecorded	—	—	£150	£325
1840	4,125	—	—	£110	£165
1841	2,574	—	—	£110	£170
1842	4,125	—	—	£110	£170
1843	4,158	—	—	£80	£140
1844	4,158	—	—	£100	£165
1845	4,158	—	—	£75	£120
1846	4,158	—	—	£110	£170
1847	4,158	—	—	£150	£200
1848	4,158	—	—	£150	£200
1849	4,158	—	—	£110	£170
1850	4,158	—	—	£85	£140
1851	4,158	—	—	£85	£140
1852	4,158	—	—	£150	£240
1853	4,158			£160	£250

DATE	MINTAGE	EF	UNC
1853 Proof	unrecorded	—	£425
1854	4,158	£80	£125
1855	4,158	£80	£125
1856	4,158	£75	£110
1857	4,158	£75	£100
1858	4,158	£70	£110
1859	4,158	£70	£105
1860	4,158	£75	£115
1861	4,158	£75	£110
1862	4,158	£80	£125
1863	4,158	£80	£125
1864	4,158	£75	£120
1865	4,158	£80	£125
1866	4,158	£75	£120
1867	4,158	£80	£130
1868	4,158	£70	£115
1869	4,158	£85	£130
1870	4,458	£80	£100
1871	4,488	£70	£95
1872	4,328	£70	£95
1873	4,162	£65	£95
1874	4,488	£65	£95
1875	4,154	£65	£95
1876	4,488	£65	£90
1877	4,488	£65	£90
1878	4,488	£65	£90
1879	4,488	£65	£90
1880	4,488	£65	£90
1881	4,488	£65	£90
1882	4,146	£70	£95
1883	4,488	£60	£85
1884	4,488	£60	£85
1885	4,488	£60	£85
1886	4,488	£60	£85
1887	4,488	£60	£85

JUBILEE HEAD ISSUES

DATE	MINTAGE	EF	UNC
1888	4,488	£60	£85
1889	4,488	£60	£85
1890	4,488	£60	£85
1891	4,488	£60	£85
1892	4,488	£60	£85

OLD HEAD ISSUES

DATE	MINTAGE	EF	UNC
1893	8,976	£50	£70
1894	8,976	£55	£75
1895	8,976	£50	£70
1897	8,976	£50	£70
1898	8,976	£50	£70
1899	8,976	£50	£70
1900	8,976	£50	£70
1901	8,976	£50	£70

EDWARD VII (1902–110)

DATE	MINTAGE	EF	UNC
1902	8,976	£35	£50
1902 Matt proof	15,123	—	£60
1903	8,976	£35	£50
1904	8,976	£40	£55
1905	8,976	£40	£55
1906	8,800	£35	£50
1907	8,760	£35	£50
1908	8,769	£35	£50
1909	1,983	£55	£85
1910	1,440	£60	£90

GEORGE V (1911–136)

DATE	MINTAGE	EF	UNC
1911	1,786	£40	£70
1911 Proof	6,007	—	£75
1912	1,246	£40	£70
1913	1,228	£50	£80
1914	982	£50	£80

DATE	MINTAGE	EF	UNC
1915	1,293	£45	£75
1916	1,128	£45	£70
1917	1,237	£45	£70
1918	1,375	£45	£70
1919	1,258	£45	£70
1920	1,399	£45	£70
1921	1,386	£45	£80
1922	1,373	£45	£70
1923	1,430	£50	£80
1924	1,515	£50	£80
1925	1,438	£45	£75
1926	1,504	£45	£75
1927	1,647	£50	£75
1928	1,642	£50	£75
1929	1,761	£50	£80
1930	1,724	£45	£70
1931	1,759	£45	£70
1932	1,835	£45	£70
1933	1,872	£45	£70
1934	1,887	£45	£70
1935	1,928	£50	£80
1936	1,323	£65	£90

GEORGE VI (1936–52)

DATE	MINTAGE	EF	UNC
1937	1,325	£45	£65
1937 Proof	20,900	£45	£65
1938	1,275	£50	£80
1939	1,234	£45	£75
1940	1,277	£45	£80
1941	1,253	£50	£80
1942	1,231	£45	£70
1943	1,239	£45	£70
1944	1,259	£45	£70
1945	1,355	£45	£70
1946	1,365	£45	£70
1947	1,375	£50	£75
1948	1,385	£55	£80
1949	1,395	£55	£75
1950	1,405	£55	£80
1951	1,468	£55	£80
1952	1,012	£60	£90

ELIZABETH II (1952–   )

DATE	MINTAGE	EF	UNC
1953	1,025	—	£300
1954	1,020	—	£70
1955	1,036	—	£70
1956	1,088	—	£70
1957	1,094	—	£70
1958	1,100	—	£70
1959	1,106	—	£70
1960	1,112	—	£70
1961	1,118	—	£70
1962	1,125	—	£70
1963	1,131	—	£70
1964	1,137	—	£70
1965	1,143	—	£70
1966	1,206	—	£70
1967	986	—	£70
1968	964	—	£75
1969	1,002	—	£70
1970	980	—	£70

Later issues are listed in the Decimal section.

Sets in contemporary dated boxes are usually worth a higher premium. For example approximately £10 can be added to sets from Victoria to George VI in contemporary undated boxes and £15 for dated boxes.

EARLY MAUNDY SILVER SINGLE COINS

DATE	F	VF	EF

It is nowadays considered that the early small denomination silver coins 4d–1d were originally struck for the Maundy ceremony although undoubtedly many subsequently circulated as small change—therefore they are listed here under "Maundy silver single coins".

FOUR PENCE

CHARLES II (1660–85)

	F	VF	EF
Undated	£22	£40	£80
1670	£34	£50	£90
1671	£19	£30	£70
1672	£19	£30	£70
1673	£19	£30	£70
1674	£19	£30	£70
1675	£19	£30	£70
1676	£19	£30	£70
*1677	£18	£27	£70
1678	£19	£30	£70
1679	£17	£26	£60
1680	£18	£29	£65
1681	£19	£30	£70
1682	£18	£30	£75
1683	£19	£30	£80
1684	£18	£30	£85

JAMES II (1685–88)

	F	VF	EF
1686	£22	£35	£80
1687	£27	£44	£90
1688	£20	£33	£75

WILLIAM & MARY (1688–94)

	F	VF	EF
*1689	£20	£32	£75
1690	£29	£42	£90
1691	£30	£45	£90
1692	£38	£47	£92
1693	£37	£50	£110
1694	£35	£45	£95

WILLIAM III (1694–1702)

	F	VF	EF
1698	£30	£42	£90
1699	£30	£40	£90
1700	£32	£42	£85
1701	£32	£45	£95
1702	£27	£37	£75

ANNE (1702–14)

	F	VF	EF
1703	£28	£45	£90
1704	£22	£40	£75
1705	£26	£42	£80
1706	£23	£40	£75
1708	£20	£40	£75
1709	£22	£41	£80
1710	£18	£27	£50
*1713	£21	£36	£75

GEORGE I (1714–27)

	F	VF	EF
1717	£22	£40	£70
1721	£22	£40	£65
1723	£30	£45	£80
1727	£25	£40	£75

DATE	F	VF	EF

GEORGE II (1727–60)

	F	VF	EF
1729	£24	£37	£60
1731	£20	£35	£55
1732	£20	£35	£55
1735	£20	£40	£55
1737	£20	£30	£50
1739	£20	£30	£50
1740	£20	£30	£50
1743	£27	£45	£75
*1746	£20	£30	£50
1760	£20	£32	£55

GEORGE III (1760–1820)

	F	VF	EF
1763 Young head	£15	£25	£40
1765	£250	£475	£725
1766	£18	£30	£50
1770	£45	£70	£100
1772	£25	£35	£70
1780	£18	£30	£50
1784	£18	£30	£50
1786	£18	£30	£55
1792 Older head, Thin 4	£35	£45	£90
1795	£16	£30	£40
1800	£15	£25	£35
*1817 New coinage	£18	£25	£40
1818	£18	£25	£40
1820	£20	£27	£45

THREEPENCE

CHARLES II (1660–85)

	F	VF	EF
Undated	£20	£32	£75
1670	£18	£31	£70
1671	£17	£29	£70
1672	£17	£30	£70
1673	£17	£30	£67
1674	£18	£28	£70
1675	£19	£30	£75
1676	£19	£31	£75
1677	£18	£27	£70
1678	£17	£29	£75
1679	£15	£25	£85
1680	£17	£30	£72
1681	£19	£32	£75
1682	£19	£33	£75
1683	£19	£32	£75
1684	£19	£32	£75

JAMES II (1685–88)

	F	VF	EF
1685	£20	£32	£70
1686	£21	£35	£75
1687	£15	£22	£65
1688	£25	£50	£90

WILLIAM & MARY (1688–94)

	F	VF	EF
1689	£21	£32	£75
1690	£30	£40	£95
1691	£85	£130	£185
1692	£30	£45	£95
1693	£70	£120	£170
1694	£35	£50	£100

DATE	F	VF	EF

WILLIAM III (1694–1702)

DATE	F	VF	EF
1698	£30	£42	£80
1699	£30	£41	£80
1700	£32	£44	£85
1701	£27	£37	£75

ANNE (1702–14)

	F	VF	EF
1703	£25	£35	£75
1704	£20	£30	£60
1705	£23	£33	£70
1706	£22	£33	£70
1707	£18	£30	£60
1708	£20	£32	£70
1709	£20	£34	£70
1710	£18	£30	£65
1713	£20	£35	£65

GEORGE I (1714–27)

	F	VF	EF
1717	£25	£35	£65
1721	£25	£33	£65
1723	£30	£40	£75
1727	£30	£40	£75

GEORGE II (1727–60)

	F	VF	EF
1729	£22	£32	£50
1731	£22	£32	£50
1732	£22	£32	£50
1735	£22	£32	£50
1737	£22	£32	£50
1739	£22	£32	£50
1740	£22	£32	£50
1743	£18	£30	£47
1746	£18	£30	£45
1760	£20	£34	£45

GEORGE III (1760–1820)

	F	VF	EF
1762	£9	£17	£29
1763	£9	£17	£29
1765	£170	£280	£475
1766	£18	£25	£50
1770	£20	£30	£50
1772	£18	£25	£45
1780	£18	£25	£45
1784	£18	£30	£50
1786	£18	£25	£45
1792	£25	£37	£70
1795	£15	£24	£35
1800	£13	£22	£35
1817	£17	£25	£35
1818	£14	£20	£31
1820	£15	£23	£33

TWOPENCE

CHARLES II (1660–85)

	F	VF	EF
Undated	£22	£32	£70
1668	£25	£35	£85
1670	£18	£30	£70
1671	£18	£30	£70
1672	£18	£30	£70

DATE	F	VF	EF
1673	£20	£32	£75
1671	£18	£30	£70
1675	£20	£32	£75
1676	£18	£30	£70
1677	£18	£30	£70
1678	£19	£30	£70
1679	£15	£25	£50
1680	£17	£30	£60
1681	£17	£30	£65
1682	£18	£30	£70
1683	£18	£30	£70
1684	£20	£32	£75

JAMES II (1685–88)

	F	VF	EF
*1686	£20	£30	£70
1687	£25	£35	£80
1688	£20	£30	70

WILLIAM & MARY (1688–94)

	F	VF	EF
1689	£16	£28	£60
1691	£22	£32	£70
1692	£40	£70	£110
1693	£25	£36	£75
1694	£22	£34	£70

WILLIAM III (1694–1702)

	F	VF	EF
1698	£30	£45	£85
1699	£25	£37	£75
1700	£25	£35	£75
1701	£27	£40	£80

ANNE (1702–14)

	F	VF	EF
1703	£25	£35	£75
1704	£18	£30	£55
1705	£22	£35	£70
1706	£25	£35	£70
1707	£18	£30	£60
1708	£19	£32	£65
1709	£25	£40	£85
1710	£15	£27	£57
1713	£30	£50	£90

GEORGE I (1714–27)

	F	VF	EF
1717	£19	£30	£55
1721	£15	£25	£45
1723	£28	£50	£70
1726	£16	£30	£50
1727	£23	£35	£70

GEORGE II (1727–60)

	F	VF	EF
1729	£15	£22	£35
1731	£15	£22	£35
1732	£15	£22	£35
1735	£15	£22	£35
1737	£15	£22	£35
1739	£16	£23	£37
1740	£17	£24	£40
1743	£15	£26	£40
1746	£15	£25	£37
1756	£15	£18	£27
1759	£15	£18	£27
1760	£19	£27	£40

DATE	F	VF	EF

GEORGE III (1760–1820)

DATE	F	VF	EF
1763	£14	£22	£37
1765	£185	£315	£575
1766	£14	£22	£35
1772	£14	£22	£31
1780	£14	£22	£31
1784	£14	£22	£31
1786	£13	£20	£30
1792	£23	£30	£48
1795	£11	£16	£23
1800	£10	£15	£21
1817	£10	£17	£25
1818	£10	£15	£20
1820	10	£15	£20

PENNY

CHARLES II (1660–85)

DATE	F	VF	EF
Undated	£22	£35	£80
1670	£22	£35	£75
1671	£22	£35	£75
1672	£22	£35	£75
1673	£22	£35	£75
*1674	£22	£35	£75
1675	£22	£35	£75
1676	£25	£40	£80
1677	£21	£35	£75
1678	£80	£140	£175
1679	£35	£50	£90
1680	£22	£35	£75
1681	£45	£70	£120
1682	£24	£40	£80
1683	£24	£40	£80
1684	£85	£120	£185

Charles II

JAMES II (1685–88)

DATE	F	VF	EF
*1685	£23	£35	£70
1686	£23	£37	£75
1687	£30	£42	£85
1688	£31	£35	£65

WILLIAM & MARY (1688–94)

DATE	F	VF	EF
1689	£250	£300	£450
1690	£35	£45	£80
1691	£35	£50	£95
1692	£60	£90	£170
1693	£35	£45	£80
1694	£35	£45	£80

James II

WILLIAM III (1694–1702)

DATE	F	VF	EF
1698	£35	£50	£80
1699	£85	£125	£185
1700	£40	£55	£90
1701	£35	£50	£75

ANNE (1702–14)

DATE	F	VF	EF
1703	£30	£40	£70
1705	£30	£45	£75
1706	£30	£35	£65
1708	£100	£150	£200
1709	£25	£35	£70
1710	£70	£120	£170
1713	£30	£45	£70

www.antiquestall.com

THE NUMISMATIC MARKET PLACE

DATE	F	VF	EF

GEORGE I (1714–27)

DATE	F	VF	EF
1716	£12	£25	£35
1718	£12	£25	£35
1720	£12	£25	£35
1723	£25	£35	£70
1725	£15	£25	£35
1726	£15	£25	£37
1727	£22	£35	£60

GEORGE II (1727–60)

DATE	F	VF	EF
1729	£22	£37	£55
1731	£20	£32	£45
1732	£15	£25	£40
1735	£15	£25	£35
1737	£15	£25	£35
1739	£15	£25	£35
1740	£15	£25	£35
1743	£15	£25	£35
1746	£20	£33	£45
1750	£12	£20	£30
1752	£12	£20	£30
1753	£12	£20	£30
1754	£12	£20	£30
1755	£12	£20	£30
1756	£12	£20	£30
1757	£12	£20	£30
1758	£12	£20	£30
1759	£12	£20	£30
1760	£17	£25	£35

George II

GEORGE III (1760–1820)

DATE	F	VF	EF
1763	£17	£24	£37
1766	£13	£18	£25
1772	£14	£19	£30
1780	£13	£18	£25
1781	£12	£18	£25
1784	£12	£18	£25
1786	£12	£18	£25
1792	£17	£22	£35
1795	£12	£16	£22
1800	£9	£12	£17
*1817	£9	£13	£18
1818	£9	£13	£15
1820	£9	£13	£15

ECIMAL COINAGE

ial introduction of the Decimal system in the UK, the ins have been issued in vast quantities, although in some years certain denominations have either not been struck at all or only limited numbers are available to collectors so, surprisingly, there are a number of potential scarcities worth looking out for—this scarcity is reflected in the prices quoted. In this section it has been decided to only include the mintage figures of coins struck in precious metals where these are available. Where dates are available in uncirculated grade at, or just above, face value no price has been quoted.

Proof issues of circulation coinage (£1–½ pence) of the decimal series were only issued as part of the appropriate year sets, but over the passage of time many of these sets have been broken up and the individual coins are now appearing on the market, hence the decision to include these coins in the appropriate sections.

A new portrait of Her Majesty the Queen, executed by Ian Rank-Broadley, FRBS, FSNAD, was introduced on the British coinage in 1998, making it the fourth portrait of Her Majesty to appear on the coins and the third since the introduction of decimal coinage in 1968.

FIVE POUNDS

DATE	Mintage	UNC
ST. GEORGE REVERSE—*Gold (issued individually and in sets)*		
1980 Proof only	10,000	£450
1981 Proof only	5,400	£450
1982 Proof only	2,500	£475
1984 Proof	905	£460
1984 with U in circle	15,104	£400
1985 New portrait Proof	6,130	£475
1985 with U in circle	13,626	£400
1986 with U in circle	7,723	£400
1987 with U in circle	5,694	£400
*1988 with U in circle	3,315	£400
1990 Proof	1,721	£500
1990 with U in circle	1,226	£400
1991 Proof	1,336	£550
1991 with U in circle	976	£400
1992 Proof	1,165	£550
1992 with U in circle	797	£400
1993 Proof	1,078	£550
1993 with U in circle	906	£400
1994 Proof	918	£550
1994 with U in circle	1,000	£400
1995 Proof	1,250	£550
1995 with U in circle	1,000	£400
1996 Proof	1,250	£550
1996 with U in circle	1,000	£400
1997 Proof	1,000	£600
1997 with U in circle	1,000	£400
1998 Proof	1,500	£650
1998 with U in circle	1,000	£425
1999 Proof	1,000	£650
1999 with U in circle	1,000	£425
2000 Proof	3,000	£650
2000 with U in circle	1,000	£450
2000	—	£350
2001 Proof	3,500	£650
2001 with U in circle	1,000	£450
2001	—	£350

The obverse of the 1989 gold coins portray HM the Queen enthroned

COMMEMORATIVE

	Mintage	UNC
*1989 500th Anniversary of the Sovereign, Gold	2,937	£500
1989 — Proof	5,000	£600
1990 Queen Mother's 90th Birthday. Crown. (Cupro-nickel)	48,477	£8
1990 — in Presentation folder	incl. above	£10
1990 — Silver Proof	56,800	£32
1990 — Gold Proof	2,500	£525
1993 40th Anniversary of the Coronation. Crown. Cu-Ni	—	£8
1993 — in Presentation folder	—	£10
1993 — Proof	—	£15
1993 — Silver Proof	100,000	£3
1993 — Gold Proof	2,500	£525
*1996 Her Majesty the Queen's 70th Birthday. Crown. Cu-Ni	—	£8
1996 — in Presentation folder	—	£10
1996 — Proof	—	£15
1996 — Silver Proof	70,000	£32
1996 — Gold Proof	2,750	£650
*1997 Golden Wedding Anniversary of Her Majesty the Queen and Prince Philip. Crown. Cu-Ni	—	£7
1997 — in Presentation folder	—	£9
1997 — — with £5 note	5,000	£50
1997 — Proof	—	£22
1997 — Silver Proof	75,000	£35
1997 — Gold Proof	2,750	£650

The obverse of the 1997 £5 crown shows the conjoined portraits of HM the Queen and Prince Philip

DATE	Mintage	UNC
1998 50th birthday of the Prince of Wales. Crown. Cu-Ni	—	£7
1998 — in Presentation folder	—	£12
1998 — Proof	—	£20
1998 — Silver Proof	—	£40
1998 — Gold Proof	—	£650
1999 Princess of Wales Memorial. Cu-Ni	—	£9
1999 — in Presentation folder	—	£12
1999 — Proof	—	£20
1999 — Silver Proof	350,000	£40
1999 — Gold Proof	7,500	£650
1999 Millennium. Cu-Ni	—	£8
1999 — in Presentation folder	—	£15
1999 — Proof	—	£20
1999 — Silver Proof	100,000	£40
1999 — Gold Proof	2,500	£600
*2000 Millennium. Cu-Ni	—	£8
2000 — with special Dome mintmark	—	£12
2000 — in Presentation folder	—	£15
2000 — Silver Proof with gold highlight	50,000	£40
2000 — Gold Proof	2,500	£500
2000 Queen Mother Centenary. Cu-Ni	—	£7
2000 — in Presentation folder	—	£12
2000 — Proof	—	£20
2000 — Silver Proof	100,000	£40
2000 — Gold Proof	2,500	£550
*2001 Victorian Era. Cu-Ni	—	£7
2001 — in Presentation folder	—	£12
2001 — Proof	—	£20
2001 — Silver Proof	20,000	£40
2001 — Gold Proof	3,500	£550
2001 — Gold Proof with frosted relief	750	£850

In addition the later cu-ni crowns are available in attractive philanumismatic covers.

TWO POUNDS

ST GEORGE REVERSE—*Gold* (issued individually and in sets)

	Mintage	UNC
1980 Proof only	10,000	£200
1982 Proof only	2,500	£200
1983 Proof only	12,500	£180
1985 Proof only	5,849	£200
1986 Proof only	15,777	£200
1987 Proof only	14,301	£200
1988 Proof only	12,743	£200
1989 Proof only	14,936	£220
*1990 Proof only	4,374	£200
1991 Proof only	3,108	£220
1992 Proof only	2,608	£210
1993 Proof only	2,155	£210
1996 Proof only	3,167	£210
1998 Proof only	4,500	£225
1999 Proof only	2,250	£300
2000 Proof	2,250	£275
2001 Proof	2,500	£300

COMMEMORATIVE

*1986 Commonwealth Games. Nickel-brass		£6
1986 — in Presentation folder		£7
1986 — Proof		£10
1986 — Silver		£15
1986 — Silver Proof		£18
1986 — Gold Proof		£250

DATE	UNC
1989 300th Anniversary of Bill of Rights. Nickel-brass	£7
1989 — in Presentation folder paired with Claim of Right	£20
1989 — Proof Pair	£25
1989 — Silver Proof Pair	£40
1989 — Silver Proof Piedfort Pair	£60
*1989 300th Anniversary of Claim of Right. Nickel-brass	£12
1989 — in Presentation folder paired with Bill of Rights	£20
1989 — Proof Pair	£25
1989 — Silver Proof Pair	£40
1989 — Silver Proof Piedfort Pair	£60
1989 500th Anniversary of the Sovereign. Gold Proof	£265
1994 Tercentenary of the Bank of England. Nickel-brass	£5
1994 — in Presentation folder	£7
1994 — Proof	£10
1994 — Silver Proof	£27
1994 — Silver Proof Piedfort	£65
1994 — Gold Proof	£400
1994 — — obverse error (no denomination, as standard £2)	£575
1995 50th Anniversary of End of WW2. Nickel-brass	£5
1994 — in Presentation folder	£6
1995 — Proof	£10
1995 — Silver Proof	£35
1995 — Silver Proof Piedfort	£55
1995 — Gold Proof	£450
1995 50th Anniversary of The United Nations. Nickel-brass	£5
1994 — in Presentation folder	£6
1995 — Silver Proof	£35
1995 — Silver Proof Piedfort	£60
1995 — Gold Proof	£450
*1996 European Football Championships. Nickel-brass	£5
1996 — in Presentation folder	£6
1996 — Proof	£8
1996 — Silver Proof	£32
1996 — Silver Proof Piedfort	£55
1996 — Gold Proof	£450
*1999 Rugby World Cup. Bi-metallic	£3
1999 — Silver Proof	£32
1999 — Silver Proof Piedfort with Hologram	£85
1999 — Gold Proof	£350
2001 Marconi, Bi-Metallic	£3
2001 — Silver Proof/gold plated ring	£30
2001 — Silver Proof Piedfort	£85
2001 — Gold Proof	£350

CIRCULATING COINAGE

*1997 First Bi-metallic currency	£4
1997 — in Presentation folder	£8
1997 — Proof	£12
1997 — Silver Proof	£35
1997 — Gold (two types) Proof	£355
1998 Bi-metallic currency. New effigy	£3
1998 — in Presentation folder	£7
1998 — Proof	£10
1998 — Silver Proof	£32
1998 — Gold Proof	£355
1999 —	£4
1999 — Proof	£10
1999 — Silver Proof	£32
1999 — Gold Proof	£355
2000 —	£4
2000 — Proof	£10
2000 — Silver Proof	£30
2000 — Gold Proof	£355
2001 —	£4
2001 — Proof	£10
2001 — Silver Proof	£30
2001 — Gold Proof	£355

SOVEREIGN

DATE	MINTAGE	UNC
1974	—	£60
1976	—	£60
1978	—	£60
1979	—	£60
1979 Proof	50,000	£75
1980	—	£60
1980 Proof	91,200	£75
1981	—	£60
1981 Proof	32,960	£75
1982	—	£60
1982 Proof	22,500	£75
1983 Proof only	21,250	£75
1984 Proof only	19,975	£85
1985 New portrait Proof only	17,242	£90
1986 Proof only	17,579	£90
1987 Proof only	22,479	£90
1988 Proof only	18,862	£90
1989 500th Anniversary of the Sovereign Proof only	23,471	£175
1990 Proof only	8,425	£130
1991 Proof only	7,201	£130
1992 Proof only	6,854	£150
1993 Proof only	6,090	£150
1994 Proof only	7,165	£150
1995 Proof only	9,500	£150
1996 Proof only	10,000	£150
1997 Proof only	9,750	£165
1998 Proof only	13,500	£165
1999 Proof only	12,250	£145
2000 (first Unc isue since 1982)	250,000	£60
2000 Proof	10,050	£125
2001	100,000	£60
2001 Proof	10,000	£125

HALF SOVEREIGN

1980 Proof only	86,700	£50
1982	—	£50
1982 Proof	21,590	£60
1983 Proof only	19,710	£60
1984 Proof only	19,505	£60
1985 New portrait Proof only	15,800	£45
1986 Proof only	17,075	£45
1987 Proof only	20,687	£45
1988 Proof only	18,266	£50
1989 500th Anniversary of the Sovereign Proof only	21,824	£80
1990 Proof only	7,889	£50
1991 Proof only	6,076	£55
1992 Proof only	5,915	£65
1993 Proof only	4,651	£65
1994 Proof only	7,167	£75
1995 Proof only	7,500	£75
1996 Proof only	10,500	£75
1997 Proof only	9,750	£75
1998 Proof only	11,000	£75
1999 Proof only	9,750	£75
2000	250,000	£40
2000 Proof	7,500	£70
2001	100,000	£40
2001 Proof	7,500	£70

ONE POUND

DATE	UNC
1983 Royal Arms Nickel-brass	£5
1983 — in Presentation folder	£7
1983 — Proof	£10
1983 — Silver Proof	£30
1983 — Silver Piedfort Proof	£120
1984 Scottish Thistle Nickel-brass	£4
1984 — in Presentation folder	£6
1984 — Proof	£7
1984 — Silver Proof	£30
1984 — Silver Piedfort Proof	£55
1985 Welsh Leek Nickel-brass	£4
1985 — in Presentation folder	£6
1985 — Proof	£7
1985 — Silver Proof	£30
1985 — Silver Piedfort Proof	£50
1986 Northern Ireland Flax Nickel-brass	£5
1986 — in Presentation folder	£6
1986 — Proof	£8
1986 — Silver Proof	£30
1986 — Silver Piedfort Proof	£50
1987 English Oak Nickel-brass	£5
1987 — in Presentation folder	£6
1987 — Proof	£8
1987 — Silver Proof	£28
1987 — Silver Piedfort Proof	£50
1988 Royal Shield Nickel-brass	£5
1988 — in Presentation folder	£6
1988 — Proof	£8
1988 — Silver Proof	£30
1988 — Silver Piedfort Proof	£55
1989 Scottish Thistle Nickel-brass	£5
1989 — Proof	£8
1989 — Silver Proof	£28
1989 — Silver Piedfort Proof	£50
1990 Welsh Leek Nickel-brass	£5
1990 — Proof	£8
1990 — Silver Proof	£28
1991 Northern Ireland Flax Nickel-brass	£5
1991 — Proof	£8
1991 — Silver Proof	£32
1992 English Oak Nickel-brass	£5
1992 — Proof	£8
1992 — Silver Proof	£32
1993 Royal Arms Nickel-brass	£5
1993 — Proof	£8
1993 — Silver Proof	£32
1993 — Silver Piedfort Proof	£65
1994 Scottish Lion Nickel-brass	£5
1994 — in Presentation folder	£6
1994 — Proof	£8
1994 — Silver Proof	£32
1994 — Silver Piedfort Proof	£65
1995 Welsh Heraldic Dragon Nickel-brass	£5
1995 — in Presentation folder (English)	£6
1995 — — (Welsh)	£8
1995 — Proof	£10
1995 — Silver Proof	£32
1995 — Silver Piedfort Proof	£65
1996 Northern Ireland Celtic Cross Nickel-brass	£5
1996 — in Presentation folder	£6
1996 — Proof	£8
1996 — Silver Proof	£33
1996 — Silver Piedfort Proof	£65

1983, 1993, 1998

1984, 1989

1985, 1990

1986, 1991

1987, 1992

1988

1994, 1999

DATE	UNC
1997 English Lions. Nickel-brass	£5
1997 — in Presentation folder	£6
1997 — Proof	£8
1997 — Silver Proof	£32
1997 — Silver Piedfort Proof	£70
1998 New portrait. Royal Arms. Nickel-brass (from Year sets only)	£6
1998 — in Presentation folder	£7
1998 — Proof	£8
1998 — Silver Proof	£30
1998 — Silver Piedfort Proof	£65
1999 Scottish Lion. Nickel-brass (from Year sets only)	£5
1999 — in Presentation folder	£6
1999 — Proof	£8
1999 — Silver Proof	£35
1999 — Silver Piedfort Proof	£75
2000 Welsh Dragon. Nickel-brass	£4
2000 — in Presentation folder	£6
2000 — Proof	£8
2000 — Silver Proof	£35
2000 — Silver Piedfort Proof	£55
2001 Northern Ireland Celtic Cross. Nickel-brass	£3
2001 — in Presentation folder	£6
2001 — Proof	£8
2001 — Silver Proof	£35
2001 — Silver Piedfort Proof	£55

1995, 2000

1996, 2001

1997

FIFTY PENCE

1969	£3
1970	£4
1971 Proof	£8
1972 Proof	£8
1973 Accession to EEC	£3
1973 — Proof	£5
1974 Proof	£5
1975 Proof	£5
1976	£3
1976 Proof	£5
1977	£3
1977 Proof	£5
1978	£3
1978 Proof	£5
1979	£3
1979 Proof	£5
1980	£3
1980 Proof	£5
1981	£2
1981 Proof	£5
1982 Legend changed to FIFTY PENCE	£3
1982 Proof	£5
1983	£3
1983 Proof	£5
1984	£3
1984 Proof	£5
1985 New portrait	£3
1985 Proof	£5
1986	£4
1986 Proof	£5
1987	£4
1987 Proof	£5
1988	£4
1988 Proof	£5
1989	£4
1989 Proof	£5
1990	£4
1990 Proof	£5
1991	£5
1991 Proof	£6

DATE	UNC
*1992 Presidency of EC Council and completion of Single Market	£8
1992 — in Presentation folder with Britannia	£9
1992 — Proof	£15
1992 — Silver Proof	£30
1992 — Silver Proof Piedfort	£50
1992 — Gold Proof	£400
1993	£5
*1994 Anniversary of the Normandy Landings	£5
1994 — in Presentation folder	£6
1994 — Proof	£8
1994 — Silver Proof	£30
1994 — Silver Proof Piedfort	£60
1994 — Gold Proof	£425
1995	£5
1995 Proof	£8
1996	£5
1996 Proof	£7
1996 Silver Proof	£22
1997	£8
1997 Proof	£10
1997 Silver Proof	£28
1997 *new reduced size*	£4
1997 Proof	£6
1997 Silver Proof	£28
1997 Silver Proof Piedfort	£65
1998 New portrait	£2
1998 Proof	£5
1998 Silver Proof	£25
1998 Silver Proof Piedfort	£65
*1998 Presidency and 25th anniversary of entry into the EU	£4
1998 — Proof	£6
1998 — Silver Proof	£25
1998 — Silver Proof Piedfort	£75
•1998 50th Anniversary of the National Health Service	£4
1998 — Proof	£6
1998 — Silver Proof	£25
1998 — Silver Proof Piedfort	£75
1999	£4
1999 Proof	£5
1999 Silver Proof	£25
1999 Silver Proof Piedfort	£75
2000	£2
2000 — Proof	£5
2000 — Silver Proof	£30
2000 — Silver Proof Piedfort	£85
•2000 150th Anniversary of Public Libraries	£4
2000 — Proof	£7
2000 — Silver Proof	£30
2000 — Gold proof	£250

TWENTY-FIVE PENCE (CROWN)

1972 Royal Silver Wedding Cu-Ni	£2
1972 — Proof	£6
1972 — Silver Proof	£20
1977 Silver Jubilee Cu-Ni	£2
1977 — in Presentation folder	£3
1977 — Proof	£5
1977 — Silver Proof	£12
1980 Queen Mother 80th Birthday Cu-Ni	£1
1980 — in Presentation folder	£3
1980 — Silver Proof	£28
1981 Royal Wedding Cu-Ni	£2
1981 — in Presentation folder	£3
1981 — Silver Proof	£25

TWENTY PENCE

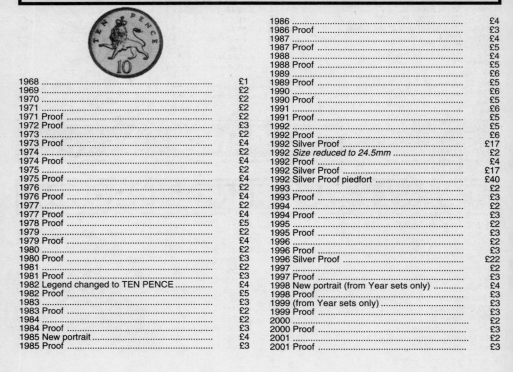

DATE	UNC	DATE	UNC
		1990	£1
		1990 Proof	£4
		1991	£2
		1991 Proof	£5
		1992	£2
		1992 Proof	£4
		1993	£2
		1993 Proof	£4
1982	£2	1994	£2
1982 Proof	£5	1994 Proof	£4
1982 Silver Piedfort Proof	£50	1995	£2
1983	£2	1995 Proof	£4
1983 Proof	£5	1996	£2
1984	£2	1996 Proof	£4
1984 Proof	£5	1996 Silver Proof	£15
1985 New portrait	£1	1997	£2
1985 Proof	£6	1997 Proof	£4
1986	£4	1998 New portrait	£2
1986 Proof	£5	1998 Proof	£4
1987	£2	1999	£2
1987 Proof	£4	1999 Proof	£4
1988	£2	2000	£2
1988 Proof	£4	2000 Proof	£4
1989	£2	2001	£2
1989 Proof	£4	2001 proof	£4

TEN PENCE

DATE	UNC	DATE	UNC
		1986	£4
		1986 Proof	£3
		1987	£4
		1987 Proof	£5
		1988	£4
		1988 Proof	£5
1968	£1	1989	£6
1969	£2	1989 Proof	£5
1970	£2	1990	£6
1971	£2	1990 Proof	£5
1971 Proof	£2	1991	£6
1972 Proof	£3	1991 Proof	£5
1973	£2	1992	£5
1973 Proof	£4	1992 Proof	£6
1974	£2	1992 Silver Proof	£17
1974 Proof	£4	1992 *Size reduced to 24.5mm*	£2
1975	£2	1992 Proof	£4
1975 Proof	£4	1992 Silver Proof	£17
1976	£2	1992 Silver Proof piedfort	£40
1976 Proof	£4	1993	£2
1977	£2	1993 Proof	£3
1977 Proof	£4	1994	£2
1978 Proof	£5	1994 Proof	£3
1979	£2	1995	£2
1979 Proof	£4	1995 Proof	£3
1980	£2	1996	£2
1980 Proof	£3	1996 Proof	£3
1981	£2	1996 Silver Proof	£22
1981 Proof	£3	1997	£2
1982 Legend changed to TEN PENCE	£4	1997 Proof	£3
1982 Proof	£5	1998 New portrait (from Year sets only)	£4
1983	£3	1998 Proof	£3
1983 Proof	£2	1999 (from Year sets only)	£3
1984	£2	1999 Proof	£3
1984 Proof	£3	2000	£2
1985 New portrait	£4	2000 Proof	£3
1985 Proof	£3	2001	£2
		2001 Proof	£3

FIVE PENCE

DATE	UNC
1968	50p
1969	50p
1970	55p
1971	50p
1971 Proof	£4
1972 Proof	£5
1973 Proof	£5
1974 Proof	£5
1975	50p
1975 Proof	£3
1976 Proof	£5
1977	50p
1977 Proof	£4
1978	£1
1978 Proof	£3
1979	£1
1979 Proof	£3
1980	£1
1980 Proof	£2
1981 Proof	£3
1982 Legend changed to FIVE PENCE	£3
1982 Proof	£3
1983	£4
1983 Proof	£3
1984	£3
1984 Proof	£4
1985 New portrait	£2
1985 Proof	£4
1986	£2
1986 Proof	£4

DATE	UNC
1987	£1
1987 Proof	£3
1988	£1
1988 Proof	£2
1989	£1
1989 Proof	£4
1990	£2
1990 Proof	£5
1990 Silver Proof	£15
1990 *Size reduced to 18mm*	£1
1990 Proof	£2
1990 Silver Proof	£15
1990 Silver Proof Piedfort	£30
1991	£1
1991 Proof	£3
1992	50p
1992 Proof	£3
1993	50p
1993 Proof	£4
1994	£1
1994 Proof	£3
1995	£1
1995 Proof	£3
1996	£1
1996 Proof	£3
1996 Silver proof	£15
1997	£1
1997 Proof	£3
1998	£1
1998 Proof	£3
1999	£2
1999 Proof	£3
2000	£2
2000 Proof	£3
2001	£2
2001 Proof	£3

TWO PENCE

Bronze

1971	50p
1971 Proof	£2
1972 Proof	£3
1973 Proof	£3
1974 Proof	£2
1975	£1
1975 Proof	£2
1976	50p

1976 Proof	£2
1977	50p
1977 Proof	£2
1978	50p
1978 Proof	£2
1979	50p
1979 Proof	£2
1980	50p
1980 Proof	£2
1981	50p
1981 Proof	£2
1982 Legend changed to TWO PENCE	£2
1982 Proof	£2
1983	£2
1983 Proof	£3
1983 Error reverse as New Pence	Rare
1984	£1
1984 Proof	£1

DATE	UNC	DATE	UNC
1985 New portrait	50p	1994 Proof	£2
1985 Proof	£1	1995	£1
1986	25p	1995 Proof	£2
1986 Proof	£1	1996	£1
1987	25p	1996 Proof	£2
1987 Proof	£1	1996 Silver Proof	£17
1988	25p	1997	£1
1988 Proof	£1	1997 Proof	£2
1989	25p	1998 New portrait	£1
1989 Proof	£1	1998 Proof	£4
1990	25p	1998 *Bronze*	£1
1990 Proof	£1	1998 *Bronze* Proof	£2
1991	25p	1999	£1
1991 Proof	£1	1999 Proof	£5
1992	£2	1999 *Bronze*	£4
1992 Proof	£1	1999 *Bronze* Proof	£4
Copper-plated steel		2000	—
1992	£1	2000 Proof	£4
1993	£1	2001	—
1993 Proof	£2	2001 Proof	£4
1994	£1		

ONE PENNY

Bronze	UNC	DATE	UNC
1971	25p	1986 Proof	£1
1971 Proof	£1	1987	25p
1972 Proof	£2	1987 Proof	£1
1973	£1	1988	25p
1973 Proof	£2	1988 Proof	£3
1974	£1	1989	25p
1974 Proof	£2	1989 Proof	£2
1975	£1	1990	25p
1975 Proof	£2	1990 Proof	£2
1976	£1	1991	25p
1976 Proof	£2	1991 Proof	£2
1977	50p	1992	£2
1977 Proof	£1	1992 Proof	£2
1978	£1	*Copper-plated steel*	
1978 Proof	£2	1992	£1
1979	£1	1993	—
1979 Proof	£2	1993 Proof	£1
1980	£1	1994	—
1980 Proof	£2	1994 Proof	£1
1981	£1	1995	—
1981 Proof	£2	1995 Proof	£1
1982 Legend changed to ONE PENNY	50p	1996	—
1982 Proof	£2	1996 Proof	£1
1983	50p	1996 Silver Proof	£15
1983 Proof	£1	1997	—
1984	£1	1997 Proof	£1
1984 Proof	£1	1998 New portrait	50p
1985 New portrait	25p	1998 Proof	£2
1985 Proof	£1	1998 *Bronze*	—
1986	25p	1998 *Bronze* Proof	£1
		1999	—
		1999 Proof	£2
		1999 *Bronze*	£3
		1999 *Bronze* Proof	£1
		2000	—
		2000 Proof	—
		2001	—
		2001 Proof	—

It would appear that 1998 and 1999 year sets *mostly* include bronze 2p and 1p coins whereas those put into general circulation are copper-plated steel. However, early in 1998 a number of 1998-dated 2ps in bronze were also put into circulation.

HALF PENNY

DATE	UNC	DATE	UNC
		1977	50p
		1977 Proof	£2
		1978	75p
		1978 Proof	£2
		1979	£1
1971	25p	1979 Proof	£2
1971 Proof	£1	1980	50p
1972 Proof	£5	1980 Proof	£1
1973	50p	1981	£1
1973 Proof	£3	1981 Proof	£2
1974	50p	1982 Legend changed to HALF PENNY	50p
1974 Proof	£2	1982 Proof	£3
1975	50p	1983	£1
1975 Proof	£2	1983 Proof	£4
1976	50p	1984 (only issued in Unc. year sets)	£4
1976 Proof	£2	1984 Proof	£5

MAUNDY SETS

DATE AND PLACE OF ISSUE	MINTAGE	UNC
1971 Tewkesbury Abbey	1,108	£70
1972 York Minster	1,026	£75
1973 Westminster Abbey	1,004	£70
1974 Salisbury Cathedral	1,042	£70
1975 Peterborough Cathedral	1,050	£70
1976 Hereford Cathedral	1,158	£75
1977 Westminster Abbey	1,138	£80
1978 Carlisle Cathedral	1,178	£70
1979 Winchester Cathedral	1,188	£70
1980 Worcester Cathedral	1,198	£75
1981 Westminster Abbey	1,178	£75
1982 St David's Cathedral	1,218	£75
1983 Exeter Cathedral	1,228	£75
1984 Southwell Minster	1,238	£75
1985 Ripon Cathedral	1,248	£75
1986 Chichester Cathedral	1,378	£75
1987 Ely Cathedral	1,390	£80
1988 Lichfield Cathedral	1,402	£80
1989 Birmingham Cathedral	1,353	£80
1990 Newcastle Cathedral	1,523	£80
1991 Westminster Abbey	1,384	£85
1992 Chester Cathedral	1,424	£85
1993 Wells Cathedral	1,440	£85
1994 Truro Cathedral	1,433	£85
1995 Coventry Cathedral	1,466	£90
1996 Norwich Cathedral	1,485	£95
1997 Birmingham Cathedral	1,486	£100
1998 Portsmouth Cathedral	1,488	£100
1999 Bristol Cathedral		£100
2000 Lincoln Cathedral		£110
2000 — Proof		£125
2001 Westminster Abbey		£120

In keeping with ancient tradition the Royal Maundy sets are made up of four silver coins of 4p, 3p, 2p and 1p. The designs for the reverse of the coins are a crowned numeral in a wreath of oak leaves—basically the same design that has been used for Maundy coins since Charles II.

PROOF AND SPECIMEN SETS

DATE	FDC
GEORGE IV	
1826 £5–farthing (11 coins)	£18,000
WILLIAM IV	
1831 Coronation £2–farthing (14 coins)	£15,500
VICTORIA	
1839 "Una and the Lion" £5–farthing (15 coins)	£30,000
1853 Sovereign–quarter farthing, including "Gothic"crown (16 coins)	£27,500
1887 Golden Jubilee £5– 3d (11 coins)	£6,500
1887 Golden Jubilee Crown–3d (7 coins)	£1,250
1893 £5–3d (10 coins)	£7,500
1893 Crown–3d (6 coins)	£1,250
EDWARD VII	
1902 Coronation £5–Maundy penny matt proofs (13 coins)	£1,550
1902 Coronation Sovereign–Maundy penny matt proofs (11 coins)	£550
GEORGE V	
1911 Coronation £5–Maundy penny (12 coins)	£2,550
1911 Sovereign–Maundy penny (10 coins)	£800
1911 Coronation Halfcrown–Maundy penny (8 coins)	£400
1927 New types Crown–3d (6 coins)	£300
GEORGE VI	
1937 Coronation £5–half sovereign (4 coins)	£1,550
1937 Coronation Crown–farthing including Maundy money (15 coins)	£125
1950 Mid-century Halfcrown–farthing (9 coins)	£55
1951 Festival of Britain, Crown–farthing (10 coins)	£75

DATE	FDC

ELIZABETH II

1953 Coronation Crown–farthing (10 coins)	£55
1953 Coronation Currency (plastic) set halfcrown–farthing (9 coins)	£12
1968 Specimen decimal set 10p, 5p, 1971 2p, 1p, ½p in wallet (5 coins)	£2.50
1970 Last £sd coins (sets issued 1971–73) Halfcrown– halfpenny (8 coins)	£18
1971 Proof (issued 1973), 50p–½p (6 coins)	£12
1972 Proof 50p–½p, Silver Wedding crown (7 coins)	£15
1973 Proof 50p–½p (6 coins)	£12
1974 Proof 50p–½p (6 coins)	£16
1975 Proof 50p–½p (6 coins)	£16
1976 Proof 50p–½p (6 coins)	£16
1977 Proof 50p–½p, Jubilee crown (7 coins)	£15
1978 Proof 50p–½p (6 coins)	£14
1979 Proof 50p–½p (6 coins)	£16
1980 Proof 50p–½p (6 coins)	£14
1980 Proof gold £5–half sovereign (4 coins)	£775
1981 Commemorative Proof £5–sovereign, Royal Wedding Silver crown, 50p–½p (9 coins)	£675
1981 Proof 50p–½p (6 coins)	£16
1982 Proof gold £5–half sovereign (4 coins)	£775
1982 Proof 50p–½p (7 coins)	£16
1982 Uncirculated 50p–½p (7 coins)	£12
1983 Proof gold £2–half sovereign (3 coins)	£355
1983 Proof £1–½p (8 coins)	£20
1983 Uncirculated £1–½p (8 coins)	£16
1984 Proof gold £5–half sovereign (3 coins)	£650
1984 Proof £1 (Scottish rev.)–½p (8 coins)	£16
1984 Uncirculated £1 (Scottish rev.)–½p (8 coins)	£15
1985 Proof Gold new portrait £5–half sovereign (4 coins)	£775
1985 Proof new portrait £1 (Welsh rev.)–1p in de luxe case (7 coins)	£25
1985 Proof as above, in standard case	£18
1985 Uncirculated £1 (Welsh rev.)–1p (7 coins)	£15
1986 Proof Gold Commonwealth Games £2–half sovereign (3 coins)	£425
1986 Proof Commonwealth Games £2, Northern Ireland £1, 50p–1p in de luxe case (8 coins)	£25
1986 Proof as above in standard case (8 coins)	£23
1986 Uncirculated as above in folder (8 coins)	£15
1987 Proof gold Britannia set 1 oz.–1/10 oz. (4 coins)	£775
1987 Proof gold Britannia ¼ oz., 1/10 oz. (2 coins)	£155
1987 Proof gold £2–half sovereign (3 coins)	£365
1987 Proof £1 (English rev.)–1p in de luxe case (7 coins)	£28
1987 Proof £1 (English rev.)–1p in standard case (7 coins)	£18
1987 Uncirculated as above in folder (7 coins)	£11
1988 Proof gold Britannia set 1 oz.–1/10 oz. (4 coins)	£755
1988 Proof gold Britannia ¼ oz., 1/10 oz. (2 coins)	£155
1988 Proof gold £2–half sovereign (3 coins)	£310
1988 Proof £1 (Royal Arms rev.)–1p in de luxe case (7 coins)	£30
1988 Proof as above in standard case (7 coins)	£25
1988 Uncirculated as above in folder (7 coins)	£12
1989 Proof gold Britannia set 1 oz.–1/10 oz. (4 coins)	£760
1989 Proof gold Britannia ¼ oz., 1/10 oz. (2 coins)	£165
1989 Proof gold 500th anniversary of the sovereign. £5–half sovereign (4 coins)	£950
1989 Proof gold 500th anniversary of the sovereign. £2–half sovereign (3 coins)	£450
1989 Proof Bill of Rights £2, Claim of Right £2 (2 coins)	£42
1989 Proof silver piedfort as above (2 coins)	£85
1989 Uncirculated £2 as above in folder (2 coins)	£14
1989 Proof Bill of Rights £2, Claim of Right £2, £1 (Scottish rev.)–1p in de luxe case (9 coins)	£32
1989 Proof as above in standard case (9 coins)	£30
1989 Uncirculated £1 (Scottish rev.)–1p (7 coins)	£18
1990 Proof gold Britannia set 1 oz.–1/10 oz. (4 coins)	£800
1990 Proof gold £5–half sovereign (4 coins)	£875
1990 Proof gold £2–half sovereign (3 coins)	£355
1990 Proof silver 5p, 2 sizes (2 coins)	£25
1990 Proof £1 (Welsh rev.)–1p, two sizes of 5p, in de luxe case (8 coins)	£32
1990 Proof as above in standard case (8 coins)	£25
1990 Uncirculated as above (8 coins)	£16
1991 Proof gold Britannia set 1 oz.–1/10 oz. (4 coins)	£775
1991 Proof gold £5–half sovereign (4 coins)	£1,250
1991 Proof gold £2–half sovereign (3 coins)	£450
1991 Proof £1 (Irish rev.)–1p in de luxe case (7 coins)	£30
1991 Proof as above in standard case (7 coins)	£25
1991 Uncirculated as above (7 coins)	£16

DATE	FDC
1992 Proof gold Britannia set 1 oz.–1/10 oz. (4 coins)	£775
1992 Proof gold £5–half sovereign (4 coins)	£950
1992 Proof gold £2–half sovereign (3 coins)	£450
1992 Proof £1 (English rev.)–1p (2x10p and 2x50p) in de luxe case (9 coins)	£35
1992 Proof as above in standard case (9 coins)	£30
1992 Uncirculated as above (9 coins)	£15
1993 Proof gold Britannia set 1 oz.–1/10 oz. (4 coins)	£900
1993 Proof gold £5–half sovereign plus silver Pistrucci medal (4 coins + medal)	£1,200
1993 Proof gold £2–half sovereign (3 coins)	£520
1993 Proof £1–1p plus Coronation anniversary £5 in red leather case (8 coins)	£38
1993 Proof as above in standard case (8 coins)	£35
1993 Uncirculated £1–1p plus European Community 50p (8 coins)	£15
1994 Proof gold Britannia set 1 oz.–1/10 oz. (4 coins)	£825
1994 Proof gold £5–half sovereign (4 coins)	£1,250
1993 Proof gold £2–half sovereign (3 coins)	£550
1994 Proof Bank of England Tercentenary £2–1p in red leather case (8 coins)	£35
1994 Proof as above in standard case (8 coins)	£32
1994 Uncirculated £1–1p including Normandy Landings 50p (7 coins)	£16
1995 Proof gold Britannia set 1 oz.–1/10 oz. (4 coins)	£810
1995 Proof gold £5–half sovereign (4 coins)	£1,250
1995 Proof gold £2–half sovereign (3 coins)	£525
1995 Proof "Peace" £2–1p in red leather case (8 coins)	£35
1995 Proof as above in standard case (8 coins)	£32
1995 Uncirculated "Peace" £2–1p (8 coins)	£14
1996 Proof gold Britannia set 1oz–¼oz (4 coins)	£950
1996 Proof gold £5–half sovereign (4 coins)	£1,250
1996 Proof gold £2–half sovereign (3 coins)	£525
1996 Proof "Royal 70th Birthday" £5–1p in red leather case (9 coins)	£42
1996 Proof as above in standard case (9 coins)	£36
1996 Uncirculated "Football" £2–1p (8 coins)	£14
1996 Proof silver 25th Anniversary of Decimal currency £1–1p (7 coins)	£125
1997 Proof gold £5–half sovereign (4 coins)	£1,250
1997 Proof gold £2–half sovereign (3 coins)	£520
1997 Proof Royal Golden Wedding £5 in cupro-nickel, Bi-metallic £2, "English" £1, 50p–1p in red leather case (10 coins)	£50
1997 Proof as above in standard case (10 coins)	£38
1997 Uncirculated "Royal Golden Wedding" £5–1p (10 coins)	£15
1997 Proof silver 50p—two sizes (2 coins)	£52
1997 Proof silver Britannia set £2–20p	£100
1998 Proof gold Britannia set (4 coins)	£1,150
1998 Proof gold £5–half sovereign (4 coins)	£1,250
1998 Proof gold £2–half sovereign (3 coins)	£500
1998 Proof silver Britannia set £2–20p	£95
1998 Proof Prince of Wales Birthday £5–1p (10 coins) in leather case	£42
1998 Proof as above in standard case (10 coins)	£36
1998 Uncirculated "Prince's Birthday" £5–1p (10 coins)	£15
1999 Proof gold Britannia set (4 coins)	£1,250
1999 Proof gold £5–half sovereign incl. £2 Rugby World Cup (4 coins)	£1,265
1999 Proof £2 Rugby World Cup–half sovereign (3 coins)	£500
1999 Proof Diana £5–1p (9 coins)	£48
1999 Proof as above in standard case (9 coins)	£36
1999 Uncirculated set £2–1p (8 coins)	£15
2000 Proof gold Britannia set (4 coins)	£1,250
2000 Proof gold £5–half sovereign (4 coins)	£1,265
2000 Proof £2–half sovereign (3 coins)	£500
2000 Proof Millennium £5–1p in de-luxe "shaped" pack (10 coins)	£48
2000 Proof as above in standard pack (10 coins)	£35
2000 Uncirculated set £2–1p (9 coins)	£12
2000 Millennium Time capsule (9 coins)	£25
2001 Proof gold Britannia set (4 coins)	£825
2001 Proof gold £5–half sovereign (4 coins)	£1,250
2001 Proof gold £2–half sovereign (3 coins)	£550
2001 Proof Executive set £5–1p in new packaging (10 coins)	£75
2001 Proof as above in red leather case (10 coins)	£48
2001 Proof as above in "Gift" packaging (10 coins)	£43
2001 Proof as above in standard case (10 coins)	£34
2001 Uncirculated set £2 (x2)–1p (9 coins)	£14

In addition to the above the Royal Mint also produce special Wedding and "Baby" gift packs each year.

SCOTLAND

The coins illustrated are pennies representative of the reign, unless otherwise stated.

DAVID I (1124–53)

Berwick, Carlisle, Edinburgh and Roxburgh Mints

	F	VF
Penny	£550	£1300

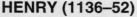

David I

HENRY (1136–52)

Bamborough, Carlisle and Corbridge Mints for the Earl of Huntingdon and Northumberland

Penny	£1200	£3000

Henry

MALCOLM IV (1153–65)

Berwick and Roxburgh Mints

Penny (5 different types)	£3500	£9500

WILLIAM THE LION (1165–1214)

Berwick, Edinburgh, Dun (Dunbar?), Perth and Roxburgh Mints

Penny	£75	£155

William the Lion

ALEXANDER II (1214–49)

Berwick and Roxburgh Mints

Penny	£750	£1500

Alexander II

ALEXANDER III (1249–86)

FIRST COINAGE (1250–80)

Pennies struck at the Mints at

Aberdeen	£80	£250
Ayr	£100	£300
Berwick	£55	£150
"Dun" (Dumfries?)	£135	£350
Edinburgh	£50	£145
Forfar	£130	£375
Forres	£145	£375
Glasgow	£155	£400
Inverness	£140	£380
Kinghorn	£165	£400
Lanark	£130	£355
Montrose	£255	£500
Perth	£65	£165
Renfrew	£175	£500
Roxburgh	£65	£175
St Andrews	£90	£225
Sterling	£135	£350

Alexander III

SECOND COINAGE (1280–86)

Penny	£35	£75
Halfpenny	£85	£195
Farthing	£165	£435

JOHN BALIOL (1292–1306)

FIRST COINAGE *(Rough Surface issue)*

Penny	£115	£255
Halfpenny		*Extremely rare*

SECOND COINAGE *(Smooth Surface issue)*

Penny	£165	£350
Halfpenny	£225	£500

John Baliol

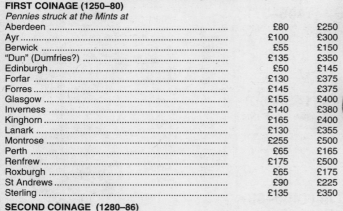

ROBERT BRUCE (1306–29)

	F	VF
Berwick Mint		
*Penny	£250	£600
Halfpenny	£350	£750
Farthing		*Extremely Rare*

Robert Bruce

DAVID II (1329–71)

Aberdeen and Edinburgh Mints		
Noble		*Extremely Rare*
Groat	£75	£225
Halfgroat	£65	£185
Penny	£50	£100
Halfpenny	£155	£350
Farthing	£500	£1500

David II

ROBERT II (1371–90)

Dundee, Edinburgh and Perth Mints		
Groat	£60	£190
Halfgroat	£90	£220
Penny	£75	£165
Halfpenny	£125	£400

Robert II

ROBERT III (1390–1406)

Aberdeen, Dumbarton, Edinburgh, Perth Mints		
*Lion or crown	£430	£900
Demy lion or halfcrown	£350	£800
Groat	£60	£175
Halfgroat	£110	£300
Penny	£155	£325
Halfpenny	£300	£1000

JAMES I (1406–37)

Aberdeen, Edinburgh, Inverness, Linlithgow, Perth, Stirling Mints		
Demy	£350	£600
Half demy	£450	£800
Groat	£125	£265
Penny	£100	£275
Halfpenny	£125	£400

JAMES II (1437–60)

Robert III Lion

Aberdeen, Edinburgh, Linlithgow, Perth, Roxburgh, Stirling Mints		
Demy	£375	£800
Lion	£450	£1400
Half lion		*Extremely rare*
*Groat	£155	£500
Halfgroat	£385	£850
Penny (billon)	£180	£500

JAMES III (1460–88)

Aberdeen, Berwick and Edinburgh Mints		
Rider	£700	£1700
Half rider	£900	£2000
Quarter rider	£900	£2000
Unicorn	£750	£1700
Groat	£155	£355
Halfgroat	£335	£850
Penny (silver)	£100	£350
Plack (billon)	£65	£165
Half plack		*Extremely rare*
Penny (billon)	£70	£175
Farthing (copper)	£155	£325

James III Groat, Berwick Mint

	F	VF

JAMES IV (1488–1513)

Edinburgh Mint

	F	VF
Unicorn	£675	£1500
Half unicorn	£550	£1100
Lion or crown	£800	£1750
Half lion	£1500	£3500
Groat	£320	£750
Halfgroat	£320	£650
Penny (silver)	£400	£1000
Plack	£40	£100
Half plack	£85	£185
*Penny (billon)	£50	£125

James IV

JAMES V (1513–42)

Edinburgh Mint

	F	VF
Unicorn	£750	£1800
Half Unicorn	£1450	£4000
Crown	£500	£1250
Ducat or Bonnet piece	£1450	£3100
Two-thirds ducat	£1850	£3200
One -third ducat	£2000	£4000
*Groat	£100	£210
One-third groat	£145	£375
Plack	£35	£125
Bawbee	£30	£100
Half bawbee	£75	£160
Quarter bawbee	*Extremely rare*	

MARY (1542–67)

Edinburgh and Stirling Mints
FIRST PERIOD (1542–58)

	F	VF
Crown	£850	£2350
Twenty shillings	£1750	£3000
Lions (Forty-four shillings)	£800	£1950
Half lions (Twenty-two shillings)	£450	£1500
Ryals (Three pounds)	£1750	£4500
Half ryal	£2750	£6000
Portrait testoon	£1000	£4000
*Non-portrait testoon	£155	£475
Half testoon	£155	£400
Bawbee	£45	£100
Half bawbee	£75	£185
Penny (facing bust)	£175	£500
Penny (no bust)	*Extremely rare*	
Lion	£30	£79
Plack	£30	£79

SECOND PERIOD (Francis and Mary, 1558–60)

	F	VF
Ducat (Sixty shillings)	*Extremely rare*	
Non-portrait testoon	£160	£425
Half testoon	£165	£475
12 penny groat	£90	£200
Lion	£30	£80

James V Edinburgh Groat

THIRD PERIOD (Widowhood, 1560–65)

	F	VF
Portrait testoon	£750	£2500
Half testoon	£800	£1850

FOURTH PERIOD (Henry and Mary, 1565–67)

	F	VF
Portrait ryal	*Extremely rare*	
Non-portrait ryal	£180	£500
Two-third ryal	£180	£550

Mary First Period Testoon

	F	VF
One-third ryal	£420	£1000
Testoon	£208	£800

FIFTH PERIOD (Second widowhood, 1567)

Non-portrait ryal	£200	£550
Two thirds ryal	£215	£525
One-third ryal	£215	£525

JAMES VI
(Before accession to the English throne)
(1567–1603)

FIRST COINAGE (1567–71)

Ryal	£185	£500
Two-third ryal	£180	£475
One-third ryal	£185	£500

SECOND COINAGE (1571–80)

Twenty pounds		*Extremely rare*
Noble	£85	£350
Half noble	£80	£275
Two merks or Thistle dollar	£900	£1700
Merk	£850	—

THIRD COINAGE (1580–81)

Ducat		*Extremely rare*
Sixteen shillings	£900	£2500
Eight shillings	£850	£2200
Four shillings		*Extremely rare*
Two shillings		*Extremely rare*

James VI Fourth coinage thirty shillings

FOURTH COINAGE (1582–88)

Lion noble	£2000	£6000
Two-third lion noble	£2500	£6500
One-third lion noble	£3000	£7750
Forty shillings	£2500	£7600
*Thirty shillings	£180	£750
Twenty shillings	£130	£400
Ten shillings	£115	£285

FIFTH COINAGE (1588)

Thistle noble	£1200	£3000

SIXTH COINAGE (1591–93)

"Hat" piece	£2500	£6000
"Balance" half merk	£175	£400
"Balance" quarter merk	£265	£600

SEVENTH COINAGE (1594–1601)

Rider	£425	£900
Half rider	£350	£750
Ten shillings	£100	£275
Five shillings	£110	£300
Thirty pence	£80	£250
Twelve pence	£65	£250

EIGHTH COINAGE (1601–04)

Sword and sceptre piece	£275	£500
Half sword and sceptre piece	£225	£400
Thistle-merk	£50	£185
Half thistle-merk	£40	£145
Quarter thistle-merk	£40	£145
Eighth thistle-merk	£45	£175

	F	VF
Billon and copper issues		
Plack	£35	£100
Half plack	£880	£400
Hardhead	£30	£85
Saltire plack	£100	£500
Twopence		Very rare
Penny		Very rare

JAMES VI
(After accession to the English throne)
(1603–25)

	F	VF
Unit	£385	£750
Double crown	£450	£1200
British crown	£325	£1000
Halfcrown	£275	£500
Thistle crown	£275	£500
Sixty shillings	£285	£650
*Thirty shillings	£80	£200
Twelve shillings	£75	£175
Six shillings	£120	£550
Two shillings	£50	£250
One shilling	£85	£300
Copper twopence	£35	£75
Copper penny	£35	£75

James VI after accession thirty shillings

CHARLES I (1625–49)

FIRST COINAGE (1625–36)

	F	VF
Unit	£450	£850
Double crown	£1200	£2500
British crown	Extremely rare	
Sixty shillings	£265	£750
Thirty shillings	£65	£250
Twelve shillings	£60	£180
Six shillings	£115	£400
Two shillings	£75	£325
One shilling	Extremely rare	

SECOND COINAGE (1636)

	F	VF
Half merk	£50	£185
Forty penny piece	£45	£155
Twenty penny piece	£55	£300

THIRD COINAGE (1637–42)

	F	VF
Unit	£425	£1000
Half unit	£550	£1750
British crown	£400	£1200
British half crown	£350	£1000
Sixty shillings	£275	£800
*Thirty shillings	£65	£165
Twelve shillings	£65	£175
Six shillings	£60	£150
Half merk	£50	£145
Forty pence	£30	£85
Twenty pence	£25	£65
Three shillings	£45	£125
Two shillings	£45	£130
Twopence (copper)	£25	£75
Penny	Extremely rare	
Twopence (CR crowned)	£20	£65
Twopence (Stirling turner)	£20	£55

Charles I Third coinage thirty shillings

	F	VF

CHARLES II (1660–85)

FIRST COINAGE

Four merks

1664 Thistle above bust	£258	£600
1664 Thistle below bust	£285	£700
1665	*Extremely rare*	
1670	£185	£550
1673	£185	£550
1674 F below bust	£300	£750
1675	£185	£500

Two merks

1664 Thistle above bust	£200	£500
1664 Thistle below bust	£220	£600
1670	£155	£450
1673	£155	£450
1673 F below bust	£275	£900
1674	£250	£900
1674 F below bust	£200	£800
1675	£155	£450

Merk

1664	£40	£150
1665	£40	£150
1666	£80	£350
1668	£45	£155
1669	£45	£155
1670	£75	£275
1671	£65	£180
1672	£65	£175
1673	£65	£200
1674	£65	£200
1674 F Below bust	£60	£200
*1675 F below bust	£60	£200
1675	£85	£275

Charles II two merks

Half merk

1664	£60	£200
1665	£60	£200
1666	£75	£225
1667	£60	£180
1668	£60	£180
1669	£80	£225
1670	£100	£350
1671	£65	£185
1672	£65	£185
1673	£55	£165
1675 F below bust	£45	£150
1675	£55	£200

SECOND COINAGE

Dollar

1676	£185	£450
1679	£185	£425
1680	£250	£1000
1681	£155	£450
1682	£145	£300

Half Dollar

1675	£165	£450
1676	£185	£475
1681	£175	£450

Quarter Dollar

1675	£70	£200
1676	£80	£250
1677	£100	£325

	F	VF
1679	£73	£325
1680	£65	£265
1681	£78	£350
1682	£95	£250
Eighth Dollar		
1676	£55	£155
1677	£55	£155
1678/7		Rare
1679	£154	£600
1680	£75	£175
1682	£103	£500
Sixteenth Dollar		
1677	£38	£110
1678/7	£77	£175
1679/7		Rare
1680	£78	£200
1681	£43	£135
Twopence CR[II] crowned	£28	£100
Bawbees	£38	£110
Turners	£28	£110

James VII ten shillings

JAMES VII 1685–9

Sixty shillings

	F	VF
1688 proof only	—	£1000
Forty shillings		
1687	£88	£325
1688	£153	£400
Ten shillings		
*1687	£86	£275
1688	£100	£300

WILLIAM & MARY 1689–94

Sixty shillings

	F	VF
1691	£155	£555
1692	£140	£500
Forty shillings		
1689	£100	£295
1690	£87	£285
1691	£75	£205
1692	£85	£285
1693	£110	£405
1694	£100	£405
Twenty shillings		
1693	£100	£385
1694	£200	£500
Ten shillings		
1689		Extremely rare
1690	£98	£275
*1691	£75	£220
1692	£47	£120
1694	£163	£400
Five shillings		
1691	£705	£265
1694	£68	£220
Bawbee		
1691–94	£45	£120
Bodle		
1691–94	£38	£85

William & Mary ten shillings

	F	VF

WILLIAM II 1694–1702

Pistole	£1550	£4000
Half pistole	£1450	£3500
Forty shillings		
1695	£80	£300
1696	£55	£250
1697	£80	£350
1698	£55	£255
1699	£120	£600
1700	£200	£800
Twenty shillings		
1695	£50	£185
1696	£50	£185
1697	£100	—
1698	£100	£350
1699	£95	£325
Ten shillings		
*1695	£80	£250
1696	£85	£285
1697	£85	£300
1698	£85	£300
1699	£115	£350
Five shillings		
1695	£65	£250
1696	£65	£250
1697	£45	£125
1699	£50	£235
1700	£50	£225
1701	£55	£250
1702	£75	£280
Bawbee		
1695–97	£35	£120
Bodle		
1695–97	£35	£150

William II ten shillings

ANNE 1702–14

PRE-UNION 1702–7

Ten shillings		
1705	£75	£200
1706	£115	£375
Five shillings		
1705	£30	£75
*1706	£35	£125

Anne five shillings

POST-UNION 1707–14
See listing in English section.

JAMES VIII 1688–1766 (The Old Pretender)

A number of Guineas and Crowns in various metals were struck in 1828 using original dies prepared by Norbert Roettiers, all bearing the date 1716. These coins are extremely rare and are keenly sought after.

ISLE OF MAN

DATE	F	VF	EF	UNC
PENNY				
*1709 Cast	£20	£65	£155	—
1709 Silver cast Proof	—	—	—	£1200
1709 Brass	£25	£78	£155	—
*1733 "Quocunque"	£15	£35	£135	£205
1733 "Ouocunoue"	£20	£45	£175	£355
1733 Bath metal "Quocunque"	£10	£20	£125	—
1733 Silver Proof	—	—	—	£450
1733 Bronze Proof	—	—	—	£275
1733 Proof	—	—	—	£400
1733 Cap frosted	£10	£25	£135	£200
1733 Brass, cap frosted	£20	£38	£155	£325
1733 Silver Proof cap frosted	—	—	—	£355
1733 Bronze annulets instead of				
pellets	£30	£55	£210	£455
1758	£15	£30	£25	£235
1758 Proof	—	—	—	£320
1758 Silver Proof	—	—	—	£625
*1786 Engrailed edge	£10	£25	£125	£285
1786 Engrailed edge Proof	—	—	—	£320
1786 Plain edge Proof	—	—	—	£650
1786 Pellet below bust	£15	£45	£155	£325
*1798	£15	£45	£125	£250
1798 Proof	—	—	—	£225
1798 Bronze Proof	—	—	—	£225
1798 Copper-gilt Proof	—	—	—	£1000
1798 Silver Proof	—	—	—	£1500
1813	£12	£30	£100	£185
1813 Proof	—	—	—	£200
1813 Bronze Proof	—	—	—	£175
1813 Copper-gilt Proof	—	—	—	£1500
1839	£10	£25	£75	£150
1839 Proof	—	—	—	£250

DATE	F	VF	EF	UNC

HALF PENCE

	F	VF	EF	UNC
*1709 Cast	£30	£45	£150	—
1709 Brass	£35	£135	£325	—
1723 Silver	£520	£1000	£2000	—
1723 Copper	£225	£455	£1100	£1600
1733 Copper	£15	£35	£135	£200
1733 Bronze	£20	£35	£135	£200
1733 Silver Proof plain cap	—	—	—	£300
1733 Silver Proof frosted cap	—	—	—	—
1733 Bronze Proof	—	—	—	£255
1733 Bath metal plain cap	£20	£25	£120	—
1733 Bath metal frosted cap	£20	£30	£125	—
*1758	£18	£34	£135	£200
1758 Proof	—	—	—	£475
1786 Engrailed edge	£12	£25	£65	£175
1786 Proof engrailed edge	—	—	—	£225
1786 Plain edge	£22	£45	£150	£200
1786 Proof plain edge	—	—	—	£400
1786 Bronze Proof	—	—	—	£225
1798	£12	£25	£65	£175
1798 Proof	—	—	—	£200
1798 Bronze Proof	—	—	—	£185
1798 Copper-gilt Proof	—	—	—	£700
1798 Silver Proof	—	—	—	£1000
1813	£10	£25	£65	£150
1813 Proof	—	—	—	£200
1813 Bronze Proof	—	—	—	£180
1813 Copper-gilt Proof	—	—	—	£750
1839	£10	£22	£40	£85
1839 Bronze Proof	—	—	—	£175

FARTHING

	F	VF	EF	UNC
*1839 Copper	£10	£20	£45	£85
1839 Bronze Proof	—	—	—	£200
1839 Copper-gilt Proof	—	—	—	£1500

The last issue of coins made in the Isle of Man had been in 1839 but in 1970 Spink & Son Ltd was commissioned to produce a modern coinage for the Isle of Man Government which was struck at the Royal Mint. From 1973 onwards the Pobjoy Mint took over the contract and has been a very prolific producer of definitive and commemorative issues. It is not proposed to give a complete listing of all these coins but the Crown and 25p, which from the collector's point of view are the most interesting in the series, have been selected. Additionally a special 50p coin is issued to celebrate Christmas each year.

The listings that follow are of the ordinary uncirculated cupro-nickel crown-size coins. The Island has also issued most of the coins listed in other metals, including silver, gold and platinum in non proof and proof form and in 1984 some were also issued in silver clad cupro-nickel in proof form.

DATE	UNC
1970 Manx Cat	£3
1972 Royal Silver Wedding	£3
1974 Centenary of Churchill's birth	£2
1975 Manx Cat	£3
1976 Bi-Centenary of American Independence	£2
1976 Centenary of the Horse Drawn Tram	£2
1977 Silver Jubilee	£2
1977 Silver Jubilee Appeal	£2
1978 25th Anniversary of the Coronation	£2
1979 300th Anniversary of Manx Coinage	£2
1979 Millennium of Tynwald (5 coins)	£8
1980 Winter Olympics	£2
1980 Derby Bicentennial	£2
1980 22nd Olympics (3 coins)	£6
1980 80th Birthday of Queen Mother	£2
1981 Duke of Edinburgh Award Scheme (4 coins)	£7
1981 Year of Disabled (4 coins)	£7
1981 Prince of Wales' Wedding (2 coins)	£4
1982 12th World Cup—Spain (4 coins)	£8
1982 Maritime Heritage (4 coins)	£8
1983 Manned Flight (4 coins)	£8
1984 23rd Olympics (4 coins)	£8
1984 Quincentenary of College of Arms (4 coins)	£8
1984 Commonwealth Parliamentary Conference (4 coins)	£8
1985 Queen Mother (6 coins)	£8
1986 13th World Cup—Mexico (6 coins)	£8
1986 Prince Andrew Wedding (2 coins)	£6
1987 200th Anniversary of the United States Constitution	£2
1987 America's Cup Races (5 coins)	£9
1988 Bicentenary of Steam Navigation (6 coins)	£9
1988 Australia Bicentennial (6 coins)	£10
1988 Manx Cat	£3
1989 Royal Visit	£3
1989 Bicentenary of the Mutiny on the Bounty (4 coins)	£8
1989 Persian Cat	£4
1989 Bicentenary of Washington's Inauguration (4 coins)	£9
1990 150th Anniversary of the Penny Black	£7
1990 World Cup—Italy (4 coins)	£8
1990 25th Anniversary of Churchill's Death (2 coins)	£5
1990 Alley Cat	£4
1990 Queen Mother's 90th Birthday	£4
1991 Norwegian Forest Cat	£4
1991 Centenary of the American Numismatic Association	£3
1991 1992 America's Cup	£4
1991 10th Anniversary of Prince of Wales' Wedding (2 coins)	£6
1992 Discovery of America (4 coins)	£12
1992 Siamese Cat	£5
1992 1992 America's Cup	£3
1993 Maine Coon Cat	£3
1993 Preserve Planet Earth—Dinosaurs (2 coins)	£7
1994 Preserve Planet Earth—Mammoth	£4
1994 Year of the Dog	£4

DATE	UNC
1994 World Football Cup (6 coins)	£22
1994 Japanese Bobtail Cat	£4
1994 Normandy Landings (8 coins)	£30
1994 Preserve Planet Earth—Endangered Animals (3 coins)	£15
1995 Man in Flight—Series i (8 coins)	£48
1995 Man in Flight—Series ii (8 coins)	£48
1995 Queen Mother's 95th Birthday	£5
1995 Year of the Pig	£5
1995 Turkish Cat	£5
1995 Preserve Planet Earth—Egret and Otter	£8
1995 America's Cup	£5
1995 Aircraft of World War II (19 coins)	£80
1995 Famous World Inventions—Series i (12 coins)	£50
1996 Year of the Rat	£5
1996 70th Birthday of HM the Queen	£8
1996 The Flower Fairies—Series i (4 coins)	£30
1996 Famous World Inventions—Series ii (6 coins)	£30
1996 Olympic Games (6 coins)	£25
1996 Preserve Planet Earth—Killer Whale and Razorbill	£8
1996 Burmese Cat	£7
1996 Robert Burns (4 coins)	£18
1996 King Arthur & the Knights of the Round Table (5 coins)	£25
1996 European Football Championships (8 coins)	£40
1996 Football Championships Winner	£8
1996 Explorers (2 coins)	£14
1997 Year of the Ox	£8
1997 The Flower Fairies—Series ii (4 coins)	£19
1997 Royal Golden Wedding (2 coins)	£10
1997 Explorers—Eriksson and Nansen (2 coins)	£10
1997 Long-haired Smoke Cat	£6
1997 10th Anniversary of the "Cats on Coins" series (silver only)	£29
1997 90th Anniversary of the TT Races (4 coins)	£22
1998 The Millennium (16 coins to be issued in the next 3 years)	—
1998 Year of the Tiger	£8
1998 FIFA World Cup (4 coins)	£20
1998 Birman Cat	£8
1998 The Flower Fairies—Series iii (4 coins)	£22
1998 18th Winter Olympics, Nagano (4 coins)	£23
1998 Explorers—Vasco da Gama and Marco Polo (2 coins)	£12
1998 125th Anniversary of Steam Railway (8 coins)	£48
1998 International Year of the Oceans (4 coins)	£26
1999 50th Birthday of HRH the Prince of Wales	£6
1999 Year of the Rabbit	£6
1999 27th Olympics in Sydney (5 coins)	£28
1999 Rugby World Cup (6 coins)	£32
1999 Wedding of HRH Prince Edward and Sophie Rhys-Jones	£7
1999 Queen Mother's 100th Birthday (4 coins)	£20
1999 The Millennium (4 coins)	£20
1999 Titanium Millennium crown	£5
*2000 Year of the Dragon	£5
2000 Scottish Fold cat	£5
2000 Millennium—own a piece of time	£5
2000 Explorers, Francisco Piarro and Wilem Brents (2 coins)	£10
2000 Life and times of the Queen Mother (4 coins)	£20
2000 Queen Mother's 100th Birthday	£5
2000 60th Anniversary of the Battle of Britain	£5
*2000 BT Global Challenge	£5
2000 18th Birthday of H.R.H. Prince William	£5
2001 Year of the Snake	£5
2001 The Somali cat	£5
2001 Life of HM Queen Mother (2 coins)	£10
2001 Explorers, Martin Frobisher and Roald Amundsen (2 coins)	£10
2001 75th Birhday of HM the Queen	£5
2001 Joey Dunlop	£5

GUERNSEY

DATE	F	VF	EF	UNC

TEN SHILLINGS
	F	VF	EF	UNC
*1966	—	£1	£1.50	£2
1966 Proof	—	—	—	£5

THREEPENCE
	F	VF	EF	UNC
1956	15p	25p	£1	£2
1956 Proof	—	—	—	£5
1959	15p	25p	£1	£2
1966 Proof	—	—	—	£3

EIGHT DOUBLES
	F	VF	EF	UNC
1834	£2	£4	£25	£88
*1858 5 berries	£2	£4	£26	£88
1858 4 berries	£2	£4	£26	£88
1864 1 stalk	£1	£2	£15	£45
1864 3 stalks	£1	£2	£16	£50
1868	£3	£6	£15	£40
1874	£2	£3	£6	£32
1885H	£2	£3	£5	£22
1889H	£1	£2	£4	£20
1893H small date	£1	£2	£4	£20
1893H large date	£1	£2	£4	£20
1902H	£1	£2	£3	£18
1903H	£1	£2	£4	£18
1910	£1	£2	£5	£20
1911H	£2	£3	£6	£25
1914H	25p	£1	£3	£15
1918H	25p	£1	£3	£14
1920H	25p	£1	£2	£14
1934H	30p	£1	£3	£18
1934H Proof	—	—	—	£85
1938H	30p	£1	£2	£10
1945H	25p	50p	£1	£6
1947H	20p	50p	£1	£6
1949H	20p	50p	£1	£6
1956	15p	25p	75p	£4
1956	15p	25p	75p	£4
1959	15p	25p	75p	£4
1966 Proof	—	—	—	£10

FOUR DOUBLES
	F	VF	EF	UNC
1830	£1	£4	£30	£65
1830 Mule with obv. St Helena ½d	—	£650	—	—
1858	£3	£6	£35	£65
1864 Single stalk	50p	£2	£8	£35
1864 3 stalks	50p	£2	£10	£40
1868	£1	£2	£15	£50
1874	50p	£1	£14	£48
1885H	50p	£1	£10	£20
1889H	50p	£1	£8	£17
1893H	50p	£1	£8	£17
1902H	50p	£1	£5	£14
1903H	50p	£1	£8	£16
1906H	50p	£2	£5	£14
1908H	50p	£1	£5	£14
1910H	50p	£1	£5	£14
1911H	50p	£1	£4	£10
1914H	50p	£1	£7	£20
1918H	50p	£1	£7	£20
1920H	50p	£1	£5	£15
1945H	50p	£1	£5	£10
1949H	£1	£2	£7	£20
1956	25p	50p	£2	£5
1966 Proof	—	—	—	£5

DATE	F	VF	EF	UNC

TWO DOUBLES

	F	VF	EF	UNC
1858	£2	£5	£30	£110
1868 Single stick	£3	£6	£35	£115
1868 3 stalks	£5	£10	£55	£125
1874	£2	£5	£30	£75
1885H	£1	£2	£6	£20
1889H	£1	£2	£5	£15
1899H	£1	£3	£10	£25
1902H	£1	£2	£8	£20
1902H	£1	£2	£9	£20
1906H	£1	£2	£9	£22
1908H	£1	£3	£9	£22
1911H	£1	£3	£12	£24
1914H	£1	£3	£12	£24
1917H	£5	£15	£50	£100
1918H	£1	£2	£6	£15
*1920H	£1	£2	£6	£15
1929H	50p	£1	£4	£8

ONE DOUBLE

	F	VF	EF	UNC
*1830	£1	£2	£15	£25
1868	£4	£8	£25	£65
1868/30	£3	£5	£20	£55
1885H	50p	£1	£3	£10
1889H	25p	50p	£2	£10
1893H	25p	50p	£2	£10
1899H	25p	50p	£2	£10
1902	25p	50p	£2	£10
1903H	25p	50p	£2	£10
1911H	25p	£1	£4	£10
1911 (new shield)	25p	50p	£2	£10
1914H	25p	£1	£4	£10
1929H	25p	50p	£2	£10
1933H	25p	50p	£2	£10
1938H	25p	50p	£2	£10

DECIMAL COINAGE

Ordinary circulating coinage from 1986 onwards is usually available in uncirculated condition at a small premium above face value thus it is not listed here. The coins listed are cupro-nickel unless otherwise stated.

TWENTY-FIVE POUNDS—*Gold*

1994 50th Anniversary of Normandy Landings	£1785
1995 Queen Mother's 95th Birthday. Proof	£225
1996 HM the Queen's 70th birthday. Proof	£225
1996 European Football Championships. Proof	£225
1997 Royal Golden Wedding. Proof	£225
1998 Royal Air Force. Proof	£225
1999 Wedding of HRH Prince Edward and Sophie Rhys-Jones. Proof ..	£225
1999 Queen Mother. Proof	£225

TEN POUNDS—*Silver*

1997 Royal Golden Wedding. Proof	£175
1999 Millennium	£375

FIVE POUNDS

1995 Queen Mother's 95th birthday	£15
1995 — Silver proof	£40
1996 HM the Queen's 70th birthday	£15
1996 — Silver proof	£40
1996 European Football Championships	£15
1996 — Silver proof	£40
1997 Royal Golden Wedding	£15
1997 — Silver proof	£40
1997 — Small size Gold. BU	£52
1997 Castles of the British Isles—Castle Cornet, Guernsey	£12
1997 — Silver proof	£42
1997 Castles of the British Isles—Caernarfon Castle. Silver proof only .	£42

DATE	UNC
1997 Castles of the British Isles—Leeds Castle. Silver proof only	£42
1998 Royal Air Force. Silver proof	£42
1999 Millennium	£12
1999 — Silver proof	£32
1999 Wedding of HRH Prince Edward and Sophie Rhys-Jones	£13
1999 — Silver proof	£48
1999 Queen Mother	£13
1999 — Silver proof	£48

TWO POUNDS

1985 40th anniversary of Liberation, crown size	£8
1985 — Silver proof	£28
1986 Commonwealth Games, in plastic case	£8
1986 — in special folder	£8
1986 — .500 Silver	£17
1986 — .925 Silver proof	£28
*1987 900th anniv. of death of William the Conqueror, in special folder .	£7
1987 — Silver proof	£28
1987 — Gold proof	£910
1988 William II, in presentation folder	£7
1988 — Silver proof	£28
1989 Henry I, in presentation folder	£7
1989 — Silver proof	£28
1989 Royal Visit	£7
1989 — Silver proof	£28
1990 Queen Mother's 90th birthday	£7
1990 — Silver proof	£32
1991 Henry II, in presentation folder	£7
1991 — Silver proof	£32

1993 40th Anniversary of the Coronation	£7
1993 — Silver proof	£32
*1994 Anniversary of the Normandy Landings	£7
1994 — Silver proof	£32
1995 50th Anniversary of Liberation	£7
1995 — Silver proof	£32
1995 — Silver Piedfort proof	£64

ONE POUND

1981	£4
1981 Gold proof	£87
1981 Gold piedfort	£255
1983 New specification, new reverse	£4
1985 New design (in folder)	£4
1995 Queen Mother's 95th Birthday. Silver proof	£28
1996 Queen's 70th Birthday. Silver proof	£28
1997 Royal Golden Wedding. Silver BU	£12
1997 — Silver proof	£28

1997 Castles of the British Isles—Tower of London. Silver proof only	£22
1998 Royal Air Force. Silver proof	£24
1999 Millennium. Silver proof (gold plated)	£32
1999 Wedding of Prince Edward and Sophie Rhys-Jones. Silver proof ..	£28
1999 Queen Mother. Silver proof	£28

FIFTY PENCE

1969	£2
1970	£4
1971 Proof	£6
1981	£2
1982	£2
1985 New design	—
2000 60th Anniversary of the Battle of Britain gold proof	£225
*2000 60th Anniversary of the Battle of Britain silver proof	£32

TWENTY-FIVE PENCE

1972 Royal Silver Wedding	£6
1972 — Silver proof	£15
1977 Royal Silver Jubilee	£2
1977 — Silver proof	£15
1978 Royal Visit	£2
1978 — Silver proof	£14
1980 Queen Mother's 80th birthday	£3
1980 — Silver proof	£15

JERSEY

DATE	F	VF	EF	UNC

FIVE SHILLINGS

1966	—	£1	£3	£5
1966 Proof	—	£1	£5	£10

ONE QUARTER OF A SHILLING

1957	—	50p	£1	£4
1960 Proof	—	—	—	£7
1964	—	—	50p	£3
1966	—	—	50p	£3

ONE TWELFTH OF A SHILLING

1877H	50p	£1	£10	£35
1877H Proof in nickel	—	—	—	£1000
1877 Proof only	—	—	—	£355
1877 Proof in nickel	—	—	—	£1000
1881	£1	£2	£10	£45
1888	50p	£1	£8	£35
1894	50p	£1	£8	£35
1909	50p	£1	£10	£25
1911	50p	£1	£4	£20
1913	50p	£1	£4	£20
1923 Spade shield	50p	£1	£4	£20
1923 Square shield	50p	£1	£4	£18
1926	50p	£1	£5	£30
1931	50p	£1	£2	£8
1933	50p	£1	£2	£8
1935	50p	£1	£2	£8
1937	50p	£1	£2	£8
1946	50p	£1	£2	£6
1947	25p	£1	£2	£7
"1945" GVI	10p	25p	50p	£4
"1945" QE2	10p	25p	50p	£4
1957	10p	20p	40p	£3
*1960 1660–1960 300th anniversary	10p	15p	30p	£2
1960 Mule	—	—	—	£85
1966 "1066–1966"	—	—	50p	£1

ONE THIRTEENTH OF A SHILLING

1841	£2	£6	£30	£120
1844	£2	£7	£35	£125
1851	£3	£10	£45	£120
1858	£2	£7	£35	£120
1861	£3	£10	£45	£120
1865 Proof only	—	—	—	£555
1866 with LCW	£1	£3	£25	£65
1866 without LCW Proof only	—	—	—	£285
1870	£2	£6	£30	£65
1871	£2	£6	£30	£65

ONE TWENTY-FOURTH OF A SHILLING

1877H	£1	£2	£6	£30
1877 Proof only	—	—	—	£220
1888	£1	£2	£6	£25
1894	£1	£2	£6	£25
1909	£1	£2	£6	£22
1911	75p	£1.50	£4	£20
1913	75p	£1.50	£4	£20

DATE	F	VF	EF	UNC
1923 Spade shield	£1	£2	£6	£25
1923 Square shield	£1	£2	£5	£25
1926	£1	£2	£5	£15
1931	75p	£1.50	£4	£15
*1933	75p	£1.50	£4	£15
1935	75p	£1.50	£4	£15
1937	50p	£1	£3	£10
1946	50p	£1	£3	£10
1947	50p	£1	£3	£10

ONE TWENTY-SIXTH OF A SHILLING

1841	£3	£6	£25	£60
1844	£3	£6	£20	£55
1851	£2.50	£5	£18	£55
1858	£3	£10	£40	£125
1861	£2.50	£5	£18	£50
*1866	£2	£5	£20	£60
1870	£2	£5	£15	£40
1871	£2	£5	£15	£40

ONE FORTY-EIGHTH OF A SHILLING

1877H	£5	£10	£45	£85
1877 Proof only	—	—	—	£255

ONE FIFTY-SECOND OF A SHILLING

1841	£8	£20	£50	£125
1861 Proof only	—	—	—	£485

DECIMAL COINAGE

Ordinary circulating coinage from 1986 onwards is usually available in uncirculated condition at a small premium above face value thus it is not listed here.

ONE HUNDRED POUNDS
1995 50th Anniversary of Liberation. Gold Proof £420

FIFTY POUNDS
1995 50th Anniversary of Liberation. Gold Proof £320

TWENTY-FIVE POUNDS
1995 50th Anniversary of Liberation. Gold Proof £220

TEN POUNDS
*1990 50th Anniversary of the Battle of Britain. Gold Proof £165
1995 50th Anniversary of Liberation. Gold Proof £165

FIVE POUNDS
*1990 50th Anniversary of the Battle of Britain. Silver Proof (5 ounces) £100
1997 Royal Golden Wedding £15
1997 — Silver proof £45
*1999 Millennium £48

TWO POUNDS FIFTY PENCE
1972 Royal Silver Wedding £10
1972 — Silver proof £20

TWO POUNDS
(note all modern Proof coins have frosted relief)
1972 Royal Silver Wedding £10
1972 — Silver proof £15
1981 Royal Wedding, nickel silver (crown size) £5
1981— in presentation pack £8
1981 — Silver proof £20
1981 — Gold proof £305
1985 40th Anniversary of Liberation (crown size) £5
1985 — in presentation pack £6
1985 — Silver proof £25

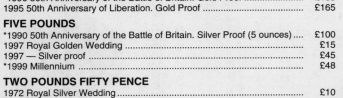

(Reduced)

(Enlarged)

DATE	UNC
1985 — Gold proof	£955
1986 Commonwealth Games	£7
1986 — in presentation case	£7
1986 — .500 silver	£20
1986 — .925 silver proof	£28
1987 World Wildlife Fund 25th Anniversary	£7
1987 — Silver proof	£26
1989 Royal Visit	£7
1989 — Silver proof	£27
1990 Queen Mother's 90th Birthday	£7
1990 — Silver proof	£40
1990 — Gold proof	£420
1990 50th Anniversary of the Battle of Britain, silver proof	£35
1993 40th Anniversary of the Coronation	£7
1993 — Silver proof	£40
*1995 50th Anniversary of Liberation	£7
1995 — Silver Proof	£40
1996 HM the Queen's 70th Birthday	£7
1996 — Silver proof	£35
1997 Bimetal	£7
1997 — Silver proof	£30
1997 — new portrait	£7

ONE POUND

1972 Royal Silver Wedding	£5
1972 — Silver proof	£6
1981	£5
1981 Silver proof	£14
1981 Gold proof	£175
1983 New designs and specifications on presentation card (St Helier)	£4
1983 — Silver proof	£20
1983 — gold proof	£355
1984 Presentation wallet (St Saviour)	£5
1984 — Silver proof	£25
1984 — Gold proof	£355
1984 Presentation wallet (St Brelade)	£5
1984 — Silver proof	£25
1984 — Gold proof	£355
1985 Presentation wallet (St Clement)	£5
1985 — Silver proof	£25
1985 — Gold proof	£355
1985 Presentation wallet (St Lawrence)	£5
1985 — Silver proof	£25
1985 — Gold proof	£355
1986 Presentation wallet (St Peter)	£5
1986 — Silver proof	£25
1986 — Gold proof	£355
1986 Presentation wallet (Grouville)	£5
1986 — Silver proof	£25
1986 — Gold proof	£355
1987 Presentation wallet (St Martin)	£5
1987 — Silver proof	£5
1987 — Gold proof	£355
1987 Presentation wallet (St Ouen)	£4
1987 — Silver proof	£24
1987 — Gold proof	£354
1988 Presentation wallet (Trinity)	£5
1988 — Silver proof	£25
1988 — Gold proof	£355
1988 Presentation wallet (St John)	£5
1988 — Silver proof	£25
1988 — Gold proof	£355
1989 Presentation wallet (St Mary)	£5
1989 — Silver proof	£25
1989 — Gold proof	£355

DATE	UNC
1991 Ship Building in Jersey Series	
1991 "Tickler" Silver proof	£40
1991 — Gold proof	£365
1991 "Percy Douglas" Silver proof	£29
1991 — Gold proof	£365
1992 "The Hebe" Silver proof	£25
1992 — Gold proof	£325
1992 "Coat of Arms" Silver proof	£25
1992 — Gold proof	£323
1993 "The Gemini" Silver proof	£25
1993 — Gold proof	£355
1993 "The Century" Silver proof	£25
1993 — Gold proof	£355
*1994 "Resolute" Silver proof	£30
1994 — Gold proof	£355

FIFTY PENCE

1969	£2
1972 Royal Silver Wedding	£4
1972 — Silver proof	£4
1983 New design	£2
1985 40th Anniversary of Liberation	£4

TWENTY-FIVE PENCE

1977 Royal Jubilee	£2
1977 — Silver proof	£14

TWENTY PENCE

1982 Date on rocks on rev. (cased)	£2
1982 — Silver proof piedfort	£38
1983 New obv. with date, rev. no date on rocks	—

SOVEREIGN

*1999 The Millennium	£95

ALDERNEY

DATE   UNC

ONE HUNDRED POUNDS
1994 50th Anniversary of D-Day Landings gold proof £465

FIFTY POUNDS
1994 50th Anniversary of D–Day Landing gold proof £255

TWENTY FIVE POUNDS
1993 40th Anniversary of Coronation gold proof £165
1994 50th Anniversary of D-Day Landings gold proof £185
1997 Royal Golden Wedding gold proof £210
*2000 60th Anniversary of the Battle of Britain gold proof £195

TEN POUNDS
1994 50th Anniversary of D–Day Landing gold proof £65

FIVE POUNDS
1995 Queen Mother Cupro-Nickel Crown £10
1995 — Silver proof £33
1995 — Silver piedfort £62
1995 — Gold proof £825
1996 HM the Queen's 70th Birthday £10
1996 — Silver proof £35
1996 — Silver piedfort £62
1996 — Gold proof £825
*1999 — Eclipse of the Sun. Silver proof with colour centre .... —
2000 60th Anniversary of the Battle of Britain £8

TWO POUNDS
1989 Royal Visit Cupro-Nickel Crown £6
1989 — Silver proof £30
1989 — Silver piedfort £60
1989 — Gold proof £925
*1990 Queen Mother's 90th Birthday £6
1990 — Silver proof £30
1990 — Silver piedfort £65
1990 — Gold proof £925
*1992 40th Anniversary of Accession £6
1992 — Silver proof £30
1992 — Silver piedfort £65
1992 — Gold proof £925
1993 40th Anniversary of Coronation £6
1993 — Silver proof £30
1993 — Silver piedfort £65
1994 50th Anniversary of D-Day Landings £6
1994 — Silver proof £35
1994 — Silver piedfort £65
1995 50th Anniversary of Return of Islanders £6
1995 — Silver proof £38
1995 — Silver piedfort £65
1995 — Gold proof £810
*1997 WWF Puffin £8
1997 — Silver proof £38
1997 Royal Golden Wedding £5
1997 — Silver proof £40

ONE POUND
1993 40th Anniversary of Coronation Silver proof £32
*1995 50th Anniversary of VE Day Silver proof £25
1995 — Gold proof £325

IRELAND

DATE	F	VF	EF	UNC

All copper unless otherwise stated

PENNIES

DATE	F	VF	EF	UNC
1805	£5	£15	£75	£150
1805 Proof	—	—	—	£150
1805 in Bronze Proof	—	—	—	£135
1805 in Copper Gilt Proof	—	—	—	£200
1805 in Silver Proof (restrike)	—	—	—	£1250
1822	£8	£18	£100	£205
1822 Proof	—	—	—	£300
1823	£5	£15	£95	£200
1823 Proof	—	—	—	£305

HALFPENNIES

DATE	F	VF	EF	UNC
1722 Holding Harp Left	£35	£95	£225	£500
1722 Holding Harp Right	£30	£85	£225	£400
1723/2 Harp Right	£30	£85	£225	£500
1723 Harp right	£12	£50	£125	£250
1723 Silver Proof	—	—	—	£1500
1723 Obv. R's altered from B's	£15	£65	£165	—
1723 No stop after date	£12	£60	£150	£275
1724 Rev. legend divided	£25	£75	£185	—
1724 Rev. legend continuous	£25	£75	£185	—
*1736	£15	£45	£125	£225
1736 Proof	—	—	—	£300
1736 Silver Proof	—	—	—	£650
1737	£15	£35	£115	—
1738	£20	£45	£125	—
1741	£20	£45	£125	—
1742	£20	£45	£125	—
1743	£20	£45	£125	—
1744/3	£20	£40	£115	—
1744	£20	£45	£135	—
1746	£20	£45	£125	—
1747	£20	£45	£125	—
1748	£20	£45	£125	—
1749	£20	£45	£125	—
1750	£20	£45	£125	—
1751	£20	£45	£125	—
1752	£20	£45	£125	—
1753	£20	£45	£125	—
1755	£22	£75	£200	—
*1760	£12	£38	£100	—
1766	£12	£38	£100	—
1769	£12	£38	£100	—
1769 Longer bust	£22	£55	£125	—
1774 Pattern only Proof	—	—	—	£1000
1775	£15	£35	£115	—
1775 Proof	—	—	—	£350
1776	£30	£95	£200	—
1781	£20	£35	£85	£180
1782	£20	£35	£85	£180
1805	£5	£8	£35	£85
1805 Copper Proof	—	—	—	£100
1805 in Bronze	—	—	—	£80
1805 in Gilt Copper	—	—	—	£150
1805 in Silver (restrike)	—	—	—	£750

DATE	F	VF	EF	UNC
1822	£10	£15	£50	£155
1822 Proof	—	—	—	£275
1823	£10	£15	£50	£145
1823	—	—	—	£275

NB Prooflike Unirculated Pennies and Halfpennies of 1822/23 are often misdescribed as Proofs. The true Proofs are rare. Some are on heavier, thicker flans.

FARTHINGS

	F	VF	EF	UNC
1722 D.G. Rex Harp to left (Pattern)	£500	£1000	£1500	—
1723 D.G. Rex Harp to right	£75	£125	£275	—
1723 Dei Gratia Rex Harp to right	£18	£45	£125	£250
1723 — Silver Proof	—	—	—	£1000
1724 Dei Gratia Rex Harp to right	£45	£85	£220	£460
1737	£20	£40	£85	£165
1737 Proof	—	—	—	£200
1737 Silver Proof	—	—	—	£400
1738	£20	£40	£100	£185
1744	£20	£40	£100	£185
1760	£12	£20	£65	£125
*1806	£8	£15	£40	£75
1806 Copper Proof	—	—	—	£120
1806 Bronzed Copper Proof	—	—	—	£75
1806 Copper Gilt Proof	—	—	—	£120
1806 Silver Proof (restrike)	—	—	—	£550
1822 George IV (Pattern) Proof	—	—	—	£750

TOKEN ISSUES BY THE BANK OF IRELAND

FIVE PENCE IN SILVER

	F	VF	EF	UNC
1805	£10	£20	£40	£100
1806	£15	£35	£85	£175
1806/5	£30	£85	£245	£550

TEN PENCE IN SILVER

	F	VF	EF	UNC
1805	£10	£20	£42	£135
1806	£12	£35	£85	£155
*1813	£10	£20	£40	£115
1813 Proof	—	—	—	£275

THIRTY PENCE IN SILVER

	F	VF	EF	UNC
1808	£20	£55	£135	£275

SIX SHILLINGS

	F	VF	EF	UNC
*1804 in Silver	£70	£135	£275	£775
1804 Proof	—	—	—	£850
1804 in Copper (restrike)	—	—	—	£455
1804 Copper Gilt	—	—	—	£1000
1804 in Gilt Silver	—	—	—	£1550

In this series fully struck specimens, with sharp hair curls, etc., are worth appreciably more than the prices quoted.

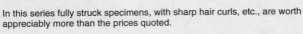

IRISH FREE STATE

DATE	F	VF	EF	UNC

TEN SHILLINGS

	F	VF	EF	UNC
*1966 Easter Rising	—	£5	£8	£12
1966 Cased Proof	—	—	—	£15
1966 special double case	—	—	—	£40

HALF CROWNS

	F	VF	EF	UNC
1928	£2	£5	£25	£40
1928 Proof	—	—	—	£45
1930	£5	£15	£85	£250
1931	£5	£20	£110	£285
1933	£5	£12	£100	£245
1934	£5	£8	£35	£100
1937	£35	£100	£350	£850
*1939	£2	£5	£15	£45
1939 Proof	—	—	—	£450
1940	£2	£5	£15	£40
1941	£3	£10	£20	£50
1942	£3	£5	£15	£40
1943	£60	£120	£525	£1250
1951	£1	£2	£10	£25
1951 Proof	—	—	—	£325
1954	£1	£2	£5	£20
1954 Proof	—	—	—	£325
1955	£1	£2	£5	£18
1955	—	—	—	£425
1959	£1	£2	£5	£15
1961	£1	£2	£12	£30
1961 Obv as 1928, rev. as 1951	£10	£15	£135	—
1962	£1	£2	£5	£10
1963	£1	£2	£4	£9
1964	£1	£2	£4	£8
1966	£1	£2	£4	£8
1967	£1	£2	£4	£8

FLORINS

	F	VF	EF	UNC
1928	£2	£4	£12	£32
1928 Proof	—	—	—	£40
1930	£3	£10	£85	£250
1930 Proof	—	—	—	*Unique*
1931	£4	£17	£115	£285
1933	£3	£15	£100	£275
1934	£5	£85	£165	£450
1934 Proof	—	—	—	£1800
1935	£2	£9	£45	£120
1937	£5	£15	£85	£250
1939	£1	£3	£15	£25
1939 Proof	—	—	—	£450
1940	£2	£4	£15	£35
1941	£2	£4	£16	£40
1941 Proof	—	—	—	£500
1942	£3	£8	£17	£40
1943	£500	£1000	£2000	£4000
1951	50p	£1	£5	£15
1951 Proof	—	—	—	£325
1954	50p	£1	£5	£18
1954 Proof	—	—	—	£250
1955	—	£1	£4	£15

DATE	F	VF	EF	UNC
1955 Proof	—	—	—	£250
1959	35p	£1	£5	£12
1961	50p	£2	£10	£28
1962	35p	£1	£5	£12
1963	25p	£1	£3	£8
1964	25p	£1	£3	£6
1965	25p	£1	£3	£6
1966	25p	£1	£3	£5
1968	25p	£1	£3	£5

SHILLINGS

	F	VF	EF	UNC
1928	£1	£3	£7	£18
1928 Proof	—	—	—	£20
1930	£2	£15	£65	£200
1930 Proof	—	—	—	£600
1931	£2	£12	£65	£120
1933	£2	£12	£65	£150
1935	£2	£8	£30	£85
1937	£5	£45	£155	£750
1939	£1	£3	£10	£25
1939 Proof	—	—	—	£450
1940	£1	£3	£12	£25
1941	£2	£5	£16	£35
1942	£2	£3	£8	£22
1951	50p	£1	£5	£12
1951 Proof	—	—	—	£300
1954	50p	£1	£4	£10
1954 Proof	—	—	—	£350
1955	50p	£1	£5	£12
1959	50p	£1	£5	£16
1962	25p	£1	£2	£6
1963	25p	£1	£2	£4
1964	25p	£1	£2	£3
1966	25p	£1	£2	£3
1968	25p	£1	£2	£3

SIXPENCES

	F	VF	EF	UNC
1928	50p	£1	£5	£15
1928 Proof	—	—	—	£18
1934	50p	£2	£15	£65
1935	75p	£2	£18	£75
1939	50p	£1	£5	£32
1939 Proof	—	—	—	£425
1940	50p	£1	£5	£35
1942	50p	£1	£8	£38
1945	£1	£5	£25	£75
1946	£2	£5	£50	£245
1947	£1	£2	£20	£55
1948	50p	£2	£12	£40
1949	50p	£1	£7	£30
1950	£1	£2	£20	£70
1952	50p	£1	£3	£15
1953	50p	£1	£3	£15
1953 Proof	—	—	—	£85
1955	50p	£1	£3	£15
1956	50p	£1	£2	£12
1956 Proof	—	—	—	£88
1958	£1	£2	£10	£45
1958 Proof	—	—	—	£250
1959	25p	50p	£2	£10
1960	25p	50p	£1	£6
1961	25p	50p	£1	£6

DATE	F	VF	EF	UNC
1962	£1	£4	£20	£45
1963	25p	£2	£5	£8
1964	25p	50p	£3	£6
1966	25p	50p	£3	£6
1967	25p	50p	£1	£4
1968	25p	50p	£1	£4
1969	£1	£2	£5	£10

THREEPENCES

	F	VF	EF	UNC
1928	£1	£2	£6	£12
1928 Proof	—	—	—	£16
1933	£2	£8	£50	£200
1934	50p	£1	£5	£35
1935	£1	£3	£12	£100
1939	£2	£6	£45	£225
1939 Proof	—	—	—	£750
1940	£1	£2	£7	£40
1942	25p	£1	£5	£30
1943	£1	£2	£10	£50
1946	25p	75p	£5	£25
1946 Proof	—	—	—	£165
1948	£1	£2	£20	£55
1949	25p	£1	£2	£20
1949 Proof	—	—	—	£165
1950	25p	£1	£3	£8
1950 Proof	—	—	—	£155
1953	25p	£1	£3	£8
1956	25p	£1	£2	£5
1961	25p	50p	£1	£3
1962	25p	50p	£1	£5
1963	25p	50p	£1	£5
1964	20p	50p	£1	£3
1965	20p	50p	£1	£2
1966	20p	50p	£1	£2
1967	20p	50p	£1	£2
1968	20p	40p	£1	£2

PENNIES

	F	VF	EF	UNC
1928	£1	£2	£7	£15
1928 Proof	—	—	—	£25
1931	£1	£3	£25	£75
1931 Proof	—	—	—	£750
1933	£1	£4	£35	£100
1935	50p	£1	£15	£35
1937	75p	£1	£20	£75
1937 Proof	—	—	—	£750
1938				*Unique*
1940	£2	£15	£85	—
1941	50p	£1	£5	£18
1942	25p	50p	£2	£10
1943	25p	£1	£3	£15
1946	25p	£1	£2	£10
1948	25p	£1	£2	£10
1949	25p	£1	£2	£10
1949 Proof	—	—	—	£250
1950	25p	75p	£3	£15
1952	25p	50p	£2	£5
1962	30p	75p	£2	£7
1962 Proof	—	—	—	£85
1963	10p	25p	£1	£3
1963 Proof	—	—	—	£75
1964	—	20p	50p	£2

253

DATE	F	VF	EF	UNC
1965	—	25p	50p	£3
1966	—	25p	50p	£3
1967	—	15p	25p	£2
1968	—	15p	25p	£2
1968 Proof	—	—	—	£155

HALFPENNIES

	F	VF	EF	UNC
1928	£1	£2	£6	£18
1928 Proof	—	—	—	£18
1933	£3	£10	£45	£325
1935	£2	£4	£25	£115
1937	£1	£3	£10	£45
1939	£2	£5	£25	£100
1939 Proof	—	—	—	£550
1940	£1	£2	£25	£100
1941	50p	£1	£5	£20
1942	50p	£1	£5	£20
1943	50p	£1	£6	£22
1946	£1	£2	£15	£55
1949	50p	£1	£5	£20
1953	25p	£1	£2	£8
1953 Proof	—	—	—	£350
1964	—	25p	50p	£2
1965	—	30p	75p	£3
1966	—	25p	50p	£2
1967	—	25p	50p	£2

FARTHINGS

	F	VF	EF	UNC
1928	£1	£2	£4	£8
1928 Proof	—	—	—	£18
1930	£1	£2	£5	£15
1931	£1	£2	£12	£22
1931 Proof	—	—	—	£550
1932	£1	£3	£15	£25
1933	50p	£1	£5	£12
1935	£1	£3	£12	£25
1936	£1	£3	£10	£25
1937	50p	£1	£3	£10
1939	50p	£1	£3	£5
1939 Proof	—	—	—	£400
1940	£1	£2	£5	£12
1941	50p	£1	£3	£6
1943	50p	£1	£3	£6
1944	50p	£1	£4	£8
1946	50p	£1	£3	£6
1949	£1	£2	£5	£14
1949 Proof	—	—	—	£265
1953	50p	£1	£2	£4
1953 Proof	—	—	—	£200
1959	£1	£2	£4	£5
1966	—	50p	£2	£5

For the 1928–50 coppper issues it is worth noting that UNC means UNC with some lustre. BU examples with full lustre are extremely elusive and are worth much more than the quoted prices.

Decimal issues are not included in this publication but it should be noted that many dates are virtually impossible to find in uncirculated grade. An example is the 1986 set which was sold exclusively through souvenir shops and included the only specimens of the ½p for that year.

Official and semi-official commemorative
Medals

It is probably a strong love of history, rather than the strict disciplines of coin collecting that make collectors turn to commemorative medals. The link between the two is intertwined, and it is to be hoped that collectors will be encouraged to venture into the wider world of medallions, encouraged by this brief guide, supplied by courtesy of Daniel Fearon, acknowledged expert and author of the *Catalogue of British Commemorative Medals*.

DATE	VF	EF
JAMES I		
1603 Coronation *(possibly by C. Anthony)*, 29mm, Silver	£325	£750
QUEEN ANNE		
1603 Coronation,29mm, AR	£375	£750
CHARLES I		
1626 Coronation *(by N. Briot)*, 30mm, Silver	£250	£650
1633 Scottish Coronation *(by N. Briot)*, 28mm, Silver	£175	£350
1649 Memorial *(by J. Roettier)*. Struck after the Restoration, 50mm, Bronze	£75	£200
CHARLES II		
1651 Scottish Coronation, in exile *(from design by Sir J. Balfour)*, 32mm, Silver	£365	£850
CROMWELL		
1651 Lord Protector *(by T. Simon)*, 38mm, Silver	£350	£800
— Cast examples	£85	£175
CHARLES II		
1661 Coronation *(by T. Simon)*, 29mm		
— Gold	£800	£1500
— Silver	£100	£250
1685 Death *(by N. Roettier)*, 39mm, Bronze	£75	£175

James I Coronation, 1603

Charles II Coronation, 1661

DATE	VF	EF

JAMES II
1685 Coronation *(by J. Roettier)*, 34mm
— Gold £850 £1600
— Silver £185 £325

MARY
1685 Coronation *(by J. Roettier)*, 34mm
— Gold £850 £1700
— Silver £150 £350

WILLIAM & MARY
1689 Coronation *(by J. Roettier)*, 32mm
— Gold £750 £1600
— Silver £125 £225
1689 Coronation,"Perseus" *(by G. Bower)*,
38mm, Gold £675 £1500

MARY
1694 Death *(by N. Roettier)*, 39mm,Bronze £55 £175

WILLIAM III
1697 "The State of Britain" *(by J. Croker)*, 69mm,
Silver £350 £800

ANNE
1702 Accession, "Entirely English" *(by J. Croker)*, 34mm
— Gold £650 £1500
— Silver £85 £175
1702 Coronation *(by J. Croker)*, 36mm
— Gold £550 £1500
— Silver £85 £175
1707 Union with Scotland *(by J. Croker, rev. by S. Bull)*, 34mm
— Gold £500 £850
— Silver £75 £150
1713 Peace of Utrecht *(by J. Croker—issued in gold to Members of Parliament)*, 34mm
— Gold £450 £950
— Silver £75 £150

GEORGE I
1714 Coronation *(by J. Croker)*, 34mm
— Gold £650 £1650
— Silver £85 £175
1727 Death *(by J. Dassier)*, 31mm, Silver £75 £150

GEORGE II
1727 Coronation *(by J. Croker)*, 34mm
— Gold £600 £1600
— Silver £85 £175

QUEEN CAROLINE
1727 Coronation *(by J. Croker)*, 34mm
— Gold £600 £1650
— Silver £85 £175
1732 The Royal Family *(by J. Croker)*, 70mm
— Silver £155 £375
— Bronze £85 £175

Charles II Coronation, 1661

George III, Coronation, 1761

DATE	VF	EF

GEORGE III
1761 Coronation *(by L. Natter)*, 34mm
— Gold £650 £1800
— Silver £125 £275
— Bronze £55 £150

QUEEN CHARLOTTE
1761 Coronation *(by L. Natter)*, 34mm
— Gold £650 £1850
— Silver £125 £275
— Bronze £55 £125
1810 Golden Jubilee, "Frogmore", 48mm, Silver £80 £175
— Bronze £55 £125

GEORGE IV
1821 Coronation *(by B. Pistrucci)*, 35mm
— Gold £400 £750
— Silver £55 £125
— Bronze £40 £75

WILLIAM IV
1831 Coronation *(by W. Wyon; rev.shows Queen Adelaide)*, 33mm
— Gold £375 £750
— Silver £50 £100
— Bronze £35 £75

George IV Coronation, 1841

QUEEN VICTORIA
1838 Coronation *(by B. Pistrucci)*, 37mm
— Gold £385 £850
— Silver £65 £150
— Bronze £30 £75

Queen Victoria Coronation, 1838

Queen Victoria Diamond Jubilee 1897

DATE	VF	EF
1887 Golden Jubilee *(by J. E. Boehm, rev. by Lord Leighton)*		
— Gold, 58mm	£800	£1100
— Silver, 78mm	£85	£200
— Bronze, 78mm	£45	£120
1897 Diamond Jubilee *(by T. Brock),*		
— Gold, 56mm	£750	£1000
— Silver, 56mm	£35	£75
— Bronze, 56mm	£20	£35
— Gold, 21mm	£125	£165
— Silver, 21mm	£20	£35

EDWARD VII

	VF	EF
1902 Coronation (August 9) *(by G. W. de Saulles)*		
— Gold, 56mm	£750	£1000
— Silver, 56mm	£35	£75
— Bronze, 56mm	£20	£35
— Gold, 31mm	£135	£185
— Silver, 31mm	£20	£35

*Some rare examples of the official medal show the date as June 26, the original date set for the Coronation which was postponed because the King developed appendicitis.

George V Silver Jubilee, 1937

GEORGE V

	VF	EF
1911 Coronation *(by B. Mackennal)*		
— Gold, 51mm	£750	£1000
— Silver, 51mm	£30	£75
— Bronze, 51mm	£15	£30
— Gold, 31mm	£135	£180
— Silver, 31mm	£15	£30
1935 Silver Jubilee *(by P. Metcalfe)*		
— Gold, 58mm	£750	£1000
— Silver, 58mm	£25	£65
— Gold, 32mm	£120	£160
— Silver, 32mm	£15	£30

PRINCE EDWARD

	VF	EF
1911 Investiture as Prince of Wales *(by W. Goscombe John)*		
— Gold, 31mm	£250	£450
— Silver, 31mm	£35	£55

EDWARD VIII

	VF	EF
1936 Abdication *(by L. E. Pinches)*, 35mm		
— Gold	£350	£650
— Silver	£35	£65
— Bronze	£15	£35

GEORGE VI

	VF	EF
1937 Coronation *(by P. Metcalfe)*		
— Gold, 58mm	£800	£1100
— Silver, 58mm	£25	£70
— Gold, 32mm	£145	£185
— Silver, 32mm	£12	£22
— Bronze, 32mm	£5	£12

Edward, Prince of Wales, 1911

DATE	VF	EF

ELIZABETH II

1953 Coronation *(by Spink & Son)*

— Gold, 57mm	£750	£950
— Silver, 57mm	£25	£60
— Bronze, 57mm	£15	£25
— Gold, 32mm	£140	£175
— Silver, 32mm	£15	£25
— Bronze, 32mm	£10	£15

1977 Silver Jubilee *(by A. Machin)*

— Silver, 57mm	—	£35
— Silver, 44mm	—	£25

*The gold medals are priced for 18ct—they can also be found as 22ct and 9ct, and prices should be adjusted accordingly.

PRINCE CHARLES

1969 Investiture as Prince of Wales *(by M. Rizello)*

— Silver, 57mm	—	£40
— Bronze gilt, 57mm	—	£25
— Silver, 45mm	—	£25
— Gold, 32mm	—	£100
— Silver, 32mm	—	£25
— Bronze, 32mm	—	£15

QUEEN ELIZABETH THE QUEEN MOTHER

1980 80th Birthday *(by L. Durbin)*

Edward VIII Abdication, 1936

— Silver, 57mm	—	£35
— Silver, 38mm	—	£25
— Bronze, 38mm	—	£20

N.B.—Official Medals usually command a premium when still in their original cases of issue.

English
Banknote
price guide

This price guide, supplied by courtesy of Pam West of British Notes, is by no means definitive. It is possible to buy notes for less than listed here, just as some may cost more. The prices quoted are for VF to EF up to the end of Peppiatt and EF and Uncirculated from O'Brien, which is usually considered to be the start of the modern period. Obviously notes in current circulation can be obtained at face value and it is always a good idea to put an uncirculated note away occasionally. Sometimes they may have "half moon" machine cutting marks, though they have never been circulated. More detailed information, as well as prices for the bank notes of Scotland, Channel Islands, Isle of Man, Northern Ireland and the Republic of Ireland, is available in the BANKNOTE YEARBOOK.

TREASURY NOTES

ISSUE	VF	EF	ISSUE	VF	EF
1st ISSUE			T16 with Anchor on rev. A1/B1 prefix	£150	£450
T1 Bradbury £1	£900	£1650	T17 Bradbury 10/-	£200	£350
T2 Bradbury £1	£900	£1650	T18 Bradbury 10/-	£150	£300
T3 Bradbury £1 5/6 digit	£300	£600	T19 Bradbury 10/-	£950	£1500
T4 Bradbury £1	£550	£1150	T20 Bradbury 10/-	£100	£250
T5 Bradbury £1	£650	£1350			
T6 Bradbury £1	£400	£950	**1st ISSUE**		
T7 Bradbury £1	—	—	T24 Fisher £1	£30	£65
T8 Bradbury 10/-	£450	£950	T25 Fisher 10/-	£65	£170
T9 Bradbury 10/-	£200	£450	T26 Fisher 10/-	£55	£145
T10 Bradbury 10/-	£650	£1250			
			2nd ISSUE		
2nd ISSUE			T30 Fisher 10/-	£60	£145
T11 Bradbury £1	£150	£450	T31 Fisher £1	£45	£100
T12 Bradbury 10/-	£100	£250	T32 Fisher £1	£65	£165
T13 Bradbury 10/-	£100	£275			
T14 Bradbury £1 Dardenelles	£2100	£4500	**3rd ISSUE (NORTHERN IRELAND)**		
T15 Bradbury 10/- Dardenelles	£450	£1000	T33 Fisher 10/-	£65	£135
3rd ISSUE			T34 Fisher £1	£45	£100
T16 Bradbury £1	£75	£150	T35 Fisher £1	£70	£165

BANK OF ENGLAND WHITE £5 NOTES

ISSUE	EF	ISSUE	EF
B208b Nairne	£300	B255 Peppiatt	£95
B209a Harvey	£200	B264 Peppiatt	£95
B215 Mahon	£200	B270 Beale	£85
B228 Catterns	£230	B275 O'Brien	£85
B241 Peppiatt	£150	B276 O'Brien	£95

White notes in better grades are becoming difficult to obtain thus earlier rarer dates and notes in exceptional condition should command a premium.

BANK OF ENGLAND ISSUES

	VF	EF
SERIES A—BRITANNIA		
B210 Mahon 10/-	£55	£95
B212 Mahon £1	£20	£65
B223 Catterns 10/-	£35	£60
B223 Catterns 10/- V prefix	£30	£80
B225 Catterns £1 LNN	£10	£25
B226 Catterns £1 NNL	£50	£100
1st PERIOD, GREEN		
B235 Peppiatt 10/- LNN	£15	£35
B235 Peppiatt 10/- LNN J Prefix	£30	£70
B236 Peppiatt 10/- NNL	£20	£50
B238 Peppiatt £1 NNL	£15	£25
B239 Peppiatt £1 LNNL	£10	£20
2nd PERIOD, BLUE (THREADED)		
B248 Peppiatt £1 Blue	£15	£25
B249 Peppiatt £1 Blue	£3	£9
B251 Peppiatt 10/- Mauve	£12	£25
3rd PERIOD, GREEN		
B256 Peppiatt 10/-	£20	£60
B258 Peppiatt £1	£8	£15
B258 Peppiatt £1 S--A	£14	£30
4th PERIOD, GREEN (THREADED)		
B260 Peppiatt £1	£10	£20
B261 Peppiatt £1 ®	£50	£150
B262 Peppiatt £1	£8	£30
B263 Peppiatt 10/- ® 01A	£350	£650
B265 Beale 10/- NNL	£12	£25
B266 Beale 10/- LNNL	£12	£25
B267 Beale 10/- ® 05A	£60	£105
B268 Beale £1	£3	£8
B269 Beale £1 ®	£20	£35
B271 O'Brien 10/-	£6	£15
B272 O'Brien 10/- ®	£45	£70
B273 O'Brien £1	£3	£6
B274 O'Brien £1 ®	£20	£35
B274 O'Brien £1 ® S--T	£20	£40

	EF	UNC
SERIES B—HELMETED BRITANNIA		
B277 O'Brien £5 Shaded Symbol	£20	£45
— A01 (first)	£75	£200
B280 O'Brien £5 White Symbol	£20	£35
SERIES C—PORTRAIT		
B281 O'Brien £1 LNN	£3	£5
B282 O'Brien £1 LNNL	£3	£6
B283 O'Brien £1 "R" EXP LNNL	£200	£300
B284 O'Brien £1 LNNL	£10	£25
B285 O'Brien £1 ®	£15	£30
B286 O'Brien 10/-	£3	£6
B287 O'Brien 10/- ®	£12	£30
B288 Hollom £1 LNNL	£2	£5
B289 Hollom £1 ® LNN	£15	£35
B290 Hollom £1 ® NNL	£12	£25
B291 Hollom £1 ® LNNL	£20	£95
B292 Hollom £1 G	£4	£10
B293 Hollom £1 G ®	£15	£45
B294 Hollom 10/- LNN	£2	£5
B295 Hollom 10/- NNL	£2	£5

	EF	UNC
B296 Hollom 10/- ®	£20	£35
B297 Hollom £5	£12	£22
B298 Hollom £5 ®	£60	£150
B299 Hollom £10	£15	£30
B301 Fforde £1	£3	£7
B302 Fforde £1 R	£20	£45
B303 Fforde £1 G	£4	£10
B304 Fforde £1 G ®	£20	£45
B305 Fforde £1	£2	£6
B306 Fforde £1 ®	£14	£20 (types)
— R01M (first)	£65	£250
— Mid	£8	£15
— S01M (first)	£65	£200
B307 Fforde £1 G	£3	£12
B308 Fforde £1 G ®	£15	£45
B308 — T--M G	£60	£185
B309 Fforde 10/- LNN	£2	£8
B310 Fforde 10/- LNNL	£2	£6
B311 Fforde 10/- ®	£10	£22
B312 Fforde £5 LNN	£14	£25
B313 Fforde £5 ®	£60	£115
B314 Fforde £5 NNL	£14	£30
B315 Fforde £5 ®	£70	£150
B316 Fforde £10	£18	£35
B318 Fforde £20	£90	£185
B319 Fforde £20 ®	£100	£250
B320 Page £1 LNNL	£3	£5
B321 Page £1 ®	£10	£20
B322 Page £1 LLNN	£3	£5
B323 Page ® (Some types rarer)	£5	£20
B324 Page £5	£20	£35
B325 Page £5 ®	£80	£150
B326 Page £10	£20	£40
B327 Page £10 ®	£30	£45
SERIES D—PICTORIAL		
B328 Page £20	£30	£60
B329 Page £20 ®	£50	£90
B330 Page £10	£20	£32
B331 Page £10 ®	£55	£95
B332 Page £5 LNN no "L" on reverse	£15	£20
B333 Page £5 ®	£80	£130
B334 Page £5 NNL	£15	£20
B335 Page £5 ®	£70	£130
B336 Page £5 LLNN	£10	£15
B337 Page £1 LNN	£2	£4
B338 Page £1 ®	£170	£250
B339 Page £1 NNL	£2	£4
B339a Page £1 8I .. various	£120	£200
B340 Page £1 LNNL	£4	£8
B341 Somerset £1 W	£3	£5
B342 Somerset £1 EXP	£350	£650
B343 Somerset £5	£10	£20

The B343 series starts DN01 and runs through a variety of prefixes to end at LZ90, although a sub-series exists of NA01 to NC90.

	EF	UNC
— DN01	£60	£125
— NA01	£100	£250
— NC90	£12	£35
— Mid on NB	£15	£22
B344 Somerset £5 OCR EXP	£450	£800

	EF	UNC
B345 Somerset £5 Wide Thread	£10	£18
B346 Somerset £10 LNN	£25	£40
B347 Somerset £10 NNL	£18	£35
B348 Somerset £10 LLNN with "L"	£18	£32
B349 Somerset £10 Window Thread	£15	£32
B350 Somerset £20 LNN	£30	£50
B351 Somerset £20 NNL Window Thread	£35	£45
B352 Somerset £50	£65	£100
B353 Gill £5	£10	£20
—SE90 (last)	£40	£80
B354 Gill £10	£15	£22
B355 Gill £20	£25	£45
— 01L (first)	£40	£110
— 20X (last)	£90	£150
B356 Gill £50 Window Thread	£60	£100
B360— E01	£65	£110

SERIES E—HISTORICAL

	EF	UNC
B357 Gill £5	—	£10
B358 Gill £20	—	£35

SERIES D

	EF	UNC
B359 Kentfield £10	—	£30
B360 Kentfield £50	—	£95

SERIES E

	EF	UNC
B361 Kentfield £5 MKI LNN	—	£10
— W18 (last)	£20	£50
B362 Kentfield £5 MKII LNN	—	£12
— AA01 (first)	£10	£18
B363 Kentfield £5 MKIII LLNN	—	£12
B364 Kentfield £10 MKI LNN	—	£20
B365 Kentfield "B" Ream £10 M/Y/Z LNN	—	£40
B366 Kentfield £10 MKII LLNN	—	£15
B367 Kentfield £20 LNN	—	£35
B368 Kentfield "B" Ream £20 A/B LNN	—	£85
& M/Z LNN	—	£85
B369 Kentfield £20 MKII LNN	—	£32
B370 Kentfield £20 MKII LLNN	—	£28
B371 Kentfield £50 LNN	—	Face
— A01	—	£100
Lowther £5 EA01	—	£12
Lowther £10 KL01	—	£50
Lowther £10 KL low nos	—	£18
Lowther "Darwin" £10	—	£12
Lowther £20 DA01	—	£65
Lowther "Elgar" £20 AA	—	£25
Lowther £50 J01	—	£120

Only some prices for true firsts and lasts, i.e. A01s–Z99s, have been quoted as often the price is dictated by availability of the notes which on earlier and some modern material, are often in short supply. Some low numbers on firsts command higher prices.

There is a series of unissued fractional notes, printed during the two wars, which are very scarce and not generally found for anything less than £2,000 in EF. These include Bradbury T21 5/–, T22 2/6, T23 1/–, Fisher T27 5/–, T28 2/6, T29 1/–, Peppiatt B253 5/–, B254 2/6.

Abbreviations			
®	Replacement	OCR	Optical Character Recognition
"R"	Research	L	Letter (of serial number)
EXP	Experimental	N	Number (of serial number)
G	Goebel		i.e. LNNL = letter, number, number, letter
W	Webb Off-set	"B"	B Ream

Why not *Bank notes?*

Millions of pounds worth of banknotes exchange hands every day, and yet most of us pay little attention to the coloured pieces of paper we are about to part with. To a collector however, they are to be studied and enjoyed. Sometimes they can be worth many times their face value. A historian, with careful study, can discover much about a county's history from prosperity through war, siege and its inflationary periods. Banknotes have also been used for spreading propaganda. The Gulf war is a recent example. Many banknotes still survive long after the country of issue has disappeared.

So how do you start and where can you get advice on forming a collection? The answers, together with a few interesting facts about paper money can be found here. But remember, this feature can only scratch the surface of this fascinating subject; its aim is to inspire and surprise you.

Paper money is not a modern phenomenon. Its origins can be found in China during the second century BC. Emperor Wu (140–86BC), frustrated with the time taken for heavily laden wagons of copper coins to complete their journey, used deerhide as a kind of tax money. Skins from white stags were cut into pieces each a foot square. The borders were decorated with designs of water plants and each skin was given a value of 40,000 copper coins. Around 105 AD paper, made from broken down plant fibres and old cotton textiles was invented by a Chinese minister of Agriculture. However, true paper money didn't appear in China until the Tang Dynasty somewhere between 650–800 AD. The earliest Chinese notes collectors are likely to come across are from the Ming Dynasty. Made from mulberry bark paper, these notes measure 230mm x 330mm. Although over six hundred years old, these notes can be bought for around £500. An interesting factor is that Asia was using paper money while Britain and Europe were still in the dark ages.

The first European bank to be established was in Stockholm, Sweden in July 1661. Unfortunately its banknotes were not government backed and

the enterprise was forced to close within a few years.

On July 27, 1694 the Bank of England was founded by Royal Charter; the first European bank to survive to the present day. From its temporary offices at the Mercers' Hall, Cheapside, London, the Bank set to work producing its first

Notgeld, issued in Germany during the period of high inflation after World War I. The appearance of these highly colourful notes greatly stimulated the hobby of banknote collecting.

265

A Confederate States of America $100 note from the Montgomery issue, 1861. At the end of the American Civil War these notes had no face value but nevertheless remain interesting to collectors today.

issues. These have become known as running cash notes. At first they were written out entirely by hand on paper bought by the Bank's staff from local stationers. Forgery however, soon put a stop to this practice. Each note was made out to the bearer for the amount they had on deposit. Although there was no guarantee of conversion into gold, the notes could be cashed in for part of their original value. This led to endorsements appearing on the notes stating the date and amount paid off. The notes would change hands for payment of goods or services just as our modern banknotes do today.

During the last century many private banks were set up in towns and cities throughout Britain. The notes they issued were usually well printed and many carry a motif or vignette identifying with the place of issue. For example coats of arms often appear, so too do famous buildings. Others simply have embellished initials. It is these simple features that help to make these provincial notes popular with collectors today, coupled with the interest of owning a banknote actually issued in your town! Unfortunately most of these banks went into liquidation and many investors lost their money—it is quite common to find provincial notes with the bankruptcy court stamp or other marks on the reverse. Notes are also encountered which have been rejoined with paper strips as it was often the practice to cut notes in half—sending half by one means and the second portion at a later date, to be joined with its counterpart before it could be redeemed. This lessened the risk of the note being stolen or lost in transit.

The expression "Safe as the Bank of England" is held in high regard today. In reality the Bank has almost collapsed on at least two occasions, and in 1696 it had its first major crisis. An act passed by parliament ordered the recoinage of all metallic currency. As the notes circulated by the Bank had status of legal tender and therefore not legally convertible into gold, people naturally had more confidence in metal currency. Accounts submitted

by the Bank to parliament in December of that year showed £764,000 worth of notes in circulation. These were backed by just under £36,000 worth of gold.

The second emergency for the Bank came in 1720 after the "bursting" of the South Sea Bubble. Holding the monopoly of trade with South America, the South Sea Company offered to take on the national debt in return for further concessions. Company shares soared but when the collapse came it was found that government ministers were deeply involved and a political crisis followed. Bankruptcy was rife and people naturally wished to obtain their money. The queue of those wanting to withdraw gold from the Bank of England stretched down Ludgate Hill into Fleet Street.

A Mafeking siege note emergency issue from the Boer War. Highly rare and very collectable.

The Bank managed to save the situation by employing it own staff to join the queue posing as customers. Each would withdraw large quantities of money and then take it round to the back of the Bank where is was redeposited. This meant the tills were kept opened until the public alarm subsided.

One modern day crisis for the Bank came during World War II when Hitler's Germany decided to forge the large white Bank of England notes in current circulation at the time, in huge quantities. This operation called for around 150 prisoners, each hand picked for their skills in engraving, printing and paper making. The original idea was to drop the undetectable forgeries on the British Isles and neutral nations in an effort to destroy Britain's economy but the plan never came to fruition, although millions of pounds in face value were produced. Most of the notes were dumped into Lake Toplitz by the fleeing German forces fearing Allied retribution. However, many have since been recovered and often appear on the market today. When encountering forgeries, collectors are in a difficult position. If they hold a note, knowing it to be a forgery, they are breaking the law. If they have the note checked, they run the risk of having it confiscated!

An example of a "skit note" (a piece of paper masquerading as a banknote). George Cruikshank's famous "Bank Restriction Note" produced as a protest against counterfeiting laws.

World War II notes. From top: Japanese Invasion Money (JIM money) intended for use by the Japanese in their occupied territories; Occupation notes issued in Guernsey during the German occupation.

A banknote need not be old to be worth collecting. Many interesting notes have been issued throughout the world each with their own story to tell. In 1954 the Canadian Central Bank issued notes in which the portrait of the Queen had what appeared to be the hidden face of the Devil in the folds of her hair. The public refused to handle them and the notes were withdrawn. To this day it is not known whether the engraving was done intentionally or not.

Most countries suffer from inflation but in 1923, Germany saw one of the biggest inflationary periods of modern times. On November 1 of that year the average wage packet was 28 million marks, equivalent to 1.3 million pounds at the 1913 exchange rate. This huge sum would not have been enough to buy a newspaper, which would have cost around 3,000 million marks. This period left a legacy of hundreds of different notes for the collector today.

Unlike coins, collecting of paper money is still in its infancy. It is still possible to obtain notes from many different countries for a modest outlay. Some dealers sell starter packs that include 50 uncirculated notes from 50 different counties, all for under £30. One reason why some notes are so cheap is that many countries devalue their currency. When a new set of notes are issued, the old set after a period, become worthless. Dealers can acquire large quantities of these notes for less than the original face value.

New collectors will find many books on the subject of paper money. A good introduction to the hobby of notaphily is *The Banknote Yearbook*. Published yearly by Token Publishing Ltd *The Banknote Yearbook* includes up to date values for notes of England, Scotland, Ireland, the Channel Islands and the Isle of Man. The useful volume also features hints and tips for the collector, a review of the current market trends, a world note identifier and much more. In short it is the essential guide to the hobby of banknote collecting. *(Call 01404 44166 for more details.)*

COIN NEWS is also a useful way of keeping in touch with the every day events of the banknote world. There is a dedicated banknote section in the magazine every month often giving vital pieces of information, for example the latest auction prices realised, forthcoming events and fairs and there are also informative articles designed to be of appeal to experienced collectors as well as newcomers.

Dealers who display this symbol are Members of the

BRITISH NUMISMATIC TRADE ASSOCIATION

The primary purpose of the Association is to promote and safeguard the highest standards of professionalism in dealings between its Members and the public. In official consultations the BNTA is the recognised representative of commercial numismatics in Britain.

The BNTA will be organising the following events in 2002

SPRING COINEX – 23rd March 2002
Old Swan Hotel, Harrogate

COINEX LONDON – 11th/12th October 2002
Hotel Marriott, Grosvenor Sq, W1

For a free Membership Directory and further information, please send a stamped addressed envelope to:

Mrs Carol Carter, General Secretary, BNTA
PO Box 474A, Thames Ditton, Surrey, KT7 0WJ
Tel: 020-8398-4290, Fax: 020-8398-4291, E-mail: bnta@lineone.net

The BNTA is a member of the International Numismatic Commission

BNTA MEMBERS IN COUNTY ORDER
(Those members with retail premises are indicated with an *)

LONDON AREA
*A.H. Baldwin & Sons Ltd.
Arsantiqva Ltd
Beaver Coin Room
Chelsea Coins
*Philip Cohen Numismatics
Andre de Clermont
Michael Dickinson
*Dix Noonan Webb
Christopher Eimer
Glendining's
Harrow Coin & Stamp Centre
Ian Jull
*Knightsbridge Coins
*Lennox Gallery
Lubbock & Son Ltd.
C.J. Martin (Coins) Ltd.
*Colin Narbeth & Son Ltd.
*Seaby Coins/C.N.G. Inc.
R.D. Shah
*Simmons Gallery
*Spink & Son Ltd.
Surena Ancient Art & Numismatic
*Vale Coins
Mark J. Vincenzi
BERKSHIRE
Frank Milward
BUCKINGHAMSHIRE
Europa Numismatics
CORNWALL
Michael Trenerry Ltd.
DORSET
*Dorset Coin Co. Ltd.
ESSEX
E.J.Brooks
HAMPSHIRE
*SPM Jewellers
Raymond Sleet
Studio Coins
West Essex Coin Investments
HERTFORDSHIRE
K B Coins
David Miller
KENT
C.J. Denton (Coins of Ireland)
Stephen Lockett
*Peter Morris

LANCASHIRE
*B.J. Dawson (Coins)
*Colin de Rouffignac
*Peter Ireland Ltd.
*Liverpool Medal Co.
*R & L Coins
LINCOLNSHIRE
Grantham Coins
NORFOLK
*Clive Dennett Coins
*Rodderick Richardson
Chris Rudd
NORTHUMBERLAND
*Corbitt Stamps Ltd.
OXFORDSHIRE
Simon R. Porter
SHROPSHIRE
*Collectors Gallery
SUFFOLK
*Lockdale Coins Ltd
Schwer Coins
SURREY
KMCC Ltd
Graeme & Linda Monk
Mark Rasmussen Numismatist
Nigel Tooley Ltd
SUSSEX
*Brighton Coin Co.
WEST MIDLANDS
*Format of Birmingham Ltd.
Mint Coins Ltd
WARWICKSHIRE
*Warwick & Warwick Ltd
WORCESTERSHIRE
Whitmore
YORKSHIRE
Airedale Coins
Paul Clayton
Paul Davies Ltd.
*J. Smith

WALES
Lloyd Bennett
*North Wales Coins Ltd.
Colin Rumney

2001/2002

COIN FAIR

KNAVESMIRE STAND
(MEZZANINE LEVEL)
YORK RACECOURSE

Featuring
> Coins
> Banknotes
> Medals
> Tokens
> Accessories
> Publications, etc.

**Friday 18th January, 11am–6pm,
Saturday 19th January, 10am–5pm**

**Friday 26th July, 11am–6pm,
Saturday 27th July, 10am–5pm**

42 Dealers – Free admission

AA signposted – Bar—Refreshments

For information please ring:
01793 513431
020 8946 4489 or 01425 656459

Directory section

ON the following pages will be found the most useful names and addresses needed by the coin collector.

At the time of going to press with this edition of the YEARBOOK the information is correct, as far as we have been able to ascertain. However, people move and establishments change, so it is always advisable to make contact with the person or organisation listed before travelling any distance, to ensure that the journey is not wasted.

Should any of the information in this section not be correct we would very much appreciate being advised in good time for the preparation of the next edition of the COIN YEARBOOK.

Museums and Libraries

Listed below are the Museums and Libraries in the UK which have coins or items of numismatic interest on display or available to the general public.

A

Anthropological Museum, University of Aberdeen, Broad Street, **Aberdeen,** AB9 1AS (01224 272014).

Curtis Museum (1855), High Street, **Alton,** Hants (01420 2802). *General collection of British coins.*

Ashburton Museum, 1 West Street, **Ashburton,** Devon. *Ancient British and Roman antiquities including local coin finds.*

Ashwell Village Museum (1930), Swan Street, **Ashwell,** Baldock, Herts. *Roman coins from local finds, local trade tokens, Anglo-Gallic coins and jetons.*

Buckinghamshire County Museum (1862), Church Street, **Aylesbury,** Bucks (01296 88849). *Roman and medieval English coins found locally, 17th/18th century Buckinghamshire tokens, commemorative medals.*

B

Public Library and Museum (1948), Marlborough Road, **Banbury,** Oxon (01295 259855). *Wrexlin Hoard of Roman coins.*

Museum of North Devon (1931), The Square, **Barnstaple,** EX32 8LN (01271 46747). *General coin and medal collection, including local finds. Medals of the Royal Devonshire Yeomanry.*

Roman Baths Museum, Pump Room, **Bath,** Avon (01225 461111 ext 2785). *Comprehensive collection of Roman coins from local finds.*

Bagshaw Museum and Art Gallery (1911), Wilton Park, **Batley,** West Yorkshire (01924 472514). *Roman, Scottish, Irish, English hammered, British and foreign coins, local traders' tokens, political medalets, campaign medals and decorations.*

Bedford Museum (1961), Castle Lane, **Bedford** (01234 353323). *Collections of the Bedford Library and Scientific Institute, the Beds Archaeological Society and Bedford Modern School (Pritchard Memorial) Museum.*

Ulster Museum (1928), Botanic Gardens, **Belfast** BT9 5AB (01232 381251). *Irish, English and British coins and commemorative medals.*

Berwick Borough Museum (1867), The Clock Block, Berwick Barracks, Ravensdowne, **Berwick**. TD15 1DQ (01289 330044). *Roman, Scottish and medievial coins.*

Public Library, Art Gallery and Museum (1910), Champney Road, **Beverley,** Humberside (01482 882255). *Beverley trade tokens, Roman, English, British and foreign coins.*

Bignor Roman Villa (1811), **Bignor,** nr Pulborough, West Sussex (017987 202). *Roman coins found locally.*

City Museum and Art Gallery (1861), Chamberlain Square, **Birmingham** B3 3DH (0121 235 2834). *Coins, medals and tokens, with special emphasis on the products of the Soho, Heaton, Birmingham and Watt mints.*

Blackburn Museum, Museum Street, **Blackburn,** Lancs (01254 667130). *Incorporates the Hart (5,000 Greek, Roman and early English) and Hornby (500 English coins) collections, as well as the museum's own collection of British and Commonwealth coins.*

Museum Collection, Town Hall, **Bognor Regis,** West Sussex. *Roman, English and British coins and trade tokens.*

Museum and Art Gallery,(1893), Civic Centre, **Bolton,** Lancashire (01204 22311 ext 2191). *General collection of about 3000 British and foreign coins, and over 500 British medals. Numismatic library.*

Art Gallery and Museum, Central Library, Oriel Road, **Bootle,** Lancs. *Greek, Roman, English, British and some foreign coins, local trade tokens.*

Roman Town and Museum (1949) Main Street, **Boroughbridge,** N. Yorks. YO2 3PH (01423 322768). *Roman coins.*

The Museum (1929), The Guildhall, **Boston,** Lincs (01205 365954). *Small collection of English coins.*

Natural Science Society Museum (1903), 39 Christchurch Road, **Bournemouth,** Dorset (01202 553525). *Greek, Roman and English hammered coins (including the Hengistbury Hoard), local trade tokens.*

Bolling Hall Museum (1915), Bolling Hall Road, **Bradford,** West Yorkshire BD4 7LP (01274 723057). *Some 2,000 coins and tokens, mostly 18th–20th centuries.*

Cartwright Hall Museum and Art Gallery (1904), Lister Park, **Bradford,** West Yorkshire BD9 4NS (01274 493313). *Roman coins found locally.*

Museum and Art Gallery (1932), South Street, **Bridport,** Dorset (01308 22116). *Roman coins, mainly from excavations at Claudian Fort.*

The City Museum (1820), Queen's Road, **Bristol** BS8 1RL (0117 9 27256). *Ancient British, Roman (mainly from local hoards), English hammered coins, especially from the Bristol mint, and several hundred local trade tokens.*

District Library and Museum (1891), Terrace Road, **Buxton,** Derbyshire SK17 6DU (01298 24658). *English and British coins, tokens and commemorative medals. Numismatic library.*

C

Segontium Museum (1928), Beddgelert Road, **Caernarfon,** Gwynedd (01286 675625) *Roman coins and artifacts excavated from the fort.*

Fitzwilliam Museum (1816), Department of Coins and Medals, Trumpington Street, **Cambridge** (01223 332900). *Ancient, English, medieval European, oriental coins, medals, plaques, seals and cameos.*

National Museum & Galleries of Wales, Cathays Park, **Cardiff** (029 20397951). *Greek, Celtic, Roman and British coins and tokens with the emphasis on Welsh interest. Also military, civilian and commemorative medals.*

Guildhall Museum (1979), Greenmarket, **Carlisle,** Cumbria (01228 819925). *General collection of coins and medals.*

Tullie House (1877), Castle Street, **Carlisle,** Cumbria (01228 34781). *Roman, medieval and later coins from local finds, including medieval counterfeiter's coin-moulds.*

Gough's Caves Museum (1934), The Cliffs, **Cheddar,** Somerset (01934 343). *Roman coins.*

Chelmsford and Essex Museum (1835), Oaklands Park, Moulsham Street, **Cheltenham,** Glos CM2 9AQ (01245 353066). *Ancient British, Roman, medieval and later coins mainly from local finds, local medals.*

Town Gate Museum (1949), **Chepstow,** Gwent. *Local coins and trade tokens.*

Grosvenor Museum (1886), Grosvenor Street, **Chester** (01244 21616). *Roman coins from the fortress site, Anglo-Saxon, English medieval and post-medieval coins of the Chester and Rhuddlan mints, trade tokens of Chester and Cheshire, English and British milled coins.*

Public Library (1879), Corporation Street, **Chesterfield,** Derbyshire (01246 2047). *Roman coins from local finds, Derbyshire trade tokens, medals, seals and railway passes. Numismatic library. Numismatic library and publications.*

Red House Museum (1919), Quay Road, **Christchurch,** Dorset (01202 482860). *Coins of archaeological significance from Hampshire and Dorset, notably the South Hants Hoard, ancient British, Armorican, Gallo-Belgic, Celtic and Roman coins, local trade tokens and medals.*

Corinium Museum (1856), Park Street, **Cirencester,** Glos (01285 655611). *Roman coins from archaeological excavations.*

Colchester and Essex Museum (1860), The Castle, **Colchester,** Essex (01206 712931/2). *Ancient British and Roman coins from local finds, medieval coins (especially the Colchester Hoard), later English coins and Essex trade tokens, commemorative medals.*

D

Public Library, Museum and Art Gallery (1921), Crown Street, **Darlington,** Co Durham (01325 463795). *General collection of coins, medals and tokens.*

Borough Museum (1908), Central Park, **Dartford,** Kent (01322 343555). *Roman, medieval and later English hammered coins, trade tokens and commemorative medals.*

Dartmouth Museum (1953), The Butterknowle, **Dartmouth,** Devon (01803 832923). *Coins and medals of a historical and maritime nature.*

Museum and Art Gallery (1878), The Strand, **Derby** (01332 255586). *Roman coins, English silver and copper regal coins, Derbyshire tradesmen's tokens, British campaign medals and decorations of the Derbyshire Yeomanry and the 9/12 Royal Lancers.*

Museum and Art Gallery (1909), Chequer Road, **Doncaster,** South Yorkshire (01302 734293). *General collection of English and foreign silver and bronze coins. Representative collection of Roman imperial silver and bronze coins, including a number from local hoards. English trade tokens, principally of local issues, medals.*

Dorset County Museum(1846), **Dorchester,** Dorset (01305 262735). *British, Roman, medieval and later coins of local interest.*

Central Museum (1884), Central Library, St James's Road, **Dudley,** West Midlands (01384 453576). *Small general collection of coins, medals and tokens.*

Burgh Museum (1835), The Observatory, Corberry Hill, **Dumfries** (01387 53374). *Greek, Roman, Anglo-Saxon, medieval English and Scottish coins, especially from local hoards. Numismatic library.*

Dundee Art Galleries and Museums (1873). Albert Square, **Dundee** DD1 1DA (01382 23141). *Coins and medals of local interest.*

The Cathedral Treasury (995 AD), The College, **Durham** (0191-384 4854). *Greek and Roman coins bequeathed by Canon Sir George Wheeler (1724), general collection of medals from the Renaissance to modern times, medieval English coins, especially those struck at the Durham ecclesiastical mint.*

Durham Heritage Centre, St Mary le Bow, North Bailey, **Durham** (0191-384 2214). *Roman, medieval and later coins, mainly from local finds.*

E

Royal Museum of Scotland (1781), Queen Street, **Edinburgh** EH1 (0131 225 7534). *Roman, Anglo-Saxon, English and Scottish coins, trade tokens, commemorative medals and communion tokens. Numismatic library. Publications.*

Royal Albert Memorial Museum (1868), Queen St, **Exeter** EX4 3RX (01392 265858). *Roman and medieval. Coins of the Exeter Mint.*

G

Hunterian Museum (1807), Glasgow University, University Avenue, **Glasgow** G12 8QQ (041 339 8855). *Greek, Roman, Byzantine, Scottish, English and Irish coins, Papal and other European medals, Indian and Oriental coins, trade and communion tokens.*

Art Gallery and Museum (1888), Kelvingrove, **Glasgow** G3 (0141 357 3929). *General collection of coins, trade tokens, communion tokens, commemorative and military medals.*

Museum of Transport (1974), Kelvin Hall, Bunhouse Road, **Glasgow** G3 (0141 357 3929). *Transport tokens and passes, commemorative medals, badges and insignia of railway companies and shipping lines.*

City Museum and Art Gallery (1859), Brunswick Road, **Gloucester** (01452 524131). *Ancient British, Roman, Anglo-Saxon (from local finds), early medieval (from local mints), Gloucestershire trade tokens.*

Guernsey Museum and Art Gallery, St Peter Port, **Guernsey** (01481 726518). *Armorican, Roman, medieval and later coins, including the coins, medals, tokens and paper money of Guernsey.*

Guildford Museum (1898), Castle Arch, **Guildford,** Surrey GU1 3SX (01483 444750). *Roman and medieval coins and later medals.*

H

Gray Museum and Art Gallery, Clarence Road, **Hartlepool,** Cleveland (01429 268916). *General collection, including coins from local finds.*

Public Museum and Art Gallery (1890), John's Place, Cambridge Road, **Hastings,** East Sussex (01424 721952). *General collection of English and British coins, collection of Anglo-Saxon coins from Sussex mints.*

City Museum (1874), Broad Street, **Hereford** (01432 268121 ext 207). *Coins from the Hereford mint and local finds, Herefordshire trade tokens, general collection of later coins and medals.*

Hertford Museum (1902), 18 Bull Plain, **Hertford** (01992 582686). *British, Roman, medieval and later English coins and medals.*

Honiton and Allhallows Public Museum (1946), High Street, **Honiton,** Devon (01404 44966). *Small general collection, including coins from local finds.*

Museum and Art Gallery (1891), 19 New Church Road, **Hove,** East Sussex (01273 779410). *English coins, Sussex trade tokens and hop tallies, campaign medals, orders and decorations, commemorative medals.*

Tolson Memorial Museum (1920), Ravensknowle Park, **Huddersfield,** West Yorkshire (01484 541455). *Representative collection of British coins and tokens, Roman and medieval coins, mainly from local finds.*

Hull and East Riding Museum (1928), 36 High Street, **Hull** (01482 593902). *Celtic, Roman and medieval coins and artifacts from local finds. Some later coins including tradesmen's tokens.*

I

The Manx Museum, Douglas, **Isle of Man** (01624 675522). *Roman, Celtic, Hiberno-Norse, Viking, medieval English and Scottish coins, mainly from local finds, Manx traders' tokens from the 17th to 19th centuries, Manx coins from 1709 to the present day.*

J

Jersey Museum, Weighbridge, St Helier, **Jersey** (01534 30511). *Armorican, Gallo-Belgic, Roman, medieval English and French coins, coins, paper money and tokens of Jersey.*

K

Dick Institute Museum and Art Gallery (1893), Elmbank Avenue, **Kilmarnock,** Ayrshire (01563 26401). *General collection of coins and medals, and the Hunter-Selkirk collection of communion tokens.*

L

City Museum (1923), Old Town Hall, Market Square, **Lancaster** (01524 64637). *Roman, Anglo-Saxon, medieval English coins, provincial trade tokens, medals of the King's Own Royal Lancashire Regiment.*

City Museum (1820), Municipal Buildings, The Headrow, **Leeds,** West Yorkshire (01532 478279). *Greek, Roman, Anglo-Saxon, English medieval, Scottish, Irish, British, Commonwealth and foreign coins. Several Roman and Saxon hoards. The Backhouse collection of Yorkshire banknotes, the Thornton collection of Yorkshire tokens, British and foreign commemorative medals.*

Leicester Museum and Art Gallery (1849), New Walk, **Leicester** (01533 554100). *Roman, medieval and later coins, mainly from local finds, tokens, commemorative medals, campaign medals and decorations.*

Pennington Hall Museum and Art Gallery, **Leigh,** Lancashire. *General collection of Roman, English and British coins and medals.*

Museum and Art Gallery (1914), Broadway, **Letchworth,** Herts (01462 65647). *Ancient British coins minted at Camulodunum, Roman, medieval and English coins, Hertfordshire trade tokens, commemorative and campaign medals.*

City Library, Art Gallery and Museum (1859), Bird Street, **Lichfield,** Staffs (01543 2177). *Roman, medieval and later English coins, Staffordshire trade tokens and commemorative medals.*

Liverpool Museum(1851), William Brown Street, **Liverpool** L3 8EN (0151 207 0001). *General collection of Roman, medievaland later British coins, tokens.*

Bank of England Museum, Threadneedle Street, **London** EC2 (020-7601 5545). *Exhibits relating to gold bullion, coins, tokens and medals, the design and manufacture of banknotes, and a comprehensive collection of bank notes dating from the 17th century to the present day.*

British Museum(1752), HSBC Coin Gallery, Great Russell Street, **London** WC1 (020-7636 1555). *Almost a million coins, medals, tokens and badges of all period from Lydia, 7th century BC to the present time. Extensive library of books and periodicals.*

British Numismatic Society (1903), Warburg Institute, Woburn Square, **London** WC1. *Library containing over 5,000 volumes, including sale catalogues, periodicals and pamphlets. Open to members only.*

Cuming Museum (1906), Walworth Road, **London** SE17 (020-7703 3324/5529). *Some 8,000 items, including Greek, Roman, medieval English and modern British coins, English tokens and commemorative medals.*

Gunnersbury Park Museum (1927), Acton, **London** W3. *Ancient British, Greek, Roman, medieval English, British and some foreign coins, tradesmen's tokens and commemorative medals, including local finds. Small numismatic library.*

Horniman Museum and Library (1890), London Road, Forest Hill, **London** SE23 (020-7699 2339). *General collection, primitive currency, some tokens.*

Imperial War Museum, Lambeth Road, **London** SE1 6HZ (020-7416 5000). *Emergency coinage of two world wars, occupation and invasion money, extensive collection of German Notgeld, commemorative, propaganda and military medals, badges and insignia.*

Sir John Soane's Museum (1833), 13 Lincoln's Inn Fields, **London** WC2 (020-7405 2107). *Napoleonic medals and medallic series of the late 18th and early 19th centuries.*

National Maritime Museum, Romney Road, Greenwich, **London** SE10 (020-8858 4422). *Commemorative medals with a nautical or maritime theme, naval medals and decorations.*

Victoria and Albert Museum (1852), South Kensington, **London** SW7 (020-7938 8441). *Byzantine gold and medieval Hispano-Mauresque coins (Department of Metalwork), large collection of Renaissance and later medals (Department of Architecture and Sculpture). Library of numismatic books.*

Ludlow Museum (1833). The Assembly Rooms. Castle Square, **Ludlow** (01584 873857). *Roman and medieval coins from local finds.*

Luton Museum and Art Gallery (1927), Wardown Park, **Luton**, Beds (01582 36941). *Coins, tokens and medals.*

M

Museum and Art Gallery (1858), **Maidstone**, Kent (01622 754497). *Ancient British, Roman, Anglo-Saxon and medieval coins found in Kent, modern British coins, Kent trade tokens, banknotes, hop tallies and tokens, primitive currency, collections of Kent Numismatic Society.*

The Manchester Museum (1868), The University, **Manchester** M13 (0161-275 2634). *Very fine collections of Greek and Roman coins, comprehensive collections of English, European and Oriental coins, over 30,000 in all.*

Margate Museum (1923), The Old Town Hall, Market Place, **Margate**, Kent (01843 225511 ext 2520). *Small collection of coins, including Roman from local finds.*

Montrose Museum and Art Gallery (1836). Panmure Place, **Montrose**, Angus DD10 8HE (01674 73232). *Scottish and British coins.*

N

Newark-on-Trent Museum (1912), Appleton Gate, **Newark**, Notts (01636 702358). *Siege pieces, trade tokens and coins from local finds and hoards.*

Newbury District Museum, The Wharf, **Newbury**, Berkshire (01635 30511). *Ancient British, Roman and medieval coins and artifacts, later coins and tokens.*

The Greek Museum, Percy Building, **Newcastle-upon-Tyne** (0191 2226000 ext 7966). *Ancient coins.*

O

Heberden Coin Room, Ashmolean Museum (1683), **Oxford** (01865 278000). *Extensive collections of all periods, notably Greek, Roman, English and Oriental coins, Renaissance portrait and later medals, tokens and paper money. Large library. Numerous publications.*

P

Peterborough Museum (1881), Priestgate, **Peterborough**, Cambs (01733 340 3329). *Roman (mainly from local hoards and finds), Anglo-Saxon, medieval English, British and modern European coins, English and British commemorative medals and tokens.*

City Museum and Art Gallery (1897), Drake Circus, **Plymouth**, Devon (01752 264878). *General collections of British and Commonwealth coins and tokens, Devon trade tokens and Plymouth tradesmen's checks, Ancient British and Roman coins from local sites.*

Waterfront Museum, 4 High Street, **Poole**, Dorset (01202 683138). *General collection of British and foreign coins, medals and tokens (view by appointment).*

City Museum (1972), Museum Road, Old **Portsmouth** PO1 (023 80827261). *Roman, medieval and later coins mainly from local finds and archaeological excavation, British coins, trade tokens of Hampshire, commemorative medals.*

Harris Museum and Art Gallery (1893), Market Square, **Preston**, Lancashire (01772 58248). *English and British coins, tokens and medals.*

R

The Museum of Reading (1883), Blagrave Street, **Reading**, Berks (0118 939 9800). *British, Roman and medieval English coins, many from local finds, tradesmen's tokens and commemorative medals.*

Rochdale Museum (1905), Sparrow Hill, **Rochdale**, Lancs (01706 41085). *Roman and medieval coins from local finds, Rochdale trade tokens, miscellaneous British and foreign coins and medals.*

Municipal Museum and Art Gallery (1893), Clifton Park, **Rotherham** (01709 382121). *Roman coins from Templeborough Forts, medieval English coins from local hoards and a general collection of British coins.*

S

Saffron Walden Museum (1832) (1939), Museum Street, **Saffron** Walden, Essex (01799 522494). *Ancient British, Roman, medieval and later coins, mainly from local finds and archaeological excavation, trade tokens and commemorative medals.*

Coin Yearbook 2002

Verulamium Museum, St Michael's, **St Albans,** Herts (01727 819339). *Coins and artifacts excavated from the Roman town.*

Salisbury and South Wiltshire Museum (1861), The Cathedral Close, **Salisbury,** Wilts (01722 332151). *Collection of coins minted or found locally, including finds of Iron Age, Roman, Saxon and medieval coins, as well as 18th and 19th century tradesmen's tokens.*

Richborough Castle Museum (1930), **Sandwich,** Kent (0304 612013). *Roman coins of 1st–5th centuries from excavations of the Richborough site.*

Scarborough Museum (1829), The Rotunda, Vernon Road, **Scarborough,** North Yorkshire (01723 374839). *Over 4,000 Roman coins, 1,500 English and 600 coins from local finds, siege pieces and trade tokens.*

Shaftesbury and Dorset Local History Museum (1946), 1 Gold Hill, **Shaftesbury,** Dorset (01747 52157). *Hoard of Saxon coins.*

City Museum (1875), Weston Park, **Sheffield** (0114 2 768588). *Over 5,000 coins of all periods, but mainly English and modern British. European coins, imperial Roman (including three hoards of about 500 coins each), Yorkshire trade tokens, British historical medals, campaign medals. Library.*

Rowley's House Museum, Barker Street, **Shrewsbury,** Salop (01743 361196). *Coins minted at Shrewsbury 925-1180, Civil War coinage of 1642, Shropshire tradesmen's tokens, English coins and medals.*

Museum of Archaeology (1951), God's House Tower, Town Quay, **Southampton,** Hants (023 8022 0007). *Main emphasis lies in Ancient British, Roman and medieval English coins from local archaeological excavations. General collection of later coins and medals.*

Atkinson Art Gallery (1878), Lord Street, **Southport,** Lancs (01704 533133). *Roman coins.*

Botanic Gardens Museum, Churchtown, **Southport,** Lancs (01704 87547). *English and British coins and medals, military medals and decorations.*

Southwold Museum (1933), St Bartholomew's Green, **Southwold,** Suffolk (01502 722375). *General collection of coins, specialised Suffolk trade tokens.*

Stamford Museum (1961), Broad Street, **Stamford,** Lincs (01780 66317). *General collection of coins, medals and tokens, including a selection from the Stamford mint.*

Municipal Museum (1860), Vernon Park, Turncroft Lane, **Stockport,** Cheshire (0161 474 4460) *Miscellaneous general collection of coins, tokens and medals.*

Stroud Museum (1899), Lansdown, **Stroud,** Glos (01453 376394). *Ancient British, Roman, Saxon, Norman, later medieval English, British coins and Gloucestershire trade tokens.*

Museum and Art Gallery (1846), Borough Road, **Sunderland,** Tyne & Wear (0191 514 1235). *Roman imperial, medieval and later English, including examples of the pennies minted at Durham, modern British and foreign coins, 17th-19th century tradesmen's tokens, local medallions and campaign medals.*

Swansea Museum (1835), Victoria Road, **Swansea,** W. Glamorgan, SA1 1SN (0792 653765). *Coins and medals of local interest.*

T

Tamworth Castle and Museum (1899), The Holloway, **Tamworth,** Staffs (01827 63563). *Anglo-Saxon coins, medieval English including coins of the Tamworth mint, later English and British coins, tokens, commemorative medallions and medals.*

Somerset County Museum, Taunton Castle, **Taunton,** Somerset (01823 255510/320200). *Celtic, Roman, Anglo-Saxon, early Medieval, tokens, medallions and banknotes. Strong emphasis on locally-found items.*

Thurrock Local History Museum (1956), Civic Square, **Tilbury,** Essex (01375 390000 ext 2414). *Roman coins.*

Royal Cornwall Museum (1818), River Street, **Truro,** Cornwall (01872 72205). *Coins, tokens and medals pertaining principally to the county of Cornwall.*

W

Wakefield Museum (1919), Wood Street, **Wakefield,** West Yorkshire (01924 295351). *Roman and medieval English silver and copper coins.*

Epping Forest District Museum, 39/41 Sun Street, **Waltham Abbey,** Essex EN 9. *Ancient British, Roman and medieval coins, Essex tradesmen's tokens of local interest.*

Warrington Museum and Art Gallery (1848). Bold Street, **Warrington,** Cheshire, WA1 1JG (01925 30550). *Coins, medals and tokens.*

Worcester City Museum (1833), Foregate Street, **Worcester** (01905 25371). *Roman, medieval and later coins and tokens. Coins of the Worcester mint.*

Wells Museum (18903), 8 Cathedral Green, **Wells,** Somerset (01749 3477). *Ancient and modern British and world coins, local trade tokens and medals.*

Municipal Museum and Art Gallery (1878), Station Road, **Wigan,** Lancashire. *British, Commonwealth and foreign coins from about 1660 to the present. Roman coins from local sites, commemorative medals.*

City Museum (1851), The Square, **Winchester,** Hants (01962 848269). *Roman and medieval coins chiefly from local hoards and finds. Hampshire tradesmen's tokens and commemorative medals. Small reference library.*

Wisbech and Fenland Museum (1835), Museum Square, **Wisbech,** Cambridgeshire (01945 583817), *British Roman, medieval and later coins, medals and tokens.*

Y

The Museum of South Somerset (1928), Hendford, **Yeovil,** Somerset (01935 24774). *Roman coins from local sites, medieval English, modern British coins and medals and a fine collection of tokens (particularly 17th century Somerset).*

Castle Museum (1938), **York** (01904 653611). *English and British coins, campaign medals, orders and decorations, commemorative medals.*

Jorvik Viking Centre (1984), Coppergate, **York** (01904 643211). *Coins and artefacts pertaining to the Viking occupation of York.*

The Yorkshire Museum (1823), **York** (01904 629745). *Roman imperial, medieval English and later coins, about 12,000 in all.*

Club directory

Details given here are the names of Numismatic Clubs and Societies, their date of foundation, and their usual venues, days and times of meetings. Meetings are monthly unless otherwise stated. Finally, the telephone number of the club secretary is given; the names and addresses of club secretaries are withheld for security reasons, but full details may be obtained by writing to the Secretary of the British Association of Numismatic Societies, Philip Mernick, c/o General Services, 42 Campbell Road, London E3 4DT. Telephone 020 8989 5672. E-mail: phil@mernicks.com.

Banbury & District Numismatic Society (1967). Banbury British Rail Working Mens Club. 2nd Mon (exc Jul & Aug), 19.45. (01295 254451).

Bath & Bristol Numismatic Society (1950). Ship Inn, Temple Street, Keynsham, Bristol. 2nd Thu, 19.30. (01275 472385).

Bedford Numismatic Society (1966). RAF Association Club, 93 Ashburnham Road, Bedford MK40 1EA. 3rd Mon, 19.30. (01234 228833/ 358369).

Bexley Coin Club (1968). St Martin's Church Hall, Erith Road, Barnehurst, Bexleyheath, Kent. 1st Mon (exc Jan & Aug), 20.00. (020 8303 0510).

Birmingham Numismatic Society (1964). Friend's Meeting House, Linden Road, Bournville, Birmingham 30. 2nd Wed, 19.45. (0121 308 1616).

Matthew Boulton Society (1994). PO Box 395, Birmingham B31 2TB (0121 781 6558 fax 0121 781 6574).

Bradford & District Numismatic Society (1967). East Bowling Unity Club, Leicester Street, Bradford, West Yorkshire. 3rd Mon, 19.00. (01532 677151).

Brighton & Hove Coin Club (1971). Methodist Church Hall, St Patrick's Road, Hove, East Sussex. Last Wed (exc Dec), 20.00. (01273 419303).

British Cheque Collectors' Society (1980). John Purser, 71 Mile Lane, Cheylesmore, Coventry, West Midlands CV3 5GB.

British Numismatic Society (1903). Warburg Institute, Woburn Square, London WC1H 0AB. Monthly (exc Aug & Dec), 18.00.

Cambridgeshire Numismatic Society (1946). Friends' Meeting House, 12 Jesus Lane (entrance in Park Street), Cambridge, CB5 8BA. 3rd Mon, Sept–June, 19.30. (01767 312112).

Chester & North Wales Coin & Banknote Society (1996). Liver Hotel, 110 Brook Street, Chester. 4th Tue, 20.00. (0151 478 4293)

Cheltenham Numismatic Society, The Reddings & District Community Association, North Road, The Reddings, Cheltenham. 3rd Mon, 19.45 (01242 673263)

Coin Correspondence Club (1988). Postal only. A.H. Chubb, 49 White Hart Lane, Barnes, London SW13 0PP. (0181-878 0472).

Cornwall Collectors' Club (1990). The Swan Inn, 40 Bosvigo Road, Truro. 1st Wed, 20.00. (01872 73376).

Crawley Coin Club (1969). Furnace Green Community Centre, Ashburnham Road, Furnace Green, Crawley, West Sussex. 1st Tue, 20.00. (01293 548671).

Crewe & District Coin & Medal Club (1968). Memorial Hall, Church Lane, Wistaston, Crewe, 2nd Tue (exc Jan & July), 19.30. (01270 69836).

Darlington & District Numismatic Society (1968). Darlington Arts Centre, Vane Terrace, Darlington, Co Durhm. 3rd Wed, 19.30. (01609 772976).

Derbyshire Numismatic Society (1964). The Friends' Meeting House, St Helens Street, Derby. 3rd Mon (exc August), 19.45. (01283 211623).

Devon & Exeter Numismatic Society (1965). Red Cross Centre, Butts Road, Heavitree, Exeter, Devon. 3rd Tue, 19.30. (01392 461013).

Edinburgh Numismatic Society (1996). Department of History and Applied Arts, Royal Museum of Scotland, Chambers Street, Edinburgh EH1 1JF. 3rd Mon, 19.30. (0131 225 7534).

Enfield & District Numismatic Society (1969). Millfield House Arts Centre, Silver Street, Edmonton, London N18 1PJ. 3rd Mon, 20.00. (0181-340 0767).

Essex Numismatic Society (1966). Chelmsford & Essex Museum, Moulsham Street, Chelmsford, Essex. 4th Fri (exc Dec), 20.00. (01376 21846).

Glasgow & West of Scotland Numismatic Society (1947). The College Club, University of Glasgow, University Avenue, Glasgow G12. 2nd Thu, Oct-May, 19.30. (0141 633 5422).

Harrow & North West Middlesex Numismatic Society (1968). YWCA, 51 Sheepcote Road, Harrow, Middlesex. 2nd and 4th Tue, 20.00. (020 8952 8765).

Havering Numismatic Society (1967). Fairkytes Arts Centre, Billet Lane, Hornchurch, Essex. 1st Tue, 19.30. (01708 704201).

Hayes & District Coin Club. The United Reformed Church Hall, Swakeleys Road, Ickenham, Middlesex. 3rd Thu, 19.45. (0181-422 9178).

Horncastle & District Coin Club (1963). Bull Hotel, Bull Ring, Horncastle, Lincs. 2nd Thu (exc Aug), 19.30. (01754 2706).

Huddersfield Numismatic Society (1947). Tolson Memorial Museum, Ravensknowle Park, Huddersfield, West Yorkshire. 1st Mon (exc Jul & Aug), 19.30. (01484 226300).

Hull & District Numismatic Society (1967). The Young People's Institute, George Street, Hull. Monthly (exc Aug & Dec), 19.30. (01482 441933).

International Bank Note Society (1961). Victory Services Club, 63–79 Seymour Street, London W1. Last Thu (exc Dec), 18.00. (020-8969 9493).

International Bank Note Society, Scottish Chapter (1995). West End Hotel, Palmerston Place, Edinburgh. Last Sat (exc Dec), 14.30.

Ireland, Numismatic Society of (Northern Branch). Denman International, Clandeboye Road, Bangor or Maysfield Leisure Centre, Belfast. 1st Fri (exc Jan) 19.30. (028 9146 6743)

Ireland, Numismatic Society of. (Southern Branch). Ely House, 8 Ely Place, Dublin. Last Fri, 20.00. (0035 3 283 2027).

Ipswich Numismatic Society (1966). Ipswich Citizens Advice Bureau, 19 Tower Street, Ipswich, Suffolk. Monthly meetings, 19.30. (01473 711158).

Kent Towns Numismatic Society (1913). Adult Education Centre, 9 Sittingbourne Road (Maidstone) and King's School Preparatory School, King Edward Road (Rochester). 1st Fri of month, 19.30 alternately at Maidstone and Rochester. (01622 843881).

Kingston Numismatic Society (1966). King Athelstan's School, Villiers Road, Kingston-upon-Thames, Surrey. 3rd Thu (exc Dec & Jan), 19.30. (020-8397 6944).

Lancashire & Cheshire Numismatic Society (1933). Manchester Central Library, St Peter's Square, Manchester M2 5PD. Monthly, Sep-June, Wed (18.30) or Sat (14.30). (0161 445 2042).

Lincolnshire Numismatic Society (1932). Grimsby Bridge Club, Bargate, Grimsby, South Humberside. 4th Wed (exc Aug), 19.30.

London Numismatic Club (1947). Institute of Archaeology, 31–34 Gordon Square, London WC1H 0PY. Monthly, 18.30.

Loughborough Coin & Search Society (1964). Wallace Humphry Room, Shelthorpe Community Centre, Loughborough, Leics. 1st Thu, 19.30. (01509 261352).

Merseyside Numismatic Society (1947). The Lecture Theatre, Liverpool Museum, William Brown Street, Liverpool L3 8EN. Monthly (exc July & Aug), 19.00. (0151-929 2143).

Mid Lanark Coin Circle (1969). Hospitality Room, The Civic Centre, Motherwell, Lanarkshire. 4th Thu, Sep–Apr (exc Dec), 19.30. (0141-552 2083).

Morecambe & Lancaster Numismatic Society. Monthly, 19.30. (01524 411036).

Newbury Coin & Medal Club (1971). Monthly, 20.00. (01635 41233).

Northampton Numismatic Society (1969). Old Scouts RFC, Rushmere Road, Northampton. 3rd Mon, 20.00.

Norwich Numismatic Society (1967). Assembly House, Theatre Street, Norwich, Norfolk. 3rd Mon, 19.30. (01493 651577).

Nottinghamshire Numismatic Society (1948). The Cecil Roberts Room, County Library, Angel Row, Nottingham NG1 6HP. 2nd Tue (Sep-Apr), 18.45. (0115 9257674).

Nuneaton & District Coin Club (1968). United Reformed Church Room, Coton Road, opposite Council House, Nuneaton, Warwickshire. 2nd Tue, 19.30. (01203 371556).

Orders & Medals Research Society (1942). National Army Museum, Royal Hospital Road, Chelsea, London SW3. Monthly, 14.30 (020-8680 2701).

Ormskirk & West Lancashire Numismatic Society (1970).The Eagle & Child, Maltkiln Lane, Bispham Green L40 1SN. 1st Thu, 20.15. (01704 531266).

Peterborough Coin & Medal Club (1967). The Club Room, APV-Baker Social Club, Alma Road, Peter-borough, Cambs. Last Tue (exc July & Aug), 19.30.

Plymouth Coin & Medal Club (1970). RAFA Club, 5 Ermington Terrace, Mutley Plain, Plymouth, Devon. 2nd Wed (exc Dec), 19.30. (01752 663803).

Preston & District Numismatic Society (1965). Eldon Hotel, Eldon Street, Preston, Lancs. 1st and 3rd Tue, 20.00. (012572 66869).

Reading Coin Club (1964). Abbey Baptist Church, Abbey Square, Reading. 1st Mon, 19.00. (0118 9332843).

Redbridge Numismatic Society (1968). Gants Hill Library, Cranbrook Road, Ilford, Essex. 4th Wed, 19.30. (020-8554 5486).

Rochford Hundred Numismatic Society. Civic Suite, Rayleigh Town Hall, Rayleigh, Essex. 2nd Thu, 20.00. (01702 230950).

Romsey Numismatic Society (1969). Romsey WM Conservative Club, Market Place, Romsey, Hants SO5 8NA. 4th Fri (exc Dec), 19.30. (01703 253921).

Rotherham & District Coin Club (1982). Rotherham Art Centre, Rotherham, South Yorkshire. 1st Wed, 19.00. (01709 528179).

Royal Mint Coin Club, PO Box 500, Cardiff CF1 1HA (01443 222111).

Royal Numismatic Society (1836). Society of Antiquaries, Piccadilly, London W1. Monthly (Oct-June), 17.30. Joe Cribb, Coins and Medals, British Museum, London WC1B 3DG (020-7323 8585).

Rye Coin Club (1955). Rye Further Education Centre, Lion Street, Rye, East Sussex. 2nd Thu (Oct-Dec, Feb-May), 19.30. (01424 422974).

St Albans & Hertfordshire Numismatic Society (1948). St Michael's Parish Centre, Museum Entrance, Verulamium Park, St Albans, Herts AL3 4SL. 2nd Tue (exc Aug), 19.30. (01727 824434).

Sheffield Numismatic Society. Telephone for venue. 2nd Wed, 19.00. (0114 2817129)

South East Hants Numismatic Society. Different locations. 1st Fri. Contact: Tony Matthews, 8 King George Road, Totton, Southampton SO4 3FE.

South Manchester Numismatic Society (1967). Nursery Inn, Green Lane, Heaton Mersey, Stockport. 1st & 3rd Mondays of each month (excl. Public hols), 20.00. (0161-485 7017).

South Wales & Monmouthshire Numismatic Society (1958). The W. R. Lysaght Institute, Corporation Road, Newport. 2nd Tues, 19.30. (029 20561564).

Thurrock Numismatic Society (1970). Stanley Lazell Hall, Dell Road, Grays, Essex. 3rd Wed, 19.00.

Torbay & District Coin Club (1967). British Rail Social Club, Brunel Road, Newton Abbott, Devon TQ12 4PB. 1st Tue, 19.45. (01803 326497).

Tyneside Numismatic Society (1954). RAFA Club, Eric Nelson House, 16 Berwick Road, Gateshead, Tyne & Wear. 2nd Wed, 19.30. (0191 372 2266).

Wessex NS (1948). Hotel Bristowe, Grange Road, Southbourne, Bournemouth, Dorset. 2nd Thurs (exc Aug), 20.00. (020 7731 1702).

Wiltshire Numismatic Society (1965). Raven Inn, Poulshot, Nr Devizes, Wiltshire. 3rd Mon, Mar-Dec, 20.00. (01225 703143).

Worthing & District Numismatic Society (1967). Kingsway Hotel, Marine Parade, Worthing, West Sussex BN11 3QQ. 3rd Thu, 20.00. (01903 241503).

Yorkshire Numismatic Society (1909). Leeds Museum, The Headrow , Leeds. 1st Sat (exc Jan, Aug & Dec) (0113 286 4914).

> *Club Secretaries: if your details as listed are incorrect please let us know in time for the next edition of the COIN YEARBOOK*

IMPORTANT ORGANISATIONS

ADA
The Antiquities
Dealers Association
Secretary: Susan Hadida, Duke's Court,
32 Duke Street, London SW1Y 6DU

BNTA
The British Numismatic
Trade Association
Secretary: Carol Carter, PO Box 474A, Thames Ditton,
Surrey KT7 0WJ

ANA
The American
Numismatic
Association
818 North Cascade Avenue, Colorado Springs, CO
80903-3279, USA

IAPN
International
Association of
Professional Numismatists
Secretary: Jean-Luc Van der Schueren, 14 Rue de la
Bourse, B–1000, Brussels.

IBNS
International Bank Note Society
Membership Secretary:
Laurence Pope, 2 Tattersall Drive
Market Steeping, Peterborough, PE6 8BS

Directory of Auctioneers

Listed here are the major UK auction houses which handle coins, medals, banknotes and other items of numismatic interest. Many of them hold regular public auctions, whilst others handle numismatic material infrequently. A number of coin companies also hold regular Postal Auctions—these are marked with a P.

Baldwin's Auctions Ltd
11 Adelphi Terrace, London WC2N 6BJ
(020 7930 9808 fax 020 7930 9450, e-mail
auctions@baldwin.sh, website:
www.baldwin.sh)

Banking Memorabilia
PO Box 14, Carlisle CA3 8DZ (0169 7476465).

A. F. Brock & Company
269 London Road, Hazel Grove, Stockport,
Cheshire SK7 4PL (0161 456 5050 fax 0161 456
5112, website www.afbrock.co.uk, email
info@afbrock.co.uk).

Christie, Manson & Wood Ltd
8 King Street, St James's, London SW1Y 6QT
(020 7839 9060).

Christie's Scotland Ltd
164–166 Bath Street, Glasgow G2 4TG (0141 332
8134 fax 0141 332 5759).

Classical Numismatic Group Inc (Seaby Coins)
14 Old Bond Street, London W1X 4JL (020 7495
1888 fax 020-7499 5916, email
cng@historicalcoins.com, website:
www.historicalcoins.com). **P**

Corbitts
5 Moseley Sreet, Newcastle upon Tyne NE1 1YE
(0191-232 7268 fax 0191-261 4130).

Croydon Coin Auctions
272 Melfort Road, Thornton Heath, Surrey CR7
7RR (020 8240 7924 or 020 8656 4583, website
www.croydoncoinauctions.co.uk,
email: croydoncoinauctions.co.uk).

Dix Noonan Webb
1 Old Bond Street, London W1XZ 3TD (020 7499
5022 fax 020 7499 5023, website:
www.dnw.co.uk, email: auctions@dnw.co.uk)

Edinburgh Coin Shop
11 West Crosscauseway, Edinburgh EH8 9JW
(0131 668 2928 fax 0131 668 2926). **P**

Fellows & Sons
Augusta House, 19 Augusta Street, Hockley,
Birmingham B18 6JA (0121-212 2131).

B. Frank & Son
3 South Avenue, Ryton, Tyne & Wear NE40 3LD
(0191 413 8749 fax 0191 413 2957,
email bfrankandson@aol.com).

T. Gillingham
42 Highbury Park, Warminster, Wilts BA12 9JF
(01985 216486).

Gillio Coins International
1013 State Street, Santa Barbara, CA 93101, USA
(805 9631345—London contact Eric Green 020-
7586 3964).

Glendining & Co
101 New Bond Street, London W1Y 9LG (020 7
493 2445 fax 020 7491 9181,
website: phillips-auctions.com)).

Graves, Son & Pilcher Fine Arts
71 Church Road, Hove, East Sussex BN3 2GL
(01273 735266 fax 01273 723813).

Hoods Postal Coin Auctions
23 High Street, Kilbirnie, Ayrshire KA25 7EX
(fax/tel 01505 682157). **P**

Kleeford Coin Auctions
19 Craythorns Crescent, Dishforth, Thirsk YO7
3LY. (tel/fax 01845 577977). *P*

W. H. Lane & Son
65 Morrab Road, Penzance, Cornwall TR18 2QT
(01736 61447 fax 01736 50097) also: Trafalgar
House, Malpas Road, Truro, Cornwall TR1 1QH
(01872 223379).

Lawrence Fine Art Auctioneers
South Street, Crewkerne, Somerset TA18 8AB
(01460 73041).

Lockdale Coins
36 Upper Orwell Street, Ipswich IP4 1BR.
Second shop at 168 London Road South,
Lowestoft (01473 218588,
website: www.lockdales.co.uk).

London Coin Auctions
31 Reigate Way, Wallington, Surrey SM6 8NU
(020 8688 5297 fax 020 8680 8071, website
www.londoncoins.co.uk).

Moreton & Eden Ltd
45 Maddox Street, London W1S 2PE (020 7470 7220 fax 020 7470 7221, email info@mortenand eden.com)

Neales
192–194 Mansfield Road, Nottingham NG1 3HU (0115 9624141 fax 0115 9856890).

Phillips
101 New Bond Street, London W1S 1SR (020-7468 8345 fax 020-7409 3466, website www.phillips-auctions.com).

R & W Coin Auctions
307 Bretch Hill, Banbury, Oxon OX16 0JD (01295 275128).

Sheffield Coin Auctions
7 Beacon Close, Sheffield S9 1AA (0114 249 0442).

Simmons Gallery
53, Lamb's Conduit Street, Holborn, London WC1N 3NB (020 7831 2080 fax 020 7831 2090). P

Spink & Son Ltd
69 Southampton Row, Bloomsbury, London. WC1B 4ET (020 7563 2820, fax 020 7563 4066, website www.spink-online.com, email info@spinkandson.com).

Sussex Auction Galleries
59 Perrymount Road, Haywards Heath, West Sussex RH16 3DS (01444 414935 fax 01444 450402).

Warwick & Warwick
Chalon House, Scarbank, Millers Road, Warwick CV34 5DB (01926 499031 fax 01926 491906, email: info@warwickandwarwick.com)

Whytes
38 Moleworth Street, Dublin 2, Republic of Ireland (+3531 676 2888 fax 676 2880, website www.whytes.ie, email whytes@iol.ie).

directory of
Fairs

Listed below are the names of the fair organisers, their venue details where known along with contact telephone numbers. Please call the organisers direct for information on dates etc.

Aberdeen
Jarvis Amatola Hotel, Great Western Road, also venues in **Glenrothes** and **Glasgow**. *Cornucopia Collectors Fairs. (01382 224946)*

Birmingham
National Motor Cycle Museum, Bickenhill, Birmingham. *Midland Stamp & Coin Fair. (024 7671 6587)*

Bristol
Jury's Hotel, Prince Street. *Gold Star Fairs. (01823 251563)*

Cardiff
City Hall. *R. J. Neil Fairs. (01873 854688)*

Cheltenham
Town Hall or White House Hotel. *R. J. Neil Fairs. (01873 854688)*

Exeter
St Georges Hall, George Street. *Gold Star Fairs. (01823 251563)*

Hereford
Holmer Church Hall. *R. J. Neil Fairs. (01873 854688)*

Leeds-Morley
Cedar Court Hotel, Denby Dale Road, Calder Grove, Wakefield WF4 3QZ. *N. C. S. Promotions. (01552 684681).*

Lichfield
Civic Hall, Castle Dyke, City Centre. *C. S. Fairs. (01562 710424)*

London
Holiday Inn, Coram St., Bloomsbury, London WC1. *London Coin Fair. (020 7831 2080)*

London
The Bonnington Hotel, 92 Southampton Row, London WC1. *West Promotions. (020 8641 3224).*

London
The Commonwealth Institute, Kensington High Street, London W8. *Davidson Monk Fairs. (020 8656 4583 or 020 8651 3890)*

Malvern
Lyttleton Rooms. *R. J. Neil Fairs. (01873 854688)*

Newport
The Holiday Inn. *R. J. Neil Fairs. (01873 854688)*

Newtown
Elephant & Castle Hotel. *R. J. Neil Fairs. (01873 854688*

Sutton Coldfield
Fellowship Hall, South Parade. *C. S. Fairs. (01562 710424)*

West Bromwich
Town Hall, High Street. *C. S. Fairs. (01562 710424)*

York
The Grandstand, York Racecourse. *York Coin Fair (01793 513431 or 020 8946 4489)*

Annual events

The B.N.T.A. (Coinex)
Tel: 020 8398 4290 for details

The I.B.N.S. (World Paper Money Fair)
Tel: 020 8360 2759 for details

Directory of
Dealers

The dealers listed below have comprehensive stocks of coins and medals, unless otherwise stated. Specialities, where known, are noted. Many of those listed are postal dealers only, so to avoid disappointment always make contact by telephone or mail in the first instance, particularly before travelling any distance.

Abbreviations:
ADA—Antiquities Dealers Association
ANA—American Numismatic Association
BADA—British Antique Dealers Association
BNTA—British Numismatic Trade Association
IAPN—International Association of Professional Numismatists
IBNS—International Bank Note Society
P—Postal only
L—Publishes regular lists

A. Ackroyd (IBNS)
62 Albert Road, Parkstone, Poole, Dorset BH12 2DB (tel/fax 01202 739039, website www.AAnotes.com). *P. L. Banknotes, cheques and related collectables.*

Airedale Coins (ANA, BNTA)
PO Box 7, Bingley, West Yorkshire, BD16 4ST (01274 770414 fax 01274 563869, website www.airedalecoins.com, email info@airedalecoins.com).
P. L. British and modern coins of the world.

David Allen Coins and Collectables
PO Box 125, Pinner, Middlesex HA5 2TX (020 866 6796). *P. L. British and world coins, tokens, banknotes.*

Joan Allen Electronics Ltd
190 Main Road, Biggin Hill, Kent TN16 3BB (01959 71255). Mon-Sat 09.00–17.00. *Metal detectors.*

Ancient Forum (ADA)
PO Box 356, Christchurch, Dorset BH23 2YD (01202 478592). *P. L. Greek, Roman and medieval antiquities with occasional groups of coins.*

Ancient World
16 High Petergate, York, YO1 2EH (01904 624062) 10.30–17.00 weekdays. *Greek, Roman, Celtic and medieval coins, also antiquities.*

Antique Boutique
54–59 Merrion Centre, Leeds, West Yorkshire (01132 444174). 09.30–17.30 (Wed 09.30 –13.30).

Antiquestall.com
On line numismatic market place. *Coins, medals, banknotes etc*

Keith Austin (IBNS)
PO Box 89, Carlise, Cumbria CA3 0GH (01228 819149, fax 01228 521176, email kaustin@kabc.freeserve.co.uk). *L. Banknotes.*

N. J. Aves
PO Box 811, Yeovil, Somerset (01935 72368). *P. Coins, tokens and medals.*

Mark Bailey
120 Sterte Court, Sterte Close, Poole, Dorset BH15 2AY (01202 674936). *P. L. Ancient, modern, world coins and antiquities.*

Baird & Co
304 High Street, Stratford, London E15 1AJ (020 8555 5217). 09.00–17.30 weekdays. *Bullion and World coins.*

A. H. Baldwin & Sons Ltd (ANA, BADA, BNTA, IAPN)
11 Adelphi Terrace, London WC2N 6BJ. 09.00–17.00 weekdays. (email coins@baldwin.sh) *Coins, tokens, commemorative medals, war medals and decorations, numismatic books.*

Banking Memorabilia (IBNS)
PO Box 14, Carlisle, Cumbria (0169 96465). 09.00–18.00 (not Sun). *Cheques, banknotes, related ephemera.*

Banknotes of Auld Scotland
Sconser, Isle of Skye IV48 8TD. (01478 650459, website www.scottish-banknotes.com, email johnaunc@aol.com).

D. G. Barney
Greenfield, Colyton Hill, Colyton, Devon EX24 6HY (01297 552702, email dougbarney@ondigital.com).
British and world coins, tokens and banknotes.

G. Barrington Smith
Cross Street, Oadby, Leicestershire LE2 4DD (01533 712114). 08.30–17.15 weekdays. *Albums, catalogues and accessories.*

Bath Stamp and Coin Shop (BNTA)
Pulteney Bridge, Bath, Avon BA2 4AY (01225 463073). Mon-Sat 09.30–17.30. *British and world coins.*

Baxters Coin & Stamp Exchange
20–22 Hapworths Arcade, Silver Street, Hull, North Humberside, HU1 1JU (01482 223875). 10.00–17.00 (closed Thurs). *British and world coins.*

Michael Beaumont
PO Box 8, Carlton, Notts NG4 4QZ (0115 9878361). *P. Coins, medals and tokens of the world.*

Beaver Coin Room (BNTA)
57 Philbeach Gardens, LondonSW5 9ED (020 7373 4553). *P. European coins and medals.*

R. P. & P. J. Beckett
Maesyderw, Capel Dewi, Llandyssul, Dyfed SA44 4PJ. (Fax only 01559 395631, email rppjbeckett@btinternet.com) *P. World crowns, coin sets and banknotes.*

Lloyd Bennett (BNTA)
PO Box 2, Monmouth, Gwent NP5 3YE (01600 890634). Abergavenny Market (Tue), Monmouth Market (Fri–Sat) 09.00–16.00. *English hammered, milled and coins of the world.*

Berkshire Coin Centre
35 Castle Street, Reading, Berkshire RG1 7SB (01734 575593). 10.00–16.00 weekdays, half-day Sat. *British and world coins.*

Beron Coins
64 Rosewood Close, Glascote, Tamworth, Staffs B77 3PD (01827 54541). *P. L. British & world coins.*

Stephen J. Betts
4 Victoria Street, Narborough, Leics LE9 5DP (0116 2864434). *P. L. Medieval and modern coins, counters, jetons and tokens, countermarks and medals.*

Bigbury Mint
River Park, Ermington Mill, Ivybridge, Devon PL21 9NT (01548 830717. *Specialists in reproduction hammered coins*

Birchin Lane Gold Coin Company
6 Castle Court, St Michael's Alley (off Cornhill), London EC3V 9DS (020 7621 0370 and 020 7263 3981). Mon-Fri 10.00–16.30. *Gold and bullion coins.*

Barry Boswell
24 Townsend Lane, Upper Boddington, Daventry, Northants NN11 6DR (01327 261877, fax 01327 261391, email Barry.Boswell@btinternet.com). *P. L. British and world banknotes.*

James & C. Brett
17 Dale Road, Lewes, East Sussex BN7 1LH. *P. L. British and world coins.*

J. Bridgeman Coins
129a Blackburn Road, Accrington, Lancs (01254 384757). 09.30–17.00. *British & World coins.*

Brighton Coin Company (ANA, BNTA)
36 Ship Street, Brighton, Sussex BN1 1AB (01273 733365 Mon-Fri 9.45–17.30, Sat 9.45–15.30. *World coins.*

Britannia Jewellery Co
234 Yorkshire Street, Rochdale, Lancs OL16 2DP (01706 341046/55507. Mon-Sat 10.00–17.00.

BRM Coins
3 Minshull Street, Knutsford, Cheshire WA16 6HG (01565) 651480 and 0606 74522). Mon-Sat 10,00–17.00. *British coins.*

Peter F. Broadbelt
10 Dragon Road, Harrogate, North Yorkshire HG1 5DF (01423 562037). Mon-Sat 11–18.00. *Specialist in Foreign coins.*

A. F. Brock & Company
269 London Road, Hazel Grove, Stockport, Cheshire SK7 4PL (0161 456 5050/5112, email info@afbrock.co.uk, www.afbrock.co.uk). Mon-Sat 09.30–17.30. *Auctioneers and valuers.*

E. J. & C. A. Brooks (BNTA, IBNS)
44 Kiln Road, Thundersley, Essex SS7 1TB (01268 753835). Any time up to 23.00. *L. British*

Iain Burn
2 Compton Gardens, 53 Park Road, Camberley, Surrey GU15 2SP (01276 23304). *Bank of England & Treasury notes*

Butler & Co
111 Promenade, Cheltenham, Glos GL50 1NN (01242 522272). Sat only. *World coins.*

BBM Coins
8–9 Lion Street, Kidderminster, Hereford & Worcester, DY10 1PT (01562 744118). Mon, Wed-Sat 10.00–17.00. *World coins.*

Cambridge Stamp Centre Ltd
9 Sussex Street, Cambridge CB4 4HU (01223 63980). Mon-Sat 09.00–17.30. *British coins.*

Castle Coins
47a High Street South, Dunstable, Beds LU6 3RZ (01582 602778). Mon-Sat 10.00–17.00. *English coins.*

Castle Curios
165 Wellgate, Rotherham, South Yorkshire S60 4DT. Wed-Sat 11.00–17.00. *English coins.*

Castle Galleries
81 Castle Street, Salisbury, Wiltshire SP1 3SP (01722 333734). Tue, Thu Fri 09.00–17.00, Sat 09.30–16.00. *British coins, medals and tokens.*

Cathedral Coins
23 Kirkgate, Ripon, North Yorkshire HG4 1PB (01765 701400). Mon-Sat 10.00–17.00.

David L. Cavanagh
49 Cockburn Street, Edinburgh EH1 1PB (0131 226 3391). Mon-Sat 10.30–17.00. *British coins.*

Cavendish Coins
14 Longfields, Ongar, Essex CM5 9BZ. *P. Modern crown-sized coins.*

CCC Coins
PO Box 192, Peterborough, PE2 5DT. *P. L. Roman, hammered and English milled silver.*

Central Bank of Ireland
Currency Centre, Sandyford Road, Dublin 16, Ireland. *New coin and banknote issues of Ireland.*

Lance Chaplin
17 Wanstead Lane, Ilford, Essex IG1 3SB (020 8554 7154). *P. L. Roman, Greek, Celtic, hammered coins and antiquities.*

Chelsea Coins Ltd (BNTA)
PO Box 2, Fulham Road, London SW10 9PQ. (020 8870 5501 Fax 020 8875 1459). *P. World coins.*

Nigel A. Clark
28 Ulundi Road, Blackheath, London SE3 7UG (020 8858 4020). *P. L. Mainly 17th century tokens.*

Classical Numismatic Group
14 Old Bond Street, London W1X 4JL. (020 7495 1888 Fax 020 7499 5916, Email cng@historicalcoins.com). *P. Ancient and world coins. Publishers of the Classical Numismatic Review.*

Paul Clayton (BNTA)
PO Box 21, Wetherby, West Yorkshire LS22 5JY. (01937 72441). *Modern gold coins.*

André de Clermont (BNTA)
PO Box 3615, London, SW10 0YD. (020 7351 5727, Fax 020 7352 8127). *World coins, especially Islamic & Oriental coins, Latin America.*

M. Coeshaw
PO Box 115, Leicester LE3 8JJ (01533 873808). *P.*

Philip Cohen Numismatics (ANA, BNTA)
20 Cecil Court, Charing Cross Road, London WC2N 4HE (020 7379 0615). Mon-Sat 10.30–17.30 (half-days Mon and Sat).

Coin & Collectors Centre
PO Box 22, Pontefract, West Yorkshire WF8 1YT (01977 704112, website www.coincentre.co.uk, email sales@coincentre.co.uk). *P. British coins.*

Coincraft (ANA, IBNS)
44/45 Great Russell Street, London WC1B 3LU
(020 7636 1188 and 020 7637 8785 fax 020 7323 2860,
Website www.coincraft.com Email
info@coincraft.com). Mon-Fri 09.30–17.00, Sat
10.00–14.30. *L (newspaper format). Coins and
banknotes.*

Coinote Services Ltd
PO Box 53, Sorting Office, Clarke Street,
Hartlepool TS26 NYL (01429 273044). *P. L. Coins
and banknotes 1615 todate. Accessories and books.*

Coins of Beeston
PO Box 19, Beeston, Notts BG9 2NE. *P. L. Tokens,
medals and paranumismatics.*

Coins of Canterbury
PO Box 47, Faversham, Kent ME13 7HX (01795
531980). *P. English coins.*

Coliseum Coins
30 Staunton Avenue, Hayling Island, Hants
PO11 0EN (01705 464332). *P. Greek, Roman,
Oriental coins.*

Collecta Coins Limited
PO Box 101, Northampton NN1 3LT (01604
766607/27076). Mon-Sat 09.00–21.00. *World coins.*

The Collector
242 High Street, Orpington, Kent BR6 0LZ (01689
890045). Mon-Sat 09.45–17.30 (closed Tue). *Coins,
medals, banknotes, badges, militaria, cigarette cards etc*

3CO
PO Box 27, Manchester, M23 9UJ. *English milled
coinage. P.*

Collectors' Corner
East Street, Crescent Road, Faversham, Kent ME13
8AD (01795 539721). Mon-Fri 10.00–15.00 (half-
day Mon, Thu). *Coins and medals.*

Collectors' Corner
Watford Market (off High Street), Watford, Herts
(020 8904 0552). Tue, Fri, Sat 09.00-17.00. *World
coins.*

Collectors' Forum
237 South Street, Romford, Essex RM1 2BE (01708
723357). Mon-Sat 09.30-18.00 Thu 09.30-14.00.
British coins and medals.

Collectors Gallery (BNTA, IBNS)
Castle Hall, Castle Gates, Shrewsbury SY1 2AD
(01743 272140 fax 01743 366041). Mon-Fri 09.00–
18.00, half-day Sat. *Coins, medals and banknotes.
Numismatic accessories and related books. Agents for
the Abafil range of coin cases.*

Collectors' World
188 Wollaton Road, Wollaton, Nottingham NG8
1HJ. (01159 280347). *Coins, Tokens, Banknotes,
Accessories.*

Constantia CB
15 Church Road, Northwood, Middlesex HA6
1AR. *P. Roman and medieval hammered coins.*

Colin Cooke
257 Brooklands Road, Manchester M23 9HF (0161
973 2395 fax 0161 962 2864, email
coins@colincooke.com). *L. British coins.*

Corbitts (BNTA)
5 Mosley Street, Newcastle Upon Tyne NE1 1YE
(0191 232 7268 fax: 0191 261 4130). *Dealers and
auctioneers of all coins and medals.*

G. D. Courtenay
58 New Peachey Lane, Uxbridge, Middlesex UB8
3SX. *P. L. Coins, medals, tokens and banknotes.*

David Craddock
PO Box 3785, Camp Hill, Birmingham B11 2NF.
(0121 733 2259) *L. Crown to farthings. Copper and
bronze specialist. Some foreign.*

John Cummings Ltd (BNTA)
Parthenon Gallery, 25 Bury Place, WC1A 2JH (020
7242 5656). *P. Greek, Roman, Byzantine, Celtic,
Saxon, Viking and English hammered coins. Quarterly
catalogue.*

Mark Davidson
PO Box 197, South Croydon, Surrey CR3 0ZD (020
8651 3890). *Ancient, hammered coinage.*

Davidson Monk Fairs
PO Box 201, Croydon, Surrey CR9 7AQ (020 8656
4583). *Organiser of monthly fairs at the Common
wealth Institute, Kensington High Street, London W8.*

Paul Davies Ltd (ANA, BNTA, IAPN)
PO Box 17, Ilkley, West Yorkshire LS29 8TZ (01943
603116 fax 01943 816326). *P. World coins.*

Paul Davis
PO Box 418, Birmingham B17 0RZ (0121 427 7179).
P. Hammered gold and silver coins.

DD Coins of Windsor
24–28 St Leonards Road, Suite 100, Windsor, Berks
SL4 3BB. (01753 739487). *L. GB milled list.*

B. J. Dawson (Coins) (BNTA)
52 St Helens Road, Lancs BL3 3NH (01204 63732).
Mon Tue Sat 09.30–16.00, Thu Fri 09.30–17.30, Wed
09.30–13.00. *L. Ancient, hammered and milled coins,
tokens and banknotes.*

Patrick Deane
PO Box 76, Orpington, Kent BR6 0UB. (01689
812222 fax 01689 898008, website
www.coinsandmedals.com, email
newissuesbureau@compuserve.com).
By appointment only. *British coins.*

Decus Coins
The Haven, Brockweir, Chepstow, Gwent NP6
7NN (01291 689216). *P.*

Dei Gratia
PO Box 3568, Buckingham MK18 4ZS (01280
848000). *P. L. Pre-Roman to modern coins,
antiquities, banknotes.*

Demesne Management Systems Ltd
3, St Mary's Hill, Stamford, Lincolnshire, PE9
2DW. *Specialist software for collectors.*

Den of Antiquity
26 West End, Haddenham, Ely, Cambs CB6 3TE
(01353 741759). *Ancients and Antiquities. L*

Clive & Richard Dennett (BNTA)
66 St Benedicts Street, Norwich, Norfolk NR2 4AR
(01603 624315). Mon-Fri 09.00–17.30, Sat 09.00–
16.00 (closed Thu). *L. World paper money.*

C. J. Denton (ANA, BNTA, FRNS)
PO Box 25, Orpington, Kent BR6 8PU (01689
873690). *P. World coins.*

Detecnicks
3 Orchard Crescent, Arundel Road, Fontwell. West
Sussex BN18 0SA (01243 545060 fax 01243 545922
Retail shop. Wide range of detectors and accessories.

Michael Dickinson (ANA, BNTA)
Ramsay House, 825 High Road Finchley, London
N12 8UB (0181 441 7175). *P. British and world coins.*

Dolphin Coins (ANA)
22 High Street, Leighton Buzzard, Beds. LU7 7EB.
(01525 383822 fax 01525 383872)
Mon-Fri 09.30– 17.00. Sat appt only. *L. British and
world coins.*

Dorset Coin Co Ltd (BNTA)
193 Ashley Road, Parkstone, Poole, Dorset BH14
9DL (01202 739606, fax 01202 739230). *P. L.
Separate coin and banknote lists.*

Drizen Coins
1 Hawthorns, Leigh-on-Sea, Essex SS9 4JT (01702
521094). *P. L. British and world coins.*

Dyas Coins & Medals
30 Shaftmoor Lane, Acocks Green, Birmingham
B27 7RS (0121 707 2808). Fri 10.30–18.30, Sun
10.30–13.00. *World coins and medals.*

Eagle Coins
Winterhaven, Mourneabbey, Mallow, Co. Cork,
Ireland (010 35322 29385). *P. L. Irish and English
coins.*

East Kent Coins
PO Box 106, Herne Bay, Kent CT6 6GN (01227
365073). *P. L. World coins*

Eden Coins
PO Box 73, Oldbury, Warley, West Midlands B68
0BT (0121 422 5357). *P. English coins, tokens and
medals.*

Edinburgh Coin Shop (ANA)
11 West Crosscauseway, Edinburgh EH8 9JW
(0131 668 2928 fax 0131 668 2926). Mon-Sat
10.00–17.30. *L. World coins and medals. Postal
auctions.*

Christopher Eimer (ANA, BNTA)
PO Box 352 London NW11 7RF (020 8458 9933 fax
020 8455 3535, email art@christophereimer.co.uk).
P. Commemorative medals.

Elm Hill Stamps & Coins
27 Elm Hill, Norwich, Norfolk NR3 1HN (01603
627413). Mon-Fri 09.00–16.45, half-day Sat. *British
and world coins.*

ELM
15 Phillimore Walk, Kensington, London W8 7SA
(020 7937 8484)P. *Egyptian Banknotes.*

Ely Stamp & Coin Shop
27 Fore Hill, Ely, Cambs CB7 1AA (01353 663919).
Mon, Wed-Sat 09.30–17.30. *World coins and medals.*

Europa Numismatics (ANA, BNTA)
PO Box 119, High Wycombe, Bucks HP11 1QL
(01494 437307). *P. European coins.*

Evesham Stamp & Coin Centre
Magpie Antiques, Paris House, 61 High Street,
Evesham, Worcs WR11 4DA (01386 41631). Mon-
Sat 09.00–17.30. *British coins.*

Michael E. Ewins
Meyrick Heights, 20 Meyrick Park Crescent,
Bournemouth, Dorset BH3 7AQ (01202 290674). *P.
World coins.*

I. Fine & Son Ltd
Victoria House, 93 Manor Farm Road, Wembley,
Middlesex HA10 1XB (020 8997 5055). *P. British &
World coins.*

Patrick Finn (BNTA)
PO Box 26, Kendal, Cumbria LA9 7AB (01539
730008, fax 01539 721800). *P. L. Early British, Irish,
Scottish and Anglo-Gallic coins.*

Robin Finnegan Stamp Shop
83 Skinnergate, Darlington, Co Durham DL3 7LX
(01325 489820/357674). Mon-Sat 10.00–17.30
(closed Wed). *World coins.*

Richard N. Flashman
54 Ebbsfleet Walk, Gravesend, Kent, DA11 9EW. *L.
P. British banknotes.*

David Fletcher (Mint Coins) (ANA, BNTA)
PO Box 64, Coventry, Warwickshire CV5 6SN (024
7671 5425, Fax 024 7667 7985). *P. World new issues*

Folley Island Coins
PO Box 361, Dunstable, Bedfordshire LU5 4YU.
(01582 667734). *World and English coins.*

Format of Birmingham Ltd (ANA, BNTA, IAPN,
IBNS)
18 Bennetts Hill, Birmingham B2 5QJ (0121 643
2058 fax 0121 643 2210). Mon-Fri 09.30-7.00. *L.
Coins, tokens and medals.*

B. Frank & Son (ANA, IBNS)
3 South Avenue, Ryton, Tyne & Wear NE40 3LD
(0191 413 8749). *P. L. Banknotes and cheques, coins
of the world. Organiser of the North of England fair.*

Frank Milward (BNTA)
2 Ravensworth Road, Mortimer, Berks, RG7 3UU
(01734 332843). Mon-Sat 09.00-18.00. *British and
World coins.*

Dennis Fudge Coins
127 Hadrian Road, Jarrow, Tyne & Wear NE32 3TS
(0191 421 6221). *P. L. Ancient coins.*

Galata Coins Ltd (ANA, BNTA)
The Old White Lion, Market Street, Llanfylin,
Powys SY22 5BX (01691 648 765). *P. British and
world coins.*

G. Gant
Glazenwood, 37 Augustus Way, Witham, Essex
CM8 1HH. *P. British and Commonwealth coins.*

James Garriock
38 Hazel Close Bemerton Heath, Salisbury,
Wiltshire SP2 977 (01722 500590). *P. L. Mainly
hammered coins.*

John Gaunt
21 Harvey Road, Bedford MK41 9LF (01234
217685). By appointment. *Numismatic books.*

Alistair Gibb (IBNS)
5 West Albert Road, Kirkcaldy, Fife KY1 1DL
(01592 269045). *P. L. Banknotes and books on
banking.*

A. & S. Gillis
20 Howard Street, Darfield, Barnsley, South
Yorkshire S73 9JD. (01226 750371, website
www.gilliscoins.com,email:
catalogues@gilliscoins.com) *P. L.
Ancient and medieval coins.*

Richard Gladdle
9 Cork Street, London W1X 1P9. (01327 858511).
Tokens. P. L.

Glance Back Books
17 Upper Street, Chepstow, Gwent NP6 5EX (01291
626562). 10.30–17.30. *World coins, medals, banknotes.*

Glendining's (ANA, BNTA)
101 New Bond Street, London W1Y 9LG (020 7493
2445). Mon-Fri 08.30-17.00, Sat 08.30–13.00.
Auctioneers.

Phil Goodwin (ANA)
PO Box 69, Portsmouth, Hants PO1 5SH (02392
423267 or 02392 752006 incl. fax). *P or by appoint
ment.L. Ancient coins and antiquities.*

K. Goulborn
12 Sussex Street, Rhyl, Clwyd. (01745 338112 or
01745 344856). *P. L. British coins and banknotes.*

Granta Stamp & Coin Shop
28 Magdalene Street, Cambridge CB3 0AF (01223
315044) Mon-Sat 10.30-18.30. *English coins and
medals.*

Grantham Coins (BNTA)
PO Box 60, Grantham, Lincs (01476 870565). *P. L. English coins and banknotes.*

Eric Green—Agent in UK for Ronald J. Gillio Inc,
1013 State Street, Santa Barbara, California, USA 93101 (020 8907 0015, Mobile 0468 454948). *Gold coins, medals and paper money of the world.*

Barry Greenaway
PO Box 2151, Swindon, Wilts SN5 3GT. (01793 771079, fax 01793 772556, email bdgreenaway@beeb.net). *Tokens, Checks. P.L.*

Grove Philatelics, Coins & Antiquities
Suite 4, Grove House, Blackheath Grove, London SE3 0DG (020 8463 0063). *P. British coins.*

R. I. Groves
82 Burntscarth Green, Locharbriggs, Dumfries DG1 1UL (01387 710636). *P. World, esp. Scandinavian coins.*

Ian Haines
PO Box 45, Hereford, HR2 7YP (01432 268178). *P. L. British and foreign coins and banknotes.*

Anthony Halse
The Headlands, Chepstow Road, Langstone, Newport, Gwent NP6 2JN (01633 413238). *P. L. English coins and tokens.*

A. D. Hamilton & Co (ANA, BNTA)
7 St Vincent Place, Glasgow G1 5JA (0141 221 5423, fax 0141 248 6019, website www.adhamiltons.com, email jeffrey@hamiltons.junglelink.co.uk). *Mon-Sat 10.00–17.00. British and World coins.*

Peter Hancock
40 West Street, Chichester, West Sussex PO19 1RP (01243 786173). *Mon-Sat. World coins.*

P. Hanson
160 Princess Road, Buckhurst Hill, Essex IG9 5DJ. *P. L. Inexpensive world coins.*

J. Hardiman & Son
PO Box 151, London SE20 7YL (020 8778 2678/4159). *P. Quality world coins, all periods.*

Munthandel G. Henzen
PO Box 42, NL - 3958ZT, Amerogngen, Nether lands. (0031 343 430564 fax 0031 343 430542, email henzen.coins@tiscali.nl *Ancients, Dutch & foreign coins. L*

Craig Holmes
6 Marlborough Drive, Bangor, Co Down BT19 1HB. *P. L. Low cost banknotes of the world.*

R. G. Holmes
11 Cross Park, Ilfracombe, Devon EX34 8BJ (01271 864474). *P. L. Coins, modern world crowns and foreign banknotes.*

John L. Homan
Oxford Grange, Marsh Lane, Barrow Haven, Barrow-on-Humber, South Humberside DN19 7ER (01469 32109). *P. Greek, Roman and Byzantine coins.*

Homeland Holding Ltd (IBNS)
Homeland, St John, Jersey, Channel Islands JE3 4AB (01534 65339). *Mon-Fri 09.00-2.00. World coins.*

HTSM Coins
26 Dosk Avenue, Glasgow G13 4LQ. *P. L. British and foreign coins and banknotes.*

T. A. Hull
15 Tangmere Crescent, Hornchurch, Essex RM12 5PL. *P. L. British coins, farthings to crowns, tokens.*

Humber Coins (BNTA)
PO Box 16, Scunthorpe, South Humberside DN15 7AA (01724 763990). *P. British coins.*

J. Hume
107 Halsbury Road East, Northolt, Middlesex UB5 4PY (020 8864 1731). *P. L. Chinese coins.*

D. D. & A. Ingle
380 Carlton Hill, Nottingham (0115 9873325). *Mon-Sat 09.30–17.00. World coins.*

Rendal Ingram Coins (English)
206 Honeysuckle Road, Bassett, Southampton, Hants SO16 3BU. (023 8032 4258, website http://www.angelfire.com/co/RIngramCoins, email ybu36@dial.pipex.co. *P. L. English milled and modern coins.*

Intercol London (ANA, BNTA, IBNS)
43 Templars Crescent, London N3 3QR (020 7349 2207). *P. Paper money of the world.*

Peter Ireland Ltd (BNTA, IBNS)
31 Clifton Street, Blackpool, Lancs FY1 1JQ (01253 21588 fax 0253 300232). *Mon-Sat 09.00-17.30.British and world coins, medals and tokens.*

JAK (IBNS)
31 Vapron Road, Mannamead, Plymouth, Devon PL3 5NJ (01752 665405). *P. L. GB and Common. banknotes.*

F. J. Jeffery & Son Ltd
23 Catalina Court, Melksham, Wiltshire SN12 6FA. (01225 703143). *P. British, Commonwealth and foreign coins.*

Richard W. Jeffery
Trebehor, Porthcurno, Penzance, Cornwall TR19 6LS (01736 871263). *P. British and world coins.*

Jersey Coin Co Ltd
26 Halkett Street, St Helier, Jersey, Channel Islands (01534 25743). *Mon-Sat 09.00–17.00. World coins.*

J. G. Coins
PO Box 206, Southshore, Blackpool FY1 6GZ. (01253 349138). *P. L British Coins.*

Ian Johnson
PO Box 28, Swinton, Manchester M27 3FR (01204 393944). *P. L. Ancient European and Oriental coins.*

I. L. Johnson
63, Sedley Close, Parkwood, Kent ME8 9QZ. (01634 261037) *P. L. English coins 1672–1967*

Robert Johnson Coin Co
PO Box 194, 15 Bury Place, London WC1A 2JN (020 7831 0305). *Mon-Fri 10.30-18.00, Sat 10.30-15.00. British and world coins.*

Ian Jull
PO Box 594, Harrow, Middx, HA2 7SG. (020 8429 3988 fax: 020 8248 1714). *British coins and medals.*

Jumbo Coins
22 Woodend Lane, Stalybridge, Cheshire SK15 2SR (0161 338 5741). *Fri-Sat 14.00-19.00. World coins, medals and tokens.*

KB Coins (BNTA)
50 Lingfield Road, Martins Wood, Stevenage, Herts SG1 5SL (01438 312661, fax 01438 311990). *09.00–18.00 by appointment only. L. Mainly British coins.*

Knightsbridge Coins (ANA, BNTA, IAPN)
43 Duke Street, St James's, London SW1Y 6DD (020 7930 8215/7597 Fax 020 7930 8214). *Mon-Fri 10.00–17.30. Quality coins of the world.*

Lancashire Coin & Medal Co
31 Adelaide Street, Fleetwood, Lancs FY7 6AD (01253 779308). *P. British coins and medals.*

Lennox Gallery Ltd
K12/13, 4 Davies Mews, London, W1Y 1AR. (020 7629 9119 fax 020 7629 9119). *Ancient coins.*

Peter Licence
31 Reigate Way, Wallington, Surrey SM6 8NU (020 8688 5297). *P. British and World coins.*

Lighthouse Publications (UK)
4 Beaufort Road, Reigate, Surrey RH2 9DJ (01737 244222 Fax 0737 24743). *L. Manufacturers and stockists of coin albums, cabinets and accessories.*

Lindner Publications Ltd
13 Fore Street, Hayle, Cornwall TR27 4DX (01736 751914 fax: 01736 751911, email lindneruk@cs.com). Mon–Fri 09.00–13.00. *L. Manufacturers of coin albums, cabinets and accessories.*

Jan Lis (BNTA)
Beaver Coin Room, 57 Philbeach Gardens, London SW5 9ED (020 7373 4553 fax 020 7373 4555). *By appointment only. European coins.*

Keith Lloyd
45 Bramblewood, The Beeches, Ipswich, Suffolk IP8 3RS (01473 603067). *P. L. Greek, Roman coins.*

Lockdale Coins
36 Upper Orwell Street, Ipswich. (01473 218588). *L.* (Shop open 9.30–4.30 Mon–Sat). *World coins, medals, banknotes and accessories.*

Stephen Lockett
59 Cedar Drive, Sutton at Hone, Kent DA4 9EW (01322 861 228). *British and world coins.*

Mike Longfield Detectors
83 Station Road, Balsall Common, nr Coventry, Warwickshire CV7 7FN (01676 533274). Mon–Sat 09.30-17.00. *Metal detectors.*

Richard M. Lubbock (ANA, BNTA, IAPN, IBNS)
PO Box 35732, London E14 7WB (020 7790 5115 fax 020 7790 5445). *World coins and medals.*

Don MacRae Coins
PO Box 233, Uxbridge, Middlesex UB9 4HY (01895 832625). *P. British and world coins.*

Mannin Collections Ltd
5 Castle Street, Peel, Isle of Man (01624 843897). Mon–Sat 10.00-17.00. Half-day Thu. *British and Isle of Man coins.*

I. Markovits
1-3 Cobbold Mews, London W12 9LB (020 8749 3000). *Enamelled coins.*

Marron Coins
7 Beacon Close, Sheffield, South Yorkshire S9 1AA (0114 2433500, website www.marroncoins.free-online.co.uk, email marronsca@aol.com). *P. English coins.*

C. J. Martin (Coins) Ltd (BNTA)
85 The Vale, Southgate, London N14 6AT (020 8882 1509, www.ancientart.co.uk). *P. L. Bi-monthly catalogue. Greek, Roman & English hammered coins.*

Clive Maxwell-Yates
21 Nicolas Road, Chorlton Manchester, M21 1LG (0161 881 7015). *P. L. World banknotes.*

M. G. Coins & Antiquities
12 Mansfield, High Wych, Herts cm21 0JT. (01279 721719).

Michael Coins
6 Hillgate Street, London W8 7SR (020 7727 1518). Mon–Fri 10.00-17.00. *World coins and banknotes.*

Midland Medals
12 Commerce House, Vicarage Lane, Water Orton, Birmingham B46 1RR (0121 7475983 fax 01564 784245). *P. Commemorative medals.*

David Miller Coins & Antiquities (ANA, BNTA)
PO Box 711, Hemel Hempstead, HP2 4UH (tel/fax 01442 251492). *Ancient and hammered English coins.*

Frank Milward (ANA, BNTA)
2 Ravensworth Road, Mortimer, Berkshire RG7 3UU (01734 322843). *P. European coins.*

Modern Coins & Stamps
24 Market Hall, Arndale Centre, Luton, Beds LU1 2TA (01582 412839). Mon–Sat 09.00-17.00. Half-day Wed. *Modern world coins.*

Graeme & Linda Monk (ANA, BNTA)
PO Box 201, Croydon, Surrey, CR9 7AQ (020 8656 4583 fax 020 8656 4583). *P. Fair organisers.*

Mike Morey
9 Elmtrees, Long Crendon, Bucks HP18 9DG. *P. L. British coins, halfcrowns to farthings.*

Peter Morris
1 Station Concourse, Bromley North Station, Bromley, BR1 1NN or PO Box 223, Bromley, BR1 4EQ (020 8313 3410 fax 020 8466 8502, website www.petermorris.co.uk, email info@petermorris.co.uk). Mon–Fri 10.00–18.00, Sat 0900-14.00 or by appointment. *L. British and world coins, proof sets and numismatic books.*

James Murphy
PO Box 122, Chorley, Lancashire PR7 2GE. *(01257 274 381). P. L. Ancient coins and antiquities.*

Colin Narbeth & Son Ltd (ANA, IBNS)
20 Cecil Court, Leicester Square, London WC2N 4HE (020 7379 6975 fax 01727 811 244, website http://www.colin-narbeth.com). Mon–Sat 10.30-17.00. *World banknotes.*

New Forest Leaves
Bisterne Close, Burley, Ringwood, Hants BH24 4BA (014253 3315). *Publishers of numismatic books.*

Peter Nichols
2 Norman Road, St Leonards on Sea, East Sussex TN37 6NH. (01424 436682, website www.coincabinets.com, email coincabinets@freezone.co.uk).

Wayne Nicholls
PO Box 44, Bilston, West Midlands. (01902 495735) *L. Choice English coins*

North Wales Coins Ltd (BNTA)
1b Penrhyn Road, Colwyn Bay, Clwyd (01492 533023/532129). Mon–Sat (closed Wed) 09.30–17.30. *British coins.*

Notability (IBNS)
'Mallards', Chirton, Devizes, Wilts SN10 3QX (01380 723961, website www.notability.org.uk, email huroper@netscapeonline.co.uk). *P. L. Banknotes of the world.*

NP Collectables
9 Main Street, Gedney Dyke, Spalding, Lincs PE12 0AJ (01406 365211Ireland (010 35322 29385). *P. L. English Hammered and Milled coins.*

The Numismery
89b Oxford Road, Reading, Berks RG1 7UZ (01734 582145). Mon–Sat 11.00–20.30. *World coins.*

Glenn S. Ogden
Duncraig, Canada Hill, Ogwell, Newton Abbot, Devon TQ12 6AF. (01626 331663) *P. L. English milled.*

John Ogden Coins
Hodge Clough Cottage, Moorside, Oldham OL1 4JW (0161 678 0709) *P. L. Ancient and hammered coins.*

Michael O'Grady (IBNS)
PO Box 307, Pinner, Middlesex HA5 4XT (020 8428 4002). *P. British and world paper money.*

Colin James O'Keefe
5 Pettits Place, Dagenham, Essex RM10 8NL. *P. British and European coins.*

Don Oliver Gold Coins
The Coin Gallery, Stanford House, 23 Market Street, Stourbridge, West Midlands DY8 1AB (01384 373899). Mon-Fri 10.00–17.00, Sat 10.00-13.00 (closed Thu). *Gold coins of the world.*

Ongar Coins
14 Longfields, Marden Ash, Ongar, Essex IG7 6DS. *P.World coins.*

Tim Owen Coins
63 Allerton Grange Rise, Leeds 17, West Yorkshire (0113 2688015). *P. L. Quality hammered coins.*

Oxford Coins
25, Weldon Road, New Marston, Oxford OX3 0HP (01865 726939). *British coins.*

P&D Medallions
PO Box 269, Berkhampstead, Herts HP4 3FT. (01442 865127, email P&D@medallions.freeserve.co.uk). *Historical and Commemorative medals of the world. P.*

Penrith Coin & Stamp Centre
37 King Street, Penrith, Cumbria CA11 7AY (01768 64185). Mon-Sat 09.00–17.30. *World coins.*

Pentland Coins (IBNS)
Pentland House, 92 High Street, Wick, Caithness KW14 L5. *P. British and world coins and world banknotes.*

Phil Phipps
PO Box 31, Emsworth, Hants PO10 7WE (tel/fax 01243 376086, email philip@worldcurrency.cc). *P. L. World and German banknotes.*

David C. Pinder
20 Princess Road West, Leicester LE1 6TP (0116 2702439). *P. Greek, Roman and Byzantine coins.*

Pobjoy Mint Ltd (ANA)
Millennium House, Kingswood Park, Bonsor Drive, Kingswood, Surrey KT20 6AY (01737 818181 fax 01737 818199). Mon-Fri 09.00–17.00. *Europe's largest private mint. New issues.*

S. R. Porter (BNTA)
18 Trinity Road, Headington Quarry, Oxford OX3 8LQ (01865 766851). *P. L. Ancient and British coins, some jewellery, tokens, banknotes and accessories.*

David Pratchett
Trafalgar Square Collectors Centre, 7 Whitcombe Street, London WC2H 7HA. (020 7930 1979, fax 020 7930 1152, website www.coinsonline.co.uk, email info@coinsonline.co.uk). Mon-Fri 10.00–7.30. *Specialist in gold and silverworld coins.*

George Rankin Coin Co Ltd (ANA, BNTA)
325 Bethnal Green Road, London E2 6AH (020 7729 1280 fax 020 7729 5023). Mon-Sat 10.00-18.00 (half-day Thu). *World coins.*

Mark Rasmussen
PO Box 42, Betchworth RH3 7YR (01737 84100, email mark.rasmussen@btinternet.com). *Hammered and milled coins. L*

Mark T. Ray (formerly MTR Coins)
22a Kingsnorth Close, Newark, Notts NG24 1PS. (01636 703152). *P. British coins.* 2379). Mon-Sat

Rhyl Coin & Stamp Centre
12 Sussex Street, Rhyl, Clwyd (01745 338112). Mon-Sat 10.00-17.30. *World coins.*

Chris Rigby
PO Box 181, Worcester WR1 1YE (01905 28028). *P. L. Modern British coins.*

Roderick Richardson
The Old Granary Antiques Centre, King's Staithe Lane, King's Lynn, Norfolk. (01553 670833) *L. English, Hammered and early milled coins.*

F. J. Rist
PO Box 4, Ibstock, Leics LE67 6ZJ (01530 264278). *P. L. Ancient and medieval coins, British coins and antiquities.*

Ian Robinson
PO Box 929, Burgess Hill, West Sussex RH15 9FN (01444 242215, website www.iamcoins.co.uk, email ian@iamcoins.co.uk). *P. L. Quality English milled coins.*

S. J. Rood & Co Ltd
52–53 Burlington Arcade, London W1V 9AE (0171 493 0739). Mon-Sat 09.30-17.00. *World gold coins.*

Bill Rosedale
17 Priory Close, Abbots Park, Chester CH1 4BX (01244 382554, email bill@banknotes40freeserve.com) *P. L. World paper money*

Royal Mint Coin Club
PO Box 500, Cardiff CF1 1YY (01443 623456). *P. New issues struck by the Royal Mint.*

Colin de Rouffignac (BNTA)
57, Wigan Lane, Wigan, Lancs WN1 2LF (01942 237927) *P. English and Scottish hammered.*

Chris A. Rudd (IAPN)
PO Box 222, Aylsham, Norfolk, NR11 6TY (01263 735007 fax 01263 731777, website www.celticcoins.com). *P. L. Celtic coins.*

Colin Rumney (BNTA)
26 Caer Felin, Llanrheadr, Denbigh, Clwyd LL16 4PR (074 578621). *All world including ancients.*

R & J Coins
21b Alexandra Street, Southend-on-Sea, Essex SS1 1DA (01702 345995). Mon-Sat 10.00–16.00 (closed Wed). *World coins.*

R & L Coins (BNTA)
521 Lytham Road, Blackpool, Lancs FY4 1RJ (01253 43081). Mon-Sat 09.00–17.00 by appointment only. *British, Commonwealth and European coins.*

Safe Albums (UK) Ltd
16 Falcon Business Park, 38 Ivanhoe Road, Finchampstead, Berkshire RG40 4QQ. (0118 932 8976 fax 0118 932 8612).

Saltford Coins
Harcourt, Bath Road, Saltford, Bristol, Avon BS31 3DQ (01225 873512). *P. British, Commonwealth and world coins.*

I. S. Sandiford & Co Ltd
3 Marriotts Court, Brown Street, Manchester M2 1EA (0161 834 9346). Mon-Sat 09.00-16.30. *British and world coins.*

Satin
PO Box 63, Stockport, Cheshire SK4 5BU. (07940 393583 answer machine)

Schwer Coins (ANA, BNTA)
6 South Hill, Felixstowe, Suffolk, IP11 8AA (01394 278580 fax 0394 271348). *P. World coins.*

David Seaman
160 Holloway Road, London N7. (020 7607 5607, email davidseamancoins@lineone.net). *P. L. Hammered, Milled, Maundy.*

Patrick Semmens
3 Hospital Road, Half Key, Malvern, Worcs WR14 1UZ (0886 33123). *P. European and British coins.*

Mark Senior
553 Falmer Road, Woodingdean, Brighton, Sussex
(01273 309359). By appointment only. *P. L.
Saxon, Norman and English hammered coins.*

S. E. Sewell
PO Box 104, Ipswich, Suffolk IP5 7QL (01473 626
950). *Mainly British milled coins.*

T. Sexton (IBNS)
19 Great Western Avenue, Bridgend, Mid Glamor
gan CF31 1NN (01656 4861). *P. World coins.*

R. D. Shah (BNTA)
9 Lansdowne Grove, Neasden, London NW10 1LP
(020 8452 5160). *Ancient India and Indian states.*

Robert Sharman Numismatist (ANA)
36 Dairsie Road, Eltham, London SE9 1XH (020
8850 6450). *P. British coins.*

Shepshed Coins & Jewellery
24 Charnwood Road, Shepshed, Leics LE12 9QF
(01509 502511). Mon, Wed-Sat 09.15-16.30. *British
coins.*

Simmons Gallery (ANA, BNTA, IBNS)
53 Lamb's Conduit Street, London WC1N 3NB
(020 7831 2080 fax 020 7831 2090, website
www.simmonsgallery.co.uk, email
info@simmonsgallery.co.uk). *Organisers of the
London Coin Fair, Holiday Inn, Bloomsbury,
London W1. L. Coins, tokens and medals.*

Raymond J. Sleet (BNTA)
11 Seagull Close, Kempshott, Basingstoke, Hants
RG22 5QR (01256 53256 fax 01256 63525) *General
world coins and tokens.*

E. Smith (ANA, IBNS)
PO Box 348, Lincoln LN6 0TX (01522 684681 fax
01522 689528). *P. Organiser of the Morley, Leeds,
monthly coin fair. World coins and paper money.*

J. Smith (BNTA)
47 The Shambles, York YO1 2LX (01904 654769).
Mon-Sat 09.30–17.00. *World coins.*

Jim Smythe
PO Box 6970, Birmingham B23 7WD (e-mail
Jimdens@aol.com). *P. L. 19th/20th century British
and world coins.*

S & B Coins
Grass Walk, Wood Lane, South Heath, Great
Missenden, Bucks HP16 0RB (01494 862161). *P. L.
British coins and medallions.*

Southern Coins
51 Beach Road, Selsey, West Sussex PO20 0LT
(01243 606698). *P. British and world coins.*

Souvereign State Coins
P.O. Box 304, Oldham OL2 6HY. ((07759 521664
Mobile). *Quality English hammered and milled coins.
Also ancient.*

George Sowden
Coins Galore, The Lizard, nr Helston, Cornwall
TR12 7NU (01326 290300). *P. World coins.*

Spink & Son Ltd (ANA, BNTA, IAPN, IBNS)
69 Southampton Row, Bloomsbury, London.
WC1B 4ET (020 7563 2820, fax 020 7563 4066,
website www.spink-online.com, email
info@spinkandson.com). *Ancient to modern world
coins, orders, medals and decorations, banknotes and
numismatic books*

SPM Jewellers (BNTA)
112 East Street, Southampton, Hants SO14 3HD
(023 80 223255/020 80 227923, fax 023 80 335634,
wwbsite www.spmgoldcoins.co.uk, email
user@spm.in2home.co.uk).
Tue-Sat 09.15–17.00, Sat 09.15–16.00. *World coins
and medals.*

Stamp & Collectors Centre
404 York Town Road, College Town, Camberley,
Surrey GU15 4PR (01276 32587 fax 01276 32505).
Mon, Tue, Thu, Sat 09.00–17.00, Wed, Fri 09.00–
1900. *World coins and medals.*

St Edmunds Coins & Banknotes
PO Box 118, Bury St Edmunds IP33 2NE. (01284
761894)

Sterling Coins & Medals
2 Somerset Road, Boscombe, Bournemouth, Dorset
BH7 6JH (01202 423881). Mon-Sat 09.30–16.30
(closed Wed). *World coins and medals.*

Strawbridge
Tanglewood, Ivy Tree Hill, Stokeinteignhead,
Newton Abbott, Devon TQ12 4QH (01626 873783,
emailjim@strawbridge.co.uk).
P. L. Coins, tokens, medals, banknotes.

Studio Coins (ANA, BNTA)
16 Kilham Lane, Winchester, Hants SO22 5PT
(01962 853156 fax 01962 624246). *P. English coins.*

Surena Numismatics (BNTA)
PO Box 2194, London NW8 6QQ (0831 220010). *P.
Parthian, Sassanian, Islamic coins.*

The Collector
PO Box 335, Tiptree, Colchester, Essex CO5 9WP
(01376 572755 fax 01376 573883, email
collector@btinternet.com). *Collectable items.*

Stuart J. Timmins
Smallwood Lodge Bookshop, Newport, Salop
(01952 813232). Mon-Sat 09.30–17.00. *Numismatic
literature.*

R. Tims
39 Villiers Road, Watford, Herts WD1 4AL. *P. L.
Uncirculated world banknotes.*

**Trafalgar Square Collectors' Centre (ANA, BNTA,
LM, OMRS)**
7 Whitcomb Street, Trafalgar Square, London
WC2H 7HA (020 7930 1979). Mon-Fri 10.00–17.30.
*World coins and commemorative medals. War medals
and decorations.*

D. A. Travis
8 Cookridge Drive, Leeds LS16 7LT. *P. L. US
coins.*

Michael Trenerry Ltd (BNTA)
PO Box 55, Truro, Cornwall TR1 2YQ (01872
277977 fax 01872 225565). By appointment only. *L.
Roman, Celtic and English hammered coins, trade
tokens.*

Vera Trinder Ltd
38 Bedford Street, Strand, London WC2E 9EU (020
7836 2365/6). Mon-Fri 08.30-17.30. *L. Coin
catalogues and books, albums, envelopes, cases etc*

Robert Tye
Poll Toran, Loch Eynort, South Uist PA81 5SJ. *P.
European and Oriental hammered coins.*

Valda Coins
80 Aberfan Road, Aberfan, Mid Glamorgan CF48
4QJ. (01443 690452). *P. L.*

Vale (ADA BNTA)
21 Tranquil Vale, Blackheath, London SE3 0BU
(020 8852 9817). Mon-Sat 10.00–17.30 (closed Thu).
British coins and medals.

Tony Vaughan Collectables
PO Box 364, Wolverhampton, WV3 9PW (01902
27351). *P. L. World coins and medals.*

Victory Coins
184 Chichester Road, North End, Portsmouth,
Hants PO2 0AX (01705 751908/663450). Mon-Sat
09.15–17.30. *British and world coins.*

Viking Metal Detectors
1 angela Street, Mill Hill, Blacburn, Lancashire BB2 4DJ (01254 55887 fax 01254 676901, email viking@metaldetectors.co.uk)). *Metal detectors and accessories*

Mark J. Vincenzi (BNTA)
Rylands, Earls Colne, Essex. CO6 2LE (01787 222555). *P. Greek, Roman, Hammered.*

Vista World Banknotes
5 Greenfields Way, Burley-in-Wharfedale, Ilkley, W. Yorks LS29 7RB. (Email vistabanknotes@barclays.net).

Mike Vosper
PO Box 32, Hockwold, Brandon IP26 4HX (01842 828292, website www.vosper4coins.co.uk, email mikevosper@vosper4coins.co.uk).

B. M. & S. A. Weeks
PO Box 1447, Salisbury, Wilts SP5 2YG (01725 510311). *L. British coins, world crowns and medals.*

John Welsh
PO Box 150, Burton-on-Trent, Staffs DE13 7LB (01543 73073 fax 0543 473234). *P. L. British coins.*

Pam West (IBNS)
PO Box 257, Sutton, Surrey SM3 9WW (020 8641 3224, website west-banknotes.co.uk, email pamwestbritnotes@compuserve.com). *P. L. English banknotes.*

West Cornwall Stamp Centre
13 Fore Street, Hayle, Cornwall TR27 4DX (01736 751910 fax: 01736 751911. *L. Coin Accessories.*

West Essex Coin Investments (BNTA, IBNS)
Croft Cottage, Station Road, Alderholt, Fordingbridge, Hants SP6 3AZ (01425 656 459). *British and World coins and paper money.*

R & J White (IBNS)
29 Shortacre, Basildon, Essex SS14 2LR (01268 522923). *P. L. Banknotes and world ephemera.*

Whites Electronics (UK) Ltd
35 Harbour Road, Inverness IV1 1UA (01463 223456 , email sales@whelects.demon.co.uk) *Metal detectors*

Whitmore (BNTA)
Teynham Lodge, Chase Road, Upper Colwall, Malvern, Worcs WR13 6DT (01684 40651). *P. World coins, tokens and medals.*

J. L. Williams
502 Clive Court, Maida Vale, London W9 1SG (020 7286 3461). *P. L. Wholesaler—dealers only.*

World Coins
35–36 Broad Street, Canterbury, Kent CT1 2LR (01227 68887). Mon-Sat 09.30–17.30 (half-day Thu). *World coins.*

World Treasure Books
PO Box 5, Newport, Isle of Wight PO30 5QE (01983 740712). *L. Coins, books, metal detectors*

Barry Wright,
54 Dooley Drive, Bootle, Merseyside. L3O 8RT. *P. L. World banknotes.*

I. S. Wright (Australia Numismatic Co)
208 Sturt Street, Ballarat, Vic. Australia 3350 (0061 3 5332 3856 fax 0061 3 5331 6426, email ausnumis@netconnect.comau. *P. Coins, banknotes, medallions, tokens.*

B. N. Yarwood (ANA)
Yarwood Hall, Luttongate Road, Sutton St Edmund, Spalding, Lincs PE12 0LH. *P. British and US coins.*

Banks, Mints and Numismatic
Bureaux
of the world

Many national banks and mints operate numismatic bureaux and sales agencies from which coins, medals and other numismatic products may be obtained direct. The conditions under which purchases may be made vary considerably. In many cases at the present time bureaux will accept orders from overseas customers quoting their credit card number and its expiry date; but in others payment can only be made by certified bank cheque, or international money order, or by girobank. Cash is seldom, if ever, acceptable. It is best to write in the first instance to enquire about methods of payment.

A

National Mint, Baghe Arg, Kabul, Afghanistan

Bank Mille Afghan, Kabul, Afghanistan

Banque d'Algerie, Sucursale d'Alger, 8 Boulevard Carnot, Alger, Algeria

Banco de Angola, Luanda, Daroal, Angola

Casa de Moneda de la Nacion, Avenida Antartica, Buenos Aires, BA, Argentina

Royal Australian Mint, Department of the Treasury, Canberra, ACT, Australia

GoldCorp Australia, Perth Mint Buildings, GPO Box M924, Perth, Western Australia 6001

Oesterreichsiches Hauptmunzamt, Am Heumarkt 1, A-1031 Wien, Postfach 225, Austria

Oesterreichische Nationalbank, A-1090 Wien, Otto Wagner-platz 3, Austria

B

Treasury Department, PO Box 557, Nassau, Bahamas (*coins*)

Ministry of Finance, PO Box 300, Nassau, Bahamas (*banknotes*)

Bank of Bahrain, PO Box 106, Manama, Bahrain

Eastern Bank, PO Box 29, Manama, Bahrain

Monnaie Royale de Belgique, Avenue de Pacheco 32, B-1000 Bruxelles, Belgium

Banque Nationale de Belgique SA, Caisse Centrale, Bruxelles, Belgium

Banque de Bruxelles SA, 2 Rue de la Regence, Bruxelles 1, Belgium

Casa de la Moneda, Potosi, Bolivia

Banco Central de Bolivia, La Paz, Bolivia

Casa da Moeda, Praca da Republica 173, Rio de Janeiro, Brazil

Hemus FTO, 7 Vasil Levski Street, Sofia C-1, Bulgaria

Banque de la Republique, Bujumbura, Burundi

C

Banque Centrale, Douala, Boite Postale 5.445, Cameroun

Royal Canadian Mint, 320 Sussex Drive, Ottawa 2, Ontario, Canada K1A 0G8

Casa de Moneda, Quinta Normal, Santiago, Chile

Casa de Moneda, Calle 11 no 4-93, Bogota, Colombia

Numismatic Section, The Treasury, Avarua, Rarotónga, Cook Islands

Banco Centrale de Costa Rica, Departamento de Contabilidad, San Jose, Costa Rica, CA

Central Bank of Cyprus, PO Box 1087, Nicosia, Cyprus

Artia, Ve Smekach 30, PO Box 790, Praha 1, Czech Republic

D

Den Kongelige Mønt, Amager Boulevard 115, København S, Denmark

Danmarks Nationalbank, Holmens Kanal 17, 1060 København K, Denmark

Banco Central de Santo Domingo, Santo Domingo, Dominican Republic

E

Banco Central, Quito, Ecuador

Mint House, Abbassia, Cairo, Egyptian Arab Republic

Exchange Control Department, National Bank of Egypt, Cairo, Egyptian Arab Republic

Banco Central de la Republica, Santa Isabel, Equatorial Guinea

Commercial Bank of Ethiopia, Foreign Branch, PO Box 255, Addis Ababa, Ethiopia

F

Currency Board, Victoria Parade, Suva, Fiji

Suomen Rahapaja, Katajanokanlaituri 3, Helsinki 16, Finland

Suomen Pankki, PO Box 10160, Helsinki 10, Finland

Hotel de Monnaie, 11 Quai de Conti, 75-Paris 6e, France

G

Banque Centrale Libreville, Boite Postale 112, Gabon

Verkaufstelle fur Sammlermunzen, D-638 Bad Homburg vdH, Bahnhofstrasse 16–18, Germany

Staatliche Munze Karlsruhe, Stephanienstrasse 28a, 75 Karlsruhe, Germany

Staatliche Munze Cannstatt, Taubenheimerstrasse 77, 7 Stuttgart-Bad, Germany

Bayerisches Hauptmunzamt, Hofgraben 4, 8 Munich, Germany

Hamburgische Munze, Norderstrasse 66, 2 Hamburg 1, Germany

Bank of Ghana, PO Box 2674, Accra, Ghana

Pobjoy Mint, Mint House, 92 Oldfields Road, Sutton, Surrey SM1 2NW

Royal Mint, Llantrisant, Mid Glamorgan, Wales, CF7 8YT

Royal Mint Coin Club, PO Box 500, Cardiff, CF1 1HA

Bank of Greece, Treasury Department, Cash, Delivery & Despatch Division, PO Box 105, Athens, Greece

Casa Nacional de Moneda, 6a Calle 4-28, Zona 1, Ciudad Guatemala, Republica de Guatemala CA

States Treasury, St Peter Port, Guernsey, Channel Islands

Bank of Guyana, PO Box 658, Georgetown, Guyana

H

Banque Nationale de la Republique d'Haiti, Rue Americaine et Rue Fereu, Port-au-Prince, Haiti

Banco Central de Honduras, Tegucigalpa DC, Honduras CA

State Mint, Ulloi utca 102, Budapest VIII, Hungary

Artex, PO Box 167, Budapest 62, Hungary

Magyar Nemzeti Bank, Board of Exchange, Budapest 54, Hungary

I

Sedlabanki Islands, Reykjavik, Iceland

Indian Government Mint, Bombay 1, India

Arthie Vasa, Keabajoran Baru, Djakarta, Indonesia

Perum Peruri, Djakarta, Indonesia

National Mint, Tehran, Iran

Bank Markazi Iran, Tehran, IranCentral Bank of Iraq, PO Box 64, Baghdad, Iraq

Central Bank of Ireland, Dublin 2, Republic of Ireland

The Treasury, Government Buildings, Prospect Hill, Douglas, Isle of Man

Israel Stamp and Coin Gallery, 4 Maze Street, Tel Aviv, Israel

Istituto Poligraphico e Zecca dello Stato, Via Principe Umberto, Roma, Italy

J

Decimal Currency Board, PO Box 8000, Kingston, Jamaica

Mint Bureau, 1 Shinkawasakicho, Kita-ku, Osaka 530, Japan

Numismatic Section, Treasury Department, St Helier, Jersey

Central Bank of Jordan, Amman, Jordan

Banque Nationale du Liban, Rue Masraf Loubnan, Beirut, Lebanon

K

Central Bank, PO Box 526, Kuwait

L

Bank of Lithuania, Cash Department, Gedimino av. 6, 2001 Vilius, Lithuania

Caisse Generale de l'Etat, 5 Rue Goethe, Luxembourg-Ville, Grande Duche de Luxembourg

M

Institut d'Emission Malgache, Boite Postale 205, Tananarive, Madagascar

Central Bank of Malta, Valletta 1, Malta

Casa de Moneda, Calle del Apartado no 13, Mexico 1, DF, Mexico

Le Tresorier General des Finances, Monte Carlo, Principaute de Monaco

Banque de l'Etat du Maroc, Rabat, Morocco

Banco Nacional Ultramarino, Maputo, Republica de Mocambique

British Bank of the Middle East, Muscat

N

Royal Mint, Dharahara, Katmandu, Nepal

Nepal Rastra Bank, Katmandu, Nepal

Rijks Munt, Leidseweg 90, Utrecht, Netherlands

Hollandsche Bank-Unie NV, Willemstad, Breedestraat 1, Curacao, Netherlands Antilles

Central Bank of Curacao, Willemstad, Curacao, Netherlands Antilles

The Treasury, Private Bag, Lambton Quay, Wellington, New Zealand

Banco de Nicaragua, Departamento de Emison, La Tresoria, Apartada 2252, Managua, Nicaragua

Nigerian Security Printing and Minting Corporation, Ahmadu Bello Road, Victoria Island, Lagos, Nigeria

Central Bank of Nigeria, Tinubu Square LB, Lagos, Nigeria

Norges Bank, Oslo, Norway

Den Kongelige Mynt, Hyttegaten, Konigsberg, Norway

P

Pakistan State Mint, Baghban Pura, Lahore 9, Pakistan

National Development Bank, Asuncion, Paraguay

Casa Nacional de Moneda, Calle Junin 791, Lima, Peru

Central Bank of the Philippines, Manila, Philippines

Bank Handlowy w Warszawie, Ul. Romuald Traugutta 7, Warsaw, Poland

Desa Foreign Trade Department, Al. Jerozolimskie 2, Warszawa, Poland

Casa da Moeda, Avenida Dr Antonio Jose de Almeida, Lisbon 1, Portugal

R

Cartimex, 14-18 Aristide Briand St, PO Box 134-135, Bucharest, Roumania

Bank of Foreign Trade, Commercial Department, Moscow K 16, Neglinnaja 12, Russian Federation

Banque Nationale du Rwanda, Boite Postale 351, Kigali, Republique Rwandaise

S

Numismatic Section, Box 194, GPO, Apia, Samoa

Azienda Autonoma di Stato Filatelica-Numismatica, Casalla Postale 1, 47031 Repubblica di San Marino

Banque Internationale pour le Commerce, 2 Avenue Roume, Dakar, Senegal

Bank of Yugoslavia, PO Box 1010, Belgrade, Serbia

The Treasury, PO Box 59, Victoria, Seychelles

Bank of Sierra Leone, PO Box 30, Freetown, Sierra Leone

The Singapore Mint, 249 Jalan Boon Lay, Jurong, Singapore

South African Mint, PO Box 464, Pretoria, South Africa

Government Printing Agency, 93 Bukchang Dong, Chungku, Seoul, Republic of South Korea

Fabrica Nacional de Moneda y Timbre, Jorge Juan 106, Madrid 9, Spain

Bank of Sri Lanka, PO Box 241, Colombo, Sri Lanka

Hong Kong and Shanghai Banking Corporation, PO Box 73, Colombo 1, Sri Lanka

Sudan Mint, PO Box 43, Khartoum, Sudan

Bank of Sudan, PO Box 313, Khartoum, Sudan

Bank of Paramaribo, Paramaribo, Suriname

Kungelige Mynt och Justeringsverket, Box 22055, Stockholm 22, Sweden

Eidgenossische Staatskasse, Bundesgasse 14, CH-3003, Berne, Switzerland

Central Bank of Syria, Damascus, Syrian Arab Republic

T

Central Mint of China, 44 Chiu Chuan Street, Taipei, Taiwan, ROC

Royal Thai Mint, 4 Chao Fah Road, Bangkok, Thailand

Numismatic Section, The Treasury, Nuku'alofa, Tonga

Central Bank of Trinidad and Tobago, PO Box 1250, Port of Spain, Trinidad

Banque Centrale de Tunisie, Tunis, Tunisia

State Mint, Maliye Bakanligi Darphane Mudurlugu, Istanbul, Turkey

U

Bank of Uganda, PO Box 7120, Kampala, Uganda

Numismatic Service, US Assay Office, 350 Duboce Avenue, San Francisco, CA, 94102, USA

Office of the Director of the Mint, Treasury Department, Washington, DC, 20220, USA

Philadelphia Mint, 16th and Spring Garden Streets, Philadelphia, PA, 19130, USA

Franklin Mint, Franklin Center, Pennsylvania, 19063, USA

Banco Central del Uruguay, Cerrito 351, Montevideo, RO del Uruguay

V

Ufficio Numismatico, Governatorato dello Stato della Citta de Vaticano, Italy

Banco Central de Venezuela, Caracas, Venezuela

Y

Yemen Bank, Sana'a, Yemen.

Z

Bank of Zambia, PO Box 80, Lusaka, Zambia

Chief Cashier, Reserve Bank, PO Box 1283, Harare, Zimbabwe

Numismatics and
The Law

Counterfeit Currency

A counterfeit is a forgery or imitation of a coin or banknote produced with the intention of defrauding the revenue of the State or deceiving members of the public. By the Coinage Offences Act (1861) it was a felony to counterfeit gold or silver coins. Lesser offences included the gilding of farthings and sixpences to pass them off as half-sovereigns, the possession of moulds, machines or tools clandestinely removed from the Royal Mint, the impairment or diminution of gold or silver coins by filing or clipping (or even the possession of such filings and clippings).

The Coinage Act of 1870 made provision for the counterfeiting of base-metal coins, or the stamping of letters or words on coins of any kind, or the forging of colonial coinage. The most celebrated prosecution under this Act occurred in 1930 when Martin Coles Harman was convicted and fined £5 for issuing bronze coins resembling the British penny and halfpenny for the island of Lundy of which he was then the proprietor. Interestingly, no attempt was made to prosecute the Birmingham Mint which actually struck the coins (prudently omitting the H mintmark).

The making of medals or coins resembling current coin became a misdemeanour under the Counterfeit Medal Act of 1883. This Act is invoked from time to time against manufacturers or distributors of medallic pieces or coin jewellery. Such pieces, often struck in 9 carat gold, are deemed to infringe the Act if, for example, they have a figure even vaguely resembling St George and the Dragon on one side. The use of the royal effigy, however, without due authorisation, is regarded as a misdemeanour punishable by an unlimited fine and the confiscation of tools, dies and instruments. At the present time it is a serious offence to make a counterfeit of a currency note or coin with the intention of passing it off or tendering it as genuine. This offence carries a maximum penalty of ten years' imprisonment or an unlimited fine, or both. Making a counterfeit of a currency note or coin without lawful authority incurs a penalty up to two years' imprisonment or an unlimited fine, or both.

Passing or tendering as genuine anything which is known or believed to be a counterfeit of a currency note or coin renders the criminal on conviction to a term of ten years' imprisonment or an unlimited fine, or both. The mere possession of any forged note or coin is itself a criminal offence. Possessing counterfeits without authority or permission so to do, and doing so knowingly, renders the possessor liable to two years' imprisonment or an unlimited fine, or both. The Act also stipulates that the reproduction of a current banknote—of the Bank of England or of the Scottish and Northern Irish banks is a serious offence. This clause covers even such apparently innocent acts as making a photocopy (whether in black and white or full colour) of a current banknote, the photography of such a note or the illustration of such a note in any book, magazine or newspaper. Strict regulations are laid down concerning the legitimate illustration of notes, whether current or not, in books and periodicals; such illustrations must be either greatly reduced or enlarged *and* must bear a prominent defacement, such as SPECIMEN or CANCELLED. It is also a serious offence to utilise a reproduction of a current British banknote in any medium. Theoretically this includes such things as tea-towels, T-shirts, mugs, plates and other souvenirs in glass or ceramics, but in practice the law seems to turn a blind eye to such practices. Imitations and parodies of notes and coins are also regarded as infringements of the law, but in these instances prosecution of the offender seldom proceeds; a warning is generally regarded as sufficient, provided that the offending article or articles are withdrawn and suppressed.

The advent of high-definition colour photocopying in recent years has brought the offence of reproduction into prominence once more. The regulations have been tightened considerably and there have been several cases of successful prosecution. In each case, however, the intent deliberately to deceive the public by uttering a colour photocopy as a genuine note was proved. Technically the offence takes places as soon as the photocopy is made, for whatever purpose, but as a rule only those cases in which an element of fraudulent deception subsequently arose are pursued with the full rigour of the law. The law is quite clear, however, and it is a criminal offence to make a photocopy or photograph of any current British note unless permission to do so has been obtained from the Treasury. The maximum penalty on conviction is an unlimited fine.

The note-issuing banks have, of course, taken steps in recent years to incorporate further security devices into their notes, notably the use of latent images and underprints in colours which are difficult, if not impossible to photocopy accurately. At the same time, the adoption of metal strips and more complex watermark devices has theoretically made the task of the forger much more difficult. If, by some unlucky chance, someone passes a dud note on to you, you must make no attempt to pass it in turn. To do so renders you liable to prosecution for uttering a forgery. Forged notes must be handed over to the police as soon as possible. If you receive a forged note in payment for goods or services you are entitled to claim its face value from the person who gave it to you. Even if the person giving you the note did not realise that it was counterfeit, it is assumed in law that he or she represented to you that the note was worth its face value at the time the note was passed. If the tenderer knew that the note was forged, he can be prosecuted; but at the end of the day he is still liable to you for the fraud and can be sued in the civil courts for the recovery of the sum involved. If, on the other hand, you received the money as a gift, you have no legal claim against the person who gave it to you. If you pay someone with a counterfeit note or coin unknowingly, you have committed no offence, but you must pay again. The degree of culpability is often difficult to prove or disprove, but it is unlikely that a prosecution would be initiated on the basis of a single note or coin.

It is also a serious offence to manufacture blanks, discs or washers which are intended to defraud the proprietors of vending machines, or to possess tools and equipment for the dishonest manufacture or alteration of such blanks for this purpose. Under the Gold and Silver Export Control Act (1920) melting down gold or silver coins to extract their precious metal content is an offence punishable by a fine of £100 or two years' imprisonment, or both.

Legal Tender

The dictionary defines this as currency which a creditor is bound by law to accept as payment of a money debt. Debts and purchases must be paid for in cash of legal tender unless the creditor or seller is willing to accept payment in another form, such as a postal order, money order, cheque or, nowadays, credit card. Bank of England notes of any denomination are legal tender in England and Wales. Formerly Bank of England pound notes (but no other) were legal tender in Scotland. Technically, since the demise of the pound note, no Bank of England notes are legal tender in Scotland, although in practice they circulate freely north of the Border. Even more surprisingly, Scottish banknotes are not legal tender anywhere, not even in Scotland! The subtle difference is reflected in the actual wording of the promise on English and Scottish banknotes. Thus English notes are inscribed "*I promise to pay the bearer on demand the sum of . . .*" without stipulating any specific place, the promise being made by the Chief Cashier. Scottish notes, on the other hand, have the promise in the third person. It is the bank itself which makes the promise "*to pay the bearer on demand . . . pounds sterling at their head office here in Edinburgh, by order of the Board*". In practice, however, Scottish banknotes are accepted without question, not only throughout Scotland but also in parts of England, and are generally accepted in London, although there is no obligation on the part of a creditor so to do.

Apart from gold coins, the base-metal pound coin is legal tender for payment of any amounts. So, too, presumably, are the various two-pound and five-pound base-metal coins of recent years, even though they have been struck as commemoratives and not intended for general circulation in the ordinary sense. Smaller denominations are only legal tender up to a maximum value in each case. In the case of 50p coins, 25p crowns and 20p coins, they may be used alone, or in combination with each other, in payment of amounts up to £10. 10p and 5p coins, alone or in combination, may be used for sums up to £5. Bronze 1p and 2p coins, however, can only be used for payment of amounts up to 20p. In practice, of course, you can probably get away with making payment in larger quantities (within reason!) although strictly speaking there is no obligation on the part of your creditor to accept them.

An Offence to Possess Legal Tender Coins

From the foregoing it will be seen that gold coins are, and always have been, legal tender. Since 1817 the legal tender gold coin of the United Kingdom has been the sovereign (with its sub-division and multiples). Yet there have been times when actual possession of these legal tender coins has been, *per se*, an illegal act. The first attempt to regulate the movement and possession of gold coins arose in 1947 with the passage of the Exchange Control Act which made it illegal to buy, borrow, lend or sell any gold or foreign currency, unless authorised to deal in gold. Moreover it was stipulated that *"any person possessing gold should offer it for sale to an authorised dealer at a price not exceeding the authorised price, unless the Treasury consented to this retention of the gold"*.

The serious implications of this Act were mitigated in the case of numismatists by the Exchange Control (Collectors' Pieces Exemption) Order 1947, which allowed collectors to hold on to *"any gold coin which was minted in 1816 or earlier, and any gold coin which was minted after 1816 and which has a numismatic value greater than the value of the gold content which would have been received if the coin had been sold to an authorised (bullion) dealer"*. In effect this meant that numismatists and coin dealers were not hindered from buying and selling gold coins as long as the coins were in collectable condition and possessed numismatic interest. This loophole was brazenly breached in the 1960s and led to the Exchange Control (Gold Coins Exemption) Order of 1966 which aimed to prevent the loss of currency reserves caused by the import of gold coins from abroad, and to eliminate the hoarding of gold by speculators. By the terms of this Order no one was permitted to hold more than four gold coins minted after 1837 unless they had received express permission from the Treasury. The maximum was set at four coins so that people who had one or two sovereigns as mementoes could keep them without breaking the law. Numismatists who possessed more than four post-1837 gold coins on April 27, 1966 had to apply to the Treasury for permission to retain them. To do so they had to prove that they were *bona fide* collectors by completing form GC 1, providing a detailed list of the coins in their possession—not only in gold, but also in silver (pre-1816, 1816–1919 and post-1919) and base metals (before and after 1860). Several individuals were successfully prosecuted under this draconian legislation and their holdings of gold sovereigns confiscated, although no one was imprisoned or heavily fined as the legislation provided. The 1966 order was rescinded in 1970, re-imposed in a modified form in 1975, and finally revoked in 1979. Since that date numismatists and speculators alike have been free to collect (or hoard) gold to their hearts' content.

Value Added Tax

This is a matter which primarily concerns dealers, but it also applies to those who dabble in coins on a part-time basis, and has implications for collectors at all levels. Briefly, anyone conducting a business, or in self-employment, who has a turnover in excess of £43,000 per annum, must register with HM Customs and Excise for the collection and payment of Value Added Tax. Anyone whose turnover is less than £43,000 is exempt from the obligation to register, but is at liberty to register if he or she feels that this would be advantageous. It is nice to think that there is an element of choice in this, although one would be hard pressed to think why anyone would voluntarily register for VAT unless they absolutely had to! Incidentally, the government raised the VAT registration level by 40 per cent to £35,000 in March 1991 with the avowed intention of relieving a large number of businesses from this burden, at a time when the rate of tax was increased from 15 per cent to 17.5 per cent. Assuming that you are a dealer with a turnover above the magic limit, then you are committing a serious offence if you fail to register. Registration then lays you open to the full machinery of the system. You have to charge VAT on all goods and services, issuing VAT invoices and receipts and keeping detailed accounts which are liable to snap inspection at any time. You have to make quarterly returns to Customs and Excise of the amount of tax you have collected. From this you are allowed to deduct VAT which you yourself have paid out in the course of your business, and you then have to remit the difference to the VAT collector. Of course, should the amount you have paid exceed the tax you have collected, you receive a repayment in due course. This arises in businesses which handle zero-rated goods and services, but coins and medals do not come within that category.

For dealers in gold bullion, coins or medals, there is a special VAT leaflet which covers regulations specific to such matters. Since January 2000 investment gold has been exempt from VAT. A coin is classified as investment gold if it satisfies the following conditions: 1. Minted after 1800; 2. At least .900 fine; 3. Is or has been legal tender of its country of origin; 4. Is of a description of coin that is normally sold at a price that does not exceed 180% of the open market value of the gold contained in the coin. This is a complicated issue and further advice can be obtained from Customs & Excise Public Notice 701/21/99. A list of coins qualifying as investment gold is published in Public Notice 701/21A/99. When VAT is applicable of course it needs to be accounted for on the profit margin. It is vital therefore to maintain accurate records of all buying and selling, and which coins and medals are subject to VAT and which are exempt. Furthermore, the onus is on you to ensure that the source of the gold you bring into the country is impeccable. There are extremely heavy penalties for smuggling gold, and ignorance of the law, or apparently innocent handling of smuggled gold subsequently, are no defence.

From January 1, 1995 the special margin scheme of accounting for VAT currently available for certain second-hand goods, such as cars, was extended to almost all second-hand goods. The scheme allows businesses buying and selling eligible goods to account for VAT only on the difference between the buying and selling prices of these items.

A special system of accounting exists which enables some dealers to account for VAT without the need to keep a detailed record of every transaction. Certain works of art, antiques and collector's items, including "secondhand" coins, defined in Notice 712 *Second-hand goods*, were exempt from VAT at import. From January 1, 1996 these items became subject to VAT at import at an effective rate of 2.5 per cent.

Export and Import

Some coins do require an export licence before they can be taken out of the country and unfortunately these controls have been extended during the past year. Following the lifting of the export regulations relating to gold coins in 1979, then prior to April 1, 1993 the only coins which required any export licence were those with a value in excess of £35,000. However the agreement by the UK to implement an EC directive on the removal of cultural goods has resulted in a fresh interpretation of previous UK legislation on these coins which are on the market as a result of an archaeological find. Therefore as from April 1, 1993, any coin *whatever its value* which has come from an archaeological source within the UK will require an export licence even to take it to another EC country. Certain other coins of EC provenance other than the UK will now require an EC export licence. The value limit for non-archaeological source coins has been increased to £39,600 (Ecu 50,000). Both types of licence are issued by the Department of National Heritage, 2–4 Cockspur Street, Trafalgar Square, London SW1Y 5DH who can also supply a handy flow-chart to enable you to tell at a glance whether a licence is needed and what type. These new regulations are imposing an enormous additional burden on the trade and the British Numismatic Trade Association has held numerous meetings with the authorities in an attempt to reduce to a minimum the number of licence applications needed. Hopefully, by next year's edition there will be better news.

The restrictions applied to the importation of gold coins were removed in 1979, as previously mentioned. Coins of any kind are now permitted under Open General Import licence from any country and a specific or individual licence is no longer required. Details of any duties which may be payable on imported coins can be obtained from HM Customs and Excise, King's Beam House, Southwark, London SE1 or any local Customs and Excise office. Until recently, the only gold coins under embargo were Krugerrands. This was a political decision, aimed at tightening sanctions against South Africa, and applied to the importation of new gold coins from that country, but not to Krugerrands which had been brought into the United Kingdom, or any of the countries of the European Community, prior to the imposition of sanctions. In practice, it was very difficult to regulate the movement, let alone the importation, of Krugerrands, and with the relaxation of Apartheid this regulation has been lifted.

Importing Coins by Mail

Elsewhere in this volume will be found the names and addresses of mints, banks and numismatic bureaux around the world from whom it may be possible to obtain currency direct. It is a wise precaution to write to these bodies in the first instance for details of their sales and distribution. In some cases they appoint a dealer in Britain as an agent and this is a method of purchase that removes a great deal of the hassle and red tape. Nowadays, however, many mints and banks are quite happy to use the credit card system to make it easy to part you from your money. The problem arises, however, when the coins are despatched. As a rule, banks and mints stipulate quite clearly that they will not accept orders prepaid in cash, and it is an offence to send coins or banknotes out of the country as payment, except through banks authorised for this purpose. Cheques drawn on British banks should not be used. Indeed, this may be actively discouraged by the imposition of heavy clearance and handling charges at the other end. The converse is also true, although Americans seem to think that dollar cheques drawn on some obscure mid-West bank will be eagerly accepted here, and are consequently aggrieved when it is tactfully pointed out to them that this creates enormous problems—to say nothing of the swingeing bank charges incurred in converting such cheques to sterling. Other than credit cards, the Girobank system is probably the best method of remitting currency from one country to another; full details may be obtained from any post office. Details on the preferred method of sending remittances, or transferring cash to another country, as well as the transmission of coins by post to different countries, will be found in the *Royal Mail International Service Guide*. This also lists, among the prohibitions pertaining to each country, which countries accept gold or silver, and which ban the transmission of precious metals by post.

The receipt of postal packets containing coins from abroad makes you liable for Value Added Tax on their importation. As a rule, the despatching mint or bank will have affixed a Customs declaration to the packet, listing the contents, their weight and value, and it is on that basis that VAT will be calculated. The position regarding the import and export of coins by post is more complicated, and applies also to goods sent on approval. In such cases you must consult your Customs and Excise office who will advise you on the correct procedure and what your liabilities will be as to tax in either case. This also applies to dealers taking stock out of the country to a coin show and then re-importing the unsold stock afterwards, or importing material purchased at the show.

Buying and Selling

When goods are sold, the seller and the buyer enter into a contract which confers rights and imposes obligations on both parties. The contract need not be in writing. There is no law governing the quality of goods sold by a private individual. If you purchase a coin from a fellow-collector as a result of an informal meeting at the local numismatic society it is incumbent on you to ensure that what you buy is what you think you are buying. If you purchase something from a dealer or shopkeeper, however, you are entitled under the Sale of Goods Act to goods of "merchantable quality" which means that they must be reasonably fit for their purpose. Items sold under a specific description, on the other hand, must correspond exactly with that description. If they do not, the seller *even a private individual* can be sued under the Sale of Goods Act. This is an important distinction because there is an erroneous notion that the Act does not apply to transactions between private individuals.

If A sells a coin to B, purporting it to be a rare date, and B subsequently discovers that the date has been deliberately altered, then B can sue A.

Even if A claims that he made the sale in good faith, believing the coin to be a genuine rare date, he will still be liable for restitution (giving B his money back) and may also face a claim for damages. The Sale of Goods Act thus overturns the traditional adage *caveat emptor* which, in its full formula, translates as "let the buyer beware for he ought not to be ignorant of the nature of the property which he is buying from another party". Traditionally this was the maxim applicable at auctions. Once the auctioneer's gavel had dropped, the successful bidder had, in effect, made a contract with the vendor and was bound to pay for the lot, even if he subsequently discovered that what he had purchased was not what he had imagined. The view was that it was up to the purchaser to ensure beforehand that what he purchased was genuine and answered the description in the sale catalogue.

Because of vexatious disputes arising from questions of authenticity, and with the Sale of Goods Act breathing down their necks, many auctioneers now have a safety net, in the form of extensions. These enable successful bidders to delay payment for two or three weeks while they seek expertisation of doubtful material. In other words, the law allows a cooling-off period, but only for he legitimate purpose of verifying the authenticity of items over which there may be some doubt. This is only operative in cases where a coin or medal is sold as genuine, and described and estimated in value accordingly. In many doubtful cases, however, an auctioneer will cover himself by adding the crucial words "as is" to the description of a lot. Then, indeed, it is a case of *caveat emptor*. The auctioneer has done everything humanly possible to draw attention to the controversial nature of the item, and it must then rest on the judgment of the purchaser.

On the subject of auctions there are legal aspects which are not always apparent, as well as subtle differences in law and practice between England and Scotland. These tend to arise in cases where coins and medals come up for sale at provincial general mixed auctions, rather than in the sales conducted by numismatic auctioneers. Goods up for auction may be subject to an upset price which is made public as the price at which the bidding will start. A reserve price, on the other hand, is known only to the auctioneer, and if it is not reached, the goods will not be sold. Upset prices are common in Scotland, reserve prices in England. If no upset price is specified and the goods are not subject to a reserve price then the highest bid secures them, even though it may not be as high as the vendor hoped for. If a seller notifies other bidders that he is bidding for his own goods, or that he has employed an agent to bid for him, the bidding is legal. If he does not give notice and bids himself, or gets someone to bid for him, thus forcing up the price, the sale is fraudulent, and the buyer can purchase the goods for the amount of the last bid he made before fraudulent bidding started.

One frequently hears dark, but usually apocryphal, tales of "the ring" in action to depress the bidding and secure items below the price commensurate with their actual value. This is a fraudulent practice and in law is regarded as a criminal conspiracy. In practice, however, it would be very difficult for a group of dealers or other individuals to keep the bidding down merely by sitting on their hands. This practice could only operate successfully in sales which were largely, if not entirely, frequented by dealers. But coin sales, like other specialist collector-orientated auctions, are characterised by a high proportion of private bidders in attendance. Any conspiracy by a ring would merely allow some private bidder to step in and secure the lot at a bargain price. Rings are illegal, but in practice prosecutions are very rare as it is extremely difficult to obtain proof of their operations. What is more likely to happen is that dealers have been known to act in concert to force up the bidding to frighten off some unwelcome interloper. Here again, such tales are legion, but astonishingly lacking in specific details. The golden rule in attending auctions is to know what you are going after, and to have a pretty precise idea of how much you are prepared to pay. Do not be stampeded in the heat of the moment into going way beyond your limit.

Taxation of Profits on Disposal

The Inland Revenue define an asset as "any form of property (other than sterling) wherever situated". A disposal includes a sale, exchange or gift of an asset, or the receipt of a capital sum in respect of them. In layman's terms you dispose of an asset when you sell it, give it away, exchange it or lose it. A transfer of assets between husband and wife doesn't count (unless they are legally separated), nor does the transfer of an asset you leave when you die. If a disposal results in a profit you could be liable to tax. Any profit made on the sale of certain assets, including coins, medals and other collectables, constitutes a capital gain and is subject to Capital Gains Tax (CGT) which is now charged at the same 25% and 40% rates as income tax. However the government allows you to make a total capital gain in the current tax year of £5,500 before tax becomes chargeable. If this is the case, and the total proceeds from disposal do not exceed £10,000, then a simple declaration to this effect is all you need to make in the relevant section of your annual tax return.

Computing the actual capital gain is a complicated matter. Suppose you purchased a coin in 1960 for £5,000 and sold it in 1993 for £12,000. On the face of it, you've made a capital gain of £7,000 and you might think that you were liable to CGT because the gain was over £5,500. However, the *length of time* you've held the asset also has to be taken into consideration. From April 6, 1988 the law was altered so that only gains made after March 31, 1982 are now taxable. In effect, you are taxed as if you acquired the coin on March 31, 1982. The initial value of the coin is deemed to be its market value at that date. If the gain from March 1982 to the time of disposal is greater than the overall gain from acquisition in 1960 to disposal in 1993, you take the lesser of the two figures. If this produces a gain, whereas the old method of working it out would have produced a loss, you will be regarded, for tax purposes, as having made neither a gain nor a loss on disposal. You have a choice of opting for computing from the time of actual acquisition or from March 1982, whichever seems the more advantageous; but once you've made your choice you cannot subsequently change your mind.

How do you establish what the coin was worth in March 1982? The Inland Revenue tend to regard Seaby, Krause or other relevant catalogues as their yardstick. The difference between the nominal or catalogue value in 1982 and what you eventually got for the coin *assuming that the latter was greater*, might be regarded as the capital gain, but even then the position is complicated by inflation in the intervening years eroding the real value of the coin.

At this stage things get really complicated as you have to work out the indexation allowance. This is determined by the Retail Prices Index (RPI), and you need to know the RPI for (a) the month of disposal, and (b) the month in which you acquired the asset, or March 1982, if later. The RPI is announced each month by the Departmenrt of Employment and is published in its *Employment Gazette* which ought to be available in your local public library. Take the RPI for the month of the disposal and subtract the RPI for the month when indexation commenced. Then divide the result by the RPI for the month when indexation began, and work out this figure to the nearest third decimal place. This is known as the indexation factor, which you then multiply by the initial value of your coin. Simple isn't it? In most cases, however, I expect you will have made a capital loss in real terms, so these sums, though necessary to satisfy the Inland Revenue, are largely academic.

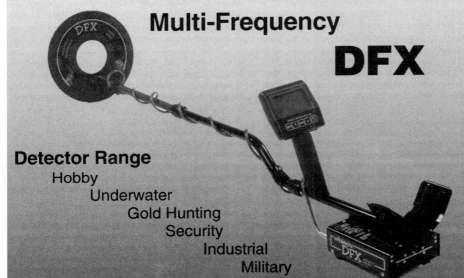

Treasure
and the Law

Until the introduction of the new Treasure Act, the legal position regarding articles of value, found long after they were hidden or abandoned, was not as simple and straightforward as it might be supposed. Furthermore, this was a case where the law in England and Wales differed fundamentally from that in Scotland.

Treasure Trove was one of the most ancient rights of the Crown, deriving from the age-old right of the monarch to grave treasure. In England and Wales, the law applied only to objects made of, or containing, gold or silver, whether in the form of coin, jewellery, plate or bullion. Moreover, the object had to be shown to have been deliberately hidden and the owner could not be readily found. The English law therefore excluded precious stones and jewels set in base metals or alloys such as bronze or pewter. It also took no account of artifacts in pottery, stone, bone, wood or glass which might be of immense antiquarian value.

In recent years, as a result of the rise in metal-detecting as a hobby, the archaeological lobby brought pressure to bear on Parliament to change the law and bring it into line with Scotland where the rules on Treasure Trove were far more rigorously interpreted. In Scotland the Crown is entitled to *all* abandoned property, even if it has not been hidden and is of little value. This applies even to objects dumped in skips on the pavement. Strictly speaking you would be committing a criminal offence if you removed an old chair from a skip without the owner's permission, although in practice such helping oneself rarely proceeds to a prosecution. In 1958 an archaeological expedition

Metal detecting can be fun—but be sure you know the rules!

from Aberdeen University found several valuable artifacts on St Ninian's Isle, Shetland. These included silver vessels and ornaments, as well as a porpoise bone which had incised decoration on it. The archaeologists challenged the rights of the Crown to this treasure, arguing that the Crown would have to prove that the articles had been deliberately hidden, and that a porpoise bone was in any case not valuable enough to count as treasure. The High Court, however, decided that as long as the property had been abandoned, it belonged automatically to the Crown. Its value, intrinsic or otherwise, or whether or not it was hidden, did not make any difference. Since then, as a result of this decision in case law, the criteria for Treasure Trove have been very strictly applied in Scotland. It would have only required a similar test case in England or Wales to result in a similar tightening of the rules. This has been resisted, mainly by the detectorist lobby, but inevitably the government considered legislation to control the use of metal detectors, if not to ban them altogether.

In England and Wales a find of gold or silver coins, artifacts or ornaments, or objects which contain some of these metals, which appears to have been concealed by the original owner, was deemed to be Treasure Trove. It was not even necessary for the articles to be buried in the ground; objects concealed in thatched roofs or under the floorboards of buildings have been judged to be Treasure Trove. Such finds had to be notified immediately to the police who then informed the district coroner. He then convened an inquest which decided whether all or part of the find was Treasure Trove. Establishing the gold or silver content was straightforward, but the coroner's inquest had to decide whether the material was hidden deliberately and not just lost or abandoned, and that the owner could not be located. A gold coin found on or near a country footpath might reasonably have been dropped by the original possessor through a hole in pocket or purse and in such cases it was very unlikely that it would be deemed Treasure Trove, even if the coin turned out to be very rare. In this instance the coroner would then have had to determine who was the lawful owner of the find: the actual finder, the owner of the land where it was found or even the tenant of the land. As a rule, however, it was left to the finder and landowner to decide between them who the owner of the coin should be, and in some cases the matter could only be resolved by referring to a civil court. For this reason it was vital that metal detectorists should secure permission *in writing* from landowners before going on to their land, defining rights and obligations on both sides, in order to determine

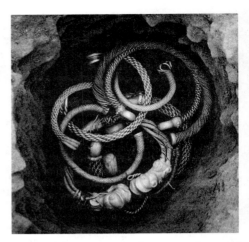

The Snettisham torcs—one of our country's greatest finds.

the disposal or share-out of any finds or proceeds from the sale of finds, *beforehand*.

If the coroner decided that the articles were deliberately concealed, and declared them to be Treasure Trove, the find automatically reverted to the Crown. In practice the find was considered by the Treasure Trove Reviewing Committee of the Treasury. They might decide that although the articles *invariably coins* were gold or silver, they were so common that they were not required by the British Museum or one of the other great national collections, and would return them to the finder to dispose of at his discretion. If some or all of the coins were deemed vital for inclusion in a national collection the finder was recompensed with the full market value of the material. On the other hand, if someone found gold or silver which might be Treasure Trove and failed to declare it at the time, that person was liable to prosecution under the Theft Act should the find subsequently come to light. Not only could he face a heavy fine but the articles would be forfeit to the Crown, and of course no reward or recompense was then payable either.

The anomalies and inconsistencies of existing law on Treasure Trove were eliminated and the position considerably tightened up by the passage, on July 5, 1996, of the Treasure Act.

Announcing that the Treasure Act had received the Royal Assent, Lord Inglewood, National Heritage Minister, said, "This represents the first legislation on treasure trove to be passed in England and Wales and will replace common law precedents and practices dating back to the

Middle Ages. The Act, which offers a clearer definition of treasure and simplified procedures for dealing with finds, will come into force after a code of practice has been drawn up and agreed by both Houses of Parliament". The Act came into force in England, Wales and Northern Ireland on September 24, 1997, replacing the common law of treasure trove.

The act was introduced as a Private Member's Bill by Sir Anthony Grant, after the failure of an earlier attempt by Lord Perth. For the first time, it would be a criminal offence to fail to report within 14 days the discovery of an item which would be declared Treasure Trove. Finders will continue to be rewarded for reporting their discoveries promptly, while landowners and occupiers will also be eligible for rewards for the first time.

The Treasure Act covers man-made objects and defines treasure as objects other than coins which are at least 300 years old and contain at least 10 per cent by weight of gold or silver; coins more than 300 years old which are found in hoards (a minimum of two coins if the precious metal content is more than 10 per cent, and a minimum of 10 coins if the precious metal content is below 10 per cent). The act also embraces all objects found in clear archaeological association with items which are treasure under the above definitions. It also covers any object which would have been Treasure Trove under the previous definitions (e.g. hoards of 19th century gold or silver coins).

The maximum penalty for failing to report the discovery of treasure within 14 days will be a fine of £50,000 or three months imprisonment, or both.

In Scotland the police pass the goods on to the procurator fiscal who acts as the local representative of the Queen's and Lord Treasurer's Remembrancer. If the articles are of little value, historically or intrinsically, the finder will usually be allowed to keep them. If they are retained for the appropriate national collection then a reward equal to the market value is payable.

A favourite haunt of metal-detectorists these days is the beach, and many hobbyists make quite a lucrative living by sweeping the beaches especially just after a Bank Holiday. It's surprising how much loose change gets lost from pockets and handbags over a holiday weekend. Technically the coins recovered from the beach are lost property, in which case they ought to be surrendered to the police, otherwise the finder may be guilty of theft. In practice, however, the law turns a blind eye to coins, on the sensible grounds that it would be impossible to prove ownership. On the other hand, banknotes are treated as lost property since someone could in theory at least identify a note as his by citing the serial number.

In the case of other objects, such as watches and jewellery, of course the law governing lost property is enforced, and the old adage of "finders keepers" does not apply. Any object of value, identifiable as belonging to someone, that is washed up on the foreshore or found in territorial waters is known technically as "wreck". This includes not just a wrecked ship, but any cargo that was being carried by a ship.

If wreck is not claimed by its owner, it falls to the Crown. In this case it is not necessary to prove deliberate concealment, as in the case of Treasure Trove. This law has a specific numismatic application in the case of the gold and silver coins washed up after storms around our shores, from Shetland to the Scillies. Such coins, emanating from wrecks of Spanish treasure ships and Dutch East Indiamen in particular, are well documented, and any such finds ought to be reported immediately to the police.

Stray finds of coins, as well as other objects of value, on public places, such as the street, a public park or a sports ground, are also subject to law. In this case the finder must take all reasonable steps to locate the owner. Anyone who keeps a coin without making reasonable effort to find the owner could be prosecuted for theft. As with the beach, however, such "reasonable effort" would clearly be impractical. Finding coins on private premises is another matter. In this case large bodies, such as the Post Office, British Rail, the British Airports Authority, bus companies, municipal authorities, hospitals, the owners of department stores, theatre and cinema proprietors and the like, may have bye-laws, rules and regulations for dealing with lost property found within their precincts, or in their vehicles. If you found a purse or wallet on a bus or train, or in a telephone kiosk or a shop, common sense (and your conscience) would tell you to hand it over to the driver, conductor, shopkeeper or official in charge. As a rule, unclaimed lost property reverts eventually to the finder, but not always; British Rail and some other organisations have a rule that in such cases the property reverts to the organisation. In any event, failure to disclose the find immediately might render you liable to prosecution for stealing by finding.

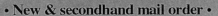

Treasure Act
Code of
Practice
—a summary

For easy reference a summary of the main points of the new law is reproduced here*. Further information will be found in the *Code of Practice on the Treasure Act*, which can be obtained free of charge from the Department for Culture, Media and Sport (formerly the Department of National Heritage) (telephone: 020 7211 6200). Metal detectorists are strongly advised to obtain a copy of the Code of Practice which, among other things, contains guidance for detectorists, sets out guidelines on rewards, gives advice on the care of finds and has lists of useful addresses.

What is the definition of treasure?

The following finds are treasure under the Act (*more detailed guidance is given in the Code of Practice*):

1. *Objects other than coins:* any object other than a coin provided that it contains at least 10 per cent of gold or silver and is a least 300 years old when found (objects with gold or silver plating normally have less than 10 per cent of precious metal).

2. *Coins:* all coins from the same find provided they are at least 300 years old when found (but if the coins contain less than 10 per cent of gold or silver there must be at least 10 of them; there is a list of these coins in the Code of Practice).

An object or coin is part of the same find as another object or coin if it is found in the same place as, or had previously been left together with, the other object. Finds may have become scattered since they were originally deposited in the ground.

Only the following groups of coins will normally be regarded as coming from the "same find":

(a) hoards that have been deliberately hidden;

(b) smaller groups of coins, such as the contents of purses, that may have been dropped or lost and

(c) votive or ritual deposits.

Single coins found on their own are not treasure and groups of coins lost one by one over a period of time (for example those found on settlement sites or on fair sites) will not normally be treasure.

3. *Associated objects:* any object, whether it is made of, that is found in the same place as, or that had previously been together with, another object that is treasure.

4. *Objects that would have been treasure trove:* any object that would previously have been treasure trove, but does not fall within the specific categories given above. These objects have to be made substantially of gold or silver; they have to have been buried with the intention of recovery and their owner or his/her heirs cannot be traced.

The following types of find are not treasure:

(a) objects whose owners can be traced;

(b) unworked natural objects, including human and animal remains, even if they are found in association with treasure;

(c) objects from the foreshore, which are wreck. If you are in any doubt, it will probably be safest to report your find.

What about objects found before the Act came into force?

You should report objects that come into any of the four categories just described (if found after September 23, 1997). There is no need to report any objects found before that date unless they may be treasure trove (see 4 above).

What should I do if I find something that may be treasure?

You must report all finds of treasure to the coroner for the district in which they are found *either* within 14 days after the date on which you made the find *or* within 14 days after the day on which you realised that the find might be treasure (for example, as a result of having it identified). The obligation to report finds applies to everyone, including archaeologists.

How do I report a find of treasure?

Very simply. You may report your find to the coroner in person, by letter, telephone or fax. The coroner or his officer will send you an acknowledgement and tell you where you should deliver your find. The Code of Practice has a list of all coroners' addresses, telephone and fax numbers.

There are special procedure for objects from a few areas for which treasure franchises exist, but they should be reported to the coroner in the usual way. The main franchise-holders (the Duchies of Lancaster and Cornwall, the Corporation of London and the City of Bristol) have confirmed that they will pay rewards for finds of treasure from their franchises in the normal way.

Where will I have to take my find?

You will normally be asked to take your find to a local museum or archaeological body. Local agreements have been drawn up for each coroner's district in England and Wales to provide the coroner with a list of such museums and archaeological organisations. The Department is publishing a series of leaflets, roughly one for each country of England and one for Wales, listing the relevant coroners, museums and archaeological services in each area.

The body which receives the find on behalf of the coroner will give you a receipt. Although they will need to know where you made the find, they will keep this information confidential if you or the landowner wish—and you should do so too.

The body receiving the find will notify the Sites and Monuments Record as soon as possible (if that has not already happened), so that the site where the find was made can be investigated by archaeologists if necessary. A list of Sites and Monuments Records is in Appendix 3 of the Code of Practice.

What if I do not report a find of treasure?

If you fail to report a find that you believe or have reasonable grounds for believing to be treasure without a reasonable excuse you may be imprisoned for up to three months or receive a fine of up to level 5 on the standard scale (currently £5,000) or both. You will not be breaking the law if you do not report a find because you do not initially recognise that it may be treasure, but you should report it once you do.

What happens if the find is not treasure?

If the object is clearly not treasure, the museum or archeological body will inform the coroner, who may then decide to give directions that the find should be returned without holding an inquest.

What happens if the find is treasure?

If the museum curator or archaeologist believes the find may be treasure, they will inform the British Museum or the National Museums & Galleries of Wales. The museums will then decide whether they or any other museum may wish to acquire it.

If no museum wishes to acquire the find, the Secretary of State will be able to disclaim it. When this happens, the coroner will notify the occupier and landowner that he intends to return the object to the finder after 28 days unless he receives an objection. If the coroner receives an objection, the find will be retained until the dispute is settled.

What if a museum wants to acquire my find?

If a museum wants to acquire part or all of a find, then the coroner will hold an inquest to decide whether it is treasure. The coroner will inform the finder, occupier and landowner and they will be able to question witnesses at the inquest. Treasure inquest will not normally be held with a jury.

If the find is declared to be treasure, then it will be taken to the British Museum or the National Museums & Galleries of Wales, so that it can be valued by the Treasure Valuation Committee.

How do I know I will receive a fair price for my find?

Any find of treasure that a museum wishes to acquire must be valued by the Treasure Valuation Committee, which consists of independent experts. The Committee will commission a valuation from one or more experts drawn from the trade. You, together with the museum that wishes to acquire the find and any other interested party, will have an opportunity to comment on the valuation and to send in a separate valuation of your own, before the Committee makes its recommendation. If you are dissatisfied you can appeal to the Secretary of State.

What if the coroner or museum loses or damages my find?

They are required to take reasonable steps to ensure that this does not happen; but, if it does, you should nonetheless be compensated.

Who will receive the reward?

This is set out in detail in the Code of Practice.

To summarise:

— where the finder has permission to be on the land, rewards should continue to be paid in full to him or her (the burden of proof as to whether he or she has permission will rest with the finder). If the finder makes an agreement with the occupier/landowner to share a reward, the Secretary of State will normally follow it;

— if the finder does not remove the whole of a find from the ground but allows archaeologists to excavate the remainder of the find, the original finder will normally be eligible for a reward for the whole find;

— rewards will not normally be payable when the find is made by an archaeologist;

— where the finder has committed an offence in relation to a find, or has trespassed, or has not followed best practice as set out in the Code of Practice, he or she may expect no reward at all or a reduced reward. Landowners and occupiers will be eligible for rewards in such cases.

How long will it take before I receive my reward?

The Code of Practice states that you should receive a reward within one year of you having delivered your find, although this may take longer in the case of very large finds or those that present special difficulties. If no museum wants to acquire the find it should be disclaimed within six months or within three months if it is a single object.

---

*Reproduced from "The Treasure Act, Information for Finders of Treasure (England and Wales)" leaflet DCMSJ0229NJ, published by the Department for Culture, Media and Sport.

Index
to COIN NEWS

Once again, in response to popular demand, we have included this basic subject index to the COIN YEARBOOK's parent magazine COIN NEWS, covering the period from September 2000 to August 2001. Entries are indicated by numbers signifying the month (e.g. 9–12 relate to September to December 2000 and 1–8 signify January to August 2001), followed by the page number.

BOOKS

Incorporating BANKNOTE NEWS

COIN NEWS

www.tokenpublishing.com

This month we value
£5 and £2 coins

...TEM... 2001   £2

Th
Ha

Plus in
BANKNOTE NEW
Notes of Algeria
Duggleby number
for Yearbook

Coins of the Jewish Revolt

A look at toy coins

ISSN 0958-13

BRITAIN'S BIGGEST-SELLING COIN MAGAZINE

CHANG
DIRECTION

Employment options
in working life

2nd edition

Sue Ward

BOOKS

Bulk orders

Age Concern England is pleased to offer customised editions of all its titles to UK companies, institutions or other organisations wishing to make a bulk purchase. For further information, please contact the Publishing Department at the address on this page. Tel: 020 8765 7200. Fax: 020 8765 7211. Email: books@ace.org.uk

© 2002 Sue Ward

Published by Age Concern England
1268 London Road
London SW16 4ER

First published 2002

Editor Gillian Clarke
Production Vinnette Marshall
Design and typesetting GreenGate Publishing Services
Printed in Great Britain by Bell & Bain Ltd, Glasgow

A catalogue record for this book is available from the British Library

ISBN 0–86242–331–7

Contents

About the author

Sue Ward is a freelance journalist and researcher specialising in pensions and social security matters.

Her publications include: *Essential Guide to Pensions*, 3rd edition (Pluto Press, 1992); *Women and Personal Pensions*, jointly with Bryn Davies (HMSO for Equal Opportunities Commission, 1992); *Planning Your Pension, a TUC Guide* (Kogan Page, 2002); and the *Pensions Handbook* (Age Concern Books, 2001). She is also the author of regular articles in specialist magazines such as *Pensions World* and *Employee Benefits*.

Sue was a member of the Occupational Pensions Regulatory Authority (Opra) from its setting up in 1996 to April 2002, and is a Governor and member of the Council of the Pensions Policy Institute.

Acknowledgements

This is the second edition of a book first published in 1996. My thanks to all those who have helped me with the preparation of both that edition and this one, and to everyone from whose experience I have quoted. I have had extensive conversations with many people, especially here on Tyneside where I live. In this region we have unrivalled experience of job losses, but also many resilient people who have gone on to make rewarding lives for themselves, whether in employment, self-employment or voluntary activity.

Special thanks for our very helpful discussions to Dot Kirton, Linda Aitken, Sheila March, Marilyn Headley and Brian Cooper of Coutts Career Consultants; Susan Wass and Deborah Know of Tyneside TEC; Jennifer Hills and Eileen Ridley of the Employment Services on Wallsend; Libby Hinson of Gateshead CAB; Betty Hill; Margaret McPhail of Tyneside Careers; Ken Burns of the (then) Employment Service; Clare Cassidy of Penna Sanders & Sidney; Stan Cooke; Valerie Irwin; and Jocelyn Marriner.

Thanks also to the Institute of Personnel and Development and the Press Offices of the Department of Work and Pensions, the Department for Education and Skills, and the Inland Revenue for dealing with my queries. Any mistakes, of course, are entirely my own.

1 Introduction

This book is aimed at people in their 40s and 50s whose current job has disappeared or is up in the air but who do not have the money or the inclination to sit back and watch their gardens grow.

There are a variety of reasons for being in this situation:

- Your employer may be closing down altogether, or closing the operating site or department where you work, perhaps after a take-over.
- Your employer could be wanting to reduce staff numbers or reorganise, and so have put together an early-retirement package and be looking for volunteers.
- You could be finding the work more stressful than before, or that your health is deteriorating and that you can no longer cope with particular aspects.
- You might have new caring responsibilities, perhaps for an older relative, that mean you can't travel so far from home or do so many hours.
- Or you may simply feel that you have had enough of that job and need a change, perhaps because the style of management has become uncongenial or perhaps because, as you get older, you realise you are missing out on life outside work.

Very often, people start thinking of a change in direction because of a combination of these reasons. You are feeling stressed and burnt-out, so when an attractive redundancy package comes along, or you hear of an opportunity elsewhere, you jump at it.

As Jocelyn, once an NHS laboratory worker but now working in a library, put it:

> 'In my last three years I had stopped enjoying the job. The pressure was becoming so great that I was frightened I was going to kill someone. Some days I was doing three people's work. You can't do that reliably for long; you are going to make mistakes.'

She felt trapped by her lack of keyboard skills, which seemed necessary in any other job she looked at. But when the local college started offering computer courses at a suitable venue and time, she jumped at the opportunity. Once she had her qualifications, she got a job – at the same pay, with longer hours, but *much* more job satisfaction.

You want something else, and you have lots of experience of work and of how the world works – though you may have no formal qualifications or only ones that you feel are out of date. You may be attracted to the idea of 'downshifting', as they call it in the USA – taking a job at a lower wage but also with less responsibility and stress – or you may want to continue at full throttle.

For anyone, a change of this sort is a major upheaval. It is only natural to feel anxious about where you start. This book is intended to guide you through the possibilities, looking much wider than the 'standard' full-time, nine-to-five job (which is far from standard any more, anyway). Chapter 2, following this introduction, looks at whether you can change your work, or the working conditions, while staying with the same employer. Chapters 3 to 6 look at the situation you may find yourself in as your job disappears: how you are likely to feel, what cash and other resources will be on offer from the employer and the state, and other financial issues that may face you. The following chapter, 7, is intended to help you decide what you want to do with your working life from now on, and to show you how to research and follow up the opportunities. The final group of chapters, 8 to 13, looks at ways of achieving your aim, whether it be employment, self-employment, voluntary work or study, and points particularly to bear in mind. At the end, there is a list of useful addresses, publications and other resources to help you.

It *is* worthwhile trying

Many older people don't try too hard to find new opportunities when they lose their jobs, or give up rather easily, because they feel depressed by the idea that society has effectively written them off as 'too old'. The message of this book is that, just because there are some prejudices and obstacles in your way, that is no reason to write *yourself* off. The opportunities are there, to a greater extent than for many years. You'll find them more easily, and probably find them more rewarding, if you:

- know what you want to do;
- plan and research how you are going to do it;
- treat getting there as a serious project in its own right.

This may be a quite different approach from the one you took when you were last looking for a job, which might be two or three decades ago. As a youngster, you might have drifted into what seemed the most attractive opportunity at the time, without thinking too much about a 'career path'. Or you took something as a stopgap till 'something better comes up' and are still there. This time round it's different. There is the chance – and the need – to organise things properly now.

Things have changed

The first edition of this book was published in 1996. This second edition has been very largely rewritten, because the environment in which you are contemplating your change of direction has altered so much.

According to the Government's statistics (using international definitions), in January 2002 unemployment in the UK was down to 5.2 per cent of the total workforce. However, within this average the figure was 7.4 per cent for the north-east of England, and only 3.3 per cent – less than half that – for the south-east of England.

There are close to 3 million people between the ages of 50 and 64 who do not have a paid job – around a third of the age group. Nearly 2 million of them are men. Of the total, over a million people are on sickness and disability benefits, and half a million have caring responsibilities. The rest are either looking for work or 'economically inactive' – not looking either because they have decided there is no point or because they feel they have enough income to live on and they do not need to work. Both employers and the Government are now becoming aware of the economic cost of this. It was put at a £16 billion reduction in the UK's Gross Domestic Product each year, in a recent Cabinet Office report.

The Government and employers have also begun to appreciate that the UK's workforce as a whole is getting older. The next ten years are going to see a major shift in the age balance of the population aged between 20 and 65. At present there are over 3 million more people aged 20 to

39 than there are those aged 45 to 64. By 2020 there will be a million fewer, with the cross-over point coming in around 2009. By 2020, around 40 per cent of the workforce will be over 45, and only 17 per cent will be under 25 according to Government Minister Margaret Hodge MP, in evidence to a House of Commons Committee in 2001. 'Strategies that retain older people in the workforce will help to fill the gap left as the number of younger people declines,' another Government report (*The Age Shift*) has suggested.

There are, though, large geographical differences, and the gap between the south-east and all the rest of the UK is widening rather than narrowing. So the experience of an older person looking for work in, say, Newbury in Berkshire, is likely to be very different from the experience of a person in Motherwell in Scotland, Rotherham in Yorkshire, or Rhyl in North Wales, or Belfast in Northern Ireland.

There are now many – perhaps over-optimistic – arguments that, with the changing economy, there is a greater need for what older people can supply. As one recent report (*Experience Necessary*) put it:

> 'The current requirement is for knowledge, but businesses are beginning to understand that knowledge is too narrow a concept to describe what they really need – people who can employ their experience and understanding, their networks and their strategic vision to add value to organisations. What businesses are really after is wisdom . . . businesses are increasingly finding that the older workers they previously had written off are the richest source of adaptable and creative labour around.'

A number of employers, such as those involved in the Employers' Forum on Age (see page 190), are also recognising the need for a changed attitude to older workers. Some might view this new attitude rather cynically. As academic Phil White has put it:

> 'Older workers have been treated extremely expediently; until the 1990s, there was little evidence that the State was regarding older workers as possessing intrinsic worth, or dignity. Rather, they were treated as a reserve army, accorded less significance than their younger colleagues.'

Expedient it may be, but the change is likely to last some time, just because of the demographic shift. It is already resulting in both new restrictions and new opportunities. For example:

- Access to ill-health early-retirement pensions is becoming more difficult, especially in the public sector. In teaching, for example, the number of pensions granted in the last few years, since changes in the rules on eligibility and the way the costs were budgeted for, has fallen dramatically, according to a report (*Review of Ill-health Retirement in the Public Sector*) published by the Treasury in 2000. There is pressure on private sector employers to do the same. While on the one hand the restrictions mean that many people who feel they have a justifiable case for ill-health retirement are being denied it, on the other hand those who feel they are being forced out have a better argument for redeployment or adjustments to the job.

- There is also now *somewhat* better employment protection, for instance with the Disability Discrimination Act 1995 (see page 15 for more details) and the national minimum wage.

- There is also the New Deal 50 Plus, for people over 50 (see page 59), which should mean that older people going to JobCentres (which are gradually being converted to provide a more comprehensive service as Jobcentre Plus offices) are given more serious help with job-finding. This also means, however, that the penalties imposed on those who do not take job-finding too seriously are heavier, in terms of loss of Jobseeker's Allowance or Income Support or both. The qualifications for receiving Incapacity Benefit have been tightened, and from April 2001 it has been offset against an occupational pension or permanent health insurance payment (see pages 67–68).

The one change in the legal framework that has not happened yet is the one that most older people looking for jobs would probably like to see – the outlawing of age discrimination. Instead, the Government, in conjunction with employers and others, have drawn up a voluntary code of practice, which research by Industrial Relations Services (IRS) suggests has not been very effective. (See page 98 for more details.) However, requirements laid down by the European Union and agreed to by the UK Government mean that, by December 2006, there must be some laws on this issue in place. The Government issued a consultation document on their plans in December 2001 and, as the Employers' Association on Age commented, 'employers who believe they can prepare for age discrimination simply by removing age from job adverts and date of birth from application forms are in for a rude shock.' There are still many details – including important ones such as whether employers will still be allowed to have compulsory retirement ages for their staff – to be decided, however.

So, over all, the picture for older people looking for changes in their jobs is mixed. To use an appropriately mixed metaphor, the world is not your oyster but the horizon is much brighter than it was a few years ago.

2 Do you really need to change?

Most of this book is about changing your employer or your employment status. This chapter, however, considers whether you can – or want to – find ways of staying with your current employer but altering the work you do or the way that you do it.

Many people feel that they 'like the work, hate the job'. Reasons for this could be that:

- The job is disappearing, either altogether or in its present form because of a reorganisation or 'downsizing', and so it looks as if you will be pushed out.
- The management style has changed, whether because of outside influences or a change of approach, and you find it difficult to adapt or don't feel it is a change in the right direction. For example, those with employers who are keen to have the standard created by the International Standards Organisation (called ISO 9000), which supposedly measures the 'quality' of their work-processes, often feel that they are involved simply with box-ticking, with no benefit to their work.
- There may be a different generation of managers, whose assumptions are also different – perhaps about people routinely putting in longer hours at work.
- The job may have altered because of changes in technology or in other parts of the organisation.
- You might be feeling that the work has not changed enough; you have been doing the same thing for much too long, it no longer presents a challenge and you are bored with it.
- You might feel that your health is not as good as it was, perhaps with arthritis or hearing difficulties, and so you are finding it more difficult to cope with work you could once handle easily. Perhaps the work itself is contributing to your health problems, through stress, working unsocial hours or the need to lift heavy weights.
- Perhaps the journey is more stressful than it used to be, for instance because of increased traffic on the roads.

■ You may have difficulties fitting together work and responsibilities at home, perhaps because of a demanding teenager or a parent or relative who is becoming increasingly frail.

All these are reasons why people jump at a voluntary redundancy package when it comes along, or calculate that, with their savings and their pensions expectations and some earnings, they would be able to manage if they gave up the job, or look for ill-health retirement. However, unless you feel you must go because the working conditions are simply intolerable, it makes sense to investigate less drastic action first. Can you change the working conditions but stay within the organisation – either by moving to a job that will survive the cutbacks or is more congenial, or by taking action to deal with the problems you are coming up against?

Redundancy versus redeployment

The payments you may get for redundancy are considered in Chapter 4. In this section we look at what your rights are if you want to continue working despite your job disappearing. Good employers go substantially beyond the legal minimum, but we will start with your statutory rights. First, there is a right to be *consulted*, both collectively and individually.

■ The collective consultation takes place either with a trade union, where there is one, or with a representative body created by the employer for this purpose (or with both if only part of the workforce is unionised). The length of time in advance that this consultation must take place depends on the number of employees involved; the minimum is 30 days in advance if there are ten or more employees to be consulted, or 90 days if there are 100 or more. These are minimum requirements, and the law also says that consultation should take place at the 'earliest opportunity'. There can be a claim for a 'protective award' (more money in lieu for those made redundant) if the employer fails to consult.

■ The individual threatened with redundancy also has the right to be consulted, with a reasonable consultation period being considered as between two and four weeks.

■ Whatever consultations go on must be genuine, and must include details of the criteria to be used, the methods for carrying out the redundancies and any possibility of reducing the numbers affected by taking other action.

This, then, is the point at which alternatives can be put forward. Is there, for instance, some way of reorganising the work that will reduce the number of jobs to be lost? Can work currently outsourced be brought in-house? Can those threatened apply for other jobs in the organisation, or be retrained to do something in another area? What about relocation?

Secondly, there is a right to be offered *suitable alternative employment*, if the employer has any available. Another name for this is 'redeployment'. If you take up the offer, you will not then be redundant, but remember that:

- 'Suitable' means work that the employee can reasonably be expected to do, and on terms or conditions not substantially less favourable.
- Usually the job would be within the same company but, if there is a group of companies involved, it could well be reasonable for the employer to look to the sister-firms as well. Whether you can be required to travel depends on whether you have a mobility clause in your contract.
- The job must be available to start within four weeks of the end of the previous job – though generally people would move straight from one to the other.

An important aspect is that, if you move jobs in this way, there is a four-week *trial period*, in order to establish whether the new job is suitable for you and you are capable of doing it. If retraining is needed, by agreement (which must be in writing) the trial period can be longer than this.

Many employers, especially in the public sector, have redeployment policies that go beyond this legal minimum. Copies should be available from your union representative or your human resources/personnel office. Even if such a policy has not existed in the past, there is nothing to stop you asking for one now, especially if you know there are skills shortages in some other parts of the organisation.

You might also be happy to look beyond what would normally be considered suitable employment – perhaps by 'downshifting' (see page 84) to something with less responsibility, going part-time or taking on a different set of tasks. It will usually be worth making this clear, either to the union or the employer or both.

Redeployment is an *alternative* to redundancy – you have not lost your job, so there is no redundancy payment to come. If you are offered different options, think carefully about which one to take up; check (preferably in writing) whether the alternative really is suitable, and then take the trial period seriously. If within the deadline you discover that the job is not for you, say so loud and clear, and get the redundancy reinstated if your employer cannot offer you anything better. Don't just suffer in the hope that 'it's sure to get better'. If it doesn't and you later find you cannot cope, legally you can be treated simply as a voluntary leaver, with no special rights.

Thirdly, there is a requirement for *fair selection for redundancy*. The employer can set the criteria but they must be reasonable, and then they must be implemented fairly.

- Obvious unfairnesses include women being selected ahead of men, or people from a particular ethnic minority ahead of others. This would be illegal, and so also would indirect discrimination – laying down criteria that worked against some groups without an 'objective justification'. To take a fairly straightforward example, using the criterion of being able to lift heavy weights would usually operate against women – and the employer would need to be able to show that this task was necessary for the job.
- Unfortunately, there is (until, at the latest, December 2006) no law against discriminating on grounds of age, as there is against discriminating on grounds of sex or race. However, there have been some employment tribunal cases where crudely using age, without relating it back to ability to do the job, has been found to be unfair – though only if the person is aged less than the normal retiring age or 65.
- Most usually, the selection criteria relate to capability and skill in performing the job, qualifications and experience. You, or the union, should argue for a balanced package of several criteria; weighting qualifications over experience, for instance, could give unfair advantage to younger people who have come in as graduates over older people who have learned on the job.

■ The criteria must be clearly defined and not too vague. Once established, the employer should not deviate from them, though they can establish different criteria for different groups of people.

Especially in larger organisations, the employer will often ask for volunteers, and may offer them an attractive package. Frequently there will be more volunteers than are needed, so the employer can then select who stays and who goes. Such selection must also be fair. If you don't want to go, but someone else does, it may be possible to negotiate so that the other person is released and you are then moved into their job. This is called 'bumping' and can also happen with compulsory redundancies – but, again, the way it is done must be fair. According to a 1998 decision at the Employment Appeals Tribunal (Church v West Lancashire NHS Trust), a 'bumping' redundancy does not qualify an employee for statutory redundancy pay, but most employers would take a broader view than this.

You may find that, as part of a reorganisation or a staffing reduction, you are required to reapply for your own job, or to apply for whichever others have been created or left vacant. For some ideas on how to go about this, look at the sections in Chapter 9 about preparing for and going through a job interview.

In all these instances, you have the right to go to an employment tribunal if you feel you have been treated unfairly. This can be a long-drawn-out and painful process, though, so think carefully before you start down this track.

The Advisory, Conciliation and Arbitration Service (ACAS) have published a free booklet on *Redundancy Handling* (reference number B10). Though aimed at employers, it is just as useful for employees to see what their bosses should be doing. According to ACAS' own summary:

'Emphasis is placed on the importance of planning an organisation's labour requirements to avoid or minimise the need for redundancies. The booklet describes some of the alternatives to redundancy and gives guidance on how to set up agreed procedures for occasions when redundancies become unavoidable. Selection criteria for redundancy are discussed, together with the need for consultation and disclosure of information, appeals procedures and methods of assisting personnel to find other work. Appendices give a checklist for redundancy agreements and an outline of the law on redundancy payments.'

There is also a *Redundancy Law Handbook*, published by Incomes Data Services, which costs £50 but is far more detailed.

Changing your role in the organisation

Even if your job is not under threat, you may be able to arrange redeployment in the same organisation, or negotiate a change in your working arrangements. What they call 'downshifting' in the USA is becoming fairly common there but is much less so here. You will probably need to make it very clear what you are asking for, and why. Some managers may assume you just want a 'cushy number' for your last few years, or that you have an unacknowledged problem (perhaps with alcohol). Make it clear that you remain committed to the employer and will give what the role requires. The more ambitious you have been, and the more of a high-flyer you were in the past, the more difficult it may be to convince your managers that you are serious. They may feel, justifiably, that you would be unable to adapt to a reduced role, or would get itchy feet and would leave anyway, after they had gone to some trouble to find you a niche.

Once you have worked out your answers to all the sceptical comments that can be thrown at you, possible ways of pursuing this are outlined below.

Are vacancies advertised internally (or can you get to hear of them on the office grapevine)? Without asking for special treatment, you ought to have a head-start on the other applicants, as you know the firm's philosophy and working practices. But you still need to prepare properly, not take it for granted – see Chapter 9 for some ideas.

Can you suggest a restructuring of your own role? Could you swap tasks with someone else or reorganise things so that some particularly tedious piece of work does not have to be done at all? Sadly, escaping from bureaucratic procedures is not easy these days – if anything, they are increasing rather than reducing – but it will be worth doing some lateral thinking about what really is necessary. Or is there a special project that needs doing, to which you could be seconded?

Might some training help? Many employers have a commitment, nominally at least, to the idea of helping with 'personal development', so they may be willing to pay for a course and give you time off, even if the topic relates only marginally to your current work. The first person to talk to is the training officer, or whoever fulfils that role, but see Chapter 12 for details about training opportunities.

If you never had a chance to sow your wild oats when you were young and are now looking wistfully at your children as they set off back-packing round the world, it could be extended leave of absence or a sabbatical that you need rather than a complete change of direction. Some organisations, for instance in the academic world, the Post Office (now called Consignia) and American Express, have standardised career-break arrangements. Others might be willing to agree something as a one-off, though much will depend on your line manager's attitude. They will tend to want you to be doing something worthy – perhaps spending time with counterparts in the same industry in a different country, perhaps doing voluntary work somewhere – so you need to be prepared for this. See Chapter 11 for some ideas about volunteering. Almost certainly this sort of extended leave will be unpaid, so think also about how you would support yourself. The Chartered Institute of Personnel and Development stresses that it is important to keep in contact, 'so that it is not out of sight, out of mind. Stay in the loop.'

There could be a chance of doing a 'job-swap' with someone abroad. The teaching profession has an arrangement for this, through the British Council, but possibilities also exist in areas such as medicine. A possibility in the USA is the Fulbright Commission (US Educational Advisory Service; see the 'Useful addresses' section for contact details), which can arrange exchanges lasting up to 18 months.

Another possibility is to look at changing your hours. Can you go part-time, perhaps with a job-share (see Chapter 8)? Or can you keep the same number of hours but move to a working pattern that suits you better? Night work, for example, takes its toll on anyone, but you may find that although you could put up with this when you were 30 you can't now that you are 50. Your employer might have had arrangements for moving older people from nights to day-work in the past but abandoned them when unemployment was higher and there was no problem in filling posts. It may now be possible to get these arrangements reinstated. (See below, if you think the current work pattern is affecting your health.)

If the working environment is the problem

It may be that the problem lies in your environment – perhaps the way you are being managed, the work you are being asked to do or the physical surroundings. If any of these is particularly bad, you may want simply to shake the dust off your feet and worry later about what you will do with your life. But it's sensible – and may do more for your self-respect and self-confidence – to consider what can be done about dealing with the problems rather than escaping from them. Again, you have legal minimum rights. For example:

- There are requirements on space, ventilation, temperature and such matters as adequate sanitary arrangements, work breaks and so on. There are also limits on the levels of noise in your workplace.
- There are limits on the number of hours you can be asked to work each week.
- Employers have a responsibility, under the Health and Safety at Work etc Act 1974, to assess both physical and mental risks to their workforce, and then do something about them.
- Harassment, victimisation and bullying could all be considered a health risk; they may also constitute unlawful sexual or racial discrimination.
- Perhaps the most common issue for people today, given the way many workplaces are managed, is stress. The Health and Safety Executive (HSE) has said quite clearly to employers that 'It's your duty in law to make sure that your employees aren't made ill by their work.' They also point out that employers who don't take stress seriously may leave themselves open to compensation claims from employees who have suffered ill-health from work-related stress.

To find out about your rights, look at the Trades Union Congress (TUC) guide *Your Rights at Work* (see the 'Further reading' section for details). For specific issues, ACAS, the Department of Trade and Industry (DTI) and the HSE publish readable material. For example, the HSE have a whole series of booklets and leaflets on different hazards. Many of them are written for employers rather than employees, but this may be an advantage, because you can use them to demonstrate to your employer just what they should be doing. The HSE's short guide on work-related stress, for instance, says that 'plain good management can reduce work-related stress when it is already occurring, and can prevent it in the first place'.

All the government bodies have websites, so if you have access to the internet you can browse around and find the information you need. (See the 'Useful addresses' section for contact details.)

You may feel, though, that whereas finding out your rights is relatively easy, enforcing them is much less so. Legally, there should be a grievance procedure at work, and there will usually be Health and Safety Representatives with whom you can raise the question of a health risk. If you belong to a trade union or professional organisation, ask them for help. If you aren't a member, it could be wise to join before you stick your neck out. Under the Employment Relations Act 1999, even if your employer does not recognise unions, they must allow you to bring a representative to a disciplinary or grievance hearing.

Other health problems

You may have a health problem that is not related to work, or that will remain even after the work-related cause has been taken away. Under the Disability Discrimination Act 1995, employers must 'make a reasonable adjustment to working conditions of the workplace that would help to accommodate a disabled person', to quote the ACAS Guide. You may not think of yourself as disabled – or wish to think of yourself in that way – but using the Act could be one way of enabling you to go on working while not harming your health.

'Disability' in the context of the Disability Discrimination Act means anyone 'with a physical or mental impairment which has a substantial and long-term adverse effect upon his or her ability to carry out normal day-to-day activities'. The Disability Rights Commission says that more than 4 million people would consider that they meet this definition. One example the Commission gives in its booklets is that 'it might be a reasonable adjustment for your employer to alter your hours of work if your disability makes it difficult for you to travel to and from work at busy times, or if you need to fit in with a carer's schedule'.

The Act currently applies only to employers of 15 or more people, but you may be able to bring moral pressure if your company has fewer staff. In the public sector, the Treasury has become very anxious about the level of ill-health retirements in areas such as the health service and teaching, and has issued guidance to other government bodies about what they should be offering. This includes saying that:

'Employers should put into place procedures which ensure that

- Redeployment is always considered when existing duties are contributing to an employee's ill-health; and
- Rehabilitation is actively addressed as part of sickness absence management.'

The Treasury also suggests that in some cases the employer should pay rehabilitation allowances, when normal sick pay has been exhausted, if this makes it more likely that someone will be able to return to work rather than taking ill-health retirement.

People working in the public sector worry that the main effect of the Treasury's pressure could be to deny those who really need ill-health retirement the opportunity to take it. However, it does provide some positive statements that can be quoted back at public employers about restructuring your work.

Effects on your pension

Whether you downshift, are redeployed, work reduced hours or take a break from work, you will need to check out the effects on your pension. There can be some problems, because of the way the maximum limits on benefits and contributions laid down by the Inland Revenue work. These are generally soluble – but it is important that action is taken at the right time.

- If you belong to an *employer's pension scheme* where the pension is calculated in terms of your *final earnings*, check whether the amount of pension you can have at retirement will be adversely affected if your earnings are reduced. Most schemes have rules that allow them to calculate the pension by taking an earnings figure from as many as ten years before retirement, revalued in line with inflation; but the Inland Revenue's rules on the maximum benefit you are allowed mean that some people cannot take advantage of this. The Local Government scheme, and some others, have specific rules to protect the pension when someone is redeployed. There will also be rules about how part-time earnings, and periods of unpaid temporary absence, are treated. Look in your pension scheme booklet for a summary of the rules. There should also be a name and address there from which you can obtain further information; ask whatever questions you need for clarification, and get answers in writing, before committing yourself.

■ If you belong to an employer's pension scheme that is *money purchase* (that is, the amount of pension depends on how much money has gone in and how well it has been invested), paying in less if your earnings go down will mean that your pension will be smaller. However, it should be possible for you to contribute a higher percentage of your reduced earnings so that the total amount going in remains roughly the same; the problem will then be whether you can afford it.

■ If you have a *personal or stakeholder pension*, again, paying in a reduced amount will mean reduced benefits, but topping up your contributions will usually be possible. Check what the charges are; there are *some* personal pensions in which making any change in the level of your contributions costs money (this would never apply to the new stakeholder pensions). It will be worth getting advice from a financial adviser, even if you have to pay a fee for it, to establish the position and if necessary renegotiate the terms.

Look in the *Pensions Handbook*, also published by Age Concern Books, for details of the different sorts of pension scheme, how to get advice and how to sort out complaints about your pension.

The Inland Revenue does not allow you, unfortunately, to draw your occupational pension while staying in the same employment, even if you have moved to part-time work. Among Government ideas for promoting the employment of older people are some proposals to introduce more flexible retirement rules. The new rules may allow people to stay with their employer and draw their pension at the same time, which would make it easier for someone to move to lighter duties or part-time working. However, there's no timetable yet for when this rule change will happen.

Some pension schemes will allow you to draw the pension (but not the lump sum) built up from Additional Voluntary Contributions (AVCs), before the main pension and while staying in the same job. This could be some help, but for most people the amount built up from AVCs is too small to make a great deal of impact. If you have a deferred pension from an earlier job, you may also be able to start drawing this early. But with either AVCs or deferred pensions drawn early, there is likely to be a reduction in the annual amount paid because the same fund has to be made to last longer, and this reduction could be considerable.

There are no restrictions on drawing a personal pension while staying in the same employment, though again you will find that your pension pot will buy a smaller pension than it would have done if you were older. It is *possible*, therefore, to get round the restrictions on occupational pensions by transferring the money instead to a personal pension, and then perhaps using Income Drawdown (explained in the *Pensions Handbook*). You would lose the very important guarantees that you have in many occupational pension schemes, however. So think carefully, and take professional advice, before doing this.

3 Your feelings about losing your job

Losing your job, or seeing the job you thought you had change out of all recognition, is unlikely to be good news. You have had a settled environment where you know people and understand how the system works. Now you are faced with all sorts of uncertainties.

However well they think they are prepared, when the break comes many people find it almost as bad as if they have been bereaved. You could find yourself feeling:

- hurt and undervalued;
- angry;
- lacking in confidence.

Even if you have volunteered for redundancy or early retirement, you've probably still felt pressure to go. This can be very unsubtle. You might have been offered redeployments that were known would be unacceptable, or had heavy hints dropped about 'leaving the jobs for younger people'. Or you may have felt that you had to take a decision quickly – a 'buy now while stocks last' sort of approach. Often it is stressed that the early retirement or redundancy package being provided is on offer for a limited time, and that any future redundancies will be on worse terms.

Feeling rejected

It is only natural that you will feel angry and hurt about what is happening. The very word 'redundancy' implies being unwanted. If you feel that you have been doing a good job for your employer, this is humiliating and may cast a shadow over all that you have achieved in the past. The employer might have looked for commitment and loyalty in the past, and you could have responded by identifying yourself with the firm. When someone employed by a household-name employer is asked what they do, they are quite likely to reply 'I work for XYZ', rather than 'I am an accountant' or 'I manage a shop'.

To have that basic framework knocked away can cast doubt on your whole self-image. Often the response is to feel that you have lost control. You knew where you were before, but now you do not. According to Clare Cassidy, of career consultants Penna Sanders & Sidney:

> 'There is certainly less stigma attached to redundancy than there used to be, and a more general acknowledgement that the reasons for redundancy are usually to do with strategic decisions at a high level, that you are not to be blamed. But even if you know this, it hurts an awful lot when it happens to you.'

Stan, who now manages a voluntary organisation but used to be a senior manager at British Gas, says that when he was having to make a change he encountered lots of people who had been in British Gas since leaving school:

> 'It was all they had ever done, they were scared of the unknown, they wanted to hold on to what they had got. The company was restructuring in a radical way, in fact being ripped apart. There were a few suicides, and some people were totally traumatised by the changes.'

People often lose confidence in themselves, feeling that they will never be able to get a job for the same salary elsewhere, or that they have no skills that will be valued or 'saleable' on the open market. It can be worse for men in this age group than for women, because they will often have a built-in feeling that they are the breadwinner, the head of the household. This gives them the self-image of someone capable of 'providing' – and redundancy reduces or destroys this.

What can make it worse is that, even in large firms, it is quite common for employers to tell people who are leaving not to work out their notice periods – either because they feel it will be bad for the morale of other staff or because they fear sabotage or misuse of confidential information once a person no longer feels a loyalty to them. So you may get the 'black plastic bag' treatment – being escorted to your desk where you empty the contents into a plastic bin-liner, handing over your keys to the company car and leaving the premises all within a couple of hours. Don't take it personally. It will be a policy decision at a high level, nothing to do with you.

However, try to resist the pressure to go immediately if you can, or appeal against it if necessary, because it can reduce your employment rights. In any case, being able to carry on in a responsible manner is important, as it allows you time to adjust, and often to hand over or complete work in progress, so allowing closure and a feeling of finishing what you have started.

Talking about your feelings

However it happens, you will need time and space to adjust. The process that people go through is almost one of grieving. Talk through your feelings with someone who will listen sympathetically, and who will also help you to see how you can move on to something else. If you can get yourself referred to an outplacement consultant (see page 26) use the opportunity to get your grievances off your chest. According to Clare Cassidy of Penna Sanders & Sidney:

'I or the managing consultant will always have the initial meeting with a new client, and this can last an hour or an hour and a half. This often takes place very shortly after they have been told about the redundancy. People feel angry and hurt, and they do need the opportunity to get their feelings off their chests. We acknowledge their feelings but say, "Now you are in contact with us and that is the first step in moving on." We tell them about their outplacement programme, give them an initial task and send them away feeling some hope.'

If you do not have access to an outplacement service, there may be other sources of help. If your employer are offering a counselling service, it is well worth taking advantage of it. The Advisory, Conciliation and Arbitration Service (ACAS, see page 186) recommends that, if employers' resources permit, they should use a trained counsellor or welfare officer for people being made redundant, or give personnel officers training for this job. Many larger employers will do this, or perhaps find a suitable person to run a group workshop. If your employer do not offer anything, it could be worth pressuring them to do so.

Counselling is available on the NHS, though in short supply, and you could ask your GP for a referral. Otherwise, you could find someone privately (try the British Association for Counselling and Psychother-apy (see page 186) for names of their members in your area), talk to a local clergyman, or perhaps ring the Samaritans. The Samaritans are not there only for people who feel suicidal, but for anyone who needs an ear to bend because they feel despairing in one way or another.

Another possibility is to look for a suitable course or workshop, per-haps on a one- or two-day basis or residential over a weekend. Word of mouth is probably the best way to ensure that it is a reputable course and that your time will not be wasted, so ask around for personal recommendations.

Of course, you will be looking for support from your family and imme-diate circle of friends. But it is not fair to dump everything on them – they will be going through much the same sort of feelings as you about what is happening, and may be too much involved themselves to be able to offer constructive help. Looking for someone else to talk to is likely to help them as much as it does you.

If you don't give yourself the chance to talk through your feelings, they will fester and could sour your life. Many of the ex-staff she knows, one adviser says, find it almost impossible to go back into the building where they once worked, even for a social occasion, because of the feel-ings it stirs up. Two and a half years on, she found herself being accosted at a party by an ex-colleague who was vitriolic about her for-mer manager and quite unable to acknowledge that she had had a generous package and special arrangements made.

Taking a break

Whatever your longer-term plans may be, in the short term you may feel you need a break, at least of a few weeks. The temptation to do this is strong but it can be a double-edged sword. One adviser likens the need to carry straight on with the search for the next opportunity to getting back on the horse after you have fallen off it – if you don't do so immediately, taking up the reins again is considerably more difficult. It is also rather easier to find another job while you are still employed.

On the other hand, if you are fortunate enough to find work while you are still finishing your notice period, it may be wise to arrange a gap between the end of one job and the beginning of the next. This gives you the time to grieve, and it marks the changeover point between one part of your life and the next. That will help reduce the amount of baggage you carry (the 'When I was at X we did it *this* way' habit) from one to the other. You may also feel stressed with all the pressures of finishing off work and planning for the future.

If you need to go straight on to Jobseeker's Allowance (see pages 51–56), taking a break is not made easy but, in any case, there may well be a few weeks before you are able to sign on – for instance, if you have been given payments in lieu of notice (as explained on page 51).

If you are pessimistic about the future, you may feel anxious about spending much of the redundancy payment or pension lump sum you have taken with you from your last employer. Alternatively, you may feel demob-happy and want to blow the lot, which is equally unwise. It is up to you how much you spend, but certainly many people feel entitled to invest a sensible proportion of their pay-off in a decent holiday or something they have always wanted to do.

Taking a longer break

Taking a lengthy break of several months or more is a rather different matter from taking the few weeks that you would have been entitled to when you were at work anyway. You might feel, for instance, that now is your chance to fulfil a dream, such as a climbing holiday in the Alps or backpacking through India. The opportunity to take a longer break than you have ever been able to before may feel too good to miss.

You do need to appreciate, though, that the longer the break you take, the more difficult it will be to get back into the same sort of role as you were in before; it is remarkable how quickly new developments happen and contacts become stale. If your aim is to set out on a radically different path, six months away may not matter and may even be an advantage if it blows the cobwebs out of your mind; but if you want to stay in the same professional area, it could mean considerable extra work picking up the threads again on your return.

It is important, therefore, to work out your future direction, make your plans and put some preparations in hand for what you are going to do when you come back. For instance, if you are planning to do some consultancy work, start telling people about it, build up your contact list, remind them that you will be back in X weeks' time and will be in touch then. If you will be looking for another job, then write your CV (see pages 116–120), find out about recruitment agencies, and perhaps book yourself on to a training course before you go. If you let things drift and think 'Oh, I'll worry about all that when I come back', the chances are that they will continue to drift after you return.

4 What you may get at the end of your old job

The package you receive when you leave your job will probably be made up of several elements. The law specifies minimum periods of notice and minimum redundancy payments, but many employers offer considerably more than these. This chapter looks at your statutory entitlements and the benefits that employers might offer in addition. It also looks at the tax position, and what happens if you have a personal pension.

In general, the entitlements outlined below apply to both full-time and part-time workers, without any lower limit on hours. See pages 38–40 for suggestions on how to sort out problems that may arise.

Time to look for new work or training

If you are being made redundant and are entitled to a statutory redundancy payment, you have a legal right to 'reasonable' time off to look for new work or training. Many redundancy agreements, or employers' practices, provide this more widely to people being made redundant whether they come under the statutory provisions or not. ACAS also recommends this. What 'reasonable' means is not specified, but there are employment tribunal cases suggesting that up to two days a week should be allowed. A survey by employment specialists Industrial Relations Services (IRS) in 1998 found that practices varied from offering just four days to virtually unlimited time. This time could be used for:

- visiting the Jobcentre Plus office and recruitment agencies;
- travelling to and attending interviews;
- finding out about training opportunities.

For more information, see the DTI booklet PL703, *Time Off for Job Hunting or to Arrange Training when Facing Redundancy* (see page 189 for contact details).

Other help with job hunting

ACAS suggests that employers should themselves contact the local Jobcentre Plus office. If there are to be large-scale redundancies, they should bring Jobcentre Plus staff to the site and give them facilities for interviewing people and discussing possibilities. The employer could also contact other local employers to see what vacancies they have.

Many employers also offer 'outplacement' services. These are run by specialist consultancy firms that can provide help with interview techniques, advice on career planning, assistance with making job applications and so on. The cost is usually borne by the employer. The survey by IRS found that more than two-thirds of the employers responding offered this, though for some it was only for people at more senior grades. Some employers used external services, while others ran in-house training courses for all staff, or took different approaches for senior and junior staff.

If you are offered outplacement help, it is generally worth taking it up. According to Clare Cassidy of consultants Penna Sanders & Sidney:

'We see a lot of people in their 50s who perceive enhanced problems because of their age. They may not be eligible for pensions yet, so they don't have financial security. If they have reached a reasonable salary level, they worry that younger candidates will be cheaper and more attractive to employers. They need to understand that they have a huge amount to offer and that they are of value.

'Really, what outplacement consultants do is not rocket science, but it involves a lot of common sense and motivational skills.'

Notice periods

Most people have a notice period specified in their contract of employment, and this should normally be followed unless *you* agree to waive it in return for a payment in lieu of notice. If you do agree to this, you must be given at least the amount of wages you would have been paid if you had remained for the notice period. (See page 42 for details of how this is taxed, and page 51 for the effect it may have on any social security benefits.) Employment advisers generally don't recommend that people waive their rights in this way.

Minimum notice periods are laid down by law:

- By the employee: 1 week.
- By the employer, where the continuous period of employment was:
  - less than two years: 1 week;
  - between two and twelve years: 1 week for each year of continuous employment (eg 3 weeks after three years' employment);
  - twelve years or more: 12 weeks.

If your contract provides for a longer notice period than the legal minimum, you are entitled to rely on whatever is the most beneficial. (This means that, even if your contract specifies that you must give, say, three months' notice, you can leave after one week.)

Never leave just because you believe redundancy is going to happen, unless this has been confirmed in writing, giving a date when it will be implemented. You will lose your rights to redundancy pay if you do – and anyway your guess could turn out to be wrong.

Right to consultation

Employers have a legal duty to consult any trade unions representing the workforce, or workplace representatives where there is no union, before declaring a redundancy. If an employer does not meet the statutory requirements for consultation, an employment tribunal can give a 'protective award' of up to 90 days' pay.

In some cases, your contract of employment may include restrictions on what work you can do after leaving that particular employer. If this is written too broadly – for instance, barring you from a whole industry – it is unlikely that a court would enforce it. More usually, it will simply bar you from approaching that employer's clients for a period.

Other employers will require, or may offer as part of a deal to get you to leave without too much fuss, what is commonly described as 'gardening leave'. This means that you have a long notice period, during which you must not come into your workplace or take up another job. The consolation is that you will be paid and you should retain all other benefits, because you are technically still employed; the disadvantage is that your skills and contacts may be becoming stale – from the employer's point of view, that is indeed the whole point! It does not stop you, of course, from making plans and brushing up your skills, nor from simply going away on holiday and coming back refreshed.

Redundancy payments

The law lays down minimum levels of redundancy pay, though many employers offer more. They are:

- one and a half weeks' pay for each year of employment in which you were aged 41 or more;
- one week's pay for each year of employment in which you were aged 22–40, inclusive;
- half a week's pay for each year of employment at any age up to 21, inclusive.

A maximum of 20 years (the last 20 years' service) can be taken into account; the maximum 'pay' for these purposes is currently (2002–3) a maximum of £250 a week. If your pay varies, perhaps because you are on piecework, it is averaged over the last 12 weeks. There is no statutory right to redundancy pay if you are over 65. However, under the Sex Discrimination Act 1987, women between the State retirement age of 60 and 65 must be given the same rights as men of the same age. In the year before your 65th birthday, statutory entitlements are reduced by 1/12th for every month after the 64th birthday, although there is a legal decision (Nash v Mash Roe Group, 1998), suggesting that this is discriminatory against men.

Redundancy pay can, in certain cases, be offset against money coming from your pension scheme. If the annual value of the pension is a third or more of your annual pay, the right to a statutory redundancy payment may be lost altogether. If it is less than a third of your annual pay, the redundancy payment can be reduced. These rules apply only where the pension is coming into effect within 90 weeks after the dismissal, and the employer must give notice in writing that they intend to do this.

It is, however, very rare for employers to make use of these rules in order to cut back on the statutory redundancy payment. As explained on page 37, they are more likely to offer a trade-off between different forms of additional payment.

> For more information, see the DTI booklets PL808, *Redundancy Payments*, and RPL1, *Offsetting Pension Payments against Redundancy Pay* (for contact details, see page 189).

Packages better than the minimum

When employers want to reduce staffing without damaging the organisation, they may offer generous terms to employees who are willing to go. There are two elements to this: the redundancy (or severance) pay, and the early retirement pension and lump sum under the employer's pension scheme, which are covered on pages 31–40.

Many larger employers give more than the legal minimum for redundancy or severance, at least for longer-serving staff. One survey, carried out in 1998 by Industrial Relations Services and cited in its journal *Employment Trends*, found that more than four-fifths of the respondents made payments above the legal minimum. According to the survey:

> 'Some use the legal minimum as a base, and make additional payments on top. Others have systems which give employees more weeks' pay per year of service than the statutory minimum. Then there are those who have developed their own arrangements for linking age and service, modelled on the statutory scheme but giving enhanced payments.'

The survey also revealed that 95 per cent of the companies responding treated part-timers in the same way as their full-time counterparts when calculating their reckonable service.

Enforcing your legal rights

Make sure you get your redundancy notice in writing, with the effective date clearly stated. Discussion and estimates will not be a strong basis on which to bring any future claim.

Before you finally leave the company, you have a legal right to a written statement setting out how the payment to you has been worked out, under section 165 of the Employment Rights Act 1996. This should break down all payments you receive on leaving, whether they are statutory or additional.

Employers, especially small ones, may not understand the legal position, or they may be unwilling to fulfil their obligations. It is not always clear when a job loss is counted as a redundancy, and you may need to dispute this. If you think your employer has got things wrong and you are a member of a trade union or staff association, go to it with any problems. A Citizens Advice Bureau or (in larger cities) a law centre, may be able to provide free advice.

Alternatively, you could ask ACAS (address on page 186) to explain to your employer what your rights are, and possibly to take enforcement action. You have six months (rather than the usual three) to bring an Employment Tribunal claim over non-payment of redundancy money.

If a package that is considerably better than the statutory minimum is included in your contract of employment, or in a collective agreement covering you, or if it has become 'custom and practice' over a period of time, this should also be legally enforceable. Even the best employers, however, often retain a certain amount of discretion, or make sure that there is some small print in the rules to allow them some room for manoeuvre if the costs become higher than they expect. So check the relevant documents before taking the matter further.

If your employer, or someone in a position to speak for the employer such as the local human resources manager, make a firm commitment relating to the package you will receive on redundancy or retirement, they may have created a contract which they are bound by, even if it turns out that they have miscalculated the figures. If they press you to take action as a result of an estimated offer and you then do so, again they could have created a binding commitment on their part. But the details do need to be in writing, with a statement of the effective date. Just discussion and estimates on their own will not be enough to let you bring a claim against them. Ask your union or professional association for help, or go to ACAS or a specialist employment lawyer.

The Citizens Advice Bureau, or a law centre if you are lucky enough to live in an area where the local authority pays for one, may also be able to help.

If the employer has gone out of business

If your employer has gone into liquidation or receivership and there is not enough left to pay the redundancy payments, *statutory* redundancy pay can be claimed from the National Insurance Fund. In these circumstances you will certainly need help from one of the sources listed above. You will probably save time and money if all those affected work as a group, rather than each doing their own thing.

Your employer's pension

What pension you will be entitled to will depend on:

- your age;
- the legal rules enforced by the Inland Revenue and the Department for Work and Pensions (DWP, replacing the Department of Social Security; deals with social security benefits and issues relating to unemployment, disability and caring: Jobcentre Plus deals with anyone below Sate pension age, and the Pension Service deals with any State pension issues);
- the provisions of the scheme;
- the willingness of the employer or the pension fund trustees to top up your pension.

Note This book does not go into detail on pensions because there is so much else to cover. For information on the legal position, and how pension schemes are set up and run, see the *Pensions Handbook* published annually by Age Concern Books (details on page 199). Make sure that you have an up-to-date copy of your own pension scheme booklet (or policy booklet if it is a personal pension), and copies of the benefit statements you should have received over the last few years. If your employer has an internet or intranet site for staff use, check that, too. Some of them include very helpful pensions calculators on their sites. Some insurance companies, financial advisers and other financial websites include similar calculators that can be used for personal pensions (but make sure you understand what assumptions they are making about the future).

If you have been in the scheme for less than two years

If you have been in an employer's pension scheme for only a short time – under two years – you are likely to receive a partial refund of your contributions. About half, possibly even less, will come back to you; the rest may go to the Inland Revenue as tax, and in some cases to buy you back into the State Second Pension (S2P) if the scheme was contracted out of it. Some employers' pension schemes, where the pension is based on the amount of money that is invested (money-purchase) rather than on your earnings, will not give a refund however short your service.

More than two years, but aged under 50

If you have been in the scheme longer than two years but are under the age of 50, you will be able to draw a pension only if you are suffering from ill-health. According to the Inland Revenue definition, this means:

> 'physical or mental deterioration which is sufficiently serious to prevent the individual from following his or her normal employment, or which seriously impairs his or her earning capacity. It does not mean simply a decline in earning capacity.'

About 50 per cent of schemes define 'ill-health' as meaning inability to do your own job or a similar one. Others define it as inability to do *any* job, which is much more rigorous. A few have different scales for different levels of disability. It could be the employer, the company doctor or the trustees who decide whether you qualify. Check in your own scheme's rules. In general, you will need to be examined by an independent medical adviser – except in the most clear-cut cases – before a pension is granted.

If you do not qualify under the ill-health rules but you are aged under 50, you will be entitled to a **deferred pension**, which you have a right to transfer elsewhere if you wish. However, whether transferring is the best idea depends very much on your circumstances; see the *Pensions*

Handbook (details on page 199) for more information. The deferred pension must be increased each year until you draw it. Under many schemes' rules, you will be able to start drawing the deferred pension once you reach 50, but it will be at a much reduced rate.

If you are 50 or over

If you are 50 or over (or sometimes 55) most schemes will allow you to draw an early-retirement pension, but the amount available can vary enormously, as explained below. What you are offered at the time when you leave may also be much more generous than what you will get later, if you take a deferred pension and then change your mind and go back later.

If yours is a final earnings scheme

The 'final-earnings' or 'final-salary' pension (the most common type for large employers) is based on:

- your years of membership of the scheme;
- your 'pensionable earnings' at the time the pension is calculated;
- and the 'accrual rate', which means the rate at which your pension builds up.

Typically, someone leaving at 65 with 40 years' service gets 40/60ths or 40/80ths of their pensionable earnings as a pension. In many schemes, some parts of the earnings are *not* pensionable, particularly items such as overtime and bonus, so you will need to check this point in your own scheme booklet.

You can usually convert part of the pension into a tax-free lump sum. In public service schemes, you get the lump sum automatically, without having to give up any part of your pension. The starting pension in these schemes is lower than it would be in a good private sector scheme (1/80th of final earnings for each year of service, rather than 1/60th), but it is then guaranteed to rise in line with inflation. (The new Civil Service scheme, PCSPS 2000, however, is a 60th scheme with the option to convert.)

If you retire early from a final-earnings scheme, your pension calculation can suffer in three ways:

- You will have had fewer years in the job, so the pension will be calculated on shorter service.
- Your earnings on which the pension is based are likely to be lower than you might have expected if you had stayed in the job.
- You are going to be drawing it for much longer. If your employer want to keep the amount spent on your pension the same as if you had worked to the normal retirement age, there has to be an 'actuarial reduction' in the pension income paid so that the same pot of money is spread over longer.

A full actuarial reduction could mean that somebody taking early retirement at 50 sees a cut in their pension (after the reduced years of service have been taken into account) of 70 per cent – leaving only 30 per cent to live on. A more typical reduction these days might be 3 per cent for each year not worked. A 55-year-old person would then lose 30 per cent of their pension by retiring ten years early.

There are also some complications relating to the Department for Work and Pensions (DWP) rules. Most schemes are 'contracted out' of the State Second Pension (S2P), which replaced the State Earnings-Related Pension Scheme (SERPS) in April 2002. Until April 1997, the scheme had to guarantee to provide the equivalent of what you would have had from SERPS, at the same age as it would have been paid by the State (60 for a woman; 65 for a man). This guaranteed amount is called the **Guaranteed Minimum Pension** (GMP). In April 1997 the rules changed and no GMPs have built up since then. However, for someone taking their pension within the next few years after a long time with their employer, the bulk of their pension will have been earned before 1997 and so will not be affected. In order to safeguard this commitment without spending extra money on it, some schemes will not allow you to draw an early retirement pension at all, or they restrict the lump sum that you can take.

How much final-earnings schemes offer

In practice, most final-earnings schemes offer rather more than the minimum. They often have different scales of benefit, depending on why you are leaving your job. The least generous pensions are usually paid when you take early retirement because you wish to, rather than because of your health or at your employer's suggestion.

A survey by the National Association of Pension Funds (NAPF) in 2000 revealed that around 50 per cent of final-earnings pension schemes in the private sector gave a pension based on all potential years of service up to normal retirement age when someone was retiring owing to serious ill-health. (For instance, a 55-year-old person received ten years' credit to take their service up to 65.) The public sector gives rather less than this. However, about 10 per cent of private sector schemes reduce the pension on early retirement whatever the reason, including ill-health. Around half the schemes surveyed had minimum service requirements, ranging from one to five years, before a person could become eligible for an ill-health pension.

Alternatively, there may be a permanent health insurance (PHI) scheme, giving a proportion of earnings for as long as you qualify under its rules, or for a certain number of years.

For retiring early 'at the employer's request', the same survey found that two-thirds of private sector schemes, and nearly all public sector ones, would allow someone to take an unreduced pension from a certain age, perhaps 55 or 60, while others might have a formula combining age and service. Voluntary early retirement tends to be treated less favourably, with many more schemes making an 'actuarial reduction'.

'Integrated' pension schemes

A number of pension schemes in the private sector are 'integrated' with the State pension. That is, when the pension is calculated, an amount is deducted to take account of the fact that you are expected to be getting the State basic pension at the same time. This is unpopular at the best of times but can cause real difficulties for those retiring too young to receive the State pension. There are various ways in which schemes deal with this:

- Most straightforwardly, this 'integration factor' may not be deducted until you reach State retirement age.
- The deduction may be made, but then a 'bridging pension' may be paid, equivalent to the amount of State pension or some other figure.
- There may be a 'variable pension option' so that you take a higher amount of pension before State retirement age, and then a lower one afterwards. There is usually an actuarial calculation of how much the reduction needs to be, to ensure that there is no cost to the scheme.

Although either of the first two will happen automatically if that is what the rules say, the third is your choice and needs some thinking about. Essentially, you are gambling on your own life expectancy; if this is longer than average, you will have that many more years of reduced pension. Check exactly how the calculation is done, and what effect it will have on future pension increases and on the pension for your spouse.

Money-purchase schemes

The type of pension most often available in small companies, and some large ones, is a 'money-purchase' scheme. It could be an employer's pension scheme, or it could be a group personal pension, or the employer's designated stakeholder pension scheme, or simply a personal or stakeholder pension you have taken out for yourself. In this money-purchase scheme, your money and any contributions from your employer are invested, usually with an insurance company. When you retire you can take a certain amount as a lump sum and the rest of the fund is used to buy an annuity, which provides you with a pension for the rest of your life.

Depending on the terms of the contract, you may find that you lose out heavily by retiring early with a pension of this sort. There are several reasons for this:

- Less money will have gone into the scheme, and it will have been invested for fewer years, so the amount available in the scheme will be less than if you had carried on until normal retirement age.
- Each pound's worth of annuity pension purchased will cost more, because you can expect to draw it for longer.
- Many insurance contracts (though not stakeholder pensions, by law) apply heavy penalties if a contract is terminated early.

Getting the best possible deal

The details in pension scheme booklets may tell only part of the story. Often there are unpublished rules, or your company's human resources department may have authorisation to go over the normal limits in some cases. So it is always worth negotiating to see whether there could be more to come. If a whole workplace, or a whole company, is being closed down, there is likely to be much less scope for this than if selected people are being asked to go. Again, there is usually a difference between large and small companies here. The larger ones, with a public relations image to think of, are likely to be much more generous than the smaller ones.

A trade-off is frequently offered between the (non-statutory) redundancy lump sum and the pension – that is, you may be able to choose between an enhanced lump sum and the standard pension, or a standard lump sum and an enhanced pension. Alternatively, you may be able to use part of the redundancy payment yourself to buy extra benefits. This can have tax advantages (see page 43) and also give you more income to live on. Check that you know exactly what is on offer and how it works out. Ask for an interview with your pensions department if you're at all unclear. Points to check out include:

- What lump sum are you being offered, and how much pension must you give up to buy it? Because you would expect to draw the pension for longer, a younger person should be offered a higher lump sum per pound of pension given up than someone of 65. So check if this is so in your case and, if not, ask why.
- How long will the pension and lump sum take to come through? There can be a nasty gap between the last pay cheque and the first pension cheque. It's easy enough to arrange an overdraft or to take money out of your lump sum, but it could be difficult if it catches you unawares.
- Are there other options that you could take to increase the amount of pension you will get? In some cases, waiting until the next tax year, or the beginning of the next month, or your next birthday can make a substantial difference to your pension. (Legally, a pensions administrator does not have to volunteer this sort of information – though a good one probably would – but would have to explain if you specifically asked. They are unlikely to give you any advice about what you should do, though, in case it should turn out badly and you decide to sue them.)
- What pension increases are being made under the scheme rules? In the public sector, no increases are given until you reach the age of 55, but then a 'catching up' increase is given, raising the pension in line with the rise in prices (not earnings). This is much less common in the private sector.

- Have the trustees given more in practice, on a discretionary basis, in the past (and so might be expected to do so again in the future)?
- What is payable if you die before starting to draw the benefit, if you defer the pension?

If the pension on offer is quite small, or heavily reduced because of early payment, it might be possible to defer it and draw it later. However, any special increases in a severance package may be on a 'take it or leave it' basis, and so you lose them if you defer. You may also find that if your health subsequently deteriorates, you cannot then start drawing the deferred pension but have to wait until the scheme's normal retirement age, or can only draw it at a much reduced rate.

A money-purchase pension (explained above) is likely to be much less flexible. It's generally not possible to renegotiate one of the contracts on which these are based at the time when the early retirement or redundancy arises. The only way to get a better deal, therefore, is for you or your employer to put in extra cash to fill the gap. How easy this is will depend on the reasons for the job loss. Norwich Union, for example, announced during 2000 that, for anyone made redundant after the age of 50, it would make a one-off contribution to their money-purchase pension of up to 24 per cent of their salary.

Again, it may be possible to make a trade-off between your lump sum and your pension. If you are buying an annuity, check that you are getting the best terms and the most suitable kind; you can usually exercise an 'open market option' to get the best rate on the market. It may also be possible to go for the alternative of 'income drawdown' – taking money directly out of your pension fund to live on for a few years at least – if your fund is large enough. See the *Pensions Handbook* for more details.

Problems over your pension

By law, every occupational pension scheme has to have an 'internal disputes procedure', and this should be your first port of call if you have a complaint or grievance. Your pension scheme booklet should give you details of this. It must have two stages, with the complaint looked at again perhaps by the pensions manager at the first stage, and then by all the trustees as a second stage (except in public sector schemes, where there are no trustees so generally the relevant government department deals with it). In many schemes there is a 'zero-stage' as well, when the administrators try to sort out complaints informally before they go into the complaint/grievance procedure, and it is usually worth using this because there might just have been a simple misunderstanding.

OPAS (Office of the Pensions Advisory Service) will help people sort out complaints and problems with their pension scheme (see page 194 for contact details). They will take up complaints after you have gone through the disputes procedure, but say that a problem is often easier to resolve if it is brought to OPAS earlier, perhaps to help you formulate the complaint to start with. The final port of call is the Pensions Ombudsman, who has the power to make a binding decision – though it can still be challenged in a court on a point of law. Going to the Ombudsman is free but it can take a very long time. Most disputes are resolved, fortunately, before they get there.

The sorts of dispute that may arise include:

- You may consider you are ill enough to justify having an ill-health retirement pension but the trustees refuse to give you one.
- Your pension scheme may have changed more than once, or your company may have been taken over, and you think you are entitled to more pension for previous service than you are being offered.
- You might have been given a quotation of one level of pension when you were discussing early retirement, but in fact it turns out to be considerably less.

It will help reduce the chances of a dispute if you ask for the details of a decision, and the reasons for it, to be in writing; also check whether a figure is just a rough estimate or a firm quotation. Make sure you understand how the figure has been arrived at, and what items have gone into the calculation. Most pension schemes are well administered but mistakes can arise even then and some are rather poor at paperwork, so it is always worthwhile checking. OPAS has a helpline (see page 194), which you could ring for an explanation if you find that your pensions manager or adviser is unable to talk in jargon-free terms. There are legal deadlines on pension schemes for giving you information you ask for – two months, for instance, for a statement of your benefits – and OPAS will be able to give you details of these for any particular case.

Since April 2001, the Pensions Ombudsman has also been dealing with maladministration in personal pensions, but the Financial Ombudsman Service covers their sales and marketing. If there is any doubt about where you should go, phone OPAS and you will be redirected as appropriate.

Other payments

You may have a number of other payments to come in your final wages – such as 'weeks in hand' (money held back by your employer from your wages when you originally started work), holiday pay, for time off in lieu or accumulated bonuses. There could also be money due from a share-save or share option scheme.

Check out carefully what you are entitled to. Try to get any disputes settled before you leave, when they will be easier to deal with. If you run into problems, talk to your union or staff association (even if your employer does not recognise it), ACAS or the local Citizens Advice Bureau. Executive share options (rights given to you to buy shares at a particular price, usually as part of your overall pay arrangement) can be particularly difficult if you are leaving voluntarily, as the rules generally say that they lapse except in cases of retirement or redundancy. But the company board may have discretion to let you exercise the option within a certain period of time after you leave. It is 'usually worth attempting to persuade the employer to exercise that discretion,' according to employment lawyer Ian Hunter, 'using the argument that it is a real benefit for you and does not increase the "headline figure" (that is, the figure that the public or other employees will notice) of what you are being paid.'

The company car and other non-wage benefits

Some employers continue certain non-pay benefits for a time after employment has finished. You may be offered the opportunity to:

■ buy your company car (though if the company has been leasing this, it will simply go back to the lessor);

- continue subscriptions to BUPA or other organisations at a preferential rate;
- continue being covered for life or disability insurance at your own expense but without needing a medical examination;
- keep a staff discount.

Companies are less generous than they used to be these days, even for those with long service. However, if the offer is made it will usually be worth taking up, if they are things you can make use of and you will be able to afford any other running costs. On the other hand, if the company car is a large high-performance one, and you are planning to move to the countryside and run a craft workshop, you might not want to take it. You may, though, be able to come to an arrangement to swap it for something more suitable; it's always worth asking. You might also be able to arrange to keep certain equipment, such as a laptop computer or a mobile phone, or to buy them at a preferential rate. If your health is dubious, insurance benefits without a medical examination could result in a substantial saving. Check (with an accountant or with the tax office) what the tax position would be.

If you have been employed in a sector such as financial services, you may have had a subsidised mortgage and other low-interest loans. Generally, anyone who leaves will lose these, but to soften the blow the employer may allow you to phase up to the full interest rate over several years. You may have to pay for a life insurance policy to cover the mortgage, if this has been included free in the past. It will be worth trying to negotiate special terms at the time you leave, or you might want to use some or all of your lump sum to reduce the debt.

Membership of associations

Your workplace, or your profession, may have a pensioners' association. Large numbers of these have sprung up in recent years, and they can be a thorn in the employer's side if pension increases are not being given or if the administration is not up to scratch. They may also have access to welfare funds or similar pots of cash for people who are experiencing hardship.

Because of the number of people who have taken early retirement in many firms, occupational pensioners' associations these days are often dominated by 'young' pensioners in their 50s. In some, there is a considerable amount of networking about employment opportunities, and an active social life.

You may be offered continued membership of your union, staff association or professional organisation. There are often reduced membership rates for retirees, or special branches. Even if you are planning to move into a different field, it will often be worth taking this up, at least for the first year or so until you are set in your new direction.

The tax and social security position

The tax position relating to payments at the end of your job varies. The first £30,000 of certain redundancy and severance payments is exempt from tax, and only the excess is taxed. Examples of such payments include:

- genuine 'ex gratia' payments on termination of employment; this means payments that are not included in the contract of employment and do not form part of the wider terms and conditions of employment, including established practices (they are treated as pay in full if they *are* included);
- statutory redundancy payments and lump sum payments for loss of employment from the employer's own non-statutory redundancy scheme;
- payments made because of breach of contract by the employer, for instance by not giving the notice required under the contract, and compensation for wrongful or unfair dismissal.

Where, as part of a package, the employer will provide something that is not a cash payment (eg the continued use of a company car for a period of time), the value of this provision has to be decided and added to the cash amount. The total amount is then taken into account for the purpose of deciding what is taxable.

The Inland Revenue is keen to narrow the circumstances in which you can get tax-free cash. Your employer ought to check the details and ensure that you do not pay more tax than you need. If there seems to be no sign that this is happening, suggest that the firm approach their accountant, or ask for information at an Inland Revenue Tax Enquiry Centre (listed in the phone book).

Lump sums payable from the pension scheme, as part of a retirement or early retirement package, are tax-free (with a very few exceptions). Your employer can also make a payment into the pension scheme, to increase your pension, tax-free. So, if you are likely to receive more than £30,000, it could be far more tax-efficient to get the extra amount paid into your pension, rather than into your hand.

Pension payments are always taxable, normally under PAYE, but not liable for National Insurance. An employer paying out a pension will deduct PAYE at source just as if it was earnings, as will an insurance company or any other provider. National Insurance, however, is not deducted. In general, payments from permanent health insurance schemes set up by the employer (see page 35) will be taxable, but if you have set up your own policy and paid premiums out of your taxable income, the payments should be tax-free. Check the position with your local tax office.

Certain social security benefits such as Incapacity Benefit (except for the short-term lower rate) and Widowed Parent's Allowance are also taxable. The value of the benefit and the employer's or personal pension are added together in order to work out your tax coding, and then all the tax is deducted from the pension.

If you are receiving earnings as well as a pension, check that your employer and the pension scheme are aware of each other's existence, so that the tax coding can be adjusted. If you are self-employed, include the pension on your tax return so that it can be taken into account. Contact your local Inland Revenue Tax Enquiry Centre (address in the phone book) if you are not sure what to do.

Chapter 6 explains what social security benefits you may be able to get when you are unemployed or in poor health. Your entitlement to these will be affected, in one way or another, by the amount you are paid at the end of your job, and how it is made up of the different elements. You are likely to find that there is an 'ineligible period' before you can apply for Jobseeker's Allowance (as explained on page 51) if you receive payments in lieu of notice. Pensions lump sums, however, are treated differently from severance lump sums.

Look at Chapter 6, and take any advice you need, to see how the rules will apply to you *before* you finalise the package. What may seem fairly minor details could have a substantial effect on your benefits.

Checklist on ending your job

- Notice period

  – statutory

  – under contract of employment

  – any payment due in lieu of notice?

- Consultation period

  – any payment due for waiver?

- Redundancy payments

  – statutory

  – employer's scheme

  – will any of it be taxable?

  – expected tax deduction

- Pension scheme – available on early retirement as

  – pension

  – lump sum

  – deferred pension

  – what annual increases are payable?

- Other payments due at end of employment

  – bonus

  – holiday money

  – weeks in hand

  – share scheme

■ Preferential terms on other company assets

   – car

   – other office equipment

   – health insurance

   – subscriptions to union, staff association or professional organisation

   – life assurance

   – other

■ Total lump sum expected (after tax) £ ...

■ Total pension (after tax) £ ...

   – has the offer been confirmed in writing?

   – do you have a breakdown of the figures?

   – when will it be payable?

   – is the package structured in the most tax-advantageous way?

   – effect on claiming Jobseeker's Allowance and other State benefits?

5 Dealing with your new financial situation

Depending on what your plans are, you will have some adjustments to make. Chapter 6 covers the benefits and other help you can ask for from the State but here we look at other financial issues, starting with the one that is probably worrying you most.

Your mortgage and other loans

If you have redundancy insurance on your mortgage, check out what you have to do about it before you leave work, if possible, and make sure you get the right documents. You may need a letter or statement from your employer making it clear that it is their choice rather than yours that you are leaving.

Mortgage insurance is notorious for the small print in the policies that reduces the chance of payouts. So you may have some trouble extracting payments from your insurance company, and need to fight. Again, the Citizens Advice Bureau, or a money advice agency if there is one locally, should be able to help.

You may also have insurance on other loans or on your credit card payments. Check these out and make claims in the same way.

It may be a good use for a redundancy or severance payment to pay off your debts, rather than invest the money. Indeed, you can regard it as an 'investment', as the interest rate you pay as a borrower is almost always going to be higher than the interest rate you receive as a lender – that's how the banks and building societies make their money! Credit cards and store cards, in particular, can have very high rates of interest if you do not pay them off in full each month – something that people do not always appreciate because of the small minimum monthly payments they are allowed to make. Reducing your mortgage by making a lump sum payment may also be a good idea, but, if it is an endowment rather than a repayment mortgage, think carefully before cashing in the insurance policy before the end of its term – you risk losing the terminal bonus by doing so. Talk to your building society or other lender about the options.

Another possibility may be to re-mortgage, with the same lender or a different one, to reduce your outgoings. Again, be cautious as you may have to spend more in capital than it is worth, and check carefully the effect on any Jobseeker's Allowance or Income Support entitlement (see pages 64–65). Get advice from a reputable adviser.

If there is a danger of your falling into arrears, explain the situation to your lender as early as you can, and ask for help in rescheduling the payments if possible.

Replacing your non-wage benefits

A car

If you have lost the use of a company car, it may be vital (or simply necessary for your current lifestyle) to replace it. This would be one use of any redundancy or severance payment, but think carefully about maintenance costs and insurance. People with company cars are sheltered from the impact of these, and they may come as a nasty shock.

If you have a good driving record, and few or no claims on the company's car insurance, you will want to ensure that this is carried over into your own policy. Find out from your employer who the insurers or brokers are, and talk to them about doing this. Although in the past it would have been quite a rare request, it is now much more common and your employer should be able to deal with it. Otherwise, if you have a trade union or professional body, it is worth checking whether they offer any special deals.

Look around for insurers who give better rates to older motorists. Several companies offer such policies, including Age Concern Insurance Services (address on page 186).

Pension

You can now pay into a personal or stakeholder pension (since April 2001) if you are not employed and therefore have no earnings, assuming you have the money to do so. Other people can pay into a pension scheme on your behalf; so, if one of a couple is earning and the other is not, the earner can help the non-earner to build up a pension in his or her own right. You may need to ask a financial adviser for help with selecting the right policy. Look in the *Pensions Handbook* for more information on this.

Getting into debt

Sadly, you can get into debt even when you have received a substantial pay-off from your employer. It could be the largest lump sum you have ever seen, and you may feel that it is inexhaustible; some people do feel the urge to 'spend, spend, spend'. Mortgage or credit card arrears are perhaps the most common problem that arises; mortgage arrears can be particularly serious because people can lose their homes as a result.

If you can foresee that you may be living on a reduced income for some time, let anyone with whom you have credit arrangements know. As Experian, a credit-reference agency, says in its leaflet for people in this situation,

> 'Never think that lenders will think less of you if you let them know that your income has become less for whatever reason. This is rubbish. They will actually think more of you and recognise you as a responsible borrower if you notify them of any change in circumstances immediately and keep them regularly updated.'

As Experian stresses, credit card companies, mortgage lenders and other finance houses *do not want* the expense and effort of chasing you to pay, or ultimately taking you to court. They would prefer to find a way of letting you pay less each month, or even freezing your repayments, while you sort out your situation.

Many people who see themselves getting into arrears are paralysed by it, and stop opening letters for fear that they will be bills or summonses. This is actually the worst thing you can do. The best thing is to talk to an informed adviser, and get their help with writing to all your creditors explaining the situation and sorting out an organised way in which you can pay off the arrears. Both the Consumer Credit Counselling Service and the National Debtline (contact details on pages 188 and 193) can help with this, and there may also be local agencies near where you live that can offer some support. Try the Citizens Advice Bureau, or a money advice centre if one exists. A book that you might find useful is *Managing Debt: a guide for older people* (details on page 199).

6 Help you may get from the State

This chapter looks at the various State benefits and assistance that may be available now you are not in your old job. It is not intended to be comprehensive. Look in Age Concern's annual publication Your Rights (for details, see page 199) for more information. The Welfare Benefits Handbook, published by the Child Poverty Action Group (details on page 184), gives very full information on an extremely complex system. It should be available in a good public library.

Signing on as unemployed

You may find that you are out of a job for only a short time while you sort out your other arrangements. Or it may be rather longer, if things don't work out quite as you had planned and the opportunities do not seem to turn up. However short or long the time, you may well have to sign on as unemployed, and this means fitting in with the Government's rules.

Jobseeker's Allowance

Jobseeker's Allowance (JSA) is the name of the benefit you can receive when you are registered as unemployed, replacing the old Unemployment Benefit. There are two elements to it:

- 'Contribution-based' JSA is paid for up to six months when you first start claiming. It is paid on the basis of the National Insurance contributions you have made, taking account of any pension and earnings you have but not of the rest of your financial situation and that of your family.
- 'Income-based' JSA is paid on a means-tested basis (that is, taking both your capital and your income into account) for as long as you continue to qualify.

Because contribution-based JSA covers only you, and not your family, you will need to start claiming income-based JSA alongside it, as soon as you become unemployed.

Claiming Jobseeker's Allowance

To claim JSA, you have to show that you are available for work and are actively seeking work. You will need to 'sign on' at your local Jobcentre Plus office, usually once a fortnight. You will be called for an interview at the beginning of your period of unemployment and at different points after that.

Make initial contact with the Jobcentre Plus office in your area as soon as you can after your job finishes. However, you may not yet be counted as being unemployed for their purposes, depending on the make-up of any final payments you have been given. This is a complex area, but essentially:

■ If you have been paid wages in lieu of notice, the payments for that purpose are still 'earnings' so far as claiming JSA is concerned. So, for example, if you leave at the end of June but your employer has paid you up to the end of July in lieu of notice, you will not be able to start signing on until the beginning of August (though you will be able to make use of some of the Jobcentre Plus office's facilities).

■ If you have not had your full entitlement of 'in lieu' payments but have had other compensation or 'ex gratia' payments (that is, payments that you do not have contractual right to), part of these may also be treated in the same way (as payments in lieu).

■ Holiday pay, if paid at the end of the job, is also treated in this way. However, if it is paid more than four weeks after you have left, it is not counted for this purpose.

■ Wages or bonus paid in arrears, or the payment of wages held under the 'week-in-hand' arrangement used by some employers, should not be counted as earnings disqualifying you for a future period, because they are money due for work you have already done.

Once you *are* entitled to make a claim, you may find that for, other reasons, you cannot get any financial help, at least to start with. (It could still be worth signing on, however, as explained later.)

For contribution-based JSA:

■ The first £50 a week of pension from any employer, or payments from a personal pension scheme, are ignored. Above that, every penny of pension reduces JSA entitlement by the same amount. So if you had £60.50 a week of occupational pension, for instance, you would lose £10.50 a week of contribution-based JSA.

■ £5 a week of any earnings is disregarded (or £20 a week for some special groups such as part-time members of fire brigades) and then benefit is reduced pound for pound above that.

To claim income-based JSA, you must have less than £8,000 in capital. If you have more than this, you will not be able to make a claim until you have spent it down at a 'reasonable' rate. The rules on what is counted as 'capital' are deeply complicated but the value of your house and your ordinary possessions are *not* counted.

On top of this, there is a rule that if you left your job 'voluntarily and without just cause' or because of 'misconduct' you can be disqualified from benefit for up to six months. If you have lost your job because of a compulsory redundancy, or the closure of the workplace or the firm, this should not apply to you. If you took voluntary redundancy, the Job-centre Plus office may try to apply the rule, but it should not. This is because, essentially, if the employer was looking for volunteers to make up a certain number of redundancies, and would have made it compulsory if enough volunteers did not come forward, you are not voluntarily unemployed. (See the *Welfare Benefits Handbook* for more information.)

On the other hand, if you chose to take early retirement and were not put under pressure to do so, you would normally be assumed to be voluntarily unemployed. But if the employer had made things intolerable for you, or you had good physical or mental health reasons (backed by medical evidence), or if there were urgent family reasons, these could count as 'just cause'. If you feel the rule is being unfairly applied to you, exercise your right of appeal to a Tribunal. Ask the Jobcentre Plus's staff for the correct form on which to do this. If you need help with filling it in, ask your union, or a local law centre or Citizens Advice Bureau.

With all this, you may wonder whether it is worth signing on as unemployed at all. For anyone aged over 60, it may well not be. A woman over 60 is above State pension age anyway, and a man over 60 automatically gets National Insurance credits and is entitled to claim means-tested Income Support without needing to show he is looking for a job.

For anyone aged under 60, even if the various rules result in no money being due to you, signing on means that:

- you protect your National Insurance position and, therefore, your future State retirement pension;
- you have access to the various New Deals (discussed later in this chapter).

It must be your decision but it would usually be wise at least to check things out at the Jobcentre Plus office, even if you do not pursue things further. The golden rules are:

- Before you leave your job, get a statement in writing of how the final payment has been worked out. Take it to your union, or the Citizens Advice Bureau, if you are unsure what effect it will have on your State benefits. You have a legal right to such a statement under section 165 of the Employment Rights Act 1996. It will also be helpful to have something in writing about the reasons for your job ending, especially where there could be questions about whether you have taken redundancy or early retirement.
- Make your enquiries at the Jobcentre Plus office as soon as possible after you stop work (even if you are aware that you will not be eligible for some time). You must do this in person, rather than by phone, and it may mean some time in a queue. This will at least give you the chance to see what is available in terms of leaflets and job-search facilities! Take all the relevant documents, including (very important) evidence of your National Insurance number, and that of your spouse as well, if you are claiming for him or her. In the new improved Jobcentre Plus service the Government announced in June 2001, you will be encouraged to make the initial contact by phone, and sort out an appointment to come in. These new arrangements are being brought in piecemeal across the country over the next few years, until 2005. By the end of 2002, around a quarter of the offices will have been converted but where they are not yet in force the old methods remain.
- Make sure you understand what you are being told, and carry on asking questions if you do not. (But don't get angry with the staff if some of the rules seem nonsensical; they will only be applying what has been laid down. Take it up with your MP instead.) If necessary,

write down a note of what is being said, and check it back with them. From their side of the desk, the system is heavily computerised, so they are likely to be entering information on the computer screen as you go on. The guidance is that they should turn this screen around so that you can see what they have put down about you; ask if they do not do this.

- Take care about what you put on the various forms you will have to fill in, especially form ES2 ('Helping You Back to Work') and about what you agree to in the Jobseeker's Agreement. If you have already been working out what you want to do next, as suggested in Chapter 7 of this book, you will be able to carry across your decisions from one place to the other. The *Welfare Benefits Handbook* has a good explanation of the dos and don'ts of what to put on these forms. If the staff feel you are being unrealistic in your plans for the future, they may pressure you to lower your sights to something more mundane. If you need the money from the Jobseeker's Allowance, they will have the whip-hand, but privately you can always regard a routine job as a temporary stop-gap while you carry on pursuing your bigger ambitions. (See below for the rules on 'permitted periods' and 'trial periods'.)

- If you are told to go away and come back another time, *make sure* you keep the appointment, and are early for it rather than running any risk of being late. If you need to change an appointment, you will need an adequate reason (like a hospital appointment or a job interview); phone well in advance of the appointment and keep a note of who you speak to and what is agreed. This applies especially to your 'new jobseeker's interview' and the appointments you are given to sign on every fortnight. Remember that you are supposed to be devoting your entire time to jobseeking. If you do not seem to be giving the task sufficient priority, they could decide you are not 'genuinely seeking work'. (You are allowed up to two weeks' holiday within the UK, but you need to notify the staff at the Jobcentre Plus office that you are taking holiday and fill in a special 'holiday form'. If you are going abroad, you will need to sign off as unemployed, and sign on again when you return.)

Jobseekers are required to be available for any work which they can reasonably be expected to do. You must be available to start work immediately, unless you are doing voluntary work without payment or are a carer, when 48 hours' notice is allowed. For a 'permitted period' of up to 13 weeks, people are generally allowed to restrict their job search to their normal line of work. Not everyone is allowed a permitted period, though, and it could be as short as one week. It should be discussed at your first interview, and included in your Jobseeker's Agreement.

To be considered 'available' for work, you must be prepared to take a job that would involve working at least 40 hours a week. You must also be prepared, however, to work for less than 40 hours if asked – though not normally less than 24 hours. You will be able to refuse a job, however, or restrict the hours of availability:

- on grounds of health;
- for religious and conscientious reasons;
- to meet caring responsibilities.

You are also allowed to refuse jobs that are vacant because of trade disputes (strikes or lock-outs).

You are *not* allowed to refuse jobs simply because the rate of pay is low (unless it is below the national minimum wage) but the guidance to staff is that they should not notify you of jobs that will leave you worse off than you are on State benefits. They should be willing to do a 'better off' calculation for you to show this, and to tell you about the various benefits you can claim when in work (including the New Deal ones explained below).

Look at the Jobcentre Plus leaflet PFL1 *The service for people of working age* for an official summary of what is available and what you are required to do. There is also a *Customer's charter* setting out the standard of service you can expect. Look also at the website www.employmentservice.gov.uk for further details, and to find out where your nearest Jobcentre Plus is.

Note The government departments that deal with jobseeking and with social security benefits are in the process of being reorganised.

The Employment Service is in the process of becoming part of 'Job-centre Plus' and the revamped offices will deal with a range of other social security benefits as well as Jobseeker's Allowance. If the changed philosophy set out in its Vision Statement (available on the website; see above) is carried through in reality, unemployed people and other claimants should be offered a much better service than at present.

Trial periods for a new job

You might want to make use of the rule that allows you to take a new job 'on trial' and leave without being penalised for it. You do not need to have agreed with the Jobcentre Plus staff that you were taking the job on this basis but you do need to fit in with its time-scales, which are quite tight.

The 'employment on trial' rule applies if:

- you have not had a job (or been self-employed or a student) for at least 13 weeks before starting the new job; and
- you give up the job some time between the beginning of the 5th week after starting it, and the end of the 12th week.

You then go back on JSA as if you had never left it. If you go over the 12th week, not only might you be penalised but a new 'jobseeking period' starts as well. Occasionally this will be in your favour, because the National Insurance contribution record that is taken into account may be better, but more often it will not.

New Deal arrangements

There is a whole clutch of 'New Deals' available for claimants without a job. The ones that are most relevant here are:

- the general New Deal, for people aged 25 or over;
- the New Deal for Disabled People;
- the New Deal 50 Plus, for people aged 50 or over.

The general New Deal for the unemployed is a mixture of carrots and sticks, with the sticks predominating. The other two New Deals have rather more carrots than sticks, so if you qualify – especially if you have reached the magic age of 50 – you should make sure that you take up all your entitlement. Ask your personal adviser at the Jobcentre Plus office for more information.

The *Welfare Benefits Handbook* gives details of all the New Deal packages, and of other employment programmes. Below is an extract from that publication (with the permission of CPAG) and covers those that are most likely to be relevant to you.

Government training and employment initiatives

New Deal for people aged 25 and over

Conditions and eligibility

- Compulsory if unemployed and claiming JSA continuously for 18 months or more or for 18 out of the previous 21 months, or have been jobseeking continuously for 18 months out of the previous 21 months and are claiming National Insurance credits only. This applies also to the claimant member of a 'joint-claim couple' for JSA after 18 months of jobseeking, to the person who has previously completed the New Deal for those aged 18–24 or the New Deal for those aged 25 and over and has then been unemployed for 18 months from the end of the 'intensive activity period' (see below).
- Not compulsory but early entry for those with particularly severe disadvantages in the labour market.
- Required to re-enter New Deal if you return to JSA within 13 weeks of leaving it.
- If you are 50 or over you are only required to enter the 'gateway' element of the New Deal (see also 'New Deal for people aged 50 and over').

Provision

- A personal adviser will guide you through the whole process.
- There is an initial 'gateway' period of up to four months, which includes advice, guidance and help to find unsubsidised work. For some there is a compulsory gateway to work course (work preparation). After four weeks you become eligible for a subsidised job.
- There is an 'intensive activity period' of up to 13 weeks in which you are referred to certain activities. Some activities last longer than 13 weeks and can be entered direct from the 'gateway'. Activities include:

- a subsidised job of up to 26 weeks;
- supported self-employment;
- education and training opportunities for 52 weeks;
- work placements (up to 6 or 13 weeks) – the employer is normally expected to take on the trainee after this period;
- work experience for up to 13 weeks;
- basic employability training up to 26 weeks;
- longer occupational training – normally between 7 and 13 weeks;
- work-focused training – normally provided using contracts via Work-Based Learning for Adults (Training for Work, in Scotland);
- other support with jobsearch, acquiring 'soft' skills, etc.

- Unless on a waged activity or in work, you will receive a training allowance, including 10p income-based JSA plus an addition (or premium) of £15.38. The allowance, including the 10p JSA, is paid without the addition if you are on the education and training opportunities option. The level of your allowance is set at the rate of the means-tested benefit you were receiving before you went on to the training allowance.
- You may be entitled to a Job Grant (see page 63).
- You may be entitled to payments from the Adviser Discretion Fund (see page 62).

Partners

Conditions and eligibility

- People aged 25 or over without children whose partner has been on JSA for six months or more.
- People aged 18–60 with or without children whose partner has been claiming Income Support (IS), Invalidity Benefit (IB), Invalid Care Allowance (ICA) or Severe Disablement Allowance (SDA) for six months or more.
- Early entry for special groups is possible.
- Involvement is voluntary.

Provision

- Offers help with jobsearch, advice on training and jobs.
- Financial help with travel and childcare costs is available for those on an approved training course or participating in an employment programme.

New Deal for disabled people

Conditions and eligibility

- People receiving any one of the following benefits:
  - Invalidity Benefit;
  - Severe Disablement Allowance;
  - Income Support including a disability premium (including IS received where appealing a decision about incapacity for work);
  - Housing Benefit (HB) or Council Tax Benefit (CTB) including a disability premium for the claimant;
  - some recipients of Disability Living Allowance (DLA), but not if in remunerative work or getting JSA;
  - war pension or industrial injuries disablement benefit if either is paid with an unemployability supplement, or European benefits equivalent to IB;
  - National Insurance credits on grounds of incapacity;
- The scheme is voluntary following a compulsory work-focused interview;
- Available nationally.

Provision

- Claimants of qualifying benefits will have an initial 'gateway' interview at the local JobCentre and be given information about job brokers in their area.
- Job brokers will help match clients' skills to job vacancies and help them find, secure and keep paid work. Job broking is provided largely by voluntary organisations and the private sector. Payment of job brokers is by results – placement of their clients in sustainable jobs.
- Claimants should get independent advice before taking up employment. There is a special linking rule for IB.
- There is some doubt about whether people can access the Adviser Discretion Fund or the Travel to Interview Scheme. Independent advisers should contact the local Jobcentre Plus or DWP office.

New Deal for people aged 50 and over

Conditions and eligibility

- People receiving a qualifying benefit (IS, IB, SDA or JSA for under two years) or who are signing on for National Insurance credits, or any combination of these and have been doing so for six months or more.
- Your partner may be eligible if you have been receiving an increase in benefit for her/him for six months or more.

- If you have been getting JSA for two years or more, you are *required* to join the New Deal for those aged 25 and over.
- The New Deal for people aged 50 and over is voluntary. You will not lose any benefit if you decide not to take it up.

Provision

- Your New Deal personal adviser will give extra help with your jobsearch and you will have access to the services of the programme centre.
- You will also be eligible for the employment credit when you start a job. You do not have to have taken a job through the JobCentre to apply for this, but you must visit the JobCentre to apply.
- An employment credit can be paid for up to 52 weeks if:
  - you are 50 or over and have been claiming one of the qualifying benefits for the immediate period of at least 26 weeks;
  - the job is expected to last for five weeks or more;
  - your gross annual income is £15,000 or less;
  - your partner is not getting an employment credit;
  - you work 16 hours or more per week.

  The lower rate of the credit is £40 for jobs between 16 and 30 hours a week. The higher rate is £60 for jobs that are 30 hours or more a week. You can also receive a training grant of up to £750 for training directly relevant to the job you have started while receiving the employment credit.

  Note that when the new tax credit scheme is introduced in April 2003 this will replace the employment credit.
- You may be able to claim some in-work benefits.

Jobcentre Plus programme centres

Conditions and eligibility

- Unemployed for six months or more.
- Access also available through the New Deals.

Provision

- There are modules covering aspects of jobsearch and guidance tailored to meet individual needs.
- There is access to a resource area with telephones, stationery, stamps, word processors, photocopiers, etc.

Work-based Learning for Adults ('Training for Work' in Scotland)

Conditions and eligibility

- Unemployed for six months if over 25.
- Aged 18–24 with a disability or not in receipt of JSA.
- Participation in some other New Deals.
- Early entry for disadvantaged groups.

Provision

- Work-based training, including short job-focused training (maximum six weeks), longer occupational training (maximum two weeks), basic employability training (maximum 26 weeks) and self-employment provision.
- The benefits you are normally entitled to and a training allowance of £10 per week.
- Help may be available with travel costs and childcare.

Help for people with disabilities – work preparation

Conditions and eligibility

- For people with disabilities usually referred by the disability employment adviser in the JobCentre.

Provision

- Programme of activity aimed at overcoming disability and health-related barriers to employment.
- You can be paid an allowance for full-time participation.
- Expenses can be covered.

Help for people with disabilities – access to work

Conditions and eligibility

- For people with disabilities entering, or already in, work.
- Access via the disability employment adviser in the JobCentre.

Provision

- Special equipment, adaptations or services to help a person with a disability start or stay in work. Costs may be shared with the employer but up to 100% of the approved costs can be provided.

Other schemes – Work trial

Conditions and eligibility

- Unemployed for six months or more and aged 25 or more (with some exceptions).

Provision

- You can take a job for up to 15 working days and continue to receive benefit.
- You can be paid travel expenses of up to £10 per day, and meal costs of up to £1.50 per day.

Financial help – Travel to Interview scheme

Conditions and eligibility

- Unemployed and on JSA, or the partner of a claimant of JSA, or in receipt of National Insurance credits.
- The job cannot be seasonal, temporary or a short-term fixed contract.

Provision

- Discretionary access for participants on most New Deals.
- Fares can be paid for travelling to interviews beyond the normal daily travel distance where the job is for at least 30 hours per week.
- You usually need to apply before travelling.

Financial help – Adviser Discretion Fund

Conditions and eligibility

- Payment is at the discretion of the New Deal personal advisers, to help participants in any of the New Deals.

Provision

- Discretionary awards of up to £300 for *anything* that will help you find or take up an offer of a job – eg clothing, tools.
- Can be made direct to you or to a third party, retrospectively or in advance.
- Payments cannot be made as an inducement to take up a job, nor to pay for items or needs funded in other way(s) by the New Deal.
- Payments cannot be made once you are in work.

Financial help – Job Grant

Conditions and eligibility

- Payable if:
  - you are starting or returning to full-time work (16 or more hours a week), or entering a New Deal scheme, including a subsidised job or waged activity; *and*
  - the job (or activity) is expected to last five weeks (if there is doubt the grant would be paid and you do not have to prove that it will last five weeks); *and*
  - you are 25 or over on the day you start work; *and*
  - you have been receiving a qualifying benefit (JSA, IS, IB or SDA) continuously for the previous 52 weeks (or any combination of these benefits during this period).

Provision

- You should apply for the grant within three weeks of starting work. Staff in DWP offices or JobCentres are also expected to identify potential applicants.
- You have a right to request a review but there is no right of appeal.
- The Job Grant is worth £100 and is paid under powers contained in section 2 of the Employment and Training Act 1973.

For more information, ask at the local Jobcentre Plus office, or look on the website www.newdeal.gov.uk. There are also leaflets available from the Jobcentre Plus offices, or downloadable from the website. Age Concern has published a leaflet on the New Deal 50 Plus, for people over 50, available from the Information Line (see page 201 for details). The Centre for Economic and Social Inclusion (address on page 188) publishes a *New Deal Handbook,* which is also available online at www.cesi.org.uk.

Other help with your income

As long as you are receiving Jobseeker's Allowance (JSA), you do not have a right to means-tested Income Support (IS) because the income-based element of JSA replaces it. You may, though, have a right to

Housing Benefit or Council Tax Benefit (paid by the local authority) on top of JSA. You may also have a right to these benefits if you are not able to claim JSA because you have too much 'capital', as the Housing Benefit/Council Tax Benefit limits are higher – £16,000 for an individual or couple (as opposed to £8,000 for income-based JSA or IS).

So, if your income is low and you have less capital than the limit (or if you are spending a redundancy or severance payment in order to live, and your capital has come down to that level), it is worth checking whether you are eligible. Any occupational or personal/stakeholder pension is taken into account, and you are assumed to have an income of £1 per week for every £250 of savings that you have over £3,000. Ask the Citizens Advice Bureau, or the local authority's welfare rights officer if one exists. For more information see Age Concern's *Your Rights* or the Child Poverty Action Group's *Welfare Benefits Handbook* (details on pages 199 and 184).

Your mortgage

Mortgage insurance was discussed on pages 46–47. In this section we cover the question of what you can get from the State to help with mortgage payments.

Unfortunately, the answer is – not a lot, at least at the beginning, if you have a recent mortgage. If you first took out the mortgage after 1 October 1995, you will get no help for the first nine months, though there are exemptions for some groups of people. If you took out the mortgage before this date, you will get no help for the payments for the first two months, and only 50 per cent for the next four months.

Very importantly, you may get no help *at all* if you take out the mortgage (or increase it) while you are on income-based JSA or IS. The rules are complex, so check the situation out carefully before committing yourself to anything.

There is a top limit on the size of mortgage that can be covered, again with some exceptions. The limit has been gradually reduced, and now stands at £100,000, but it can be lower if in your particular case the DWP considers that you are paying more than you need.

When you do start getting help, only the *interest* payments are covered, not the capital, and a special 'notional' figure is used to calculate the interest, rather than the real one. This is calculated centrally by the DWP, and at the time of writing this was 5.34 per cent. There is generally a shortfall, so you will need to eat into other income, or capital, to make it up.

Payment of the mortgage-interest element of your benefit will usually be made direct to the lender.

Financial help when starting a new job

There are some special rules intended to ease people back into work, if they have been unemployed for some time. They include:

- Employment Credit under the New Deal 50 Plus (covered in the section on page 59 – to be replaced in April 2003 by an equivalent element in the Working Tax Credit, paid by the Inland Revenue through the employer).
- Back to Work Bonus, if you have been doing part-time work for a period before getting a full-time job (or increasing your hours with the same employer). The name is misleading, because what it really means is that, if part of your Jobseeker's Allowance or Income Support has been deducted because of the level of your part-time earnings, half of that deduction is paid back to you (up to £1,000) once you stop claiming JSA. There are various conditions to fulfil, so check whether they apply to you. (You can also get the bonus if you reach pensionable age while on JSA or, for a man, if you reach 60 and stop claiming Income Support.)
- Mortgage interest run-on. Subject to some fairly strict conditions, you can have the mortgage interest element of Income Support paid for up to four weeks (direct to you, not to the lender) when you come off Income Support or JSA. However, once you get past this period, there will be no further help with the mortgage.
- Housing Benefit and Council Tax Benefit extended payments. These benefits can also continue for four weeks. In these cases, however, you are quite likely to have continued claims for the benefits, though at a lower rate. The local authority, which administers them, should give your claim priority so that the transition between the different rates is smooth.

With all these possible payments, it is essential to make the claim at the right point. You can take advantage of them only if you claim as you are starting work. Tell your personal adviser at the Jobcentre Plus office as soon as you know you are going to start work, and ask for help with claiming whatever is available.

If your earnings are low, you might also have some entitlement to Working Families Tax Credit (if you have dependent children) or Disabled Person's Tax Credit (if you have poor health or a disability). You can claim these at any time. Indeed, you may only become eligible once one of the other payments (such as the Employment Credit) runs out. From April 2003, these benefits will all be replaced by the Working Tax Credit, which is also available to people without children. If in doubt, make enquiries and put in a claim.

There is also some help if you take up short-term employment, or start a permanent job but it does not work and you become unemployed again within a short time. Rapid Re-Claim means that you can start claiming again, without having to go through all the bureaucracy, if you have taken up a job (or been doing something else, such as jury service) that lasts for less than 12 weeks. For gaps in claiming, of up to 52 weeks, there is a 'linking rule' for mortgage and home loan interest payments, so that you do not have to wait nine months again (as explained above) before getting help with these payments.

If your health is not good

If you are leaving work because of health problems – or they develop after you have left work – you may be eligible for Incapacity Benefit. (Check also whether you could qualify for an ill-health pension under your own pension scheme's rules, rather than an ordinary early retirement pension.)

If you are receiving Statutory Sick Pay at the time when your job ends, or if you become sick when you are unemployed, you will need to claim Incapacity Benefit, on the lowest rate to start with (see page 67 for information on the different rates). The fact that you are already claiming Jobseeker's Allowance does *not* stop you claiming Incapacity Benefit if you fall ill or if a condition you already had worsens.

However, if you claim Incapacity Benefit when you are unemployed, you immediately become subject to the 'personal capability' test. The aim of this is to decide whether, on a supposedly objective test of the extent to which your illness or disability impairs your performance of certain physical and mental functions, you are capable of work. There is no reference to your last job, and no account is taken of education or training, or of any language or literacy problems.

The *Welfare Benefits Handbook* explains the details of the test and how it works in practice. Jobcentre Plus leaflets *A guide to Incapacity Benefit* and *A guide to the personal capability assessment* give more details, and it is also possible to download the lengthy claim form from the internet (via www.dwp.gov.uk).

Once you have filled in the claim form, you will be called up for an examination by the Medical Service (MS), which is run by a private company under contract to the Department for Work and Pensions (DWP; formerly the Department of Social Security). Your own GP will be asked to give information and to release your medical records (with your permission), but does not have any other role. The results of the medical examination are then passed to a 'decision-maker' in the social security or Jobcentre Plus office. In some pilot areas there is also a 'capability report', which is intended to assist in efforts to help you back to work. This is sent to your New Deal personal adviser.

Anyone who disputes the decision can appeal to an Appeal Tribunal. Success rates are quite high, but it is important that you turn up in person and can supply additional written evidence from your GP or consultant. While you are waiting for an appeal to be heard, you will not be paid Incapacity Benefit and may need to claim Income Support.

If your condition is one that is likely to improve over time, or with treatment, you are likely to be called up for a further examination in due course – perhaps in six months, or 18 months. The DWP also plans to make all Incapacity Benefit claims 'time-limited' so everyone will have to apply again after (probably) three years, but the full details of this are not yet known.

Rates and deductions

There are three basic rates of Incapacity Benefit. The rates for 2002/3 are:

- First 28 weeks of sickness (if not getting Statutory Sick Pay): short-term lower rate (no increases for children) – £53.50 a week.
- From 29 to 52 weeks: short-term higher rate – £63.25, with increases for children if applicable.
- After one year: long-term rate – £70.95, with increases for children if applicable.

Very disabled people, or those with a terminal illness, receive the long-term rate from week 29.

There is also an age-related allowance, paid with the long-term rate, where the person was under 45 on the first day of their present illness and a larger allowance for those under 35 at the start. An increase for your spouse is paid only if the spouse is aged 60 or over, or is caring for a child for whom *you* are getting a child increase with your benefit. There is also an earnings rule for adult dependants, which means that if they earn more than a certain amount no increase will be paid. The short-term higher rate of benefit and the long-term rate are both taxable.

For anyone who started receiving Incapacity Benefit after April 2001, this benefit is reduced if you have an occupational or personal pension (or a combination) of more than £85 a week. For each £1 that your pension is over this limit, your benefit is reduced by 50p. For example, if you had a pension of £100 a week (£15 over the limit), your Incapacity Benefit will be reduced by £7.50.

This rule also applies to any permanent health insurance arranged by your employer – but not to a policy that you have arranged yourself, and not if you contributed more than 50 per cent to the cost of the policy.

Even if these various rules do wipe out any financial entitlement you may have, it can be worth claiming if you seem to be eligible. It will mean that you have:

- entitlement to National Insurance credits; and
- access to the New Deal packages, for yourself and, in some cases, for your spouse or partner.

Industrial injuries benefits

If you feel that your ill-health has been caused by an accident at work, or is the result of a disease that you picked up at work, it will be worth checking whether you are entitled to industrial injuries benefits.

These can be paid where an employee has had an accident 'arising out of and in the course of employment' or where he or she is suffering from a 'prescribed disease'. A prescribed disease is an illness that is on a DWP list in relation to the particular occupation in which you worked. It covers, for instance, a number of cancers and skin diseases, occupational deafness (but only for some occupations), some chest diseases, and some types of work-related limb disorders such as carpal tunnel syndrome.

The main form of industrial injuries benefit is **Disablement Benefit**, paid either for a limited period or for life, if your industrial disease or injury is serious enough. The payments can be made *on top* of wages or other benefits. There are also some additional benefits for very badly disabled people.

There is also a **Reduced Earnings Allowance** (REA), though this is now limited to cases where the accident happened, or the disease arose, before October 1990. If you are already claiming REA, or are changing or leaving your job because you are now permanently incapable of employment of the same standard as before, it will be worth checking whether there is anything extra to come from this source.

All industrial injuries benefits are non-contributory, so they cover all 'employed earners', including married women paying reduced-rate National Insurance contributions. They can also act as a passport to other benefits. They are quite separate from the right to sue the employer in the courts for negligence (but if you win a damages award, the DWP will reclaim the benefit it has paid out).

If you think that you might be able to claim an industrial injuries benefit, talk to your union or staff association if you have one, or the Citizens Advice Bureau if not.

Working after going onto Incapacity Benefit

The Government is keen that people should not regard themselves as 'written off' once they qualify for Incapacity Benefit. If you find yourself recovered enough to do at least some work, it will be worth taking up what is on offer under the New Deal for Disabled People (summarised on page 59). There are also various benefits rules that can help. These changed in April 2002, and they now say that:

- You can do voluntary work, as long as it is not for a close relative and the only payment is to cover your 'reasonable expenses', without it affecting your Incapacity Benefit. This means that you could try yourself out for a while, for instance by helping in a local charity shop, to see how you stand up to a work environment.
- Under the 'welfare to work' rules, someone who has been receiving Incapacity Benefit for at least six months can stop claiming the benefit, go into work or training, and if necessary start claiming again at the old rate within a year. (There are some tight conditions here; talk to your personal adviser at the Jobcentre Plus office to make sure you get the timing and procedure right.)
- People receiving Incapacity Benefit will be able to do work for a maximum of £20 a week, with no limit on the number of hours worked, and no limit on the length of time this can go on.
- They will also be able to work for up to 16 hours a week, and earn up to £66 a week for up to six months, with a six month extension if they have a personal adviser, job broker (under the New Deal for Disabled People) or disability employment adviser at the Jobcentre Plus office, who agrees that it will help towards work of 16 or more hours a week. After a gap of at least a year, people can do another session of this sort of work, this time lasting up to a year. This time, they must have a job broker, personal adviser or disability employment adviser who is supporting the work from the outset.
- They can work in 'supported permitted work' for earnings of up to and including £66 a week for an unlimited period. This means work done with the ongoing support or supervision from a professional caseworker in the community or in a sheltered workshop. It also includes work done under medical supervision as part of a hospital treatment programme. In both cases, however, there will be the condition – as there is at present – that 'the nature of the activity undertaken should not call the person's incapacity into question'. In other words, the type of voluntary work done should not indicate that the incapacity could be less severe than has been claimed.

Other help with your income

If you find that you do not have enough money to live on, there are means-tested benefits for which you may be eligible, though not while you have capital over a certain limit. These include:

- **Income Support** if neither you nor your spouse/partner works for more than 16 hours a week. Any earnings you have under the arrangements explained in the previous section will be counted for the purposes of the means-test.
- **Working Families Tax Credit** or **Disabled Person's Tax Credit** (DPTC) if either you or your spouse/partner works more than 16 hours a week. (These benefits will be replaced in April 2003 by the Working Tax Credit.)

In addition, you may be entitled to Housing Benefit and Council Tax Benefit, explained earlier (page 64). For more information about the various means-tested benefits, see Age Concern's *Your Rights* or the Child Poverty Action Group's *Welfare Benefits Handbook* (details on pages 199 and 184).

7   What do you want to do now?

The fact that your current job is coming to an end gives you an opportunity – one you may never have had before, or not for a very long time. Unlike our sons and daughters, most 50-somethings today first started work at a time of pretty full employment. So you may well have drifted into something that came along, that you did not care that much about, and then continued along the same career path because it seemed inevitable. There are many people in jobs where they actively dislike some or even all of what they are doing day by day. Now that there's a push behind you, this is your chance to work out what you really want and how to get there.

So this chapter sets out the homework that needs doing. This divides broadly into two parts – analysis about yourself, and research on what is out there – though it is not a very tidy division and there is considerable overlap.

Note In this chapter, the words 'work' and 'job' are used in a very broad sense, as meaning not just the tasks a new employer will pay you for but also a changed role with your current employer, self-employment and voluntary work. Later chapters look more specifically at these, and also at training and education.

Finding a new role may not be very easy, and it could take some time. You may have to take a 'stop-gap' job while you work on getting what you want in the longer term. The need for money and the rules for claiming Jobseeker's Allowance (explained in Chapter 6) may, however, mean that you have to take something that is not what you want. If you find that you have to accept a job you don't want, treat it as a learning opportunity and a way of proving to other employers that you can be flexible, while carrying on looking for what you do want.

You could be very lucky and fall into the ideal role almost immediately. It's far more likely, though, that you will need to do quite a lot of analysis and research before you even start making specific applications, and then more research while you are doing so.

See Chapter 13, 'Organising your time and other commitments', for ideas on how best to use your time in planning your change of direction. If this sounds rather daunting, it's worth remembering that:

- The more you are working to your strengths, the more likely you are to succeed in your search. Your feelings about particular subjects are going to come over to potential employers and customers. 'Infectious enthusiasm' really does exist. If you are bubbling over with anticipation and ideas about what can be done, you will come over as positive and a good bet. If, on the other hand, you put yourself forward for something you are indifferent to, or know very little about, because 'it's a job', you will probably come over as negative and downcast – so why should an employer pick you out from anyone else?

- You are by no means alone. There is a plethora of books, internet sites and advisers to help you. Some cost money but many others are free; you need to keep your wits about you because there are plenty of sharks and cowboys around, but there is enough good quality assistance out there to be helpful.

- The more time and trouble you take to get it right, the more likely it is that you will be able to stick with what you get, rather than having to do it all again in a few years' time. You could be unlucky – even the most secure firm can be brought down by the loss of a major contract, for instance – but the more care you take, the more you will reduce your chances of being 'a square peg in a round hole' this time. If you have had a bad experience in your last job, or in the way it ended, this could be vital to your self-confidence. But it does matter to almost everyone. As the author of *What Color is your Parachute?* (an excellent, if very American, book on the subject; see page 184 for details) puts it:

  'Every worker in the world takes the measure of their organisation, and decides whether or not they would enjoy working there. Trouble is, most job-hunters or career-changers do so, *after* they are hired there.'

One other point to bear in mind, as you set about your homework, is that what you turn out to be looking for may not be 'a job' at all. It might be:

- part-time work, perhaps for several employers in different fields;
- self-employment;
- voluntary work;
- education;
- a mix of all these (often called a 'portfolio');

Or you might want to develop a 'portfolio' over time. Just because you are middle-aged does not mean that you are stuck with doing one thing for the rest of your life. You might, for instance, want to do full-time education for two to three years – to get a qualification, for fun, or both – and then move into a full-time job.

Valerie had not been working for some years in her 50s because of a back problem. At 60, however, she decided she would 'show the world'. She went to an interview for a book-keeping job in a small firm two days after her 60th birthday, and fibbed about her age 'but probably didn't need to', she says. She got the job, and worked there for three years but finally gave up because she was finding it difficult to take time off, because she was the only book-keeper there. Before she left, she thought about what to do, made plans for the pressed flower business that she is now developing, revived earlier contacts with a debt-collecting agency for whom she does occasional work and, on the side, enrolled for a part-time degree at the local university.

As Valerie's example shows, planning your change of direction does not have to wait until you have cleared your desk. Indeed, the earlier you start, the better – it is often easier to obtain work when you are currently employed than when you are already unemployed. Ideally, the time to start planning is when you feel the haze of gloom descending over the workplace, or are beginning to loathe Mondays because of the management style you have to put up with.

The key issues

The three key issues to think about are:

- what you like doing, are interested in and feel you are good at;
- what money you want or need to survive on;
- the limits around you – such matters as geographical location, time travelling to and from work, your health and that of your dependants, other family commitments.

Your first step is to audit yourself on all these points. After that, you can move to establishing what sort of work would fit your 'profile', and putting yourself forward for the opportunities that exist in that field.

How to decide what you want

One possibility is simply to go on your gut feelings. But it is difficult for most of us to see the wood for the trees – there's a tendency just to think, 'Well, what I have been doing but with X difference'. A systematic analysis will help you to see the opportunities more widely.

There are plenty of personality and aptitude tests, and pro-formas that will help you move from them to real work opportunities. You can also find people who will help you work through them – though this will be easier in some areas than others. Some of the places to get help are:

- **A commercial careers or employment consultancy** You will find them listed in the phone book under 'Careers Advice' and 'Employment Agencies and Consultants', or see the 'Useful publications' section on page 182 for a directory. Avoid wasting money (and your own time) by checking out first exactly what they can offer, and preferably getting recommendations from someone else. One of your first questions should be whether they have other clients like yourself. The cost, if you have to pay yourself, could be £1,000 for 'individual counselling and a general CV and career brush-up', but it could be much less if you simply want a few hours' help going through the various tests and being shown the options. Firms that describe themselves as 'outplacement consultants' work only on the basis of referrals from employers, who also pay the fees.
- **A personal adviser** at the Jobcentre Plus office. Where the new arrangements are in force, they will have responsibility for most of

the work in this area, and are intended to work in 'partnership' with other local organisations. So they are likely to refer you elsewhere, possibly to a private contractor, but should meet the bill for whatever the contractor charges.

Different organisations have different approaches, and some allow much more time for thought than others. At outplacement advisers Coutts Career Consultants, for instance, they suggest that clients should virtually write a life history in a 'workbook', setting out what they have done. They expect the clients to spend a week or more over it. An interview arranged by Jobcentre Plus will be much quicker, and concentrates more on fitting square pegs into square (or possibly round) holes.

It is also quite possible to **do it yourself**. There is a sizeable industry publishing material – not just books but CD-ROMs, tapes and internet pages – on career development. If you can't find a specialist to talk to (or in addition to doing so) there is plenty to work with.

There are, for instance, a number of books and websites that allow you to take yourself through the most common tests, as well as more specialist ones for particular selection tests such as the Police Initial Recruitment test (see 'Further reading' for details). The danger is, in fact, that you will not know what to buy or will spend far too much buying everything that looks relevant. You could invest a few hours in browsing through your local bookshop (especially if you are lucky enough have one of those that provides seats and coffee and does not mind how long you stay), and then go on to the reference section of your area's central library and see what they have, or can get for you through the inter-library lending system. Look under 'Business and Management' when browsing for books – many bookshops have these sections, but nothing called 'Careers' – and don't hesitate to ask. Reference librarians take pride in being able to track down answers to even the most obscure queries! You can also do the equivalent on the internet (see below).

Some of the books and websites are very idiosyncratic. Others, such as the US-based *What Color is your Parachute?* (now in its 30th edition) are so relentlessly upbeat and optimistic that they may turn you off if you are a reserved Brit! You don't have to buy all the message, though – pick and choose the activities and worksheets that seem useful.

A note about using computers and the internet

It's not yet essential to understand computers and know your way around the internet to find a new job but things are developing that way. It is certainly extremely useful, though it can also lead to much time-wasting. The internet gives you access to an enormous range of resources, but it is rather like sitting in a public library that is very good at accumulating stock but dreadful at cataloguing it! You can find not only factual information but also activities, worksheets and tests, and an enormous amount of educational material of all sorts. There are also opinions and rumours, some much better founded than others. The internet also allows you to communicate with other people, for instance through chatrooms, email and feedback forms on different sites.

So you need to be selective about how you use the internet. According to Clare Cassidy of career consultants Penna Sanders & Sidney:

'There is still a lot of commerce around that is not internet-reliant. But the internet is vital for doing research on companies. People do a lot more preparation for interviews than they used to, say, ten years ago. Now a well-prepared candidate will look up full financial and historical details, market analysis and comparisons as well as press cuttings about the company they are interested in joining. The internet is much better for research than actually finding jobs to apply for. Unfortunately, some of the jobs that are advertised do not really exist. I would hesitate to say that sending out CVs on the internet is a waste of time but people need to be careful. Some of the leads can be a distraction, consume a lot of time and can be depressing if they fail to bring results.'

You may not have used a computer at work before or have used one only for very limited purposes. You may not have access to a good computer at home, either. Fortunately, there are many classes and places where you can learn about computers. Irene Krechowiecka, in *Net that Job* (a good basic guide to using the internet to develop your career and find work; details on page 183), suggests the following places:

■ Libraries – many offer internet access and short courses to get you started, at a charge of around £5 an hour.

- Jobcentre Plus offices – these offer free internet access to help job-seekers find work.
- Cybercafés – places you can have a drink and a meal, and access the internet for an hourly charge.
- Schools and colleges – many of which offer introductory courses on the use of computers and the internet. The Government are promoting this, and have an organisation called Learndirect with a freephone number, 0800 100900, for you to phone and find out details of courses in your area.
- Another alternative is Age Resource, part of Age Concern's ActivAge Unit. This operates via a national network of Age Resource Desks, computer points located in Age Concern groups and organisations and run predominantly by older volunteers. Most offer computer and internet 'taster' sessions.
- Friends and relatives – those who have already found their way into the internet world may be very ready to help you do the same. Offer to cover the phone costs for the time you spend on-line. Your selection of sites may not be the same as your 17-year-old son or daughter's but the principles will be the same.

The resources available will vary considerably from area to area. Ask around and try places out. If you find one uncongenial, try another. As an example of what might be on offer, the University of Newcastle upon Tyne's Centre for Lifelong Learning (what older people may still think of as the Extra-Mural Department) says in its course brochure:

'iPAD is the Centre's innovative on-line system for giving you information and resources to support your learning with us. We provide free introductory web sessions that will have you surfing in next to no time, and you can access iPAD and the internet at large via our dedicated library.'

You may well be able to obtain help and access free or, if you have to pay, at reduced rates. Otherwise, shop around for the best value. Regard it as an investment. However, to quote *Net that job*:

'The Web is one medium, one source of information among many. You need to integrate it with other forms of communication. It is not always the best or the most appropriate method. You have to exercise judgement and discrimination.'

In the rest of this book we assume you are able to get access to the internet and make use of the resources there. If you have a lump sum at the end of your job, using part of it to buy the right equipment might be a good idea. Try to get some advice on what to buy, though – there are many people around who have bought systems that are much more high-powered, and therefore expensive, than they need.

Support from friends and colleagues

Another way of getting assistance with your audit is to enlist a supportive colleague, friend or partner (with the emphasis on the *supportive* – some people thrive on putting down their nearest and dearest). You may also have a support group available who can work together. For instance:

Stan was one of ten who left his firm within the same four to six weeks. They went to the outplacement consultants together and formed a support group of their own. Some of them are still meeting, though those who have not yet found work tend to use the group, Stan says, mainly for a 'moan session' nowadays. If not, you may be able to create your own.

What do you like doing?

What do you like doing, and what are you interested in and feel you are good at? These factors do generally go together; it is easier to get to be good at the things we enjoy doing than the things we find dull (if only because we practise more). It is also difficult to like things we feel a fool doing. For example, some people enjoy selling – whether it's themselves as people, products or ideas. Others cringe at the thought. The first group are far more likely to be successful as sales representatives – no matter what they are selling – than the second group.

Most occupations include some aspects that people like and some that they don't. One complaint that many people have when they reach a certain level is that they don't spend enough time doing *real* work, and they spend too much time doing paperwork and in meetings. In the public sector and large private firms, there is a growing tendency for everyone to have to do more form-filling, as appraisal, performance measurement and checking of standards take hold. Many teachers, for example, feel ground down by the demands of the National Curriculum and the inspections by the Office for Standards in Education (OFSTED).

It is not just the job title that matters. There could be aspects that would make a potentially dull job interesting for you, or that would make a potentially good one unappealing. Being a receptionist in a lively office, with lots of people coming and going and a lot of phone calls, might suit a gregarious person perfectly, for example. The same job in a different office might mean being shut away in a small room with piles of routine work to get on with.

It could well be that the things you really like doing are the things you have been doing outside work. You might be the backbone of the Parent–Teacher Association, treasurer of half a dozen groups, or champion cook for all the church fêtes and socials. Many people who are in dull jobs where they are unable to exercise their talents compensate for this by leading a far more interesting life in their own time. Have you developed skills outside work that you could make use of – and would enjoy doing so – in a paid capacity?

What's important for this purpose is to be specific, and to find evidence, as far as possible, of what you claim to like doing or to be good at – not just gut feeling. One approach – there are many others – is to create a grid on a large sheet of paper, or on your computer, and put down, on the left-hand side:

- current (or last) job
- previous jobs
- family responsibilities
- activities you do in your own time
- formal education
- training

List all these and then add three columns to your spreadsheet, headed 'Likes/Dislikes', 'Important to me' and 'Good at/Bad at'. When you fill in these new columns, think of less tangible things as well as more concrete factors. These columns could include:

- liking a secure pay cheque at the end of each week or month;
- being bad at dealing with financial uncertainty and insecurity;
- feeling that it is important to work with a congenial group of people;
- being good at relating to people and helping with their problems.

Then create some more columns headed 'What I actually do or did', 'The responsibilities involved', 'Skills/Competences this demonstrates' and 'My achievements'.

'Competences' is just another word for skills, but it is very much in vogue at present. All it really means is what you are competent at. It is in this area that you may find it particularly difficult to work on your own. Ask other people what they think you are good at. To quote the authors of *Finding the Right Job*, the BBC book on the subject, 'It's surprising what they will include that, through false modesty, you will have missed.'

If you have been doing a job for a long time, and have perhaps developed it as you went along, it is easy to take what you do for granted. You may think 'there's nothing to it' simply because, for you, there isn't – it comes as second nature after so long. You may also feel that your skill is in something very specific, when in fact it can quite easily be used elsewhere. Computing is a good example of this. Perhaps you have always worked with one particular accounting package and feel that is all you know. But there are strong similarities between different accounting packages; with some practice and a short period of training, you could be just as proficient in many others. It would certainly take you far less time to pick it up than someone starting from scratch.

According to Brian Cooper of Coutts Career Consultants:

'People often find it very difficult to put down their achievements, because they were just "part of the job". I had one ex-sales manager who had succeeded in replacing a major competitor's products with his own in a whole new area of the market, but it took a lot of discussion to get this out of him.'

So make sure you blow your trumpet from the beginning – you'll need to at any interview.

If you have done some aptitude tests recently, now is the time to feed in what you have learnt from them. If not, try to do them now. *Test Yourself* by Jim Barrett (see 'Useful publications' for details) is one example of a self-help book for this, but there are many others, and also many internet sites. If the tests are looking at your personality rather than simply your aptitudes, try to get an accredited person – either a chartered occupational psychologist or someone qualified under the British Psychological Society's scheme – to take you through them, and ensure that there is enough time for a proper follow-up discussion. The last thing you want, if you are already feeling bruised by the loss or potential loss of your job, is to be left feeling inadequate by a test!

Doing this activity may help you identify obvious gaps in your training, skills or paper qualifications. So take another piece of paper (or another section on your computer file), head it 'Action Plan', and start making a list of actions you must take. You might, for instance, conclude that:

- if you are no longer able to go to that job round the corner, you will finally have to pass a driving test; or
- you might need to develop skills in a particular area of computing; or
- you might have become fluent in another language over the years, but have never taken an exam in it.

See Chapter 12 for details of where and how to get training. There may be some financial help available for this.

Jocelyn very much wanted to leave her part-time job as a health service laboratory worker. She knew she had plenty of experience working with computers but she did not have keyboard skills. So she went on a part-time course with the local college, passed three RSA exams with distinction, and was then ready to look for jobs – and in fact got the second one she applied for.

The money you need or want

If you are single or the sole earner in the family, the answers to the questions in this section will be based on your whole family unit. If, on the other hand, you have been a dual-earner couple so far (or your partner is in a similar position to you and seeking new employment), start by deciding whether you are working out everything on a shared basis or looking at each person's needs and income independently. Although you may manage your finances separately, in practice people who live together are almost always interdependent financially, so it usually makes sense to work it out on a shared basis.

How much money do you need?

Ideally, before you do this part of the exercise, you should keep a record of your spending over several months. If this is not really feasible, you can probably reconstruct much of it from your bank and credit card statements.

Basic living expenses

It's important first to define what is meant by 'need'. First of all, there are the inescapable commitments of yourself and your spouse and family, such as:

- mortgage or rent;
- Council Tax;
- household contents and buildings insurance;
- food and other basic necessities;
- hire purchase and similar payments;
- heating/lighting/water bills;
- transport.

You may also have commitments to other people – putting a student son or daughter through university, for instance, or paying maintenance to an ex-spouse.

Tot up the cost of these essentials at their current level (that is, not taking account of any inflation). If you have a computer, put all these figures on to a spreadsheet; it will make it much easier to play around with the calculations later.

Leisure activities and extras

Many people find it difficult to enjoy life if they pare their finances down to essentials only. Enjoyment tends to cost money, and some hobbies and interests cost a lot more than others. Some people feel that life is not worth living unless they can go on an expensive ski-ing holiday each year, while others prefer a quiet walk in the country.

If you have not done this sort of calculation before, discovering how much you spend on your leisure activities can be quite a shock. There is no need to feel guilty or ashamed about this. Neither should you feel that you have an obligation to cut back your expectations of life, though you may have to if your plans do not work out as you had hoped. In the short term you may want to be rather frugal until you see how things work out. But no one should feel that they have to pitch their sights too low at this stage. On the other hand, you may come to realise that much of your spending is either compensation for the stress of work – buying escapist books or expensive cosmetics, for example – or made necessary by a shortage of time, for instance buying takeaways rather than cooking yourself. So these are areas where you could probably cut down without much of a pang, if life were less pressured.

Even without this, there could well be ways in which you can limit your spending on different activities without really altering the enjoyment – for example, buying cheaper seats at the theatre or a concert, and having a sandwich beforehand rather than buying a meal there. Or if you are someone who is always buying books or clothes, would you be able to live within a ration of say, one purchase a month and go to the library more? Look realistically at what savings you think you are capable of making, without becoming miserable as a result.

Some people may specifically want to simplify their lives, and lower their standard of living, as part of a whole change in their lifestyle. *Downshifting*, by Andy Bull, discusses how to go about this in detail (see 'Useful publications'). As he suggests, it is sensible – though it may not always be feasible – to test out any change in your living standards before taking the plunge. Waiting an hour for the bus with a load of shopping may be a step too far for those who have been used to driving a powerful car everywhere.

Providing for your retirement

Think also about your needs when you reach the age when you retire and have to live on whatever pension you may have. It is difficult even to guess how much you will need in 15 or 20 years' time in money terms, because of the effects of inflation. However, you will be able to find out (by looking in the booklet or asking the pensions administrator) whether the pension is guaranteed to keep up with prices (as with most public sector pensions) or gives a lower level of increase or even no increase at all, and it is important to take this into account. Even at a 3 per cent rate of inflation, prices will double in around 23 years – and you could be living on a pension for a lot longer than that.

It is possible to estimate what contributions you need to put into a pension scheme to get a decent amount. If you find employment that includes a pension scheme, you could expect to pay an average of about 5 per cent of your earnings as an employee's contribution. If you are on your own and having to buy a pension out of your own resources, you need to think of putting away **at least** 15 per cent of your net earnings each year. Many of the large insurance companies and other providers have 'pension calculators' on their websites, which take you through the arithmetic.

In both cases, if the pension you have built up already is not very good, or non-existent, you will need to put in a lot more if you are to build up enough for a comfortable retirement over a short period. Only if you already have a very good pension, and you are sure that it is going to keep up with inflation, can you say that you do not need to worry about any further provision for your retirement.

By adding a pension contribution figure to the amount you have calculated you need for a comfortable lifestyle, you will now have a net figure for your income needs. To find the gross figure (which is what you see in job advertisements or what would be quoted to you in an interview), you need to add in tax and National Insurance. Working this out is complicated, because of the need to take account of your personal allowances (the amount of income you are allowed to receive before you become liable to pay Income Tax) and the part of your earnings on which you pay National Insurance and tax at lower rates.

Roughly speaking, if you are looking for a lower-paid job you will need to add about another 20 per cent; you will need around another 30 per cent if you will be paying basic-rate tax. If your expectations are higher and you would be paying tax at the 40 per cent tax rate if you achieved them, it is more complicated. You would be paying 40 per cent tax on part of your income only, and above a certain level your National Insurance contributions will not rise any more. So add perhaps 37 per cent to the take-home pay figure you have worked out (unless you feel like doing it more exactly).

Jack and Mary have decided they could just about manage on an income of £12,000 a year after tax. Grossing that up by adding 30 per cent brings them to £15,600. They decide that they need £20,000 a year to live on reasonably comfortably, which is £26,000 after grossing up.

What income will you have?

On the other side of the equation comes your income. If you have started drawing a pension from your employer, this can go into the balance sheet on that side (at its gross, pre-tax figure, as you have already worked out a gross needs figure).

If you have a lump sum from your pension scheme or a severance payment, think about how much of it you will want to invest and what income you could receive. Alternatively, you might want to use some of it to reduce your outgoings, by paying off mortgage or hire purchase debts for instance. You may want to do some research at this stage (you will certainly need to do this at some point) to see what options are open to you, and decide on your preferred investment strategy – especially the level of risk you will feel happy with, which will affect the level of returns you can expect. Then put a rough figure – probably a pessimistic rather than an optimistic one – into the income side of the balance sheet.

For an explanation of the different types of investment, and of how to decide on a strategy, look in Age Concern's *Your Taxes and Savings* (updated annually). You may also want to talk to a financial adviser. It could be better to find one to whom you pay a fee, even though they are not cheap, rather than one who will be paid by commission by those providing the financial products the adviser recommends you buy. See the *Guide to Financial Advice*, published by the Financial Services Authority (FSA), for information on how to go about finding an adviser.

If you have no pension yet, either because you are too young to draw one or because the terms offered were too bad for it to be worthwhile taking it now, all or most of your income needs will have to be met by earnings.

If there is a shortfall between your income and your outgoings, is it likely to be for the short or long term? If you are due to get a reasonable pension and a lump sum in four or five years' time, your attitude to the income you want now may be different from that of someone who has not yet built up much by way of a pension.

Jack and Mary will have Jack's early retirement pension of £7,000 from his firm. They will have £50,000 altogether in savings after they have spent part of Jack's severance payment on a trip to Australia. So they can look for investment income of £2,000 a year, at a cautious 4 per cent rate of return, giving them a total pre-tax income of £9,000.

So the gap between their currently expected income and their 'comfortable' budget is £17,000 a year. The gap between their income and the 'just about managing' budget is £6,600.

If they are going to manage at all, one of them has to earn *some* other income. But even to reach their 'comfortable' budget neither of them needs a 'proper' job like Jack's previous professional management job, which was more than full-time and really took over his life. A limited amount of consultancy work, full-time work at a less taxing level or reasonably well-paid part-time jobs would do. And they need to do rather less if they are happy to move to the 'just about managing' lifestyle – in effect, buying extra leisure through reduced working time.

What are you worth?

In parallel with looking at your financial position, consider what you might be worth to an employer or to those who might buy your services.

You know what you *were* worth, because you were being paid a wage or salary by an employer until you lost your job.

Go through the job ads to see what is being paid for jobs that compare with yours. It is important not to underprice yourself, because if you do so others will undervalue you too. (Even if you don't need the money and are planning to offer your services as a volunteer, it is worth knowing the value of what you are giving.) One outplacement adviser says:

> 'I've had people assume that they are bound to have to take a cut in pay, which is not always the case. They may take a lot of convincing that the work they have been doing for their firm has given them skills which are readily transferable elsewhere.'

She cites the example of one woman, with considerable financial skills, who assumed she would need to look for a job earning around £20,000 and ended up with one paying £100,000.

However, there is also research evidence (quoted in *Winning the Generation Game*) that older workers can face a 'pay gap' of 25–35 per cent between their previous earnings and potential earnings in a new job, a considerably larger gap than for those under 50. So it is important to be realistic and test the market. Remember that there may be some financial help from the State, such as the Employment Credit and, in future, the Working Tax Credit under the New Deal 50 Plus, if you do take a pay cut.

If your health is not good

There are people who are not well – perhaps have not been for a long time – but who have found it possible to manage their job in an environment that they know and where people are sympathetic. There are people who have struggled through their work each day but have been completely exhausted by the time they got home and collapsed into bed at six o'clock. A person with back problems, for example, might have had their work rearranged by management or sympathetic colleagues to ensure that they did not have to do heavy lifting. Once you are on the wider labour market, this may not be possible if people at the new job are not so sympathetic.

However, the Disability Discrimination Act (explained on pages 15–16) does require employers to make 'reasonable adjustments' to assist people with disabilities, and there is also help with finding jobs for people with disabilities – through the New Deal for Disabled People and a means-tested benefit called the Disabled Person's Tax Credit which subsidises (to some extent) your wages if what you can earn is reduced by illness or disability. The Disabled Person's Tax Credit (to be merged into the new Working Tax Credit from April 2003) is also some help in finding employment, though it has a good many let-outs for employers. If you feel you want to carry on working, or it is a necessity, now is the time to find out what can be done to improve your health, what activities you would be able to do and what help you might be able to get – for example, with adaptations to make moving around easier, or training to allow you to take a sedentary job.

Every Jobcentre Plus office should have a disability employment adviser, and it should be possible to get referred immediately by your personal adviser without having to serve a waiting period as with other New Deal packages. It should even be possible to get some advice even if you have not been signing on as unemployed or sick, as it is a Government priority to get back into work more people who are currently not in work for health reasons.

For other advice, there are a number of specialist organisations for people with disabilities, and support groups for those with particular conditions, which you can find through the internet or through your reference library. Skill UK (www.skill.org.uk) is an example of one such group, which has plenty of links through to others.

It is possible that you will find that your health problems are work-related to a greater extent than you had realised. Back pain, for example, could have been caused by poor design of office equipment, and so reduce once you have left. Once you have identified this, you will be able to sort out what you need to avoid in future. (You may also want to take advice from your union or a solicitor about whether you have a claim against your previous employer.)

Other limitations

Whatever you may want to do, and however adaptable you may feel you are, there will still be some limits that you want, or feel it is necessary, to impose:

- If you do not have your own car, for example, you will need to work somewhere accessible by public transport from your home.
- If you have caring responsibilities, perhaps for a parent or an in-law, you may not be able to move away from your present home even if the perfect job comes up elsewhere.
- Even without these responsibilities, you may not want to leave the area where you have friends and links with the local community.
- You might be interested in moving, but only to an area that would bring you closer to your children or grandchildren. That would rule out large parts of the country.

Any of these factors, and others, could limit the hours you can work (both the length of time and when the hours are worked) and the places where you could work. Shiftwork and unsocial hours, for instance, are difficult for many people, but there are others whom they suit. Someone with a family and plenty of social life might not want to work weekends or evenings; a single person without much going on in their life might even prefer to work those times.

The hours you want to do will also affect the time and money you want to spend on travelling. A journey that takes, say, an hour each way will be a waste of a good chunk of your life if you work only a three-hour session when you get there. You could either restrict yourself to jobs closer to home or plan to work two or three full days in the week, to cut down on the travelling time and the fares.

Putting it all together

The end-result of all this should be a profile of the sort of work that you want and that you will be happy doing. If you are working on this with an organisation, or through a book or a website, each will have its own ways of setting this out. Or you may want to create your own. At least, though, you should cover the items in the following checklist.

Checklist

Sort of work Tick any of the following that apply – or, if you have been very open-minded about what you would be happy doing, prioritise. Cross out the items that appeal to you least, and rate the rest from 1 to 10. Try not to contradict yourself!

routine

developmental

stimulating

needing use of imagination

office-based

management role

caring tasks

using craft skills

using new technology

manual labour

indoors/out of doors

sitting down

involving travel

physically strenuous

not strenuous

working under close supervision

using own initiative

other (*add*)

Hours Tick one of the following, or put in order of preference:

under 10 hours a week

between 10 and 20 hours

between 20 and 30 hours

full-time

Working pattern Tick one of the following, or put in order of preference:

    regular 9–5 type hours

    regular but not necessarily 9–5

    happy with irregular working pattern

Place Tick one of the following, or put in order of preference:

    very close to home

    within half an hour's travelling distance

    within an hour's travelling distance

    prepared to move house or live away from home if necessary

Working Tick one of the following:

    for someone else

    as my own boss

    in a partnership

    employing other people

Weekly or monthly figure needed £ ...

Moving on to job research

By now you should have a pretty detailed specification of what you can do and what you want to do. It's only at this stage that you really need to start pinning yourself down to a job description. What sorts of labels are there going to be on the work you want to do?

Again, there are plenty of guides and tests available for you to investigate. One example is in *Test Yourself*, which has a series of activities to help you to relate your interests to particular careers. As it says:

'The profile is not meant to be exact, only to serve as a basis for you to think through whether what you choose to do seems to fit well with your underlying motivation ... '

It is important to think 'out of the box' – in the current jargon which for once does say something useful. There are two elements in any occupation – the task and the organisation you are doing it in.

For example, a theatre company needs actors, of course, but it also needs stage hands, electricians, carpenters, accountants, administrators, box office staff, ushers and so on. If you are an accountant but have concluded that you love the theatre, perhaps what you are really after is a finance job in a theatre company (and they might even let you carry a spear on stage now and then!).

What you are looking for may change over time, or you might realise you have to do one thing in order to achieve a longer-term goal of something else. Perhaps you are an accountant who fancies being a playwright. A few years in a theatrical environment would really help a good deal with understanding what writing a play involves, and give you contacts with people in the right field.

Alternatively, you may only want to work full-time until, say, 55, because you have a pension that will kick in at that stage and give you enough to live on while working only part-time, doing voluntary work the rest of the time. So put that in the plan too.

This plan, though, is a living document, not a once-for-all exercise. If when you reach 55 you are bouncing with energy and loving your full-time job (or if our accountant's few years in the theatre have put her off actors for life!) you can go back and change your plans.

Doing your research

What you have now is a broad outline of what you think you want – a proposal. It could be based on a lot of information, especially if you intend to carry on doing roughly the same as you are now but need a new employer to do it with. Or it could be based on an idea. Either way, you need to find out as much as you can about your proposal before you start applying for the new role, and refining – or if necessary drastically changing – that proposal as you go. You can get a long way by doing this on paper or a computer screen, but in the end you will also need to talk to people.

Desk research

There are a number of general career guides available, not all geared towards people in their 20s. For example, the *Penguin Careers Guide* (see 'Useful publications') lists over 300 careers and occupational areas in alphabetical order; as well as the sub-headings within each article for 'Entry qualifications', 'The work' and 'Training and personal attributes', there are also 'Late start', 'Career break', 'Part-time' and 'Position of women'. You might find that the information you obtain from such research rules you out of occupations you had been thinking about; for example, in the unlikely event of your feeling inspired to become an actuary, the Penguin guide advises that a late start is 'Only advisable for very able mathematicians because of the long training; also difficulty in finding training posts,' which will effectively stop you wasting further time on the idea. But it also offers a list of related careers that you could follow up instead.

If there is a professional body or a trade body, they are likely to have literature you can write off for. Most such organisations, and most potential employers of any size, also have websites. Remember, though, that generally these are promotional tools. They won't ever tell you, 'this is a terrible job, don't touch it with a barge pole'. You do need to read between the lines to some extent.

It is also worth looking at websites and publications that will help if you are thinking about ways of working. For instance, if you thought job-sharing might be a way forward, the organisation New Ways to Work (contact details on page 194) has a wealth of material both for individuals and aimed at persuading employers.

Talking to people

Useful as books, brochures and websites are, they don't replace human contact. Now is also the time to talk to people who will know about the topic, both about the particular occupation and about the way of working. Make *very clear*, when approaching people, that what you are doing is research about jobs, *not* asking for a job. Some books on job-hunting suggest using information-seeking as a 'foot in the door' to get yourself an interview, but, as *What Color is your Parachute* (see page 184) puts it:

> 'You've botched it, whenever you're telling a lie to someone. The whole point of informational interviewing [the author's term for this stage] is that it is a search for Truth.'

The people who can give you the most helpful information about what it is like to work in a particular field, he points out, are anyway not so much the people with the power to hire you as the ordinary workers, people at the sort of level you might aspire to. Nevertheless, you might find yourself being offered an opportunity even so. Unless you are desperate, he suggests that you say 'Thanks, but can I come back to you?' at this stage. You don't yet know whether this field suits you, or you it, so moving too fast could be 'out of the frying pan, into the fire'.

For a shy person, going round talking to people you don't know well, or at all, may be very difficult. Try practising on family and friends first. Once you get into it, you will find that many people are very willing to talk about what they do, provided they do not feel that you are exploiting them or using them to weasel your way in. Ask for an hour of their time and don't go over it, go prepared with your questions, and always remember to thank them afterwards.

Finding the contacts to talk to is not as difficult as it sounds; in fact, for many people they will be there ready-made. Take our example above, of an accountant with a hankering to write plays. He or she probably belongs to the Friends of the local theatre, or knows someone who does. Their Secretary will know the paid staff at the theatre. So our accountant could ask the Secretary who to speak to, and then use his or her name (with permission) in making the contact.

If you don't know people in your chosen field, ask around for those who do. There is a theory of 'six degrees of separation' (which has been turned into a film). This says that anyone can link up with anyone else, through no more than six intermediate stages of friends-of-friends. It may be an exaggeration, but it is not far from the truth. Prepare yourself a little speech: for instance, 'I've been an accountant so far, but that job has come/is coming to an end, and what I would really love is a job where I could both use those skills and be in contact with theatre administration. Do you know anyone who could tell me more about what the possibilities are?' Use it to friends, acquaintances and contacts at parties, and pretty soon someone is going to say to you, 'Oh, you ought to contact so-and-so'.

Sometimes what you are told will be unwelcome – you will find out that you are out of date or simply wrong in your ideas about a job.

However, regard this as a good thing rather than a setback. The earlier you lose your preconceptions, the better. According to one careers adviser, for example:

> 'A lot of people seem to have a vague idea that they'd like to "work for a charity", and that this would be an easy and unstressed role. But these days, nothing could be further from the truth. There's an organisation which runs courses about working for a charity (Working for a Charity; address on page 197) and I persuade them to go on one if I can.'

If as a result of doing some research you decide that your chosen area of work is not for you, don't despair. Go back and revise your life plan. You haven't wasted the time if it enables you to make another constructive move. In any case, you are not likely to be successful in your search if it is clear that your heart isn't in it and you know the employment you are pursuing is not for you.

For some ideas about how to organise your time when doing your research, look at Chapter 13.

But am I not too old for all this?

Chapter 8 looks at the question of ageism in employers, and how to tackle it. You also have to look at ageism in yourself, however.

These days, the average 50-year-old has easily 20 more years of energetic life ahead. Many people will have 30, 40 or even 50 years to go. It is known that one of the best ways to lengthen your lifespan is to keep busy and active. Or to put it the other way round, it really is possible to die of boredom, of lack of stimulation.

Whatever you do, don't assume that you are too old to learn. You *can* teach an old dog new tricks. Research projects have shown time and again that, to quote a 1993 report, *Age and Employment: policies, attitudes and practices*, from the then Institute of Personnel Management (now the Chartered Institute of Personnel and Development):

> 'although older people do not learn as quickly as their younger colleagues, they can in fact acquire substantial new knowledge

and skills ... Older people can be particularly effective learners after their anxiety in learning situations has been overcome and opportunities for practice have been provided. Further, older workers do not forget new knowledge and skills any faster than their younger colleagues.'

The next step

Armed with this specification and your plans, you are ready to start your search, whether it is for a job, a business to set up in, training or education opportunities, or voluntary work. The next few chapters cover the different factors that arise in each case, and how to set about the search for what you want.

8 Working for an employer

This chapter looks at the different types of paid work that are available, such as:

- *full-time*
- *part-time*
- *job-shares*
- *temporary*
- *casual (including zero-hours contracts)*
- *teleworking (working from home)*

Before looking at any of this, however, here is the best place to tackle the problem that may have been worrying you – ageism.

Age discrimination and how to combat it

However hard you try, will the new job ever be there, at your age? That there is age discrimination cannot be doubted. A recent evaluation of the Code of Practice on age diversity in employment for the Department for Education and Skills (DfES; formerly the Department for Education and Employment) found that 20 per cent of those in the sample had experienced discrimination in relation to an actual or possible job because of their age, and for half of these the discrimination was in getting an interview – so they were not even given the chance to show their mettle. (Responsibility for combating age discrimination has now moved to the Department of Work and Pensions, and you can find out more about the Code of Practice, and other activities, on their Age Positive website www.agepositive.gov.uk.)

A very high 85 per cent thought that employers discriminated against older workers in some way, and 75 per cent thought this in relation to recruitment or taking on new staff. More depressingly, another recent study found that even in an area with skills shortages such as information technology, ageism – starting as early as 45 – was, according to a report in the *Financial Times*, 'rife'. Of those surveyed, 56 per cent thought that young managers found it difficult to manage older employees.

There does seem to be some improvement, however. The most recent summary of the DfES research, published in March 2001, showed that the proportion of companies that say they take account of age in selection and recruitment has more than halved since 1999, decreasing from 27 per cent to 13 per cent.

The most obvious example of age discrimination is in job adverts in the newspapers and magazines. The DfES study quoted above found that 13 per cent of advertisements mention a preferred age range, and 6 per cent specify age limits, though there's no obvious reason why a 46-year-old accountant, for instance, should be any worse at doing the job than a 45-year-old. This does limit the field in which it is going to be useful to look, because whoever is doing the short-listing is likely to weed out automatically anyone who does not fit the age criteria.

On the other hand, this is only a small proportion of the total number of advertisements, and in any case the majority of jobs are *not* filled through the advertisement. Instead, they are filled via speculative approaches or contacts – people being asked if they are interested, or hearing about the job and expressing an interest. Lower-paid, manual or routine clerical jobs, and part-time jobs, are often filled in the traditional way by people calling in at the firm after the Vacancies board has gone up, or through cards in newsagents' windows. With higher-paid and higher-status jobs it tends to happen more elegantly, through 'networking' – getting to know the right people and persuading them that you are worth considering for a vacancy.

Guidance to employers

The DfES has had a non-statutory Code of Practice on Age Diversity in Employment since June 1999. The Government will need to draw up legislation by December 2006, as a result of the new European Directive on the subject. The UK Government has convened a working group to go through the details. The aim is, according to Government ministers, that compulsory retirement based on age will be possible only where it is objectively justified by a legitimate aim.

Currently, even though the Code of Practice is voluntary, it is at least worth quoting back at employers if you feel you are running into age discrimination. More ammunition comes from the professional organisation dealing with personnel and human resources management, the Chartered Institute of Personnel and Development, which takes a strong line against age discrimination. Its Key Facts document on *Age and Employment* says bluntly that:

'Employment decisions based on age are never justifiable because:

- age is not a genuine employment criterion;
- age is a poor predictor of performance;
- it is misleading to equate physical and mental ability with age.'

The document expands this with detailed arguments and recommendations. If you are dealing with an organisation with a human resources department, you could raise this with them. Find out also whether the employer who has treated you badly has an Equal Opportunities statement; most of these today mention age as well as other issues. It could be that policy decisions at the top level have not filtered down to the people with whom you are dealing. Even if raising the issue does not help you directly, it could assist others who come after you.

As an individual older person faced with employers' prejudices, it is the initial step – getting an interview – that is probably the most difficult. So you need to make the maximum use of all the informal contacts you have, and to ensure that the applications you make are as well prepared and as relevant as possible. Stress the skills and competence you have, what *you* can bring to the job. It is not wise to leave your age out of a CV altogether (see pages 116–120) but it can come well down the list, *after* you have explained all the things you can do.

Encouragingly, with fuller employment there are signs that employers are now taking a more reasonable view about older workers. The DWP's Age Positive Campaign has named a number of employers as Champions for their experience of turning Age Positive policies into action. These are listed on their website, with brief case studies and quotes from the employers concerned. Supermarket group Safeways, for instance, says:

'Our customers value the maturity and experience of our older staff. We have also found that labour turnover in the over-50 age group is significantly lower compared to other age groups. This saves on recruitment and training costs, and we are looking to increase the percentage of employees aged over 50.'

There are of course many areas of the country where unemployment is still far too high, and lack of good transport may mean that you have to look for work in a fairly limited area. But as Clare Cassidy of Penna Sanders & Sidney on Tyneside points out, there are opportunities even in these areas from some of the new industries starting up.

'The predominance of call centres in the north-east means that there is more flexibility now, and people can get jobs who never had access before.'

Such work is likely to be extremely boring, of course, and not something you will want to stick to for very long. But you can treat it as a stop-gap and a way of learning how to develop new skills and fit in with new environments, while continuing your hunt for more interesting work that will use your real skills. Don't let difficulty in finding the right thing make you downhearted. The problem lies in the general jobs market, and the high level of unemployment, exacerbated by age discrimination – *not*, it must be stressed, by any personal qualities you gain or lose as you get older!

Different types of work

Full-time work

'Conventional' full-time jobs are probably the most difficult jobs to find, simply because everyone wants them and the number available is shrinking rather than growing. Much depends on whether there is a surplus or a shortage of skilled staff in your field. If you have a nursing or teaching qualification, for instance, obtaining work may be comparatively easy. You may need a refresher course if you have not been working in those occupations for a while (see Chapter 12).

If your occupation is one without staff shortages, a possible way in is to find temporary work in that field, perhaps as a holiday relief or for casual employment to start with. Often, employers wanting to fill a permanent job will look first at those they know already and can trust.

They can even create, or bring forward, a job for someone who has already shown that they fit in with the organisation.

Part-time work

Part-time work tends to be easier to find than full-time, but it is a lot more variable in terms of what is offered and how well paid it is. It can be worse paid than a full-time job doing much the same thing. Part-timers can also find themselves treated as 'non-people' when it comes to discussions of policy, opportunities for training and promotion, and so on. However, under the Part-Time Workers (Prevention of Less Favourable Treatment) Regulations 2000, part-timers now have the same employment rights as full-timers doing comparable jobs.

Although part-time work is spreading to almost every sector, it is particularly common in areas where there are marked peaks and troughs of work, or where the job needs covering for longer than a working day. Examples are retail shops, catering and hotels, banking and other financial services, and caring jobs in residential homes and hospitals. There are also possibilities where there is a specialist job to be done but it does not warrant someone full-time – a part-time accountant or bookkeeper might be needed for a small business, for instance.

Your own previous employer, or a similar one, might be able to afford to employ you part-time though it could not afford to have you full-time. For instance, owing to public spending cuts, many schools are having to replace full-time staff with part-timers. It may also be worth applying for jobs that are advertised as full-time but for which the employer may be happy to accept one or more part-timers, or to arrange a job-share (see below), if people with the right skills come along.

Part-time work can be stressful, however, if there is simply too much to do to fit into the time. Jocelyn, for instance (in the example on page 1) found that a full-time job, in a less pressured organisation, took less out of her than part-time work in an NHS laboratory working against the clock all the time. Some part-timers can find that they turn into cheap full-timers, doing extra work that they are not paid to do just because there is too much to fit into their part-time hours. People working for voluntary organisations, and in demanding jobs such as social work or teaching, can find themselves caught up in this way. You need to be strong-minded enough to make it clear with the employer, from the start, what your hours are going to be, and what work you are expected to do in those hours. Stress from the start that you have other commitments you intend to maintain.

Don't confuse *part-time* work with *temporary* work. There are many jobs that are both part-time and temporary, and some indeed shade over into casual work. But there are also permanent part-time jobs in which people can, and do, stay for many years.

Job-sharing

This is a particular form of part-time work in which a full-time job is divided into two. The job is usually split down the middle, with half the wages and half the non-wage benefits for each person. One person can work mornings and the other afternoons, or one can work at the beginning of the week and the other at the end, or you can do alternate weeks. There may also be a session of 'overlap time' when you are both in the workplace in order to hand over tasks and bring each other up to date.

Although the costs might be slightly higher than when employing a single person, the attraction for employers is that the job-sharers will usually arrange to cover for each other during sickness, holidays and other absences. Vacant 'halves' of an already established job-share are sometimes advertised, or two people can get together and apply for a job on a job-share basis. Employers that have not heard of the concept before, or have not tried it, may take some convincing that it will work. The organisation New Ways to Work (address on page 194) can provide material explaining how it works. Their website offers a lot of help and includes publications aimed at management, unions and particular sectors – such as schools and the legal profession. Job-sharing is slowly spreading now to management roles. One research study (by The Resource Connections, Savile and Holdsworth, and the Industrial Society) has found that 'most managers who share a job or work flexibly are seen by their bosses as outperforming their full-time counterparts.'

Because job-sharers will usually be working part-time, their employment rights will be protected under the Part-Time Workers (Prevention of Less Favourable Treatment) Regulations 2000 in the same way.

Temporary work

For most people this is a stop-gap, but some people enjoy doing it as a way of life because of the variety it brings. It is possible to do temporary work in almost every field, including professional areas. If you have been in management, there is a growing number of 'interim managers' who may be brought in just to fill a gap while someone is long-term sick or might be faced with a real challenge of sorting out a company in a mess.

The easiest way to get into temporary work is through an employment agency. The best agencies realise that 'permanently temporary' workers on their books are a valuable resource, and may offer the sort of non-wage benefits as ordinary employers do, over and above the statutory requirements such as a minimum amount of paid holiday. Manpower UK, for example, offer life insurance, share options, and even discounted gym membership! Like many other agencies, they also offer help with career-planning, and opportunities for on-line training.

Shop around for the right agency for you, in the same way as for the right employer; you want to be able to build up a long-term relationship with them. For these and other occupations, the *Yellow Pages* for your area will have pages of different employment agencies, some of them general, some covering specialist fields such as sales, accountancy and engineering. The very large multinational agencies have a host of specialist subsidiaries; you might find, however, that you prefer to deal with a small local agency where you can get to know the owners and be part of a team. There are several agencies that specialise in dealing with mature workers. You will find details of them on the Age Positive website, among the case studies.

The trade association for recruitment and employment agencies, the Federation of Recruitment and Employment Services (FRES), set standards for their members; check whether any agency you are using has the FRES symbol on its notepaper. There is also a government-run Employment Agency Standards Line on 0645 555 105 where you can obtain advice about your rights and help take up complaints.

As with part-time work, European law is strengthening the legal rights of temporary workers. A Directive on Fixed-Term Work (which includes most temporary employees) was agreed by the European Union in 1999, and the UK plans to bring it into force by July 2002. Agency workers are not covered (there is another Directive in preparation for them), and neither are the self-employed. The draft Fixed-Term Employees (Prevention of Less Favourable Treatment) Regulations say that fixed-term employees should not be treated less favourably than similar permanent employees in their contractual terms and conditions of employment unless there is an 'objective reason' to justify it. The DTI have concluded that this will have to include pay and pensions, and a clause covering this is included in the Employment Bill currently (spring 2002) on its way through Parliament.

Casual or sessional work

In some areas of work, such as the media, there are widespread opportunities for casual work and they are spreading still further. As with part-time work, your old employer or a similar one may be willing to employ you for odd sessions.

Ian used to be a senior cameraman with a TV company. He took early retirement but is now working for his previous employer on a sessional basis, about one day a week.

If you have nursing qualifications, you may well be able to find work through a 'nurse bank', established by a local health services trust. Teachers may be able to work on 'supply' with the local authority or the specialist employment agencies in different sectors of education and further education.

If the work involves a lot of preparation – as lecturing or teaching may do, for instance – the hourly rate you are offered for the occasional session may not be worthwhile. But working in this way could give you a way in to more regular employment, and might also be a way of testing out whether you will really take to some new activity you are thinking about. If, for instance, you were thinking of running a pub, doing some evening shifts in several different pubs would be a way of seeing all sides of the operation.

Doing casual or sessional work can play havoc with your social life and other commitments. Nor will it suit a person who needs to know where they are and hates uncertainty. But if you can build up a relationship with one particular source of work, you should quite soon be able to predict when the calls will come and how much notice you will get. As a casual worker you will almost certainly be working some unsocial hours, because those will be just the times when the full-time regular workers are off and your services are needed.

Zero hours contracts are a particular form of part-time work, very close to casual work. The idea is that you are offered no regular pattern of employment but are called in as and when you are needed by the employer. Some of these contracts virtually require you to sit by the phone all the time, waiting for the employer's call. They are popular with certain types of employer whose demands for labour are irregular and unpredictable but not, in general, with employees (for fairly obvious reasons). They also tend to pay pretty badly. If you take on work of this sort, check the terms of the contract and what your rights and responsibilities are. If the workplace has a union, join it to reduce the chances of being exploited.

So far as legal protection is concerned, there is a distinction between 'workers' and 'employees'. An 'employee' is someone who has a contract of employment, which gives them various statutory and contractual rights. Someone is a worker who, to quote the TUC guide *Your Rights at Work*, 'works for someone else but usually on the basis of providing a service' and has fewer rights. Those doing casual work may well fall the wrong side of the line on this.

In many casual jobs, the line between employment and self-employment is blurred. There can be tax problems if it is not clear which category you are in – see page 141 for more details.

Teleworking

This means working for an employer but based at home (or you may be treated as self-employed; see page 141 for information on this). Usually, it means work that involves new technology, with computers and telephones. The AA, for instance, has 150 people in its 'virtual call centre' taking calls for its emergency breakdown service and routing them to the mobile workers.

The Institute of Employment Studies has estimated that in 2000 there were nearly 1.5 million teleworkers, and that nearly three in ten firms have employees who work from home or are planning to do so. This can be useful if you have caring responsibilities, or if you need to work in the evenings or at weekends but don't want to travel late at night. However, especially if you are living alone, working like this can become very isolating, and you may come to feel almost a prisoner of the phone or the computer. Some firms offering teleworking also offer ways of getting people together now and then, so check whether this is possible. The Telework Association publishes the *Teleworking Handbook* (details on page 183), which is essential reading for anyone thinking of working in this way.

There are many other forms of home-based work available, like addressing or stuffing envelopes or sewing clothes. Though they will suit some people, they can be very poorly paid (though legally they have to pay at least the national minimum wage), with few legal rights and sometimes dangerous or unhealthy work. The National Group on Homeworking (see page 194 for address) also warn that some of the attractive-looking advertisements for recruitment, or for making up toys or lampshades or kits, are little short of scams. So take great care before getting into this sort of work and give a wide berth to any scheme that involves paying up front for materials or a deposit. Think instead about getting training that would allow you to work at the more 'high-tech' end of the homeworking spectrum, or about genuine self-employment building up your own business.

For more information, see the *Which? Guide to Working from Home* and the website www.workingfromhome.co.uk.

9 Looking for a job

This chapter deals with the whole process of looking for a job. It covers:

- *researching the employers in the fields in which you are looking;*
- *how to go about looking for work, including approaching people 'on spec' when you don't know if they have a job going or not;*
- *developing job-hunting skills and putting together information about yourself (almost always known by the Latin term* curriculum vitae *or CV, or in American terms a* résumé*);*
- *preparing for an interview.*

Researching the employers available

Chapter 7 suggested the sort of research and information gathering you will need to do, if you are planning to change direction in your working life. If you have done this, you are likely to have a fair idea of the sort of employers you are looking for, and on whom it is worth concentrating. Now is the time to focus more closely and find out whatever you can about which sort of employer you might like to work for – and who might like to employ you.

Where you start looking – to draw up a 'long-list' (possibly a very long list) of potential employers – will depend on what sort of job you are after. If your occupation exists in many different places, such as being a clerical worker or a book-keeper, the best place to start will be local directories, or even the *Yellow Pages*. If, on the other hand, your occupation is specific to certain sectors, you will want the more specialist trade directories or lists of members of professional organisations. A good reference library is the most likely source of all these, and many will also be on the internet. Look, too, at job advertisements – even if you are not yet ready to apply – and the trade magazines to see who is looking for staff or is likely to do so in future. *Net that Job* (see 'Useful publications', page 183) is a starting point for a list of useful sites.

108

Having got your 'long-list' you will then want to find out what you can about the potential employer. This is where the internet becomes very valuable (see Chapter 7 for more discussion of this). Most employers of any size now run a website, which can give you a general impression of the organisation; in addition, most have a page at least about jobs or opportunities with them.

For example, the big accountancy firm KPMG has a button on its website home page that leads you through to its jobs pages, with a special 'opportunities' section. Going into this allows you to find out what is currently available – full-time, part-time, temporary and permanent, in which business areas and locations, and what skills are needed. Both this section and the site as a whole allow you to surf around and find out a good deal about the firm's culture and activities.

It will also be useful to find out how any particular firm rates as an employer. Check, for example, whether it carries the Investors in People logo. If you have a disability, or even if you do not but you want to see if it is a caring employer, there is also the 'double tick' logo for employers who have agreed to guarantee a job interview to applicants with disabilities (this is called the *Positive about disability symbol*). You might also want to explore:

- what the annual report says, including issues such as average pay, what is spent on training, what is said about environmental and social issues. You can get most annual reports for companies, charities or public bodies simply by phoning and asking for one. Company annual reports are also available on-line at www.carol.co.uk;
- which of your possible employers belong to the Employers' Forum on Age or is an Age Positive Champion;
- for companies quoted on the Stock Exchange, whether they figure in the FT4Good index, or the Good Corporation list; these are for companies that meet specific ethical and environmental standards;
- what press coverage they have had recently, and how they come out.

The information available on small local employers, of course, will be much less than that on a major national firm, but you may still be able to find out something. Local newspaper files, for instance, may cover them. The idea is to build up a short-list of employers you would most like to work for, so that you can put your chief effort into getting a job with them.

(See Chapter 13 for ideas about how to keep your job-hunting research and activities in some order, so that you do not drown in paper or electronic files.)

How to start looking

There are a number of ways to look for jobs. There is a lot of overlap between them, and they are all worth trying at once. They are:

- by word of mouth and 'networking' through people you know;
- answering advertisements;
- making speculative inquiries by phone, letter or via the internet/email.

What is *not* useful, however – though regrettably some organisations still encourage or even enforce it – is sending off dozens or even hundreds of standard letters with CVs attached, in answer to any job advertisement that looks even vaguely possible, or simply going through trade directories and sending letters to everyone. As *What Color is your Parachute* explains, this is unlikely to work because of the sheer numbers involved:

> 'Some companies receive as many as 250,000 *résumés* a year; even small companies may receive as many as ten to fifteen a week … Consequently, employers' first intent is not *selection*, but *elimination*.'

This 'scattergun' approach makes you look and feel busy, and can make a good living for the people who promote it as an activity. A lot of it, however, is meaningless activity. It is likely to make you feel depressed and rejected as you get your *N*th letter turning you down – or, more likely, hear nothing at all.

The more you can target your activities, the better your chances of success. 'Targeting' doesn't mean you work any less hard at getting a job; it means that the work you do is more meaningful, with a higher chance of the contact you make leading to something.

Networking

This simply means making use of all your contacts to find out about openings and to get yourself interviewed when you might not otherwise be. Quite often, an employer will leave open a short-term vacancy (such as a maternity leave replacement) because it is too much trouble to go through a full advertising and interviewing process for the sake of a few months. Or they may be thinking about creating a new job but have not yet got round to it. But if the right person turns up, this may stimulate them to do something about it.

This is a stage beyond the 'informational interviewing' suggested in Chapter 7. You are now trying to present yourself as the right person for the sort of job they have or might have in the future.

The people you approach may not be able to help you directly, but they may be able to offer you new leads about where to look and information you should have; they may also share experiences. It is not a one-way process and you are not 'begging' for help in any way. You will be reciprocating by giving them ideas about what's going on in the world outside their own jobs, and offering your own ideas and information. People will also know that they can network with you in the same way when they need to, and this is valuable: no one feels altogether secure in their jobs today.

> 'Networking is really something we all do informally,' says Stan Cooke. 'You've just got to be organised about it. It *doesn't* mean you are using people. You are communicating to people, raising your profile in other people's lives a little bit. It does help, though, if you are sensitive to people's moods – for instance, if you have caught them at bad moment. I always ask on the phone "is it convenient to speak to me now?"'

Start by making a list of all the contacts – family, personal, social and work-related – that you have. Then systematically make contact with anyone you think might be able to help. This could be just for a drink and a chat or for a more formal 'information meeting'. Prepare for this as you would for any other interview (see pages 123–124). Keep a note of what you're told, follow up further leads, and always send a letter to thank those whose time you have taken up.

What comes out of this sort of contact may be a suggestion of temporary or casual work, or a short-term contract on a particular project. The employer will be effectively testing you out (and you can test them at the same time) to see if you will hit it off. It is frequently worth taking up such an offer, so long as it is on reasonable terms and will not prevent you from continuing your job-hunting activities. In some cases, the Government's New Deal and work-trial arrangements (explained in Chapter 6) could allow you to take on such work at a lower pay rate than you would if you were starting a permanent job.

In larger companies and in the public sector there will be codes of practice requiring all jobs to be advertised, and no one may give you a job outside this formal framework. Making and keeping up your contacts is still worthwhile, however, because it will help you to know when and where the advertisements will come out, whether you and the organisation would suit each other, and the important issues when it comes to deciding between candidates.

Advertisements

Newspapers and magazines

Job advertisements are the bread and butter of many national and local newspapers, and you should always study them. Go systematically through all the newspapers that carry job advertising, for a week or more (not forgetting Sunday), and establish which carries what category of jobs on which days. Then concentrate on the ones that are going to be of use to you. You may find that you have to buy some of the papers in order to be able to clip out the advertisements but, to keep your newsagent's bill down, establish where you can obtain free access to the papers you need. Sources such as the public library, programme centres (run on behalf of the Jobcentre Plus) and outplacement agencies should all have these papers themselves. Your particular trade or profession probably has some specialist magazines that you can look at in the reference library. Many professional organisations also send out bulletins to their members.

You might find it worthwhile advertising yourself, in the local papers at least (display advertisements in the national ones are very expensive), especially if you are looking for something that is local and/or casual.

Websites

Job advertisements will be found on:

- the websites running in parallel with the newspapers, magazines and journals you are looking at;
- employers' and employment agencies' websites;
- the Government's Jobcentre Plus and Worktrain websites, and the Jobpoints (computer screens allowing you to search for jobs) in the Jobcentre Plus offices themselves;
- commercial job-advertising websites.

These last need treating with care. On some, the employers can post job advertisements, while on others the lists have been lifted from elsewhere. In the worst cases, the jobs may not exist at all. The smaller and more specialist ones are far more likely to be useful than the huge general ones. They need evaluating, just as you would a newspaper with adverts, to see how useful they are *to you*. If they have just one or two nuggets and a load of out-of-date dross, or the search arrangements leave you scrolling through masses of irrelevant material, don't waste your time. There are plenty of others.

Display cards

A final source of advertising is display cards in employment agencies and shop windows. If you are looking for something fairly limited and local, whether permanent or while doing some training or working on your next move, shop windows may well be the best place to look. You could put your own advertisement in the shop windows also, specifying what you will do, to see what response you get.

Following up an advertisement

When you see an advertisement that interests you, take down all the details or make a photocopy, and *do what you are told*. If it tells you to write or phone for an application form, it is a waste of time to send in a CV (see pages 116–120) at this point; wait for the form. If it sets a closing date, make sure you stick to it. Keep a note of the advertisements you have answered and the progress you have made.

The usual formula is that any enquirer is sent a *job description* explaining what the job is and what you would have to do. In some cases you may also get a *person specification* explaining what sort of person they are looking for, and the skills, training and personal qualities they must have. (When you actually get into the job, you may find that these are works of fiction rather than fact!) It is essential that you read these through carefully, along with any information you are sent, or can find, about the employer and the job, before going on to the next stage. The more you can demonstrate that you match the needs that have been set out, the more likely you are to be short-listed.

Speculative contacts

If you are having difficulty finding contacts who can put you in touch with your target organisations, or if you are finding that it is going too slowly, you may want to make speculative contacts. Check – on their websites, or via a phone call – whether they have specific arrangements for handling enquiries of this sort. Some big organisations will have general forms that they ask all enquirers to fill in, for instance.

However speculative your letter and however much of a 'long shot' an approach seems, you need to take the same care as you would over an application for a job you know a lot about.

Speculative letters need to be short and to the point. They should be personalised and not photocopies, which give the impression that they are just 'round robins'. Say that you are interested in working for that organisation, and explain what you are looking for and what your skills are. Enclose a copy of your CV (see pages 116–120). Ask for an appointment to visit the company, to discuss the chances of employment there. Enclose a stamped addressed envelope for the reply.

Some companies will not respond at all, some will send a curt acknowledgement and others will say that they will keep your details on file until a vacancy comes up. Others, again, may invite you for an informal interview. Prepare for this just as you would for a formal interview (see pages 123–124).

If you do have an informal interview, send a thank-you letter afterwards, saying how keen you are to work in the organisation. If later you see an advertisement for a job with them, when you write in you can remind them of your previous contact. Even if the interview has shown you that the job, or the organisation, is not the right one for you, it is still important to send a thank-you letter for their time and trouble. They might well be in contact with other organisations that would suit you better.

Registering with employment agencies and internet sites

It is worth registering with appropriate agencies, because many employers go there for staff before advertising publicly, and the agencies may also have other resources to offer you (see page 104). The more specialist your area of work, the more important it is to find agencies that are knowledgeable about that area. This is something that networking can help you with, as others will be able to say which agencies they have found most helpful. Some trade and professional bodies run their own employment agencies, as do some trade unions. It will be worth keeping in close touch with them. They may also be able to offer you support when you are feeling depressed by the effort.

Posting your CV on an internet site is also a possibility. Going for the specialist, targeted sites aimed at people doing the sort of job you are looking for is your best bet. The large commercial sites are generally reckoned to be rather a waste of time. What employer, after all, will waste time looking at these when there are so many more relevant places to look?

Finding resources and developing job-hunting skills

An early task in the job search project is getting the right equipment for the job, however modest: paper, envelopes, stamps and cardboard files so that you can sort everything properly without wasting time. A second step is to identify the nearest sources for things such as photocopying and printing good-looking letters and CVs. If you have the money, this could mean spending some of it to upgrade your equipment. If, for example, you possess a computer but only a poor-quality printer, or none at all, it will be worth investing in one that produces good quality print. This could be in combination with a fax, or you may want to buy a separate fax. If there is no one else around much of the time to take messages, or if they are unreliable, invest in an answering machine as well.

Alternatively, there will be places where you can get access to this equipment. If your employer has referred you to an outplacement agency, it should offer all the resources of this sort that you need. The Jobcentre Plus service can provide resources through its Programme Centres. At present (March 2002), though, much of the help available under their New Deal 50 Plus is restricted to people who have been receiving a social security benefit for six months or more (see Chapter 6). If you live in an area (particularly an inner city) that is getting regeneration money from the Government, there may be a range of other agencies that can help.

These sources can also offer help with job-hunting skills. For example:

- how to draft a CV;
- how to fill in an application form;
- how to make a speculative enquiry by telephone and write a follow-up letter;
- how to do well at interviews (sometimes with the help of a video, which can be terrifying but worthwhile).

There are also many internet sites that offer guidance; if you feel terrified by the range of choice, the Jobcentre Plus one (www.jobcentreplus. gov.uk) is as good a place as any to start.

The following sections go into these various aspects.

Preparing your CV

CV stands for *curriculum vitae*, which is a Latin term meaning, essentially, the course of your life. It should be brief. If it's longer than two sides of A4 the potential employer may not take the trouble to read through it.

It has to be accurate and well thought out, because its aim is to present you to the employer as someone worth interviewing. Ideally, you should write a new one for each job you apply for, but this may not be practical if you are following up several leads each week and cannot easily churn out different versions on a computer. If you do have to create one standardised one, send off print-outs or good photocopies as required with a personalised covering letter.

There are any number of books on finding a job that go into the details of writing a CV and give examples. See the 'Useful publications' section (pages 182–185) for some of them, or go and look along the shelves in

116

your local library or bookshop. There are also many websites. They should enable you to put together a good one. If you don't feel confident about it, an employment agency you have registered with, or the Jobcentre Plus service, can help. What used to be called the Careers Service (now being revamped as Connexions and aimed more at younger people) may also be able to offer help – free in some areas or for a flat-rate fee in others. On Tyneside, for instance, it will charge £47.50 for an hour's session, but tells clients to phone (at no charge) if they need some more advice later.

There are also firms of consultants who, for a fee, will help you draft and produce a CV. They are of very variable quality, however, so ask to see examples of their work before parting with your money. According to Anne-Marie Bewley of Tyneside Careers:

'There are still some scams around on CVs. People will bring in ones they have done privately, and some are awful. People need to shop around and have a look before they jump in. Lots of agencies will do them free of charge.'

Keep your CV clear, simple and *positive*. Stress what your skills are, not what your formal job title was. Nurses, for example, have considerable knowledge of computers these days. But an employer faced with an application from a nurse for a job involving work on computer databases may not look twice at it unless the relevant skills are highlighted; the employer may not know what nursing involves today. Make as much use as possible of 'action' words, rather than passive ones. These are words such as 'accomplished', 'approved', 'assisted', 'authorised', 'budgeted', 'completed', 'succeeded'. For example:

'I was required to set up a new project within six months,' and
'I successfully completed, within six months, the setting-up of a new project'

could both refer to the same task but give very different impressions.

There are several different formats for a CV, but the information that always needs to be included is:

- **Name and personal details**, such as address, phone number, age (or date of birth) and marital status. Some people say you should leave out your age here, but recruiters tend to become suspicious about gaps, so it is probably better to put it in.

- **Skills, competences and achievements** Include any major successes, and refer not just to the various jobs you have done but also to voluntary work or activities at home that have helped you develop particular skills. ('Competences' used in this way is just a bit of fashionable jargon used by human resources/personnel people. It just means what you are competent at – that is, what you're good at.)

- **Employment details** It is usual to start with the most recent job and work backwards. Say what the organisation was and what department you were in. If you had a career break, say so (recruiters hate unexplained gaps). If you took on particular roles such as acting as secretary of a voluntary organisation while you were on your career break, say so. Make it sound positive, not just a period when you were doing nothing.

- **Education, training and qualifications** from secondary school onwards, including any vocational training you have done and short courses within or outside the firm. You may find it best to work in reverse order, so your list starts with the most recent education. For the examinations you took in the distant past at school, there's no need to go into enormous detail; you need simply say '8 O-levels' without racking your brains to remember all of them. Don't be tempted to exaggerate or mislead – it's too easy to get caught out.

- **Interests, hobbies and voluntary work** If you are looking for a job in which your main skills and experience will come from something you have done outside your previous jobs, put this section before the employment details and explain why.

- **Additional information** that is relevant to the job you are looking for.

- **References** (see below).

Write or type the CV in draft first, read it through (preferably with someone else who will pick up the errors you miss), and then type or print up a neat version. This is crucial – remember that your pieces of paper are competing with hundreds of others, and one of the quickest ways to get eliminated is to produce something that is difficult to read. Occasionally, employers will ask for something hand-written (possibly because they want to do graphology tests or because some of the work involves neat handwriting), but more usually they will want it typed. If you can't type, find someone who can who can help you, and think hard about training so that you acquire at least basic keyboard skills as quickly as possible.

An example of a CV

Name Elaine Jones

Address 5 Any Street, Anytown, AB1 2CD

Telephone 0123 456 7890

Age 53

Skills and competences:

I am an experienced administrator with knowledge of:

- the management of an annual budget of £50,000
- a wide variety of computer programs including Word, Excel, Powerpoint
- desktop publishing work
- organisation and management of a communications programme for a large organisation.

My recent work in health services administration has involved successfully creating and taking responsibility for the internal communications programme for a Trust with a budget of £X million. With an annual budget of £X, I accomplished the drafting, printing and distribution of posters, leaflets and newsletters for X staff, on time and within budget. As part of this, I acquired hands-on skills in a number of word processing, database and desktop publishing computer programs. I also have project management skills, working with both internal departments and external contractors.

This work has been in addition to taking a key role in the day-to-day activities of the Central Administration Unit in which I was based. I have created and maintained a workflow system for the Unit to ensure that the paperwork is dealt with speedily and that customers' demands are met rapidly and accurately.

Employment details

1996–2002   Senior Administrative Officer, Central Administration Unit, X Health Services Trust

1988–1996	Administrative Officer, Administration Unit, X Health Authority
1978–1988	Clerical Assistant, Y Health Authority, promoted to Clerical Officer, 1983
1971–1978	Career break while bringing up three children. During this time I also studied French and German at evening classes, leading to success at A-level French and O-level German; acted as Secretary of the Pre-School Playgroups Association; organised the school Christmas bazaar for three years in succession.
1964–1971	Office junior, promoted to Office Assistant, Bloggs & Co, Anytown

Education and training

I have been accepted for an Open University Business School management course commencing September 2002.

1992–2001	In-service training courses in computer technology (including specific software packages including Word, Excel, Powerpoint), administration, working with the media, project management
1985	ONC in Commerce
1973–5	O-level German, A-level French, Anytown Adult Education College
1965	Pitman Shorthand and Typing, Certificate of Proficiency
1958–64	St X School for Girls, Anytown

Other information

Outside my working time I am involved with a number of voluntary organisations in the local community and have used my desktop publishing skills to produce newsletters and leaflets for, among others, the Anytown Townswomen's Guild, the Council of Voluntary Services and St X School.

References

(Two names and addresses)

References

You will want to include details of a couple of referees on your CV, and most application forms also ask for names. It is normal to give your last employer as a reference but if there is a good reason not to (for instance, that the company has gone into liquidation), give the name of someone else who knows your work and explain why. The other referee could be work-related or someone who knows you socially or from your leisure interests.

Check first with the individuals concerned that they are happy to give you a reference, and ask them if you could see what they are sending, to be sure it is accurate. (Some people don't like showing them, though.)

If you have parted on bad terms with your previous employer, you may suspect that they will give you a poor reference. Talk to your union or staff association, or your solicitor, about this if necessary; there may well be action that you can take.

For certain jobs, for instance in the financial services industry, you may need a financial or credit reference. Talk to your bank manager about this.

The covering letter

This can be a standard letter but adapted for each job. It is best to produce a new letter each time, rather than send a photocopy.

The covering letter is your introduction to the person who is recruiting for the job. It is there to explain why you are sending in your CV to this particular person. So it needs to say:

- what position you are interested in (including any reference number and where you saw or heard about it);
- why you are suitable: highlight reasons that are explained further in the CV;
- a polite ending saying that you hope to hear from them soon.

As always, check the draft before finishing it off. And check the final version, too!

An example of a covering letter

Dear ...

I am writing in response to your advertisement concerning the job of Publicity Officer for the National Association of X.

I enclose a CV for your information. From this, you will see that I have been running publicity programmes for a major NHS trust for the last few years, and have skills in communications, desktop publishing and project management. I believe that I am well suited to your requirements and look forward to hearing from you.

Yours sincerely,

Filling in application forms

These are used commonly by employers who have large numbers of applications, so being able to deal with information in standardised form is important. They are also used by companies anxious to provide equal opportunities and to ensure that people do not have an unfair advantage by the quality of their own presentation of information about themselves.

Before you do anything else, photocopy the form (or print off an extra copy if you are downloading from the internet) and read the job description and any other material that has come with it. Also check back on whatever research material you have found about that employer.

Then start drafting on to the photocopy, and copy the information on to the original only when you are satisfied. Type the answers, unless you are specifically requested to write them – in which case, do so neatly in black ink. Put all the relevant information that you have already gathered from your CV on to the form, making sure you answer the specific questions they ask. If there is not enough room for your reply in any section, use an extra sheet rather than cramming things in too tight. Some application forms these days are very complicated, so check that you understand what is being asked, and if necessary get some help.

Many employers today do not acknowledge forms but simply say that, if you haven't heard within X weeks, you can assume that you haven't been short-listed. This may seem rather impolite but it is understandable given the numbers they have to deal with. It's permissible to ring up to check that the form has arrived, but if you do any more you risk being marked down as 'pestering'.

Preparing for an interview

You may well have done a lot of interviewing in your time and feel that you know all about it. But it looks very different from the other side of the table and you will need some serious preparation. 'I've known people like accountants go to an interview without having looked at the accounts for the company they're seeing,' one careers adviser says. 'That seems to me an extraordinary lack of preparation, and must make one wonder about how serious they are.'

Whether it is a formal or informal interview, always check out before you go:

- **Where the interview is**, how you get there and how long you will need. It's far better to arrive early than late and flurried. If something goes wrong and you have a problem, phone and explain – they may well be forgiving.
- **What the organisation does** and how the department you are dealing with fits in. Send off for the annual report; look the company up on the internet or in the reference library; ask if they have any brochures and reference material.
- **What you should wear** It's not entirely true that interviewers make up their minds as a person walks into the room but appearance certainly has a lot to do with it. If in doubt, dress more smartly than may be necessary, rather than risk appearing too casual. Whether male or female, you are unlikely to go wrong with a good dark suit and very clean shoes. If you don't possess a suit, can you borrow one from a friend when needed?

Prepare by thinking about what questions the interviewers are likely to ask, and what will provide a confident, knowledgeable response. Play to your strengths. What you have that younger people haven't is *experience*, so make the most of it. Talk about the things you have done, the lessons you have learnt and what you could bring to the new employer. Show yourself to be approachable and adaptable. Don't give in to the temptation to rubbish your old employer, even if you are feeling bitter. That goes down very badly with interviewers, because they are afraid you will do the same to them in due course.

You could be interviewed by one person or by a panel of several people at once. You may be asked to do psychometric or aptitude tests, and you may find yourself plunged into a group interview (where several applicants are in the room at the same time). Or there may be more than one interview – perhaps on different days – with different people. Usually you are warned beforehand of all these points, but if you are told nothing, ring up and ask what form the interview will take. At a senior level, you might find yourself involved in an 'assessment centre', where you could spend two days or more doing different tests and doing role-play and other exercises.

You may be asked to make a presentation to a panel. Candidates are usually informed about this well in advance, even if the subject for the presentation is revealed after the interview date is notified.

There are also some techniques of 'stress interviewing' which can create a very unpleasant experience. Some interviewers, as David Greenwood in *The Job Hunter's Handbook* (details on page 183) puts it, 'seem to feel that an interview is an intellectual point-scoring exercise'. Faced with this, he suggests that you keep calm, appear unruffled and 'think long and hard about whether you want to work for someone as inadequate as that'.

You normally get your travelling expenses paid if you are interviewed but you may have to ask. The only case in which you may not get them paid is if you are offered the job and then turn it down. Check the position in advance, before you spend money out of your own pocket. In some cases, the Jobcentre Plus office may be able to pay travel costs (see Chapter 6) but you need to meet its conditions and there is little leeway if you get things wrong.

If you don't succeed at an interview

If you don't get offered the job, don't treat it as an aspersion on you personally: you simply did not fit with what they wanted. Treat it as a learning experience; 'debrief' yourself about what you did right and what you did wrong, and make a list of points to remember for next time. If the interviewer used a technique you had not encountered before, make some notes about what to watch out for if you come across it again. If you are offered feedback after the interview, take up the offer. If the offer is not made, it is worth phoning to ask for feedback

If you think you have been discriminated against – perhaps because of your age or your gender – you may want to take the issue further. Talk to the Jobcentre Plus adviser, or your trade union, before doing anything in the heat of the moment. Look in *Rights at Work* for details of when you have a right to ask for specific information to help you take up a legal case.

10 Working for yourself

Many people have an itch to be self-employed, and cash from a reasonable redundancy or severance payment can offer a golden opportunity. A recent survey published by Barclays Bank in 2001 showed that 'Third Age entrepreneurs' are responsible for 50 per cent more business start-ups now than ten years ago.

There is considerable help available, so long as you fit into one of the Government programmes. You can take on work on a small scale, doing a certain amount of consultancy or specific projects. Or you can set up a small business, which might perhaps grow.

There are more and more self-employed people around, and many commentators see it as the trend for the future. But the failure rate for those setting up in business on their own is uncomfortably high: 400,000 new businesses start up each year, but one in four ceases to trade within four years. Small businesses are vulnerable in a recession, and can also be hit by outside influences about which they can do very little. The closure of the countryside to visitors because of the foot-and-mouth epidemic in spring and summer 2001 affected well-run and badly run bed-and-breakfast businesses alike, for example.

The type of business can vary enormously, from those where the sole asset is yourself and your brainpower or physical skills to those that require very considerable capital and are intended to grow into something sizeable. On pages 128–135 we consider some broad categories of self-employment. First, however, we look at the sort of person you need to be and the skills and resources you need.

What sort of person do you need to be?

To make a living in any sort of self-employment, you need some organisational skills and a certain amount of self-discipline. In her book *Start a Successful Business*, Rosemary Phipps has suggested the following golden rules:

- **Adapt to the market** She says, 'It's all too easy to do what you want to do, or what you think the market needs, without ever checking to see whether you're right ... Nothing ever exists in a vacuum and you need to position yourself, your business and your product/service in relation to what is already in the market.'
- **Create objectives** You need clear personal objectives and a realistic sense of your own strengths and weaknesses, along with the will to adapt as conditions change. Decide before you start whether you want to employ others or to work only for yourself. Also decide how hard you want to work – though if the business takes off you may find yourself working substantially harder than you bargained for.
- **Have the right attitude** 'Overwhelming optimism tempered with common sense (or, rather, uncommon sense)' is Rosemary Phipps' prescription. Among other things, you need to be able to persevere, and also to check people out (even your friends) rather than naively trusting them. Most people are to be trusted – but some are not.
- **Be willing to do things you don't enjoy**, for the sake of the business. Very few people enjoy paperwork and chasing up overdue debts – but to survive, you have to do these things. Some people enjoy selling their services, but for many phone calls marketing themselves are agony. It is important, though, to do it, and you are most unlikely to be able to employ someone to do it for you at the start. If you feel you just cannot do it, self-employment is not for you. As another author puts it, the worst thing can be the experience of sitting before a silent phone. You've done everything you can think of to advertise your services and no one seems to have noticed. 'The only thing to do is to get out and sell yourself and your services – relentlessly if necessary. Always expect to have to make the first move, to make things happen.'
- **Don't let failure get you down** A lot of things will not go right first time. You will have a good many false starts when people don't respond as you hope, or when suppliers, contractors and competitors seem to be putting obstacles in your way. It helps if you have someone you can moan to about these things, but also someone who can offer constructive suggestions. This is where business counselling, discussed on pages 135–136, can help. If you are someone whose equilibrium is a bit fragile, and who perhaps gets easily depressed, self-employment may not suit you.

However, you do need to be realistic. Though you should not let yourself be put off too easily, equally it is not worth fighting on if the situation becomes hopeless. Nor is it worth adapting yourself to the market so much that you dislike, or even actively hate, what you end up doing. There has to come a point when you cut your losses, rethink your business plan, and start again.

Think from the start about the effect on your family and other relationships, especially if you are planning something that will require capital and you will be eating into savings, and perhaps also going into debt. It is not a decision that should be taken by just one person in the family – all of you will be involved. So it is crucial that you talk it through, in depth, before committing yourself.

In addition, if you are planning to employ anyone else, you will need some management skills as well, and the willpower to check out the law and abide by it. The legal responsibilities of small employers have increased considerably in recent years.

What skills do you need?

To make a success of starting out on your own, you need two different sorts of skill or ability:

- **The skill to make the product** (using the term in its broadest sense) that you are marketing. So it might be knowing how to make corn-dollies or advising on the way corrosion affects the paintwork on ships.
- **Business skills** – the ability to organise yourself and your finances, to deliver the work on time, and to go out and find new orders.

Different types of self-employment

No self-employed person is quite like any other! But there are certain broad groups into which people fall, discussed below.

Skill-based work

Your skill might be the one you learnt and practised in your job, such as repairing cars, dressmaking or computer programming, or something you have developed since. If there is a market for it, almost any activity can be carried out on a self-employed rather than an employed basis these days. Even the clergy can now find ways of doing this, for example officiating at weddings or funerals or taking services in parishes where there is no permanent vicar.

You will often be able to work at home or to use your home as a base. Many people starting up in a small way don't employ anyone else. Often some other member of the family keeps the books and sends out the invoices. Frequently all the family members get involved in answering the phone and taking messages. Invest in another phone line and an answering machine and/or a mobile phone, however, so that you do not have to rely on them.

Some areas of employment are overcrowded and poorly paid, such as window-cleaning and sandwich-selling. Others can pay very well for someone who is properly skilled, treats the customers well and is *reliable*. We all have experience of builders and other tradespeople letting us down or doing a shoddy job. Those who can be trusted can get premium rates, and people are willing to wait for their services.

Consultancy

'Consultancy' is a very broad term but it covers mainly people who are selling professional or technical skills and knowledge. Many people think of doing this, and they may well get their first piece of consultancy work from their old employer or from other professional and business contacts who know their work.

An important factor in success is keeping yourself up to date. People pay consultants for their accumulated knowledge, not just for the hours they spend on the job. This means reading the journals, keeping up contacts with your colleagues, attending conferences, and – in many scientific areas – carrying out hands-on research, and all this takes time. One day's consultancy could mean spending another two days briefing yourself. So doing only a few hours a week of consultancy work, even in the area that you already know from your job, will not be practicable for all that long. You need to go into consultancy wholeheartedly or not at all.

The best book for someone starting in consultancy is probably Tom Lambert's *High Income Consulting* (see 'Useful publications', page 183).

In general, much of the work will come from word of mouth or from satisfied clients you have already done work for. You may also build up a pattern of repeat business from a few good clients. Even so, it is wise not to operate too informally. Draw up a contract for any assignment that lasts longer than a day. (There is a sample contract in Lambert's book.)

Lambert (and others) stresses the importance of not undercutting your own rates even if work is short. Once you have set a daily rate, he suggests that you should treat it as non-negotiable. If the client says it is too expensive, go through the plan with them and see what can be done internally, or what may not need to be done at all, to save them money rather than cutting your rate.

Casual work for an employer

In some occupations and professions there are jobs that are treated as self-employment by the firm but which are really little different from employment. Sales representatives for insurance companies and other firms are one example of this, and media jobs such as subediting, camera work and sound engineering are another. In some sectors it may not be possible to find work in any other way but this type of self-employment can represent the worst of both worlds. You have the insecurity of someone setting up on their own – and particularly in sales work you may be paid entirely on a commission and so depend on the results of your own hard work. You may have to invest a considerable amount in equipment for yourself, or pay a monthly subscription for 'office services', before you earn a penny on your own account. But the actual work you do will be dictated by others.

Make sure you understand the terms of what is being offered before you take on this sort of work. With sales work in particular, think about your own personality if it is not the type of work you have been doing already. Some teachers went to work for insurance companies after taking early retirement, often thinking that they could sell products to their ex-colleagues in the staff rooms. Some were very successful but others hated it, especially the 'close' when they had to persuade the prospective buyers to commit themselves.

See page 141 for the definitions of employment and self-employment for tax purposes. If your work comes wholly or mainly from one source, the Inland Revenue may question your self-employed status at some point.

Setting up a co-operative

Legally you are likely to be employed rather than self-employed in this situation, but it is included here because it is more akin to setting up your own business than to joining someone else's. The basic idea of a workers' co-operative is that those who work in it own it. There are a number around, including some that have resulted from employee buy-outs of existing firms which have gone into liquidation, or of privatised companies in the public sector.

You can set up a co-operative with only seven people, though many grow larger than this. You will need some people with ordinary business skills if you are to succeed, and you will also need to develop skills in working co-operatively, planning and running meetings. The Cooperative Union (see page 188) has publications and training courses on this, and can also offer legal advice and registration services.

Some parts of the country also have local co-operative support organisations, which can give a range of practical help. According to one of them, Leicester and County Co-operative Development Agency, if you are thinking of setting up you need:

- a rough idea of what you want to do;
- other people who are interested;
- energy and commitment;
- willingness to learn new things;
- some skills appropriate to the planned business; and
- to be prepared for it to take longer than you think!

The Cooperative Union, a co-operative support organisation, or your local Business Links office (see page 187), will be able to help with finding sources of finance.

Buying a franchise

A growing number of franchise opportunities are available – you have probably come across some of the more widespread ones, such as Prontaprint and some Body Shops, without even realising that they are franchises. To quote Rosemary Phipps again: 'What you will be doing is taking on an idea that the franchiser has already tested commercially. You then pay for the right to use the business name and pay the franchiser a royalty fee based on your sales.'

There are fewer risks in this than in starting up your own business from scratch. According to the *Daily Telegraph* guide on the subject (*Guide to Taking Up a Franchise*; see page 182), although 70 per cent of all new businesses fail, 90 per cent of franchises succeed. It is in the interests of the franchiser to pull out all the stops to prevent them from failing. A bank may be willing to lend a greater proportion of the capital needed for a franchise than for a completely new business – perhaps two-thirds as opposed to only half. You may, however, be asked to sign a release so they can tell the franchiser if you go over their borrowing limits.

The size of your initial investment, the level of royalty you pay and the scope for developing things yourself rather than sticking to a predetermined plan will vary from one franchiser to another. Check out all the details just as you would if you were buying a business from someone else (see pages 133–134). Most banks have someone who can advise you on franchising, and the British Franchise Association (BFA; address on page 187) can help. They also publish a code of practice and an explanatory guide, *The Ethics of Franchising*. Any franchiser who does not meet the BFA's requirements should be treated with great caution.

Setting up your own small business

This could be almost anything that involves a marketable idea. For many mature people looking for a new start, the natural inclination may be to look at things such as pubs, restaurants and bed-and-breakfasts, which one might call 'I've always wanted to ...' projects. Some of these provide a good and satisfying living for their owners but many others fail because of insufficient research or capital, or both. The key is to check out exactly what is going to be needed, and not to proceed unless you are satisfied that those requirements are going to be met. Think about:

- **Your own skills and abilities** Can you manage the staff, deal with the accounts and produce the quality your customers are going to expect, day in and day out?
- **Your stamina** Pub landlords and restaurateurs, in particular, work extremely long hours and may take very little time off. The job can be pretty stressful when things are not going well.
- **The capital required** This can be substantial. If you have taken over premises that have already been in the same use, you will still want to refurbish them in your own style. Conversion is even more expen-

sive. It can then take some time to build up trade, but all the time you will be paying staff and suppliers.

The best way to find out all about it is to talk to people who have experience in that field. In addition, you may be able to find a specific course to go on, and there are certainly books and websites to read. The local Business Links (or the equivalent bodies in Scotland, Wales and Northern Ireland) (see page 135) and the relevant trade or professional organisations will be able to point you towards the right information and possibly also contacts. Otherwise, use the same strategy as suggested in Chapter 7 to find out as much as you can by 'informational interviewing' before taking the plunge.

Your dream idea is probably based on a favourite pub, restaurant or guest-house, so why not ask the proprietor to sit down with you for an hour and go through all the important issues? You could also ask if you could work behind the bar or in the kitchens for a while, perhaps as a holiday relief, to see how it suits you. Make sure you are given your share of the worst jobs – these are what you will be doing, as proprietor, when one of your staff doesn't turn up.

Buying someone else's business

If you are buying a business from someone else, all the points already made about researching it to make sure it suits you apply. In addition, it is crucial to carry out 'due diligence' – which simply means checking everything. Make sure that the accounts add up and that you have been told everything important. A pub that looks viable at a certain rent from the brewery, for instance, may be totally impossible as a going concern if the rent is trebled. Ask as many questions as you need, get the answers in writing and don't be satisfied with evasive answers. Use professionals to help you: an accountant and a solicitor, and a surveyor if it involves property.

Kenneth Lysons, in the Age Concern publication *Earning Money in Retirement* (details on page 182), suggests the following checklist of points to find out about, both by asking the vendor directly and by researching in the library and the immediate area:

■ When was the business established, and by whom?
■ How many subsequent owners has it had, and why did they sell?

- What are the annual profits? Are these audited? Is the profit trend increasing or decreasing? What are the reasons for the increase or decrease?
- Are the premises freehold or leasehold? If leasehold, how long has the lease to run? Can it be renewed?
- What condition are the premises in? Will much renovation be required?
- Are equipment, fixtures and fittings in good condition? Who owns them?
- What is the condition of stocks? Are they new or obsolete, shop-soiled or deteriorated?
- Are suppliers dependable? Are any agreements due for renewal?
- What is the present and likely future competition?
- What is the location like?
- Why does the present owner wish to sell? Are the reasons given the true ones?
- What is the reputation of the business in the area? To what extent does this depend on the personality of the present owner?
- Are the present staff efficient and willing to stay on?
- How does the business compare with others that are available?

Although the failure rate is high, success can bring considerable rewards. One group of early retirees – a former computer engineer, a sea captain and a farmer – started the Wylam Brewery in the Tyne Valley, in northern England. As a press report said about them at their launch, 'That's the enthusiasm that the Wylam Three engender – hardly a week into production and they're already thinking of improvements.' Wylam Brewery was awarded Champion Beer of the CAMRA Newcastle Festival in April 2001.

Get-rich-quick schemes, pyramid sales, and the like

There are all sorts of schemes around promising you riches if you just undertake this course, or start producing or selling that product. Some are honest but bring your income only up to the point where you have saturated a rather small market. Others are plain dishonest. There is only one good piece of advice so far as they are concerned, and that is **avoid them**. As David Greenwood says in *The Job Hunter's Handbook* (details on page 183):

'If you discovered a means of making a huge amount of money legally for very little effort, what would you do? Would you share your secret with the world or would you sit back and quietly watch your bank balance grow? ...

'Beware! Their effortless way of making money is probably through the stream of cheques and postal orders which they attract from gullible punters who respond to their advertisement.'

Or, to quote a cliché that must have been around for several centuries, 'If something seems too good to be true, it probably is.' Don't hand over money without asking someone independent to check the project out, and report it to the police and the Trading Standards department at the local authority if it looks dodgy.

Where to get help

Information and advice

The best place to start looking for information and advice is likely to be your local Business Links office. To quote the DTI's material on them:

'These are local business advice centres [with people] who under-stand the special needs of new and existing small firms and can offer practical help and useful information.'

You can find your nearest Business Link office by ringing the main telephone number or via its website (details on page 187). (They go by different names in Scotland, Wales and Northern Ireland, but do the same job.)

Business Link Tyne and Wear, based in Sunderland, as one example, offers one-to-one advice and guidance, training in business skills, and regulatory and financial information to start-up businesses. Most of this is free to new entrepreneurs, though there may be a charge for con-tinuing services as time goes on.

Other places to get help include:

- The banks; all the major ones have a Small Business service.
- Libraries; either your local library will have a commercial/business section or it will be able to point you in the direction of one that does.
- Enterprise Agencies; there is a network of these, though they do not cover the whole country.

- In areas of high unemployment, particularly those that are designated 'Employment Zones', there may be other agencies funded by the Government or the local authority, which can help.

An organisation that specifically promotes enterprise among people over 50 is PRIME, part of Age Concern England. This aims to enable people over 50 to set themselves up in business successfully. It has an interactive website, a central helpline to point you to where else to go, and a loan fund that can act as a lender of last resort for promising business ventures. It also has a network of Loan Associates and partners around the country. (See page 195 for address.)

Training

Again, Business Links can point you in the right direction, and offer training courses themselves. On the internet, Learndirect has a number of computer-based courses for people setting up or in the early stages of running a business. Local universities and colleges may have courses in what you need to know; the Wylam Three, in the example on page 134, managed to find a Start Up Brewing course at Sunderland University, for instance.

There is some financial help available for training. Under New Deal 50 Plus (explained in Chapter 6), the training grant of £750 can be used for in-work training when you have started work, and the local Jobcentre Plus office should be able to tell you where you can find local work-based training.

Funding

The major source of finance, if you need substantial amounts of capital, will be the bank. The DTI's Small Business Service runs a Loan Guarantee Scheme (see 'Useful addresses' page 189) that 'guarantees loans from banks and financial institutions with viable business proposals which have tried and failed to obtain a conventional loan because of lack of security'.

Other possible sources of finance include:

- A mortgage on your house or other property.
- Borrowing from friends and family.
- Help from 'business angels' (individuals who invest relatively small

amounts in start-up businesses they think have growth prospects) or, on a larger scale, venture capitalists.

■ Grants from the Government, the European Commission or the local authority. DTI Enterprise Grants, for example, can give grants of up to £75,000 on projects with up to £500,000 capital investment. But they warn that grants are discretionary, and 'high growth businesses seeking to maximise value-added projects with quality output are given preference'.

> See the DTI free booklet, *A Guide to Help for Small Business*; look also on its website for small businesses, www.sbs.gov.uk

All the sources of information suggested elsewhere in this chapter can give advice about sources of finance and ways to apply for it. Channel 4's 'Real Deal' section of its website (based on earlier TV programmes) is aimed at would-be entrepreneurs looking for investment in their business.

Note There are also commercial firms that have set themselves up as 'grant-finders', charging a fee to give you information that is available freely from most Business Links. Using one of these would generally be a waste of time and money.

Finding the money to live on

Claiming social security benefits

You are allowed to spend up to eight weeks while on Jobseeker's Allowance developing ideas for a small business without having to divert energy into seeking a paid job at the same time. However, it has to be part of one of the various schemes funded by the Government, either directly or indirectly. Talk to your personal adviser at the Jobcentre Plus office about this.

While your business is developing, you may be entitled to something from the State to help you survive. In particular, there is Working Families' Tax Credit (WFTC) if you have dependent children, or Disabled Person's Tax Credit (DPTC) if you have a disability that limits your earning capacity. Both of these are means-tested benefits, which means that your income is made up to a certain level or an 'applicable amount' laid down by the Government. For self-employed people, 'earnings' mean net profit after various expenses have been met.

Under the rules for WFTC and DPTC, your net profit is calculated from your profit and loss account, and your trading account and balance sheet where appropriate. If you are only just starting, estimated figures based on a shorter period can be used. A weekly figure is then calculated by averaging your earnings over the period covered by the profit and loss account (or a different assessment period, if you have given estimated figures). Complete weeks when you are not working – for instance, if you are off sick or on holiday – are ignored.

The Employment Credit available under the New Deal 50 Plus (explained on page 59) can also be paid for self-employment. It counts in full as income for WFTC, so you are unlikely to be able to get both. There are also some other weekly benefits available under the Employment Zone arrangements and some local government programmes. Ask the Business Links advisers what is available in your area.

Timing your claims can be difficult: WFTC runs for six months at a time, so if you claim it before another benefit has come to an end, you may lose out. Again, ask for advice from your New Deal adviser, or a Welfare Benefits adviser if one is available in your area.

Note All these benefits are to be replaced by Working Tax Credit in April 2003. This is also a means-tested benefit, but paid by the Inland Revenue via the employer. For more details see *The child and Working Tax Credits: the modernisation of Britain's tax and benefits system* published by the Treasury in April 2002 (available on their website or from their Public Enquiry Unit 020 7270 4558). Other leaflets should be available nearer the start date.

Developing a business plan and management accounts

To receive almost any sort of financial assistance, you need a business plan. This plays the same sort of role for someone starting up on their own as a CV does for someone looking for a job. Work on the plan can take quite some time, as it involves:

- developing the details of your idea;
- doing market research, for instance by contacting potential customers to see if they are interested;

- investigating premises and staffing;
- working out budgets and cash-flow estimates;
- finding out what sources of finance are available and which offer the best prospects.

The time taken drawing up the plan will be well spent if it means that you have thought out how you will work and the issues involved. There are standard formats, and a business counsellor (from Business Links or another organisation that advises small businesses) or accountant will help you with them. There is also masses of literature on the subject – both on paper and on the internet. The 'Useful publications' section gives just a few titles that can help.

Any competent adviser will insist that you be involved in drawing up the plan rather than leaving it to them; you have to 'own' it and be committed to what it says you will do, if it is to work. The plan is likely to need revision several times in the course of your first few months or years.

A business where the finances are at all complicated will need *management accounts*, so that you can tell if you are making a profit or loss and if there will be enough cash to pay the bills next month. Management accounts are best done as you go along; the courses and other sources of advice discussed on pages 135–136 will explain what is needed.

Tax, social security and VAT

If you are self-employed, you are responsible for your own tax and National Insurance and you must tell the tax office and the National Insurance Contributions Office (NICO) that you are now in business for yourself. Initially your tax office will be the one you dealt with when you were employed, though it may later transfer your file elsewhere. You can find the phone numbers for both the tax office and NICO for your area in the phone book under 'Inland Revenue'.

National Insurance contributions

You will need to set up an arrangement for paying Class 2 National Insurance contributions. These are flat rate, and only £2 a week, so you can pay these every three months in arrears, or monthly by direct debit. They are paid at a flat rate and qualify you for most social security benefits, though not for Jobseeker's Allowance, nor the State Earnings-Related Pension (SERPS) or its replacement the State Second Pension (S2P).

If you are just starting, your self-employed earnings may be low and you can apply for a 'certificate of exception'; fill in the form in DWP leaflet NI 27A. Apply as soon as possible, because this can be back-dated for only 13 weeks. In 2002/3, you are entitled to this certificate if your estimated earnings are less than £4,025 for the year. If you have paid contributions for the year and it then turns out that you are below the limit, you can reclaim them by writing to the National Insurance Contributions Office (address on page 192 under 'Inland Revenue') before the end of December that year. But you will be creating gaps in your contribution record, which could affect your pension later.

It is possible to be employed and self-employed at the same time in different jobs – perhaps working as a part-time assistant to someone for half the day and running your own business for the other half. You would then be taxed through PAYE on your income from the employment and pay tax on a self-employed basis on the rest of your income. If this is your situation, you can apply to postpone paying self-employed National Insurance contributions until after the end of the year, so that the employed contributions can be taken into account in working out what you should pay. Fill in and return the form in DWP (formerly DSS) leaflet NP 18.

Income Tax

You will also need to contact your local tax office. As a self-employed person you have to send in accounts and tax returns each year. On the basis of these, you pay Income Tax and Class 4 National Insurance contributions, collected at the same time. Class 4 contributions don't qualify you for any extra benefits, so really they are just another form of tax.

It is generally best, if your business involves much use of capital and any great amount of purchases and sales, to employ an accountant to sort out your annual accounts for the Inland Revenue. It costs money but is well worth it to prevent your paying more tax than you need. Even if you are only doing freelance work as an individual, you will find it useful to ensure that you have claimed everything you are entitled to as business expenses.

Employed or self-employed?

There can be problems on the margin between employment and self-employment. Some firms will pressure the people who are working for them into being 'self-employed'. There are advantages, they will point out, in that you are able to offset the expenses of doing the work – such as buying equipment and supplies and travelling to see clients – against your income. You also save in National Insurance contributions (but get fewer benefits). The rather bigger advantage for the employer is that it saves on National Insurance contributions, does not have the same contractual commitments as to employees, and may be able to disclaim responsibility for you.

However, the Inland Revenue is tightening up on this, and conducts frequent 'blitzes' in certain trades and professions where it suspects that there is a level of phoney self-employment. It will then insist on treating people as employed, and will require the employer to deduct PAYE and National Insurance from their earnings. This has happened, for instance, with many media workers such as subeditors who work on a casual basis. The National Union of Journalists has taken test cases through the Inland Revenue's appeal system against this, and won. Some other professions have had to accept the Inland Revenue's ruling.

Inland Revenue's views on the distinction between employment and self-employment are set out in leaflet IR 56 *Employed or self-employed*. If you answer 'yes' to any or all of the following questions, you are probably employed:

- Do you have to do all the work yourself, rather than hire someone else to do it for you?
- Can someone tell you at any time what to do, or when and how to do it?
- Are you paid by the hour, week or month? Do you get overtime pay?
- Do you work set hours, or a given number of hours a week or month?
- Do you work at the premises of the person you work for, or at a place or places he or she decides?

On the other hand, if you answer 'yes' to most or all of the next questions, you would usually be considered self-employed:

- Do you have the final say in how the business is run?
- Are you risking your own money in the business?
- Are you responsible for meeting the losses as well as taking the profits?
- Do you provide the main items of equipment you need to do your job (not just small tools)?
- Are you free to hire other people on your own terms to do the work you have taken on? Do you pay them out of your own pocket?
- Do you have to correct unsatisfactory work in your own time and at your own expense?

There are some special rules for 'labour-only subcontractors', who exist especially in the building trade. They receive a '715 certificate' authorising them to be treated as self-employed if they meet certain conditions. There are also rules (since April 2000) aimed at stopping people using service companies as intermediaries as a way of avoiding paying tax and National Insurance. These rules, generally known as NI 35, mainly affect people working as consultants in industries such as computer software, who set themselves up as single-person companies rather than working as individuals.

> See Inland Revenue leaflet IR 175, *Supplying services through a limited company or a partnership*.

VAT

You have to register for VAT once the value of your 'taxable supplies' reaches a certain level – £55,000 a year in 2002/3 – or if you do more than a certain amount of business overseas. You *can* register, on a voluntary basis, if your taxable supplies figure is less than this. The rules are complicated and vary between types of activity but the Treasury have promised to simplify them for small businesses, after April 2003. Ask for expert help to sort out what should and should not be VATable in your particular case – try your accountant, or a business adviser.

Insurance

There are some types of insurance that businesses must have by law, and others that it is a sensible precaution to take out. This section summarises the position.

- **Consequential loss insurance** or **business interruption insurance** covers you while your business is out of action, for instance if the premises burn down.
- **Credit insurance** covers you against the risk of your customers not paying up. You may not be able to obtain this until you have a track record in business, however.
- **Employer's liability insurance** If you are employing someone outside your home, you are legally obliged to have this to the value of at least £2 million, and to display the certificate on the premises.
- **Motor insurance** If you have a car or other vehicle for your business, you must insure it just as with any other vehicle, but you may need to pay extra because you are using it for business purposes.
- **Product liability insurance** covers you for damage caused by your products.
- **Professional indemnity insurance** is useful (and in some professions compulsory) if your business involves giving advice. Many professional bodies bulk-buy insurance at a saving for their members. You may have had such insurance in your previous job, so check that the insurers will take your track record into account rather than treating you as a new entrant to the profession.
- **Public liability insurance** The law does not require you to have this but it is not wise to try to do without. It covers you against damages awards to members of the public who are injured on your premises or by your activities. (You will need this if you are trying to get a 715 certificate as a subcontractor.)

Consult an insurance broker who has experience of organising insurance packages for small businesses. Some trade associations, trade unions and professional bodies will have a link with a particular broker who has built up a specialism in your area, so look there first. SAGA, which specialises in insurance for the over-50s, can now include a limited amount of business insurance in its home insurance policies, and most big insurance companies offer policies that package together the various types of insurance you need. The costs vary depending on the type of business and where it is based. Fire and theft insurance, for example, can be extremely expensive in some inner city areas.

Loan insurance

If you need capital to get your business started, this may involve borrowing money, re-mortgaging your house or personally guaranteeing a loan to the company. Go to reputable advisers to arrange this, and check that you and any co-signatories fully understand the implications.

Consider taking out insurance to cover the loan in the event of your falling ill or some other disaster happening. This insurance is expensive, however, and you need to be careful of the small print. A recent report revealed that in all too many cases the insurers managed to disclaim responsibility once a serious problem arose. So take expert advice before committing yourself and possibly wasting your money.

Note Before taking out any sort of loan, always check with your spouse or partner, who may otherwise find him- or herself committed without realising it. The complications caused by this can be even worse if the marriage breaks up.

Pensions

Unless you are happy that the pension you are already entitled to from a past employer will see you through into a comfortable retirement, you will need to set money aside every year for a pension. The contributions you make towards a personal or stakeholder pension get full tax relief.

The older you are, the more you are allowed to put into a personal pension (30 per cent of your 'net relevant earnings' – broadly speaking, your income after tax – between the ages of 51 and 55; 35 per cent between 56 and 60; 40 per cent if you are over 60). Unless you have already built up a substantial pension, you will need to put that sort of amount away.

The *Pensions Handbook*, published annually by Age Concern Books (details on page 199), explains the rules, and gives details of what to look for and the pitfalls to avoid. Get independent financial advice, and check that the terms of the policy you buy are properly explained and that they suit you.

11 Voluntary work

If you have plenty of energy, even if you have enough money not to need any paid work you may still want to make good use of your time. There are many opportunities for this, both with voluntary organisations and in public duties.

Searching for the right organisation

Voluntary work can be as rewarding or as unrewarding as a paid job, and for much the same reasons. Some organisations know how to use people properly; others simply waste people's potential and then wonder why the turnover of volunteers is so high.

If you find an organisation to work with and then discover that it doesn't work out well, you may be made to feel guilty about leaving them in the lurch. So it makes sense to take care in deciding what organisation to work for, just as you would with a paid job.

Start by making an audit of your position, as suggested in Chapter 7. Think about what you have to offer them, and look at your skills and experience – again just as you would with a paid job. Think, too, about how much time you want to commit. It is better to understate than overstate the time you want to give, at least at the beginning.

Different types of voluntary work

Although it is a very broad generalisation, it would be fair to say that there are two sorts of voluntary work open to you – or you might want to do both, at different times or for different organisations. One type makes use of your particular skills and experience, while the other uses you as a more general worker, part of their 'personpower'.

Making use of your skills

The first type involves using specialist skills and talents for the organisation. These might be the same as those you used in your job, or a

145

development of them. Someone with management skills nurtured in a large organisation, for instance, might find themselves chairing a voluntary organisation's management committee.

You might already be involved with a group and now be able to take more on. Former bank managers, for instance, are likely to find themselves suddenly in demand to be treasurer of whatever groups they are involved in.

If you are a member of a particular profession or trade, you may be dragged into its administration – for instance, acting as an examiner or tutor for student members, or sitting on one of the professional committees that usually burgeon.

Another possibility is to offer your services to a local charity or self-help group that seems to have the right sort of gap. Age Concern England, the publishers of this book, is one organisation that relies heavily on older volunteers to run its groups and services. You can find out what is available either on a local level or nationally (or both, of course).

At local level, there is a network of Volunteer Bureaux around the country. In some areas, they are also called Volunteer Centres, Councils for Voluntary Action Services or Volunteer Development Agencies. There are more than 350 in the UK. Ask in the local library where your nearest one is, or look on the Do-It website (contact details on page 190). According to Do-It (a voluntary body working with the National Association of Volunteer Bureaux and the Home Office, among others):

> 'They can act as a recruitment agent between you and an organisation of your choice, introducing you to them and in some cases negotiating or developing the role that you want … All Volunteer Bureaux can help you if your volunteering experience does not work out or if something goes wrong. They are committed to ensuring people have access to the best possible volunteering experience so work closely with organisations who provide opportunities.'

Many areas also have Volunteer Fairs (often in the autumn when new students come on the scene) where organisations needing help set out their stalls and try to attract people to volunteer their services.

At national level, a specialist body for older people is REACH (contact details on page 195). It has no upper age limits, and looks particularly for people with managerial and professional experience with time to spare – this might be one or two part days a week, or just occasional time. They then identify jobs brought to them by voluntary organisations and set up interviews between the volunteer and the organisation selected. There is a network of (volunteer) Area Managers who can keep in touch with volunteers and develop further opportunities.

Some examples of the sorts of vacancy they had in mid-2001, alongside a number of places for committee members and treasurers, were:

- a fund-raiser in Skipton;
- an archivist in London;
- a questionnaire analyst in Macclesfield.

Among volunteers on their books at the time were:

- a deputy head teacher from Slough;
- a research scientist in Buckinghamshire;
- a company director in Sheffield.

The Home Office has also set up an 'Experience Corps', to 'encourage people over 50 to get more involved in their communities'. This has some ambitious goals. It aims to 'run the largest campaign this country has ever seen to recruit people over the age of 50, who want to give their time and experience but may not know where to start'. It has been granted the largest amount of money the Home Office has ever given to a new volunteering venture. It has a target of attracting 250,000 volunteers by March 2004.

A prime example of an organisation that makes intensive use of volunteers, and also gives them a well-planned training and work structure, is the Citizens Advice Bureau (CAB). Originally CABs were run almost entirely by volunteers, but now most bureaux have at least a handful of paid staff. Much of the interviewing and follow-up work, though, and a large proportion of the administration, is done by volunteers; there are tens of thousands of volunteers involved in some 900 CABs. According to Libby Hinson, Bureau Manager of Gateshead CAB:

'Speaking for ourselves, we'd be extremely glad to see older volunteers. Many of those we have now are younger, and move on to a job or a course quite quickly, so that we have a constant turnover of vacancies. An older person can bring some stability and experience. Most of the problems we deal with are problems of everyday life. So someone who has had experience of life themselves, whether they have specialist knowledge or not, is suitable to be a volunteer.'

The essential skills, she says, are:

- being a good listener;
- being patient;
- being understanding without being critical;
- being non-judgemental towards people and their problems;
- keeping whatever you hear confidential;
- working as a member of a team.

Volunteers have to commit themselves for a minimum of six hours a week. The National Association of Citizens Advice Bureaux (NACAB; address on page 192) provides an eight-day training course spread over a number of weeks, plus self-study packs to help people find their way through the information systems. There is a heavy concentration on interviewing and case-recording skills, which will come in useful in many other places as well.

Many people carry on working for a day or two a week at a CAB for years, though there is generally an upper age limit of 70 for volunteers. The work can also act as a stepping stone to another job or to further education, as it rebuilds confidence and helps you develop and achieve recognition for skills. Once you have got through the training programme, Libby Hinson says, the most important factor – and this is true of many types of voluntary work – is reliability. You can be more flexible in your comings and goings than was possible in your paid job, but if you don't keep the managers informed so that they can plan a rota, you will be letting down the clients. 'Most clients don't know, and wouldn't consider it relevant, that they are being interviewed by a volunteer,' she says. 'They've a right to just the same standards as if the interviewers were paid staff.'

Volunteering overseas

Another possibility is to re-live your youth and do a stint in a developing country overseas. Voluntary Services Overseas (VSO) is a long-standing charity involved in recruiting 1,000 volunteers a year. They don't have an upper age limit, though obviously you do need some stamina; they say that they welcome people with disabilities and will try to tailor-make placements for them. In the past many of their placements have been of teachers, but now they are also inundated with demand for business people – accountants, IT experts and marketing staff among others. According to a research report commissioned by VSO and published in 2001, professional women now make up the majority of volunteers overseas. They tended to be in either their 20s or their 50s, with the older volunteers 'prompted by freedom from family ties, an urge to see the world and travel with a purpose'. You do need to be sure about what you are letting yourself in for, however, and for this reason VSO has a fairly gruelling interview process and rejects people it does not feel will be able to adapt.

Returned Volunteer Action (see page 196) can also help with this.

Doing more general work

If you don't want to use your particular skills any more, the alternative is to do 'general' work. This could be helping in a charity shop or sitting with people who have Alzheimer's disease while their carers have some time on their own. If what you want is the company and to give active support to the cause, this may be enough. Your local Volunteer Bureau is probably the best place to look for this sort of task.

You could, however, find that after a while, when you have recovered from the trauma of leaving your job, this sort of work is rather frustrating; you may well decide that you want more. One advantage of voluntary organisations is that they tend to be considerably more flexible than ordinary employers. If you want to expand your work or take on more responsibility, they will probably let you. If you have been open about what skills you have, the organisation may in any case be begging you to take on more. Voluntary organisations are remarkably good at pulling people into their net and persuading them to give more of their time and effort than they ever intended.

Public service work

British society, especially at a local level, depends very heavily on the public spirit of retired and non-employed people. They sit as magistrates, as local councillors and on all sorts of tribunals and committees. Some of these tasks involve a certain amount of payment, some of them do no more than reimburse your expenses.

Election to the local council

There are parish, district and county councils. In some areas of the country it is possible to win a council seat as an independent. In most cases, though, for a district or county council you will need to have been a member of your political party for quite a while before you get selected (though not necessarily a very active one; for 'unwinnable' seats they may be searching simply for candidates who will stand).

Tony started off by volunteering to start a Labour Party branch in his village. But he was persuaded to show the flag by being nominated as a candidate for the local council, and unexpectedly won the seat. 'I had to get my letterbox enlarged,' he says ruefully.

Councils do not have nearly as much power as they used to. People are still a great deal more ready to give brickbats than bouquets, however, and you can find yourself dealing with a mountain of paperwork and long, complex meetings. So being a councillor is not a task for someone who wants a little light work to keep them going.

Becoming a magistrate

Much of our system of criminal justice depends on the work of magistrates, local people who commit themselves to operate at the lowest tier of the court system. You must retire at the age of 70, but if you have taken early retirement this still allows plenty of time to carry out a worthwhile role. The selection process is very similar to that for a job

– you get an application form from your local court, and then have two interviews. One thing the Lord Chancellor's Department (which makes the final selection) has to take into account is balancing the 'bench' to reflect the local community. 'For example, it would not be appropriate to have 70 per cent of a bench who were all retired, white males,' according to the Magistrates' Association handout on the topic. So if you get rejected, it may simply be that you do not fit the present requirements but could re-apply another time.

There is quite a time commitment involved; magistrates have to commit themselves to sitting at least 26 half-days a year but in practice most sit for more. Training is given but is almost always done at weekends or in the evenings. According to Betty, a former health visitor who became a magistrate after taking early retirement:

'You know well in advance what your days are, and you can plan round them. If you say you're available to do extra sessions at short notice they will probably call you in to do just that, so you have to harden your heart and say you cannot, on occasions.'

Betty was offered six initial evening training sessions, spread over a number of weeks. During this time she and her fellow trainees sat in on various court sessions, and also went on visits to the sort of places they might be sending people to, such as the local prison. After six months' experience on the bench, there were six more evening training sessions to complete the initial training. Every year there are optional refresher courses and specialist training for experienced magistrates.

Sitting on a tribunal

In addition to the court system, there is a sizeable network of tribunals dispensing 'administrative justice'. Some of these require particular knowledge of an area of the law, so people sitting on them will tend to come out of a specific profession. Disability Appeal Tribunals, for instance, always include a member who is 'experienced in dealing with the needs of disabled persons … in a professional or voluntary capacity … or because they are themselves disabled'.

Another example is Employment Tribunals, which have a legally qualified chairman and two lay members at each sitting. The members need, according to the DTI,

- practical experience of employee relations in the workplace;
- some knowledge of the employment rights legislation; and
- the ability to make sound judgements.

Tribunals need, they say, good quality members with the skills and adaptability necessary for the changing world of employment relations. They should also be as representative as possible of the working population, especially with regard to the proportion of women, ethnic minorities and people with disabilities. This might suit someone who has been active in their union, or in human resources management, very well.

Other public bodies

There is an enormous – and growing – range of other non-elected public bodies distributing large amounts of public money, such as health trusts or school governing bodies. Some of the jobs, especially those chairing such bodies, are well paid but also demand a high level of commitment. Others may involve only monthly or quarterly meetings – though there is usually a pile of paperwork to get through as well. They may pay a flat fee for each day's sitting, or nothing at all.

Check that you know what the terms of reference are, including your liability if things go wrong. Decide also whether you support the policy that the organisation has been set up to promote. The health service trusts, for instance, have to follow the policy the Government lays down for the National Health Service. If you do not agree with the general thrust of policy, you could find yourself a lone voice on the committee and rather unhappy. Check whether you will have some allies.

You can apply to have your name included in the list held by the Public Appointments Unit in the Cabinet Office (address on page 195). It puts forward names to departments for several hundred appointments that fall vacant each year.

In addition, many public appointments are now advertised in newspapers and on the Government's websites. Look out for them – there is no reason why these jobs should be confined to the people 'in the know'.

The effect on your finances

In most cases, voluntary work is just that, though you may get your direct expenses paid, some help in kind such as lunches, and an 'honorarium' to cover indirect and unquantified expenses. Volunteer bureaux do stress that out-of-pocket expenses should be reimbursed to the volunteer (who may then choose to donate the money to the charity); this helps charities to keep track of the true cost of their operations. Public bodies may pay rather more; local councillors, for example, get their expenses and an attendance allowance for each meeting they attend.

Straightforward expense payments are not taxable but other allowances may be. They *might* also affect your social security benefits. Check this before starting any sort of voluntary or public service work.

Jobseeker's Allowance

As explained on page 55, you need to meet some pretty rigorous conditions as the price of receiving Jobseeker's Allowance. However, volunteers are allowed 48 hours in which to rearrange their duties in order to take up an available job. To qualify for the benefit, you must be working for a charity or other not-for-profit organisation and not receiving payments other than expenses.

If you are receiving other payments, you are likely to be treated as a part-time or casual worker. This could mean that your benefit is cut or stopped altogether for weeks in which you do the work. The National Centre on Volunteering suggests that a letter from the volunteer organiser to the Jobcentre Plus may be useful. This should state:

- the type of payments you receive;
- that you have discussed methods of seeking work with the volunteer organiser, that you may be contacted on a stated telephone number and that the organisation will do its best to pass on messages to you;
- that the organisation understands and accepts that you have to give up volunteering at a maximum of 48 hours' notice;

- that volunteering will help you to develop skills, get a reference for job applications, etc.

Although local interpretation can make the system more flexible, the National Centre for Volunteering says that it may also lead to inconsistencies; it would like to hear of any problems so that it can help to sort them out.

Incapacity Benefit

Voluntary work, so long as it is not for a close relative and the only payment you receive is for reasonable expenses, is not considered 'work' for Incapacity Benefit purposes. There are also some special rules for people sitting on social security appeal tribunals and the Disability Living Allowance Advisory Board. However, the rules for Incapacity Benefit require you to be unable to perform certain work-related functions (as explained on page 67).

If you have a clear-cut disability that scores sufficient points in the tariff system – such as being in a wheelchair or being almost entirely deaf – you would be able to do voluntary work without any problem, though it will still be wise to tell the Jobcentre Plus office about it. If, however, your case is more marginal, so that it is a matter of interpretation and the opinion of the medical authorities whether you are eligible for Incapacity Benefit, the simple fact that you are doing voluntary work, even for a few hours a week, could be used to show that you are *not* incapacitated for work. A light task at which you could be sitting down most of the time would probably be treated very differently from, say, conservation work restoring Hadrian's Wall.

From April 2002, the rules on earnings and Incapacity Benefit have been more flexible (as explained on pages 69–70), so it is now possible to receive something more than only expenses. However, ask for advice from your doctor *and* from someone who understands the social security system (such as a local welfare rights officer) before committing yourself.

Means-tested benefits

If you receive expenses for volunteering, which are no more than the amount you actually spend, they should be allowed and not affect

Income Support or other means-tested benefits. Other payments will generally be taken into account in full. Again, ask for advice if you are unsure of the situation. Most voluntary organisations will have checked on the position for their own volunteers.

Occupational pension or other payments from your employer

If you have taken an ill-health pension, which can be reduced or suspended if you recover, then doing voluntary work might be considered to be evidence that you no longer qualify, especially if it is similar in any way to the paid work from which you have retired. Check the small print of your own pension scheme.

However, if your early retirement was for any other reason, doing voluntary work should have no effect on your pension.

12 Retraining and educational opportunities

No one is ever too old to learn. You may want to go back to education in order to take an academic path that was not available to you when younger. Or you may want to develop a hobby or interest you have always had, or simply to keep your brain stimulated.

Alternatively, you might be looking for ways to improve your position in the job market or sharpen your business skills. If you have been in a job for much of your adult life, or looking after a family, you may not have had much formal training or education since the year you left school or college. You could have developed all sorts of skills 'on the job' and through in-company training courses, but have little to show for it in terms of letters after your name or bits of paper. You might, for instance, have developed your computer skills by trial and error or by being shown what to do by a ten-year-old grandchild, so you need to formalise them before you can make use of them in the job market.

Other reasons for studying include:

- You have qualifications but are unsure whether they are up to date and still of value in today's labour market.
- You need some specific new training for a new project you have in mind.
- You realise that you are lacking in some very basic skills that you will need to help get another job. (You can be perfectly intelligent and have held down a good job for some time, and still have trouble with spelling and arithmetic.)

If you did the skills audit suggested on pages 80–81 – and especially if you had some expert help with it – you will probably have identified areas where you need new skills, or recognition of those you already have. There are probably far more ways of obtaining these than when you were last looking for education. But the money available to finance courses is more limited and you have to know whom and what to ask.

Recognition of existing skills

Many people have been carrying out specific tasks in their employment for many years, without having sought or obtained any sort of certificate to say that they have done so. You might, for instance, have gradually taken on all the book-keeping, or developed very substantial expertise in the welfare benefits system, but never tried to gain a qualification. Perhaps you were too busy, it didn't seem necessary, or there wasn't an immediately suitable one. Or you might have a degree or A-levels in subjects completely different from those you are dealing with now.

You can obtain recognition for what you already know in a number of different ways. One possibility, for anyone who has been working in a particular discipline for years but has never bothered to gain a professional qualification, might be to put yourself through a crash course in it and take the exam at the end. Many of these qualifications are designed for people who are studying after work and in the evenings. They include correspondence material and some tutorials. It is worth finding out how quickly you could undertake what would normally be a slow process, and what the costs and demands would be. You could link in with courses run by a local college or another training provider. This might be a good move, for instance, for someone who has been acting as an accountant or book-keeper at a higher level than their formal qualifications would show.

Or you could take an A-level in a suitable subject, perhaps a language you are already good at.

National Vocational Qualifications (NVQs) or **Scottish Vocational Qualifications** (SVQs) are the new form of practical training qualifications, replacing or running alongside older forms such as RSA, City and Guilds, and BTecs. (Many of these in fact now work as dual qualifications, so you get something that is recognised under more than one body's rules.)

In general, you achieve an NVQ through your workplace: your employer works with an assessment centre to accredit you when you have reached a certain level of competence. There is no exam as such. But it is also possible to achieve one via a college instead, by means of work experience gained there and assessment by the tutor, and perhaps also the co-operation of your previous employer. So long as the evidence that you can carry out the required tasks is 'authentic, relevant and current', it can come from previous work and life experience as well as from formal learning.

Accreditation of Prior Learning (APL) and **Accreditation of Experiential Learning** (APEL) allow you to be given credit for existing qualifications, and to have your experience taken into account by demonstrating your skills and knowledge. Generally this is intended for people thinking of doing courses, but it can also be used to show employers (or yourself) what your knowledge and skill would equate to in terms of a qualification.

You are required to compile a 'portfolio of achievement' related to the course you are comparing with. Through the portfolio you can achieve credits for the formal entry requirements, or for part of a course. If you are interested in this, ask at your local college or university whether they offer the service (or ask them for information about one that does). They ought then to be able to say whether this is a runner for you, and what the fees would be. Some places will offer support to help you with compiling a portfolio.

Developing new skills

An alternative (or additional) possibility is to achieve new skills or to bring those you already have to a higher level. If you have decided to change direction completely, you may need to achieve a qualification before you can start your new career. There are numerous courses available (see below on how to find out more about them). They might be provided by:

- schools and community colleges;
- universities;
- colleges of further and higher education;
- the Open University;
- specialist institutes;
- work-based learning courses provided through Jobcentre Plus;
- other providers, both voluntary (such as the Workers' Educational Association) and commercial.

It is quite possible to do a course up to quite a high level without ever leaving your home, by using correspondence- or computer-based material. However, the face-to-face contact with fellow students and with tutors is a large part of the fun, and also helps with the learning process. Even if you live somewhere that means regular travel to a college is difficult, it is worth it at least to get on a weekend or short residential course.

There are a great many mature students on courses at all levels, from the most basic numeracy and literacy courses to further and higher education; most institutions are keen to recruit them. There are a number of 'Access', 'Return to Learning' and 'taster' courses for people who have not been in education for a long time, to help them find out what they can do and the best way to organise their lives around study. As the DfES 'Second Chances' website puts it (see page 185 for details):

> 'Courses geared specifically to give adults a "second chance" work to build up the individual's confidence and are designed to take into account the fact that most people need a lot of encouragement to start learning after a break.'

A good college will also give support and counselling to students, especially if they seem to be floundering. Open University courses, and others provided on a distance learning basis, are perhaps less geared to picking up such problems, but for those with some confidence in their learning skills they may meet the right needs.

There are also some specific skills-updating courses for particular professions, for those who have been away from the workplace for a number of years and had skills qualifications before. For example, there are courses for returning to teaching or nursing, re-entry to general practice (medicine), and updating in information technology and office skills.

It is even possible to get on to a degree-level course (and certainly one at a lower level) without *any* formal qualifications, and the DfES is planning to extend the opportunities further. Most institutions will interview potential mature students, to find out their experience and knowledge, and how committed they are.

Many courses at all levels are 'modular' now, which means that you may be able to join them at any point and pick up the bits you miss later. There are generally also 'transfer credits', so you can go elsewhere and have the work you have already done accepted without needing to repeat it.

Do you have what it takes?

You will need a fair bit of dedication and staying power to do a course, especially if you are doing it on your own. Think about:

- The time commitment. You need to research possible courses carefully, checking out how much time will be needed, both in the classroom or lecture theatre and for 'homework', and for your own independent learning. It can be useful to work out your own time management plan.
- How to acquire (or re-acquire) study skills and techniques. There is a lot of help available for study skills. Some courses incorporate elements about this, and there are also free-standing courses and workshops. Many establishments have learning-support units that students can take advantage of. The course tutor should also be able to help.
- How you can try it out. It's worth easing yourself in, if you are planning to do a lot of studying; try first with an evening class, a weekend study course, or an Open University module. This will help to increase your confidence as a learner, give you some learning skills and give you a 'track record' when you apply for further courses. Some providers offer 'taster' courses to enable potential students to sample the work and setting before making a major commitment.
- How much support you will get from your family. Hopefully, they will also be interested and supportive. They will need to understand, however, that you will need somewhere to study where you won't be interrupted, and that at times (when you have an exam or there's an essay due) you may be quite stressed. There will be ways round some problems – such as studying in the university library if your teenage children insist on playing loud music so you cannot do so at home – but you will need more confidence and stamina, if finding the space for yourself is an uphill battle. Mature students often develop strong informal support mechanisms for each other, particularly where they feel that they form an identifiable group which has distinctive needs and problems.

You will find at some institutions – for instance in further education colleges – there are always vast numbers of young people milling around, so even going for a coffee is daunting. The younger students look a bit askance at you, and even ask strange questions (one sixth-former asked me, on a French weekend school, 'Why does someone your age want to study a language?'). But with a reasonable amount of mutual tolerance, it becomes less daunting and both age groups can learn a lot.

Finding what's available

Before you start looking seriously at what's available, you need to decide whether you want to study:

- full-time
- part-time
- mainly at home/mainly in the college or other institution/away altogether in a residential setting

and what topics and what for (if you want to improve skill X with the aim of setting up in a business in a year's time, you won't want an academic course on how X was done in the fifteenth century; that can wait until you retire fully).

There is an enormous amount of information around. The DfES has a large, rather unwieldy, section on its website called Second Chances (www.dfee.gov.uk/secondchances) giving all the addresses and publication details you could want, and guidance on what is available. Use it as a starting point only, though, as they do not seem very good at keeping it up to date. Many areas have an adult education and training advisory service that provides advice and guidance to local adults on local and national education/training opportunities. They tend to run under a different name in each locality, and may even form part of a wider service, but a local education authority, local library or college should be able to provide contact details. Other places to find useful help, and in some cases the chance of an individual discussion, include Learndirect, Training Access Points and a local college or other educational establishment.

Learndirect is a national learning advice line. It has over 500,000 courses on its database, and can also help with career guidance and information and advice on funding your learning. If you want a human being to help you, you can phone and speak to an independent adviser, or e-mail them. You can also use the searchable database on its website for courses, or search over 800 job profiles on its online career diagnostic package (called 'learndirect futures') to help you to decide which career is right for you.

Training Access Points (TAPs) are databases of information on education and training opportunities in a particular geographical area, covering the whole range of learning providers, including public, private and voluntary sectors. There is now a national network of TAP databases which, collectively, hold information on over half a million learning opportunities across the UK. Local TAP databases can be found in guidance shops, libraries, careers centres and Jobcentre Plus offices. The service may also be available by phone or post, and in some cases also on the internet. There isn't a single national website for all the TAPs but, if you go to www.tap.org.uk/links/index.html (run by bodies in the south-west of England), its index page will allow you to find the website for your area.

A college or other education institution All further education colleges today are required to provide impartial advice and guidance on entry, and other places such as universities also try to do so. Most will have a full-time worker to do this, with extra staff seconded to help out during the busy enrolment periods in the autumn. They should be able to guide you around and find the best course for you, and will have access to information about the aptitudes and skills needed for a particular area.

Don't take no for an answer, but be prepared to be adaptable. If you can't get on a course in one place, or through one particular route, there is very likely to be another.

Valerie, now in her 60s, was put off by the admissions tutor the first time she tried to get into university a few years ago. She discovered afterwards that if she had followed things up with the subject tutor who had interviewed her, she would probably have got a place. Later she started on a course at a university some distance from her home but gave up after the first year because the journey was difficult. Only after that did she find out that she could do a part-time rather than a full-time degree at her local university, and that because her income was low she would be able to get considerable help with the fees.

Finding the resources

As usual, this is the difficult bit. How can you find the money to pay for a course, which may cost several thousand pounds, and your living expenses as well? Resources are more limited today than they used to be, and students are expected to dig in their own pockets more and more. However, there are still sources of money available if you fit in with the various sets of rules.

Note Because of devolution, Scotland and Northern Ireland have different rules from England and Wales in a number of areas. This section covers only the English/Welsh situation, so it will be important to check the details if you live elsewhere.

Through the Jobcentre Plus service

Work-based Learning is the new name for Training for Work (Scotland still uses the old name). Courses under the Work-based Learning system are free to people who are unemployed (though you need not be actually receiving benefit to qualify), because they are paid for by Jobcentre Plus funding. The upper age limit for being accepted on these is 63, and generally you also need to have been registered as unemployed for six months. There are some exceptions to this, however – for instance, for people with disabilities, people returning to the labour market after a gap of more than two years (perhaps while looking after a child), and those who have lost their jobs due to a large-scale redundancy – so it will always be worth asking.

People have their training needs assessed before they join, and an 'individual training plan' is agreed. This could include job-specific training, working towards National Vocational Qualifications (NVQs) and work experience. Training is generally full-time, but it is possible to do it part-time if that fits better with your domestic circumstances.

What is on offer can also include training for self-employment, with initial support and advice, help to develop business plans, skills training and mentoring.

While doing the training, you receive an allowance that is equivalent to whichever benefit you are entitled to, plus £10 a week. Also available is some help with childcare and travel expenses.

If you come under the New Deal 50 Plus (explained on page 59), there is also a training grant – initially of up to £750 – available once you are back in work and claiming Employment Credit (Working Tax Credit from April 2003). This can be used for training that will improve current or future job prospects, not necessarily for the employer you are with. According to Ken Burns, running the programme at a JobCentre in East Newcastle:

'One lady has used two small amounts to go on courses for food hygiene and first aid training. Another person used all £600 [the maximum figure at that time] in one go, to get a qualification so he could carry out higher level MOT tests. The whole course cost £750, and the employer said he would not be able to afford it, so he used the £600 and somehow made up the rest. Another person used the money to get a forklift qualification.'

These courses need not be arranged via the employer, and can be in the private sector.

See also the section 'Learning while unemployed' on page 166 if you are claiming Jobseeker's Allowance or Income Support.

Courses at further education colleges

These are free to people receiving social security benefits or Housing Benefit, and there may be an alternative low-income test for those not on benefit but without much income. People over 50 not on benefit may anyway be exempt from tuition fees, though they may have to pay for exams. The arrangements can vary considerably between different colleges, and if you are near several you may need to shop around for the best bet.

Degree level courses

In general, student grants do not exist any more. There are loans instead. However, for full-time 'independent' students (that is, anyone over age 25) the position is a little different:

- You are likely to get help with paying tuition fees. According to the DfES, almost 85 per cent of all independent students pay no fees whatsoever.
- Student loans are available – between £3,000 and £5,000 a year depending on your circumstances. However, there is an upper age limit of 54 for these, and for those aged between 50 and 54 they are available only to people who are planning to return to work after studying. There are also grants for dependent children and childcare, and for books, equipment and travel.

■ The university or college may be able to provide a hardship loan of up to £500, and there are also some hardship funds provided according to need.

What you will be asked to contribute towards the cost of your fees or living costs will depend mainly on your income. The amount is calculated by the local education authority when you apply to them for 'student support'. The DfES warns that:

> 'Previous study at higher education level which included help from UK or EU public funds, or if the college where the course was taken was publicly funded, may exclude students from entitlement to further financial support. *It is important that such students seek information and advice from their LEA, as the rules relating to previous study are complex.*'

The DfES website (www.dfes.gov.uk/studentsupport), includes a section for mature students. It allows you to access both online and downloadable versions of the eligibility form and the financial assessment form together with a range of useful supporting information.

Career Development Loans

Another way to finance yourself is a Career Development Loan (CDL). These started in 1988 with the objective of 'encouraging individuals to take greater responsibility for their vocational training'.

They are run by four of the clearing banks for the DfES. You can apply for a loan of between £200 and £8,000 to pay 80 per cent of the course fees and associated expenses, including the cost of books and materials (and living expenses for full-time courses). You normally still have to cover the remaining 20 per cent of the cost yourself. If you have been unemployed for more than three months, however, you can receive 100 per cent if your local Learning and Skills Council (LSC) agrees. LSCs also have the discretion to offer top-up grants to cover the remaining 20 per cent or to reduce the cost of borrowing.

There are various eligibility rules for CDLs, including:

■ You must not be receiving other funding that covers the expenses applied for.

- You must be without access to funds to pay for the training course without a CDL.
- You must intend to use the training for work in the UK or elsewhere in the European Union.

Courses can be full-time, part-time or by distance learning, but they must not last more than two years. Loan repayments do not begin until the course has finished and you have found work, and can be deferred for up to 18 months after the end of the course.

People doing some vocational courses are eligible for Vocational Tax Relief (VTR) on the course costs. Ask the course providers about this.

Take-up of CDLs is much lower than the Government had hoped, despite advertising campaigns. According to one careers adviser, 'People see them as very much a last resort. If you are doing a lengthy course, you may need to borrow thousands of pounds, and people generally don't want to get into that sort of debt.' They are, nevertheless, worth considering for something that will definitely improve your career prospects.

Financing yourself

If you have a lump-sum leaving payment from your previous job, you could invest this in training or education. If you can't afford a full-time course, doing it part-time or on a distance learning basis may be cheaper, and could allow you to earn some income at the same time.

Learning while unemployed

The position for those wanting to study full-time while signing on as unemployed is complicated. Essentially, it's heavily discouraged unless it's a course within the Work-based Learning system (explained above). The only exceptions are for:

- **Full-time employment-related courses** You are allowed to go on one full-time course of up to two weeks in any year and continue to receive Jobseeker's Allowance, and be treated as available for and actively seeking employment while you are on the course, provided your Jobcentre Plus adviser agrees that you may go on the course before it starts.
- **Open University courses** You are allowed to attend a residential

session *where it is a requirement of the course,* for one week per course, and continue to get Jobseeker's Allowance.

You will lose Jobseeker's Allowance if you undertake any other course of study that involves more than 16 'guided-learning' hours per week. The number of guided-learning hours will be set out in the 'learning agreement' signed by you and the college.

If the full-time course of study is not funded (in whole or in part) by the Learning and Skills Council, there won't be a straightforward definition of 'full-time', and the benefits officer will make a decision based on the description of the course given by the educational establishment. If a description is not available, the officer 'takes account of all the relevant facts, including hours of guided and private study'.

For part-time courses (under 16 hours), however, things are rather easier. As explained on page 55, you are entitled to put 'reasonable restrictions' on the hours during which you are able to work. So, if you have said that you are available from 8–6 each day, five days a week, the fact that you are doing an evening or weekend course is really none of their business. Colleges will often arrange 'access' and other courses targeted at mature students so that they fit in under the 16-hour rule, and the Learning Agreement will state this.

If the part-time course does cut into your working hours, however, you *may* still be entitled to Jobseeker's Allowance provided you can show that:

- you are available to start work immediately;
- you have not put restrictions on the work you are available to do, which would leave you with no real prospect of finding a job; and
- you are taking steps each week to look for a job.

You will almost certainly be interviewed, and the internal Jobcentre Plus guidance says that different students on the same course may be treated differently, depending on their circumstances. Look in the *Welfare Benefits Handbook*, published by Child Poverty Action Group (which should be available in libraries) for more details on the sorts of factors they will take into account.

You have a right to have your case reviewed, or to make a formal appeal, if you feel you are being treated unfairly.

13 Organising your time and other commitments

If you were employed for a long period before your current job fin-ished, the idea of organising your own timetable from now on probably seems both attractive and daunting. Unless you step straight into another full-time job, you will have new spaces in your day and no fixed pattern for filling them; at the same time you will have new commitments to meet. What these commitments are will depend on what your position is, and so they will change as your own pattern of activity changes. But you will also find that other people have new expectations of you – some that you appreciate and some that you do not.

The major issues – and the adjustment process that has to go on – will tend to differ between men and women. If you are a woman with a fam-ily still at home, or with older relatives living close by, you may find an expectation in the family that once you have left your job you will sim-ply stay at home and 'housekeep'. The demands put on your time may build up quite rapidly, on the assumption that you have nothing better to do; you may then find it quite difficult to pursue your own projects.

On the other hand, if you are a man who has always been at work, the family perhaps won't make the same demands on you. Quite rightly, though, there is likely to be an expectation that you will do *something* in the home. You may find it difficult to cope with this. You may be spending more time with your family than you have done for many years, except on holiday, and this too will take some getting used to.

One warning often given to men is that they should not start trying to reorganise and manage the home. It has got on perfectly well without you so far, so why should it be changed? There can be irritations all round as different people in the family adapt. It would usually be bet-ter to fit in and take on a fair share of the routine tasks rather than create a major upheaval.

Whether you are a man or a woman, it will help you to work out all these problems if you make a sensible and constructive plan about how you will use your time and negotiate that with the rest of your family. This chapter looks at some of the points to think about:

- during the job search process;
- when starting a new job;
- when starting to work from home;
- when coping with caring responsibilities;
- when you have undertaken a 'portfolio' of activities.

Hunting for a job

A job search is a serious project, quite time-consuming and possibly stressful. You need to plan and allocate time accordingly. It is a project that you could need to undertake more than once, because the first job you get may be only temporary, it may not suit you, or it may not be what you want as time goes on and your financial position and other commitments change.

Whatever type of work you are looking for, the commitment is going to be much the same. It is a full-time job looking for work these days, whether full-time or part-time.

Chapter 9 looked at the practical steps to be taken. Just as important, though, is working out how to use your time and energy effectively on the project. To quote the authors of the BBC handbook *Making Time*,

'Like every plan of campaign you must have objectives and targets to aim for. If you don't know where you are going it is highly unlikely you will get there – or know if you have arrived.'

If you are claiming Jobseeker's Allowance (explained on pages 51–56), you will be required to sign a Jobseeker's Agreement committing you to a certain plan of action. Treat it as a framework in which to fit your job-hunting activities. Recording what you do is an important part of the Agreement. Rather than have an extra chore, build these record-keeping activities into your own system, by using the Jobseeker's Activity Log (given to you at the Jobcentre Plus office) to put down, for example, a note of phone calls to potential employers as you make them.

Problems with managing your time

Particular problems with managing your time could include:

- **The lack of framework or structure to your day** You may have been used to getting up early and dashing off to catch a bus or train, and then getting back home again at the same time each evening with barely enough time to eat before dashing off to a leisure activity. Now – especially if you are feeling rather depressed about the whole experience – there may seem to be no good reason to get up at any particular hour, and too little to do to fill your time. Some people find it helpful to give themselves a period of 'being a slob' to start with, but it's not wise to let this go on for more than a couple of weeks. The longer it goes on, the harder it is to stop.

- **The lack of a support system** In the past you may have relied heavily on colleagues, especially if you were in a position where you had staff to whom you could delegate tasks. You may not even have known how to work the photocopier or the coffee machine, if someone else always did it for you. Now the only coffee machine is the one you switch on, and the photocopier is in the newsagents down the road, if you are lucky.

- **The impact on your family** They won't be used to seeing you at home, and may feel that, now you have all this free time, you could just carry out this or that chore without trouble. If your partner has unexpectedly become the sole breadwinner, you will both have problems adjusting. The tensions are likely to be much worse if they are not talked through. You really need to make it plain to yourself and others that you are going to devote your ordinary working hours to your job search, and not have them eaten into by other activities. But since you are no longer travelling to work, there will still be extra time available for doing housework or for spending with the family as well.

Set yourself targets

A useful tactic, suggested in *Making Time*, is to set a target time, say three months, and then break that down into weeks during which you carry out specific tasks. These could include writing and revising your CV, drawing up a contacts list and following up a certain number each day, going systematically through job advertisements and useful internet sites. Draw up a daily 'Things to do' list, and then make sure you do them.

A work discipline is especially important for the tasks you hate doing. Hardly anyone really likes phoning to pursue contacts or applications. Many of us, even if quite outgoing, feel shy at the thought that their 'contact' may have forgotten altogether who she or he is. So, *Making Time* suggests, set aside, say, four 15-minute stints a day for the phone calls you don't want to make. (Always keep a note of whom you have phoned, or who has phoned you, and what was said – it is extremely easy to confuse two conversations in your mind.)

Writing yourself lists of things you need to do means that you will go to the Jobcentre Plus office or the reference library to deal with specific tasks, rather than just dropping in to while away time.

Review the situation

Once you have got organised, don't just let your search drift on and become a routine in itself. One outplacement adviser had a client who has been coming in to the offices regularly for two and a half years. Perhaps he was unlucky, but he could also have been looking for the wrong type of job or in the wrong place.

Review the way you are working, and your progress, regularly. If things don't seem to be working out, think about whether your original plans were realistic, and whether you are going about things in the right way. Talk it over with someone else such as an outplacement consultant or staff at an employment agency. Other possibilities are to work again through the various exercises and activities available in books and on the internet (explained in previous chapters), perhaps questioning yourself rather more than you did in the first round.

If you are claiming Jobseeker's Allowance, your personal adviser at the Jobcentre Plus office will probably require reviews at intervals in any case, but you may find that the agenda is largely to persuade you to downgrade your expectations. If you are certain that what you are doing is reasonable, but you can't persuade them of that, then the answer may be to agree to look for temporary work at a lower level, and treat this as a learning experience as suggested in other chapters.

Starting a new job

When you start a new job – whether full-time or part-time – you may well find yourself in a very different environment from where you last worked. If you came out of a large organisation, you are now far more likely to be working in a small one, perhaps a small business or a partnership. If you have taken on a less taxing job, or one in a new field, you could also find that you are now a subordinate where before you were in charge (and you may not think much of the people to whom you are subordinated, either).

On top of that, there is the 'new child at school' feeling; you don't know where everything is and what the office habits are. Even if people mean to be helpful, they may simply forget that you don't know what time the coffee break is, or the details of the National Lottery syndicate.

Starting in a new place is never easy, but you can help yourself by:

- thinking through some of the issues in advance, for instance how you will react if your boss is younger than you, and perhaps of the opposite sex when you were used to a single-sex environment;
- asking what you need to know (even if you are not given a proper induction course) and then writing down the details so you don't forget them;
- biting your tongue when it wants to start saying 'In my old job we did …' It is irritating for others and will make them feel that you are less flexible than you suggested in the interview. If you think that the way they did something at your last workplace was better, why not suggest it as if it is your own idea and take the credit? You can always own up later if your conscience is troubling you!

A good employer does thorough induction training for new recruits. Some also appoint a 'mentor' for a new person, or people may informally take on the same role. If there is such a person, ask for a review meeting once you have been there a week, and then again a few weeks later, to establish how you are doing and what improvements (if any) you could make in your work.

You may also need to spend a little time working out the best route to work. Give yourself the space to prepare properly; try your route by public transport the week before you start work, for instance.

Check on the dress code in advance if you can. Otherwise, arrive looking as smart as you think can possibly be required on the first day, and dress down on future days if it turns out not to be necessary.

If you are being paid at the end of the month, this may leave a gap in your finances. You could ask the employer for a 'sub' to tide you over, or get a short-term overdraft from the bank. Check whether you can get a loan for a travel season ticket, for instance. (The State can also give some short-term help here; see Chapter 6.)

Looking after your pension

When you start in a new job and your new employer provides pensions or death benefits, it will almost always be worth joining the scheme. (You won't necessarily want to transfer your money from any previous scheme; that will depend on what is on offer from each.) You may have to undergo a medical examination, and if your health is not good you could be refused entry, though that would be rare.

If you are working part-time for a new employer, the amount you and they are contributing, and the earnings on which the pension or death benefit will be based, could be low. You might want to start paying Additional Voluntary Contributions (AVCs), or take out a personal or stakeholder pension, up to the limit that you are allowed by the Inland Revenue, in order to build up a larger amount of pension.

For most people, the pension they have earned in one job need have no bearing on the amount of pension they can build up in the next job. There are some exceptions, however, for the higher paid and those in very good pension schemes. Check with your new employer's pensions department if you fall into one of these categories. They will be able to tell you whether, as a result, you will have special limits applied to the maximum pension you can get in the new job.

The alternative, if there is no pension scheme available via an employer, is to take out a personal or stakeholder pension and your own life assurance. Unfortunately, the cost of buying a good pension rises sharply as you get older, so work out what you can afford to spend without over-committing yourself. All but the smallest employers are required to have arrangements to deduct money from your earnings and pass it on to a pension provider, if they do not have their own pension arrangements. If you prefer to set up your own, a monthly direct debit is comparatively painless.

See the *Pensions Handbook*, published annually by Age Concern Books, for more information on pensions.

Permanent health insurance

You may find that your new employer provides a decent sick pay scheme, or it may be Statutory Sick Pay only. There could also be a qualifying period before you are entitled to full benefits.

If a reasonable scheme is not available to you, you may need to take out permanent health insurance (PHI; also called 'income protection insurance') on your own account – though it is sadly expensive for older people, and especially for women. Self-employed people may also need to do this.

PHI pays up to three-quarters of your earnings, less any State and company benefits, if you are prevented from working through disability or long-term illness. Benefits will be tax-free if you have paid the premiums yourself out of taxed income, and are paid as long as you qualify on health grounds, or until retirement age if that is earlier.

However, the policies tend to be full of small print conditions, so specialist independent advice is essential. Check out particularly whether the premium rate is 'reviewable' (which means that it can be increased without warning), what the definition of disability is, and what exclusions there are.

Starting to work from home

Organising your time when working from home, whether as a self-employed person or in some form of telework, is one of the most difficult things to get right. It is not easy to control the flow of work, and this can result in periods when you hardly have time to turn around and feel that you cannot possibly chase another order. But the result of that, a few months later, is a work famine instead, when you have to spend a lot of time chasing work and so cannot earn what you need.

Again the answer is to organise your time properly and make allowance for the necessary but tedious chores. There may also be some office skills that, if you have them, will cut down immensely on the time that things will take – such as typing/word processing and using computer spreadsheets and databases. See Chapter 12 for some suggestions of where to look for relevant training.

Set yourself targets

The first step is to set yourself some objectives, in fairly concrete terms. In Chapter 3 it was suggested that you should work out your income requirements on a monthly or weekly basis, so that gives you a clear target to aim for. You can then assess how many products/contracts/assignments that means.

Making Time suggests that you make yourself a chart of monthly, weekly and daily targets and keep them under your nose at all times. Keep referring to your plan: tick off what you achieve, and change the targets if they are too hard or too easy.

'Make sure you include all the activities you need to do in order to achieve your goals; remember the things you don't like doing but know you must.'

Include in this the time you will need to get your contacts and support system set up, which can be surprisingly lengthy. Some of the things you may need to allow time for are:

- sorting out a bank or building society account;
- VAT registration;
- getting planning permission (you won't need this if you are simply using part of your home as an office, but you might if you were setting up a workshop, or running tea-rooms, for example);
- notifying the tax office;
- arranging to pay Class 2 (self-employed) National Insurance contributions;
- seeing Business Links counsellors and attending training courses (see pages 135–136);
- getting hold of the right equipment;
- taking out subscriptions to magazines, or finding where you can get access to them;

■ buying office equipment and stationery.

It is necessary to invest in the proper equipment to do the job – though not to spend extravagantly on it. It is worth investing in the right equipment to make light work of necessary routine tasks (eg a computer with the right software and peripherals); the trick is to identify exactly what you need and to seek advice before buying. Second-hand office equipment is perfectly adequate, but you will need filing cabinets and shelving if your work is likely to generate paper. (There is no such thing as the paperless office, whatever the new technology gurus might like to tell us! In fact, the internet and email probably generate even more paper than the old-fashioned way of doing things.)

Find space and time away from your family

You also need to create office or workshop space. If you take over the sitting room there will be friction with your family but, equally, you won't do yourself justice if you perch on a corner of the kitchen table with other activities going on around you. You need some exclusive space for your work, even if it is the boxroom or part of your bedroom, but you also need to leave your family their own space.

Finding time in your own home may also mean some thought and negotiation. Teenagers who are never off the phone, or who wander into the sitting room looking dishevelled when you have a client there, don't help with the starting up of any business. You can, to some extent, adjust your working times to fit in with the realities of home life but you will also need to work out some rules together and then get everyone to stick to them.

If you live on your own

If you live on your own, rather than in a family, you may find the opposite problem: that you never stop working. When your office or workspace is in your own home, it is too easy to carry on tinkering away all the time and never take a real break. The quality of your work will suffer, though, if you let yourself do this.

Set yourself definite working times, with gaps between them when you go for a walk, make coffee, eat a genuine sit-down meal and so on. Build in time when you see friends and indulge in leisure activities.

Occasionally you will have to break this pattern, when you are asked to do something in a rush and it can't be completed in any other way but by working all hours, but that should be the exception rather than the rule.

Allowing time for non-productive activities

There are some crucial activities for which you cannot charge anyone, and which you probably won't much enjoy, but without which your business will founder. These include marketing, invoicing and keeping your accounts, and preparing your work.

Initially, much of your time will be spent marketing yourself and your services. As your business develops, you may need to spend rather less time on this, but the requirement will never go away. Even when you are at your busiest, you have to keep on thinking about where the next chunk of work will come from, and go out and find it if it does not arrive on your doorstep.

Set yourself a definite number of tasks to do each day – 'two phone calls and two follow-up letters to prospective customers' – or make yourself some rules, however arbitrary, about when and how to do marketing.

You will probably have to spend quite a lot of (unpaid) time discussing possibilities, making presentations and drawing up estimates. Though it will vary between different types of work, one rule of thumb is that no more than half the people who say they are interested in you will actually follow it up, and no more than half of *them* will turn into serious customers. So the more regular customers you can build up, for whom there is no need to spend time introducing yourself and explaining what you can do, the better from this point of view.

After the work is done, you again need to set aside time to send out invoices, and then chase up anyone who does not pay. Another rule of thumb is that the larger the organisation that is your customer, the slower it will be at paying its bills! In theory, under the law a company should pay invoices within 30 days, if there is no reasonable query, but in practice you may find you need to do considerable chasing. It is wise to keep your accounts up to date (or to put the paperwork in the form in which your accountant will want it) as you go along. Waiting until near the deadline for VAT or Income Tax payments is likely to mean a wild rush to complete, and it can be expensive if you miss that dead-line and find yourself penalised by the tax authorities.

Finally, when allocating time for the work you have taken on, don't forget about preparation time. It is easy to skimp on this now and then, but disastrous in the long run. If you are teaching a course, for instance, you can expect to spend at least as long writing the material, or doing major revisions, as running the course itself. The standard of presentation is becoming steadily more important (sometimes, one feels, at the expense of the content). So give yourself time to do things properly. Reflect it in the amount you charge.

Coping with caring responsibilities

This section is only a very brief look at a very big subject. There are about 750,000 people caring for someone who is disabled or elderly for over 20 hours each week at the same time as they are carrying on paid employment. Without underestimating the work of all the rest of the 6 million carers in this country, it is this group that we are concentrating on here. (See the *Carers Handbook: what to do and who to turn to* (details on page 182) or contact Carers UK (formerly Carers National Association; address on page 187) for much more information on this.)

You may find that, when your work situation changes, you are asked, or expected, to take on the care of a relative or partner. Or you may already have been spending a substantial amount of time caring when you were in your previous employment. Either way, caring can be strenuous and stressful, especially if you are combining it with paid work.

Don't feel you have to manage on your own; there is help and support available. But it is unlikely to come unless you ask for it. As Jane Brotchie says in *Help at Hand: the home carers' survival guide* (details on page 183):

'If you can be clear about what would help you, professionals and people around you are more likely to respond. There are some very good schemes around that can give you a break or help you in some other ways. How good the response to your request will be will vary enormously according to who you ask and where you live. But don't give up; keep on asking. Even if a service does not exist it should not stop you asking.'

Your GP and the local authority's social services department are the places to start looking for help. You may also find that there are local specialist services run by voluntary organisations (for instance 'sitters' provided by the Alzheimer's Society). There are also many carers' support groups (some with paid staff) around the country. It can help ease the strain considerably just to sit down and talk to people with the same sort of problems as yourself. Contact Carers UK for details of groups in your area (address on page 187). There is also a *Directory of British Self Help Groups* (details on page 182 but not, unfortunately, on the Web) and an internet site at www.patient.co.uk/selfhelp/groups.htm

Aids and adaptations in the home, and training – for instance, in the best way to lift a bed-bound person – can also make life easier. Ask the GP or social services.

If you are going to cope, you will need time for yourself, however little, to go out and pursue your own interests. You may need to be quite assertive to ensure that your needs, as well as those of the person you are caring for, are taken into account.

You are only too likely to come under pressure to do more than you want, or feel capable of doing, to save money on the social services budget. You are perfectly entitled to resist this; you have a life to lead as well. It will be easier to do this if you have planned out your own time already and know what you can reasonably offer.

If you are working and caring, you do have limited rights to 'reasonable' time off to help people who are dependent on you. This time off does not have to be paid, but some employers will give paid leave in the circumstances. In general, this covers close relatives and people living in the same house as you, but it also applies to anyone who 'reasonably' relies on you for assistance if they are ill or injured. The TUC guide *Your Rights at Work* gives details on this and on how to exercise your rights in practice.

In the USA some employers offer workplace day centres for their employees' older or disabled relatives, and a very few employers in the UK are experimenting with a similar system. Keep your eyes out for any such arrangements in your area.

Benefits for carers

You may be able to get a small addition to your income from the State (really, no more than a token recognition of what you are doing, £42.45 a week in 2002/3) if you spend a substantial amount of your time caring for a person with a disability. This is called the **Invalid Care Allowance** (ICA). The first condition is that the person being cared for is receiving the care component of *Disability Living Allowance* at the middle or highest rate, or *Attendance Allowance* if they are over pension age. (Details of these benefits are not covered here; see DWP leaflets DS 704 and HB 6, or DS 702, or look on its website.)

If this condition is satisfied, you as carer will be entitled to ICA if you are:

- not gainfully employed or in full-time education (this means that you earn less than £75 after deduction of reasonable expenses, or are on a course that involves fewer than 21 hours of supervised study);
- 'regularly and substantially' caring – this means caring for 35 hours a week or more;
- aged between 16 and 65.

ICA is taxable (except for any child addition). You also receive Class 1 National Insurance credits towards your pension.

If you are doing a mixture of activities

You may have found yourself taking on a 'portfolio' of activities, including part-time employment, self-employment, perhaps a college course, perhaps caring and family commitments. Women who have brought up families in the past will probably find it easier than men to juggle the time spent on these various elements. But, for everyone, it is important to organise your life well and exercise great self-discipline so that you don't run yourself into the ground and become unreliable.

The essential requirement is to set up the space and time *at home* to enable you to operate elsewhere, and to plan what you are doing when. Draw up a weekly timetable of when you are supposed to be where, taking account of travelling time, preparation (especially important for learning and teaching activities) and administration.

Get a wall calendar with space to write on, and fill it in each weekend for the following week. Get your spouse or partner and the rest of your family to do the same, so you each know where the others are.

If one element seems to be squeezing out the others, think about the reasons for it and what can be adjusted. You may need to renegotiate some of the arrangements. This may be particularly necessary with family commitments, which can be very demanding.

Useful publications

Books

Some of the older books in this list may now be out of print. However, your local library may have a copy or be able to obtain it through an inter-library loan.

Age Shift: a consultation documents (2000) by Ageing Population Panel, Foresight. London: Department of Trade and Industry.

Carers Handbook: what to do and who to turn to (1998) by Marina Lewycka. London: Age Concern Books.

Directory of British Self Help Groups and Support Organisations (2002) by Steve and Julie Garrill. Blackburn: self-published ISBN 0–9538246–1–6 [also on CD]; £10 for either plus £2.50 postage.

Disability Rights Handbook (published annually) London: Disability Alliance ERA. £8.95 (£5 for individuals receiving any State benefits).

Downshifting (1998) by Andy Bull. London: Thorsons.

Earning Money in Retirement (1992) by Kenneth Lysons. London: Age Concern England.

Essential Guide to Age Discrimination Legislation (2001) London: Employers' Forum on Age.

European Directory of Career Management and Training Consultants (2000) London: Executive Grapevine.

Experience Necessary: the business case for wisdom (2000) by Charlotte Thorne. London: Industrial Society.

Finding the Right Job (1994) by Ann Segal with William Grierson. London: BBC Books.

FSA Guide to Financial Advice, free from Financial Services Authority.

The Good Retirement Guide (2000) London: Kogan Page.

Guide to Taking up a Franchise: Daily Telegraph guide (2000) by Colin Barrow, Godfrey Golzen and Helen Kogan. London: Kogan Page.

Help at Hand: the home carers' survival guide (1990) by Jane Brotchie. London: Bedford Square Press.

High Income Consulting: how to build and market your professional practice, 2nd edition (1997) by Tom Lambert. London: Nicholas Brealey Books.

Job Hunter's Handbook (1999) by David Greenwood. London: Kogan Page.

Making Time (1993) by Gerard Hargreaves, Dorothy Morfett and Geraldine Bown. London: BBC Books.

Net that Job (2000) by Irene Krechowiecka. London: Kogan Page.

New Deal Handbook (1999) London: Centre for Economic and Social Inclusion [download free from www.uuy.org.uk]

Penguin Careers Guide (1996) by Anna Alston and Anne Daniel. London: Penguin.

Pensions Handbook (updated annually) by Sue Ward. London: Age Concern Books.

Public Bodies (1994) by the Cabinet Office. London: HMSO.

Redundancy Law Handbook (2000) by Incomes Data Services. [available from 77 Bastwick Street, London EC1V 3TT, or via IDS Customer Services on 020 7324 2599, or email sales@incomesdata.co.uk]

Start a Successful Business (1994) by Rosemary Phipps. London: BBC Books.

Taking a Career Break (2001) by Joshua White. London: Vacation Work Publications.

Teleworking Handbook: new ways of working in the information society, 3rd edition [£19.95 plus £2 p&p from TCA, Freepost CV2312, Wren, Kenilworth CV8 2RR]

Test Yourself! (2000) by Jim Barrett. London: Kogan Page.

Third Age Entrepreneurs: profiting from experience (2001). London: Barclays Bank

Welfare Benefits Handbook (published annually). London: Child Poverty Action Group.

What Color is your Parachute? a practical manual for job-hunters and career changers, 30th edition (2000) by Richard N Bolles. Berkeley: Ten Speed Press.

Which? Guide to Changing Careers, 2nd edition (2001) by Sue Bennett. London: Consumers Association.

Which? Guide to Working from Home (1999) by Lynn Brittney. London: Which? Books.

Winning the Generation Game (2000) London: Performance and Innovation Unit, Cabinet Office [see also www.cabinetoffice.gov.uk/innovation/2000/winning/winning_index_page.htm.

Your Rights at Work (2000) a TUC Guide. London: Kogan Page.

Your Taxes and Savings (updated annually) by Paul Lewis. London: Age Concern Books.

Booklets

Disability Discrimination Act 1995. Booklet DLE3 by the DfES [can be downloaded from their website]

Guide to Help for Small Business. A DTI free booklet available from 0870 1502 500

Help on Work-related Stress: a short guide. Booklet INDG2/81 by the Health and Safety Executive [can be downloaded from their website]

Key Facts on Age and Employment (1999) by the Chartered Institute of Personnel and Development. [free from CIPD, 35 Camp Road, London SW19 4UX]

Offsetting Pension Payments against Redundancy Pay, DTI booklet RPL1

Redundancy Handling, ACAS booklet B10, free from ACAS

Redundancy Payments, DTI booklet PL808

Student Grants and Loans: a brief guide for higher education students, DFE booklet, free from DfES Publications Centre, PO Box 2193, London E15 2EU

Time Off for Job Hunting or to Arrange Training when Facing Redundancy. DTI booklet PL703

Leaflets

Caring for someone? DWP leaflet SD4; free from your local DWP office.

The child and Working Tax Credit: the modernisation of Britain's tax and benefits system. Treasury leaflet available on their website or from their Public Enquiry Unit 020 7270 4558.

Customer's charter. Jobcentre Plus leaflet.

Employed or self-employed. Inland Revenue leaflet IR 56.

A guide to Incapacity Benefit. A DWP leaflet.

A guide to the personal capability assessment. A DWP leaflet.

New Deal for the Over 50s. Age Concern leaflet available from the Age Concern Information Line.

The service for people of working age. Jobcentre Plus leaflet PFL1.

Supplying services through a limited company or a partnership. Inland Revenue leaflet IR 175.

What do you know about magistrates? Magistrates Association leaflet, free from 28 Fitzroy Square, London W1T 6DD.

Websites

Age Positive: www.agepositive.gov.uk – a Government site to help employers end age discrimination. Gives news about legislation, good practice guidance, case studies.

Do-It: the National Volunteering Database: www.do-it.org.uk – a central online database for volunteering opportunities.

Second chances, in DfES website: www.dfes.gov.uk/secondchances.

Worktrain: www.worktrain.gov.uk – Government's website for job advertisements.

Useful addresses

Organisations' names and addresses, especially their website and email addresses, change frequently. If an organisation seems to have disappeared, it is generally worth using an internet search engine, or making enquiries at your reference library, to see if it has transmuted into something else. If it really has disappeared, there may well be another body that has taken on its functions.

Advisory, Conciliation and Arbitration Service (ACAS)
Brandon House
180 Borough High Street
London SE1 1LW
Tel: 020 7210 3613
Website: www.acas.org.uk
Public enquiry points in 12 regional offices in the UK (not Northern Ireland); numbers listed in every phone directory. Can help with advice and conciliation concerning your employment rights.

Age Concern Insurance Services
Lowthian House
Market Street
Preston PR1 2ET
Tel: 01883 834887
For home insurance protection for building and contents. Also offers motor insurance and travel insurance.

British Association for Counselling and Psychotherapy
1 Regent Place
Rugby
Warwickshire CV21 2PJ
Tel: 0870 443 5252
Website: www.counselling.co.uk
Can put you in touch with members who can offer counselling help.

British Association of Psychotherapists
37 Mapesbury Road
London NW2 4HJ
Tel: 020 8452 9823

Website: www.bap-psychotherapy.org.uk
Can put you in touch with members who can offer psychotherapy help.

British Franchise Association
Thames View
Newtown Road
Henley on Thames
Oxon RG9 1HG
Tel: 01491 578050
Website: www.british-franchise.org.uk
Regulatory body for franchising in the UK, responsible for developing and promoting fair and ethical franchising through its member franchisor companies. Aims to help potential franchisees recognise the good, the bad and the ugly for what they are, and to help businesses involved in franchising to secure their own position among the 'good' operators.

Business Link Network Ltd
Small Business Service
1 Victoria Street
London SW1H 0ET
Tel: 0845 600 9006
website: www.businesslink.org.uk
Advice to small businesses. Website includes directory of local organisations throughout the UK.

Career Development Loans
Freepost
Warrington WA4 6FB
Information line: 0800 585 505
Website: www.lifelonglearning.co.uk/cdl
For information on loans for career training.

Carers UK (formerly Carers National Association)
20–25 Glasshouse Yard
London EC1A 4JT
Tel: 020 7490 8818
Helpline 0808 808 7777 (Mon–Fri, 10am–12 and 2–4pm)
Website: www.carersuk.demon.co.uk
Gives information and support to people who are caring at home, and produces a wide range of information leaflets.

Centre for Economic and Social Inclusion
Camelford House
89 Albert Embankment
London SE1 7TP
Tel: 020 7582 7221
Website www.cesi.org.uk
Publishes a guide to New Deal rights and benefits, and researches all aspects of unemployment rights and developments.

Chartered Institute of Personnel and Development (formerly **Institute of Personnel Management**)
35 Camp Road
London SW19 4UX
Tel: 020 8971 9000
Website: www.cipd.co.uk
The professional body for personnel and human resources managers; has produced a strong policy statement on age discrimination in employment.

Community Service Volunteers
237 Pentonville Road
London N1 9NJ
Tel: 020 7278 6601
Email: information@csv.org.uk
Website: www.csv.org.uk
Creates opportunities for people to take an active part in the life of their community through volunteering, training and community action.

Consumer Credit Counselling Service
Tel: 0800 138 1111
Email: info@cccs.co.uk
Website: www.cccs.co.uk
A free confidential service providing independent counselling to help you achieve realistic solutions to your debt problems, avoid bankruptcy and learn to handle money.

Cooperative Union (incorporating ICOM)
Holyoak House
Hanover Street
Manchester M60 0AS
Tel: 0161 246 2959
Website: www.co-opunion.org.uk

Can offer advice and training to those wanting to set up a workers' co-op, or put you in touch with local sources of help.

Department for Education and Skills
Sanctuary Building
Great Smith Street
London SW1P 3BT
Tel: 0870 000 2288
Website: www.dfes.gov.uk
Deals with education at all levels; includes website www.dfee.gov.uk/ secondchances and www.dfee.gov.uk/studentsupport

Department of Trade and Industry (DTI)
Customer Service Unit
7th Floor, Hagley House
83–85 Hagley Road
Birmingham B16 8QG
Tel: 0121 456 4411
Website: www.dti.gov.uk/
Deals with queries about redundancy pay and how to make a claim.

For Cumbria, Durham, Yorkshire, Cleveland, Tyne & Wear and Merseyside
Ladywell House
Ladywell Road
Edinburgh EH12 7UR
Tel: 0131 316 5600
Helpline: 0500 84 84 89 (Mon–Thur 9am–5pm; Fri 9am–4.30pm)

For London and the Home Counties
PO Box 15
Exchange House
60 Exchange Road
Watford WD18 0YP
Tel: 01923 210 700
Helpline: 0500 84 84 89 (Mon–Thur, 9am–5pm; Fri 9am–4.30pm)

Small Business Service Loan Guarantee Unit
St Mary's House
c/o Moorfoot
Sheffield S1 4PQ
Tel: 0114 259 7308/9

Fax: 0114 259 7316
Email: sflgs@sbs.gsi.gov.uk
Guarantees loans from banks and financial institutions with viable business propositions that have failed to obtain a conventional loan because of lack of security.

Disability Alliance

Universal House
88–94 Wentworth Streeet
London E1 7SA
Tel and textphone: 020 7247 8776
Fax: 020 7247 8765
Website: www.disabilityalliance.org
Provides information and advice to disabled people, their families and advisers about entitlement to social security benefits and services, runs training courses for advisers, carries out research into the income needs of disabled people, and campaigns for improvements in provision and for increases in disability benefits so that they better reflect the real costs of disability.

Disability Rights Commission

DDA Information Line
Freepost MID 02164
Stratford upon Avon CV37 9BR
Information Line: 08457 622 633 or (textphone) 08457 622 644
Website: www.drc-gb.org.uk
Working with existing bodies, it promotes civil rights for disabled people and gives advice and information.

Do-It: the National Volunteering Database

Email: info@do-it.org.uk
Website: www.do-it.org.uk
A central online database for volunteering opportunities.

Employers' Forum on Age

Astral House
1268 London Road
London SW16 4ER
Tel: 020 8765 7280
Fax: 020 8765 7293
Email: efa@ace.org.uk
Website: www.efa.org.uk

Working in association with Age Concern, it promotes the business benefits of a mixed-age workforce.

Employment Agency Standards Line
Tel: 0845 955 5105
A government-run helpline where you can obtain advice about your rights and helping with taking up complaints.

Financial Services Authority
25 The North Colonnade
Canary Wharf
London E14 5HS
Tel: 020 7676 1000
Website: www.fsa.gov.uk
Regulates the provision of financial services, and educates consumers on what to look for.

Health and Safety Executive
Local offices in the phone book
Website: www.hse.gov.uk
Responsible for enforcing the law on workplace health and safety.

Sheffield Information Centre
Broad Lane
Sheffield S3 7HQ
InfoLine: 08701 545500 (a confidential phone line service)

London Information Centre
Rose Court
Ground Floor North
2 Southwark Bridge
London SE1 9HS
InfoLine: 08701 545500 (a confidential phone line service)

Publications available from:
HSE Books
PO Box 1999
Sudbury
Suffolk CO10 2WA
Tel: 01787 881165
Fax: 01787 313995

Inland Revenue
National Insurance Contributions Office
Self-employed Service
Longbenton
Newcastle upon Tyne NE98 1ZZ
Tel: 0845 915 4655
Address from which to reclaim National Insurance contributions paid when self-employed before finding that your earnings for the year are below the limit at which contributions are compulsory.

Learndirect
Tel: 0800 100 900
Email: enquiries@learndirect.net
Website: www.learndirect.co.uk
National learning advice line; can search through over 500,000 courses to find one to suit you. Can also help with career guidance and information and advice on funding your learning.

Learndirect Scotland
FREEPOST SCO5775
PO Box 3816
Glasgow G12 8BR
Tel: 0808 100 9000
       0800 917 8000
Email: info@learndirectscotland.com
Website: www.learndirectscotland.com
For information and advice on computer and internet information in TV pro-grammes and free IT 'taster' sessions in libraries, shopping centres, buses and pubs.

Magistrates' Association
28 Fitzroy Square
London W1P 6DD
Tel: 020 7387 6099
Website: www.magistrates-association.org.uk/
Association for people appointed as magistrates (formerly called justices of the peace).

National Association of Citizens Advice Bureaux
115–123 Pentonville Road
London N1 9LZ

Tel: 020 7833 2181
Website: www.nacab.org.uk
Information about your local Citizens Advice Bureau.

National Association of Councils for Voluntary Service (NACVS)
3rd Floor, Arundel Court
177 Arundel Street
Sheffield S1 2NU
Tel: 0114 278 6636
Website: www.nacvs.org.uk
Can tell you about local Councils for Voluntary Service.

National Association of Volunteer Bureaux
New Oxford House
Waterloo Street
Birmingham B2 5UG
Tel: 0121 633 4555
Email: info@navb.org.uk
Website: www.navb.org.uk
Can tell you if there is a Volunteer Bureau in your area.

National Centre for Volunteering
Regents Wharf
8 All Saints Street
London N1 9RL
Tel: 020 7520 8900
Fax: 020 7520 8910
Website: www.volunteering.org.uk
Freephone number (UK only): 0800 028 3304
Non UK:+44 (0)20 7520 8900
Offers a range of services designed to support volunteer managers and organisations that involve volunteers. Believes that increasing the quality, quantity, contribution and accessibility of volunteering will benefit both individuals and the community at large.

National Debtline
Birmingham Settlement
318 Summer Lane
Newtown
Birmingham B19 3RL

Tel: 0808 808 4000
Fax: 0121 248 3070
Can help with sorting out your financial affairs if you get badly into debt.

National Group on Homeworking
Office 26
30–38 Dock Street
Leeds LS10 1JF
Tel: 0113 245 4273
Advice Line: 0800 174 095 (Mon–Fri, 10am–12.30pm; 1–3.30pm)
Fax: 0113 246 5616
A non-governmental organisation that campaigns for improved employment rights and conditions for homeworkers.

New Ways to Work
26 Shacklewell Lane
London E8 2EZ
Tel: 020 7503 3283
Helpline: 020 7503 3578
Email: info@new-ways.co.uk
Website: www.new-ways.co.uk
Gives advice and assistance on job-sharing.

Office of the Pensions Advisory Service (OPAS)
11 Belgrave Road
London SW1V 1RB
Tel: 020 7233 8080
Fax: 020 7233 8016
Email: enquiries@opas.org.uk
Website: www.opas.org.uk/
A voluntary organisation that gives advice and information on occupational and personal pensions, and helps sort out problems.

Pensions Ombudsman
11 Belgrave Road
London SW1V 1RB
Tel: 020 7834 9144
Fax: 020 7821 0065
Website: www.pensions-ombudsman.org.uk
Deals with complaints or disputes about occupational and personal pension

schemes. The Ombudsman is appointed by the Government and is independent of the pension providers.

PRIME
Walkden House
3–10 Melton Street
London NW1 2EJ
Tel: 0208 765 7852
Fax: 0208 765 7879
Email: prime@ace.org.uk
A national not-for-profit organisation whose goal is to enable the over-50s to set up their own businesses.

Public Appointments Unit
Cabinet Office
Room 202
4 Central Buildings
Matthew Parker Street
London SW1H 9NL
Tel: 020 7276 2489
Website: www.quango.gov.uk
There are around 1,000 public bodies in the UK with over 30,000 people serving on them. The Unit keeps a list of people willing to serve, and a directory of public bodies.

REACH
89 Albert Embankment
London SE1 7TP
Tel: 020 7582 6543
Fax: 020 7582 2423
Email: volwork@btinternet.com
Website: www.volwork.org.uk/
Places older people in voluntary work with charities.

Retired and Senior Volunteer Programme
237 Pentonville Road
London N1 9NJ
Tel: 020 7278 6601
Website: www.csv-rsvp.org.uk
Part of Community Service Volunteers.

Returned Volunteer Action
1 Amwell Street
London EC1R 1TH
Tel: 020 7278 7019
Email: retvolact@lineone.net
Provides a range of information on overseas volunteering opportunities, and points to think about, through its various publications.

Skill UK
Chapter House
18–20 Crucifix Lane
London SE1 3JW
Tel: 020 7450 0620
Information service: 0800 328 5050
Fax: 020 7450 0650
Website: www.skill.org.uk
Promotes opportunities for young people and adults with any kind of disability in post-16 education, training and employment across the UK.

Small Business Service
see under Department of Trade and Industry

Telework Association
WREN
Kenilworth
Warwickshire CV8 2RR
Tel: 0800 616008
Website: www.telework.org.uk
Promotes teleworking both for companies and for individuals.

Third Age Employment Network (TAEN)
207–221 Pentonville Road
London N1 9UZ
Tel: 020 7843 1590
Email: taen@helptheaged.org.uk
Website: www.taen.org.uk
Campaigning organisation, committed to better opportunities for mature people to continue to learn, work and earn.

Trades Union Congress (TUC)
Congress House

Great Russell Street
London WC1B 3LS
Tel: 020 7636 4030
Fax: 020 7636 0632
Website: www.tuc.org.uk
TUC Know Your Rights Line: 0870 600 4882
Can provide you with up-to-date leaflets and information on what union to join (but not detailed advice).

US Educational Advisory Service
The Fulbright Commission
Fulbright House
62 Doughty Street
London WC1N 2JZ
Tel: 020 7404 6994
Fax: 020 7404 6874
Email: education@fulbright.co.uk
Website: www.fulbright.co.uk
Can arrange educational exchanges and secondments with the USA.

Voluntary Service Overseas
317 Putney Bridge Road
London SW15 2PN
Tel: 020 8780 7200
Fax: 020 8780 7300
Email: enquiry@vso.org.uk
Website: www.vso.org.uk
An international development charity that works through volunteers.

Working for a Charity
The Peel Centre
Percy Circus
London WC1X 9EY
Tel: 020 7833 8220
Fax: 020 7833 1820
Email: enquiries@wfac.org.uk
Website: www.wfac.org.uk
Promotes the voluntary sector as a positive career option, and the options and benefits of becoming a volunteer.

About Age Concern

Changing Direction is one of a wide range of publications produced by Age Concern England, the National Council on Ageing. Age Concern works on behalf of all older people and believes that later life should be fulfilling and enjoyable. For too many this is impossible. As the leading charitable movement in the UK concerned with ageing and older people, Age Concern finds effective ways to change that situation.

Where possible, we enable older people to solve problems themselves, providing as much or as little support as they need. A network of local Age Concerns, supported by many thousands of volunteers, provides community-based services such as lunch clubs, day centres and home visiting.

Nationally, we take a lead role in campaigning, parliamentary work, policy analysis, research, specialist information and advice provision, and publishing. Innovative programmes promote healthier lifestyles and provide older people with opportunities to give the experience of a lifetime back to their communities.

Age Concern is dependent on donations, covenants and legacies.

Age Concern England
1268 London Road
London SW16 4ER
Tel: 020 8765 7200
Fax: 020 8765 7211

Age Concern Cymru
4th Floor
1 Cathedral Road
Cardiff CF11 9SD
Tel: 029 2037 1566
Fax: 029 2039 9562

Age Concern Scotland
113 Rose Street
Edinburgh EH2 3DT
Tel: 0131 220 3345
Fax: 0131 220 2779

Age Concern Northern Ireland
3 Lower Crescent
Belfast BT7 1NR
Tel: 028 9024 5729
Fax: 028 9023 5497

Publications from Age Concern Books

Pensions Handbook: planning ahead to boost retirement income
Sue Ward

The Pensions Handbook is an essential guide for people in their mid-life years who are keen to improve their pension arrangements. It explores in detail the main types of pension scheme – state, stakeholder, occupational and personal – and offers guidance on increasing their value.

For more information, please contact Age Concern Books on 0870 44 22 044

Your Rights: a guide to money benefits for older people
Sally West

A highly acclaimed annual guide to the State benefits available to older people, *Your Rights* is divided into five parts, giving details about:

- pensions and retirement
- financial help for people on a low income
- benefits for disabled people and their carers
- types of financial help, including the system for paying for care
- sources of national and local help

For more information, please contact Age Concern Books on 0870 44 22 044

Managing Debt: a guide for older people
edited by Yvonne Gallacher and Jim Gray

Despite the general increase in disposable income and the rise in living standards enjoyed generally, there is no doubt that a significant proportion of older people continue to experience financial problems in retirement. This comprehensive book aims to help those people break free from the vicious debt cycle. It provides information, advice and guidance on managing debt. Topics covered in detail include:

- getting into debt
- negotiating with creditors
- money advice
- prioritising debts and dealing with emergencies
- bankruptcy

■ understanding the law and your rights

Written in clear, jargon-free language, the book contains examples, sample letters, case studies and a glossary of terms, and is a complete self-help guide for people with financial problems.

£7.99 0–86242–236–1

The Retirement Handbook, 2nd edition
Ro Lyon

A comprehensive handbook for retired people of any age, this book is packed full of practical information and advice on all the opportunities available. Drawing on Age Concern's wealth of experience, it covers everything you need to know, including:

■ managing your money
■ staying healthy
■ using your time
■ leisure activities
■ housing options
■ relationships
■ educational opportunities
■ community involvement

The Retirement Handbook is designed to encourage everyone to view retirement as an opportunity not to be missed. Positive and upbeat, reading this book will make you wonder how you had time for work!

£7.99 0–86242–350–3

Healthy Eating on a Budget
Sara Lewis and Dr Juliet Gray

This book shows how, even on a tight budget, it is possible to produce meals that are both healthy and delicious. Opening with a comprehensive introduction to achieving a nutritionally balanced diet, there are over 100 closely costed recipes for the health-conscious cook, all of which are flagged up to show their nutritional values and calorie content.

£6.95 0–86242–170–5

Know Your Complementary Therapies
Eileen Inge Herzberg

People who practise natural medicine have many different ideas and philosophies, but they all share a common basic belief: that we can all heal ourselves – we just need a little help from time to time.

Written in clear, jargon-free language, the book provides an introduction to complementary therapies, including acupuncture, herbal medicine, aromatherapy, homoeopathy and osteopathy. Uniquely focusing on complementary therapies and older people, the book helps readers to decide which therapies are best suited to their needs, and where to go for help.

£9.99   0–86242–309–0

If you would like to order any of these titles, please write to the address below, enclosing a cheque or money order for the appropriate amount made payable to Age Concern England. Credit card orders may be made on 0870 44 22 044 (for individuals); 0870 44 22 120 (AC federation, other organisations and institutions). Fax: 0870 44 22 034.

Age Concern Books
PO Box 232
Newton Abbot
Devon TQ12 4XQ

Age Concern Information Line/Factsheets subscription

Age Concern produces over 45 comprehensive factsheets designed to answer many of the questions older people (or those advising them) may have. Topics covered include money and benefits, health, community care, leisure and education, and housing. For up to five free factsheets, telephone: 0800 00 99 66 (7am–7pm, seven days a week, every day of the year). Alternatively you may prefer to write to Age Concern, FREEPOST (SWB 30375), Ashburton, Devon TQ13 7ZZ.

For professionals working with older people, the factsheets are available on an annual subscription service, which includes updates throughout the year. For further details and costs of the subscription, please write to Age Concern at the above Freepost address.

Index